A TREATISE ON
ADVANCED CALCULUS

INCLUDING THOSE PARTS OF THE THEORY OF FUNCTIONS
OF REAL AND COMPLEX VARIABLES WHICH FORM
THE LOGICAL BASIS OF THE INFINITESIMAL
ANALYSIS AND ITS APPLICATIONS TO
GEOMETRY AND PHYSICS

BY

PHILIP FRANKLIN, Ph.D.

Professor of Mathematics, Massachusetts Institute of Technology

DOVER PUBLICATIONS, INC.
NEW YORK

This Dover edition, first published in 1964, is an unabridged and corrected republication of the work first published by John Wiley and Sons, Inc., in 1940.

Library of Congress Catalog Card Number: 64-21659

Manufactured in the United States of America

Dover Publications, Inc.
180 Varick Street
New York 14, N. Y.

PREFACE

This treatise is addressed to a reader who has already acquired some proficiency in the technique of the calculus and who desires a more logical treatment of the subject than is feasible in a first course. It is suitable as a text for upper classmen, particularly those in reading or honors classes, and for graduate students. It may also prove a convenience to teachers in that it includes in a single volume proofs of a number of theorems which are usually assumed without proof in elementary textbooks.

While the book deals primarily with infinitesimal calculus, prerequisite parts of algebra and analysis and concepts needed for applications to geometry and physics have not been excluded. Thus the real number system, complex numbers, limits, continuous functions and infinite series, products and sequences are discussed as necessary preliminaries. Adequate definitions of the elementary functions are also given. For the trigonometric functions, the arithmetic definition given here is believed to be new in detail, although in principle it goes back to Ptolemy. Unlike definitions based on integrals or series, it avoids giving the student the impression that trigonometry is dependent on integration or function theory. The treatment permits the introduction of the trigonometric functions at an early stage. Similarly, the Gauss proof of the fundamental theorem of algebra makes possible the presentation of the decomposition of rational functions into partial fractions before integration.

The presentation of differentiation is complete in itself, with the elementary derivations briefly recapitulated. This frees the work from dependence on any particular first course. Taylor's developments and indeterminate forms are studied at length. Several properties of Taylor's series are derived later by using analytic functions. An existence theorem for implicit functions is established in connection with partial differentiation. The statements of the relations of Jacobians to solvability and functional dependence avoid a common error resulting from the confusion of the term " vanishing " with " identically vanishing." The existence theorems for ordinary and first-order partial differential equations, generally omitted from the formal course in differential equations, are demonstrated. The theory of envelopes is introduced as an application of the condition for a differential equation to have a unique solution. Analytic functions of several complex vari-

iii

ables are defined, and it is shown that the total differentiation rule applies to them.

Integration is treated in several of its aspects. The subject begins with the integration of continuous functions and deals with integration in explicit terms. A rough classification of those integrals which are reducible to elementary functions is given. As among the simplest non-elementary integrals, elliptic integrals are defined and proved to be reducible to a combination of elementary functions and Legendre's three normal forms. The discussion of the Riemann integration of bounded functions includes Lebesgue's condition, as well as those of Darboux and Jordan. With a view to physical applications, a simple type of Stieltjes integral is discussed. Multiple integrals and their relation to repeated integrals are treated. Satisfactory definitions of arc length, surface area, and such mechanical concepts as center of gravity and moment of inertia of continuous distributions are formulated.

The discussion of the theory of functions, Fourier series, and Fourier and Laplace transforms is facilitated by a preliminary chapter on uniformity and other conditions for the inversion of limit processes. So much of the theory of functions is given as is necessary for the computation of definite integrals by the method of residues. Several of the better known definite integrals capable of evaluation by the use of Fourier transforms, residues, or inversion of order in repeated integrals are given in the exercises. Because of the large number of particular definite integrals reducible to, or related to, the Gamma function, this function forms the subject of a special chapter. Here many asymptotic expansions are developed, including that of Stirling. This is established for complex, as well as for real, values of the argument.

My primary object has been to provide a sound foundation for the methods of the calculus. However, enough theory has been included so that the student who has thoroughly mastered this book will be well prepared to pursue graduate work in analysis. A selected list of references for further study, topically arranged, is given in the bibliography.

The number of problems is large. Many of them concern fairly general forms. It is assumed that numerical problems can easily be constructed from these forms by any reader or teacher who feels the need of them. Hints for their solution, in many cases amounting to the solution in outline, are appended whenever any real difficulty is involved or when the method of proof, using only the material of preceding chapters, is not easy to see. A few of the problems contain important results, and the name of the discoverer is mentioned. For instance, Peano's example of a continuous function nowhere differentiable and

Fejér's example of a continuous function whose Fourier series diverges appear as exercises.

The principal works which I have consulted in preparing the text and the problems are included in the bibliography. I have found Hardy's *Pure Mathematics* and de la Vallée Poussin's *Cours d'Analyse* especially helpful. I also owe much to discussions with colleagues and students.

PHILIP FRANKLIN

CAMBRIDGE, MASS.
January, 1940

CONTENTS

CHAPTER I. REAL NUMBERS

CHAPTER II. LIMITS OF FUNCTIONS

CHAPTER III. EXPONENTIAL, LOGARITHMIC, AND TRIGONOMETRIC FUNCTIONS

CHAPTER IV. DIFFERENTIATION

CHAPTER V. COMPLEX NUMBERS

CHAPTER VI. INTEGRATION

CHAPTER VII. INTEGRABLE FUNCTIONS

CHAPTER VIII. EXTENSIONS AND APPLICATIONS OF INTEGRATION

CHAPTER IX. INFINITE SERIES AND INFINITE PRODUCTS

CHAPTER XIV. FOURIER SERIES AND INTEGRALS

CHAPTER XV. DIFFERENTIAL EQUATIONS

CHAPTER XVI.   THE GAMMA FUNCTION AND OTHER DEFINITE INTEGRALS

A TREATISE ON
ADVANCED CALCULUS

CHAPTER I

REAL NUMBERS

We assume that the reader is already acquainted with the rules of reckoning for positive and negative numbers, as well as the use of such numbers as coördinates to determine points on a line or in a plane. However, certain abstract properties of numbers or of points in one or more dimensions may be unfamiliar to the reader. To lead up to these properties, we shall sketch one method of starting with the positive integers and logically developing the complete system of positive and negative, rational and irrational numbers.

1. Mathematical Induction. The positive integers are the numbers used in counting, $1, 2, 3, \cdots$. We assume that their elementary properties are known. In particular, an integer n is less than n' if, and only if, there is a positive integer k such that $n' = n + k$. In this case n' is greater than n.

In any finite, non-empty collection of integers there is a greatest integer and a least integer. By non-empty, we mean that the collection contains at least one integer. By greatest integer, we mean one greater than, or equal to, any other integer of the collection. The definition of least integer is similar.

If each of the members of I, an infinite collection of positive integers, is less than, or equal to, N, every integer of the collection I is equal to some member of the finite collection $1, 2, \cdots N$ Thus there is a finite collection of distinct integers, F, such that each member of I is equal to a member of F. The greatest integer of F is the greatest of I, so that the first collection I has a greatest integer.

Again, if an infinite collection of positive integers contains the integer N, the integers of the collection less than, or equal to, N determine a finite collection of distinct integers. If M is the least of these, then M is less than, or equal to, all the integers in the collection which do not exceed N. But, since M is less than $N + 1$, it is less than all those integers in the collection which do exceed N. Thus the original infinite collection has a least number M.

1

It follows that any non-empty collection of positive integers contains a least integer. This has as a consequence the principle of *mathematical induction,* which is often useful. We may express it as a theorem:

If the statement of a theorem involves a positive integer n, and if the theorem for any particular value of n implies the theorem for the value n + 1, then the truth of the theorem for the value 1 implies its truth for all positive integral values of n.

To prove this, let $S(n)$ denote the statement of the theorem involving the particular value n. Then consider the collection of positive integers m, such that the statement $S(m)$ is false. If there is at least one integer m, there will be a least integer in this collection. Call this integer k. Since the theorem $S(1)$ is true, and the theorem $S(k)$ is false, k cannot be 1. Therefore, there is a positive integer $k - 1$ which precedes k in the natural order.

Since every value m equals or exceeds k, the integer $k - 1$ is not a value m. Therefore the statement $S(k - 1)$ is true, and by the assumed nature of $S(n)$, this implies that the theorem $S(k)$ is true. Thus we arrive at a contradiction, which shows that the assumption that there was at least one integer m was false. Since the statement $S(n)$ is false for no positive integral values, it is true for all such values.

2. Rational Numbers. In discussing the rational numbers, we take the positive integers and the rules for their addition and multiplication as our starting point. Division is defined as the inverse of multiplication. That is:

$$\frac{a}{b} = x \quad \text{if} \quad bx = a. \tag{1}$$

When we restrict ourselves to the positive integers, division is not always possible since there may not be any integer x which satisfies the second equation for a given pair of integers a and b.

To overcome this difficulty, we introduce the *positive rational numbers.* These are defined in terms of pairs of positive integers. We define equality of two rational numbers by the rule:

$$\frac{a}{b} = \frac{a'}{b'} \quad \text{if} \quad ab' = a'b. \tag{2}$$

We identify certain rational numbers with integers by regarding

$$a = \frac{a}{1}. \tag{3}$$

Addition and multiplication are defined by the rules

$$\frac{a}{b} + \frac{a'}{b'} = \frac{ab' + a'b}{bb'} \tag{4}$$

and

$$\frac{a}{b} \cdot \frac{a'}{b'} = \frac{aa'}{bb'}. \tag{5}$$

Subtraction is defined as the inverse of addition. That is,

$$\frac{a}{b} - \frac{a'}{b'} = x \quad \text{if} \quad \frac{a'}{b'} + x = \frac{a}{b}. \tag{6}$$

If the integer ab' exceeds $a'b$, there is a rational value of x,

$$x = \frac{ab' - a'b}{bb'} \tag{7}$$

which satisfies the second equation (6), but if ab' does not exceed $a'b$, there is no positive rational value of x which satisfies this equation (6).

To overcome this difficulty, we introduce *zero* and the *negative rational numbers*. The rules for combining zero with an integer in the case of addition and multiplication are:

$$a + 0 = a, \quad a \cdot 0 = 0. \tag{8}$$

We indicate negative integers by positive integers with a minus sign affixed and define addition for them by such rules as

$$a + (-b) = a - b = -(b - a), \quad \text{etc.} \tag{9}$$

Multiplication of positive and negative integers is defined by such rules as

$$a(-b) = -ab, \quad (-a)(-b) = ab, \quad \text{etc.} \tag{10}$$

We indicate negative rational numbers in any one of three ways, identifying

$$-\left(\frac{a}{b}\right) = \frac{-a}{b} = \frac{a}{-b}. \tag{11}$$

We also agree to consider

$$\frac{a}{b} = \frac{-a}{-b}. \tag{12}$$

Certain rational numbers are identified with negative integers by the convention that

$$-a = \frac{-a}{1}. \tag{13}$$

We then extend the application of equations (1) through (6) to the case where a and a' are positive or negative integers or zero and where b and b' are positive or negative integers, equations (8) through (12) being used when necessary. We thus find that the relations (8) through (10) hold when a and b are replaced by any positive or negative rational numbers. They will also hold if a or b is replaced by zero and the other is replaced by a rational number, provided we extend the application of equations (8) through (10) to the case where a or b or both are zero. We extend equations (11) and (12) to the case where a is zero and b is not zero, but we do not define division by zero or admit rational fractions with zero as denominator.

The positive and negative rational numbers together with zero constitute the *rational number system*. The system includes the positive and negative integers by the conventions made in equations (3) and (13).

Addition and multiplication when applied to positive integers satisfy the *commutative laws:*

$$a + b = b + a, \quad ab = ba, \tag{14}$$

the *associative laws:*

$$a + (b + c) = (a + b) + c, \quad a(bc) = (ab)c, \tag{15}$$

and the *distributive law:*

$$a(b + c) = ab + ac. \tag{16}$$

We extend these by definition to the case in which a and b are positive or negative integers or zero. These laws then necessarily hold for any numbers of the rational number system in view of our earlier definitions.

We note that, in the rational number system, multiplication, addition, and subtraction are always possible. Division is possible except when the divisor is zero.

We indicate that a rational number is positive by writing

$$r > 0. \tag{17}$$

This enables us to introduce *order* into the rational number system. We do this by writing

$$r' > r \quad \text{or} \quad r < r' \quad \text{if} \quad r' - r > 0. \tag{18}$$

In particular, if $r > 0$, $-r < 0$. Also

$$r' > r \text{ implies } -r' < -r. \tag{19}$$

For any two unequal rational numbers, equation (18) determines which precedes and which follows. However, unlike the set of integers, there is no next greater rational number to any given one, in the way that 3 is the next greater integer to 2.　In fact, we may always insert one rational number, and hence as many as we please, between any two unequal rational numbers.

The positive integers, in their natural order, are enumerated, and any collection of numbers or objects which can be arranged in a single sequence with a first, second, $\cdots$, nth object is said to be *enumerable*. The collection of rational numbers is enumerable, since there are only a finite number of rational fractions a/b with $|a| + |b| = N$.　Here $|a|$ means the *numerical value* of a, that is, a if a is positive and $-a$ if a is negative.　Thus we may take a series of blocks of terms, for which $N = 1, 2, \cdots$ in succession.　The first few terms are:

$$0; \quad 1, \ -1; \quad 2, \ \tfrac{1}{2}, \ -2, \ -\tfrac{1}{2}; \quad 3, \ \tfrac{1}{3}, \ -3, \ -\tfrac{1}{3};$$
$$4, \ \tfrac{3}{2}, \ \tfrac{2}{3}, \ \tfrac{1}{4}, \ -4, \ -\tfrac{3}{2}, \ -\tfrac{2}{3}, \ -\tfrac{1}{4}; \quad \cdots .$$

The terms in each block are arranged according to decreasing numerator for the positive term, followed by the corresponding negative terms. Any number is omitted from the sequence if an equal number has been already listed.

3. Irrational Numbers.　Irrational numbers, and operations with irrational numbers, may be defined in terms of classes of rational numbers in a way similar to the definition of rational numbers in terms of pairs of integers.　We begin by defining a *cut* in the system of rational numbers as a separation of the rational number system into two classes, A and B, with the following properties:

P1.　*Every number in A, the left-hand class, precedes every number in B, the right-hand class.*

P2.　*There are some numbers in each class.*

P3.　*Each number of the rational number system is in one of the two classes.*

Let us denote by a or a_i typical rational numbers of class A, and similarly by b or b_i typical elements of class B.　It follows from the properties P1 and P3 that every number less than any one a is in A.　Similarly, every rational greater than any one b is in B.　There may be a rational number, c, such that for all the elements a and b,

$$a \leqq c \leqq b. \tag{20}$$

In this case, we say that the cut is rational, and identify the rational number c with it.　By the property P3, c is in one of the classes.　But, by equation (20), if it is in A, it is the last number in A and if it is in B, it is the first number in B.　There cannot be two distinct rational numbers c satisfying the relation (20) for all a and b, since if c' were a second such number, numbers between c and c' would have to belong to both classes. Hence as examples of rational cuts, for each of which $c = 3$, we may have:

$$x \text{ in A, if } x < 3; \quad x \text{ in B, if } x \geqq 3, \tag{21}$$

or

$$x \text{ in A, if } x \leqq 3; \quad x \text{ in B, if } x > 3. \tag{22}$$

However, for a given cut, there may not be any rational number c which satisfies the relation (20). In this case, we say that the cut is irrational and regard the cut itself as the definition of an irrational number y. We define y as following all the numbers in A, and preceding all those in B, so that for all elements a and b,

$$a < y < b. \tag{23}$$

As an example of an irrational cut, we have

$$x \text{ in A if either } x < 0 \text{ or } x^2 < 3;$$
$$x \text{ in B if } x > 0 \text{ and also } x^2 > 3.$$

When multiplication is defined for irrational numbers, we shall see that the y for this cut has $y^2 = 3$, so that this cut defines $\sqrt{3}$.

Two irrational numbers y and y' are equal if the elements of A are all elements of A' and if the elements of B are all elements of B'. If the irrational numbers y and y' are not equal, there are two possibilities. Either some element of A, a is an element of B', b', in which case

$$y' < b' = a < y \quad \text{and} \quad y' < y, \tag{24}$$

or some element of B, b is an element of A', a', in which case

$$y < b = a' < y' \quad \text{and} \quad y < y'. \tag{25}$$

Thus the natural order of precedence of two irrational numbers is determined. For a pair of numbers, one of which is rational and one of which is irrational, the order of precedence is determined by the cut defining the irrational number in accordance with the relation (23).

The rational and irrational numbers together make up the *real number system*.

4. Real Numbers. It follows from our definition that every cut **in** the system of rational numbers with the properties P1, P2, P3 determines a single real number. It is often desirable to replace P3 by an alternative property:

P3′. *Given any positive real number ϵ, it is possible to find a number a of the class* A *and a number b of the class* B *such that* $b - a$ *is at most* ϵ.

The property P3$'$ is of such a nature that if it holds for a particular ϵ, it will necessarily hold for any larger value of ϵ. Thus in most applications of P3$'$ we shall be concerned with small values of ϵ. Again, for any given irrational positive number, we may find a smaller rational positive number. Consequently, to show that P3$'$ holds, it will only be necessary to show that it holds for rational values of ϵ.

We shall now show that any cut satisfying the properties P1, P2, P3 also has the alternative property P3$'$. Let a_1 be any element belonging to class A for the given cut, and consider any rational value of ϵ for which we desire to test P3$'$. Form the sequence

$$a_1, \; a_1 + \epsilon, \; a_1 + 2\epsilon, \; \cdots, \; a_1 + N\epsilon. \tag{26}$$

If b_1 is any element of class B, and we take N large enough, the last number of the sequence, $a_1 + N\epsilon$, will exceed b_1 and hence will itself be a member of class B. Thus the elements of the sequence (26) will be in A, up to a certain one, $a_1 + n\epsilon$, and from there on they will be in B. Consequently, the property P3$'$ may be satisfied for the ϵ considered by taking

$$a = a_1 + n\epsilon, \quad b = a_1 + (n+1)\epsilon, \quad b - a = \epsilon. \tag{27}$$

We next show that any cut satisfying the properties P1, P2, P3$'$ determines a single real number. Let A$'$ and B$'$ denote the two classes for the given cut. We replace class A$'$ by an enlarged class A, which contains not only all the elements of A$'$ but all the rational numbers less than any number in A$'$ Similarly we enlarge the class B$'$ to a class B containing all the rational numbers greater than any element of B$'$ as well as all the elements of B$'$.

If the enlarged classes A and B include all the rational numbers, P3 is satisfied and a real number is defined.

If the enlarged classes include all the rational numbers except one, r, this number must be greater than all the elements of A and less than all the elements of B. Consequently, if we add r to the class A, we have a cut defining the rational number r.

Finally, suppose that at least two distinct rational numbers r and r' are not included in the enlarged classes A and B. Then, for any elements a of A and b of B, we would have:

$$a < r, \quad b > r', \tag{28}$$

where r' is taken as the greater of the two. Hence

$$b - a > r' - r, \tag{29}$$

since $b - a - (r' - r) = (b - r') + (r - a)$ is positive. But, since $r' > r, r' - r$ is positive and we may take it as the ϵ of the property P3$'$

We thus obtain a pair of elements a of A′ and hence of A, b of B′ and hence of B, for which

$$b - a \leqq \epsilon, \quad \text{or} \quad b - a \leqq r' - r. \tag{30}$$

As this contradicts the relation (29), the possibility of there being more than one rational number omitted from the classes A and B is excluded.

Since a cut which has the properties P1, P2, P3 also has the property P3′, while a cut with the properties P1, P2, P3′ may be modified to give a cut with the property P3, we usually consider a given cut which determines a real number as having all four properties: P1, P2, P3, P3′. However, in constructing a cut to determine a new real number, it is only necessary to establish P1, P2, and either P3 or P3′. We shall frequently find P3′ the more convenient.

5. Operations on Real Numbers. If two given real numbers y and y' are defined by cuts, and if we denote typical elements so that:

$$a \leqq y \leqq b, \quad a' \leqq y' \leqq b', \tag{31}$$

the sum of the numbers y and y' is defined by requiring that:

$$a + a' \leqq y + y' \leqq b + b' \tag{32}$$

for all choices of a, b, a', b'.

Since the property P1 holds for the two given cuts, the equality cannot take place in both cases in either of the relations (31). Hence for all choices, $a + a' < b + b'$, and the cut with all sums $a + a'$ in class A and with all sums $b + b'$ in class B will satisfy the property P1.

The property P2 will obviously hold for the new cut if it holds for the original cuts.

Finally, from property P3′ applied to the two original cuts, we may find pairs a, b and a', b' such that:

$$b - a \leqq \tfrac{1}{2}\epsilon, \quad b' - a' \leqq \tfrac{1}{2}\epsilon, \tag{33}$$

where ϵ is any positive quantity. It follows from this that

$$(b + b') - (a + a') = (b - a) + (b' - a') \leqq \epsilon. \tag{34}$$

Thus the new cut satisfies the property P3′, as well as the properties P1 and P2, and so defines a single real number.

By extending the application of the second equation (8) and the equation (10) to real numbers, we may reduce the multiplication of real numbers to the multiplication of positive numbers. For two positive real numbers, we put:

$$aa' \leqq yy' \leqq bb', \quad \text{if} \quad y > 0, y' > 0, a > 0, a' > 0. \tag{35}$$

By an argument similar to that used in the case of addition, we may show that this leads to a cut satisfying the properties P1, P2, and P3′ and hence defines a single real number.

In deducing the products of negative real numbers from the products of the corresponding positive numbers, we need a method of finding the cut for $-y$ when that for y is given. If a and b are typical elements of the cut for y, as in the relation (31), $-b$ and $-a$ are typical elements of the cut for $-y$, since:

$$-b \leqq -y \leqq -a. \tag{36}$$

This relation also enables us to define subtraction by the relation:

$$y' - y = y' + (-y). \tag{37}$$

To define division, we first define the reciprocal of a positive number y by using only the elements a which are positive. We use a subscript p to indicate the restriction to positive elements. Then we put:

$$\frac{1}{b} \leqq \frac{1}{y} \leqq \frac{1}{a_p}, \quad \text{if} \quad y > 0, \quad \text{where} \quad a_p > 0. \tag{38}$$

We then define the reciprocal of a negative number by

$$\frac{1}{-y} = -\frac{1}{y}, \tag{39}$$

and finally define division by

$$\frac{y'}{y} = y'\left(\frac{1}{y}\right). \tag{40}$$

We may show that the cut given by the relation (38) leads to a single real number, by showing that the properties P1, P2, and P3′ hold.

The definitions of the four fundamental operations for real numbers given in this section are in agreement with all our earlier rules. In particular, we continue to have subtraction the inverse of addition and division the inverse of multiplication.

6. Cuts in the Real Number System. It is a natural extension of our previous definition to consider as a cut in the real number system any separation of the real numbers into two classes A and B if it satisfies the three properties:

R1. *Every number in A, the left-hand class, precedes every number in B, the right-hand class.*

R2. *There are some numbers in each class.*

R3. *Each number of the real number system is in one of the two classes.*

These statements differ from the corresponding ones of section 3 only in having rational replaced by real in R3 and in having the word number mean real number instead of rational number.

We shall show that for cuts in the real number system there is always a real number which makes the separation. We first observe that the separation of the real numbers which satisfies the properties R1, R2, R3 involves a separation of the rational numbers which satisfies the properties P1, P2, P3. This cut defines a single real number y. If a_1 is any rational element of A, and b_1 is any rational element of B, we shall have:

$$a_1 \leqq y \leqq b_1. \tag{41}$$

Again, if a is any irrational number less than y, there are rational numbers between a and y. Let a_1 be one of them. Then

$$a < a_1 < y, \tag{42}$$

and since a_1 is in A, a is also in A. Similarly, any irrational number greater than y is in B. Thus for all real numbers a in A and b in B, and the y defined by the relation (41), we must have:

$$a \leqq y \leqq b, \tag{43}$$

with one of the equality signs holding for y itself, which must be in one class or the other, in view of the property R3.

Thus cuts in the real number system bear the same relation to that system that rational cuts bear to the system of rational numbers. In particular, cuts in the real number system do not lead to any new numbers. These results are expressed in the theorem of Dedekind:

Every cut in the real number system satisfying the properties R1, R2, R3 *is effected by a unique real number.*

By using the results of section 4, we may show that all the conclusions of this section continue to hold if we replace R3 by the alternative R3′:

R3′. *Given any positive real number* ϵ, *it is possible to find a number* a *of class* A, *and a number* b *of class* B *such that* $b - a$ *is at most* ϵ.

This statement does not differ in wording from P3 but differs slightly in intent, since the a and b of R3′ may be irrational. However, it is not difficult to show that if irrational values can be found, rational ones can also be found with $b - a$ at most ϵ, for any given positive ϵ.

7. Geometric Representation. If we take a straight line, regarded as indefinitely extended in both directions, we may match up its points with real numbers, coördinates of the points, in the following way. We select one point as an origin, which we mark zero. We take one of the directions on the line as positive and mark a point one unit away from the origin in this direction with one. By repeating this operation, we obtain the points for two, three, and the other positive integers. Points on the opposite side of the origin, found in a similar way, are marked with the negative integers. We may view the line from such a position that the positive is the right-hand direction and the negative is the left-hand direction. To suggest this image, we shall sometimes use the terms right and left in place of positive and negative direction. By a familiar construction of elementary geometry, a point for any rational number may be found. We take it as a geometric assumption that there is a single point on the line for any irrational number which separates the points with rational coördinates in the same way that the irrational number separates the rational numbers. We also assume that for each point on the line there is a single real coördinate.

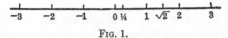

Fig. 1.

The geometric picture is helpful in following analytic arguments. To suggest this picture, we use an abbreviated form of language. Thus we speak of rational points when we mean points with rational coördinates. Also we use the phrase " the point a " in place of the expression " the point with a as its coördinate."

By numbers x, or points x, in the interval a,b where $a < b$, we mean the coördinates of the points, or the points themselves inside the interval with the points a and b as end points. Thus the numbers x satisfy the relation:

$$a < x < b. \tag{44}$$

When we wish to emphasize that the end points a and b are not included, we use the phrase " points of the *open interval a,b* " to mean " those points x which satisfy the relation (44)."

If we wish to include the end points a and b, we use the phrase " points of the *closed interval a,b* " to mean those points x which satisfy the relation:

$$a \leqq x \leqq b. \tag{45}$$

8. Limit Points. A collection of real numbers or their corresponding points on a line is called a *point set*. A point set may have only a finite number of points, or it may have an infinite number of points. It may include whole intervals or, as an extreme case, consist of all the points of the coördinate axis.

Consider a set of points, denoted by S, and a point x, corresponding to a real number x, which may or may not belong to S. If every open interval which includes x includes at least one point of S different from x, then x is said to be a *limit point* of the set. It follows from this definition that every open interval which includes x contains an infinite number of points of S. For suppose that x is a limit point of S and that the open interval a,b includes x. If y_1 is one point of S in the interval, since it is distinct from x, the point x will be included in one of the open intervals a,y_1 or y_1,b. Thus this interval will include a second point of S, y_2, distinct from x. We may repeat this process to obtain a sequence of points $y_1, y_2, y_3, \cdots$, each of which is distinct from x and from all those which precede it.

A limit point of a set may or may not belong to the set. Thus the set consisting of the numbers

$$1, \ 0.9, \ 0.99, \ 0.999, \ \cdots \tag{46}$$

has 1 as a limit point and 1 as a member of the set. On the other hand, the set consisting of the numbers

$$1, \ \tfrac{1}{2}, \ \tfrac{1}{3}, \ \tfrac{1}{4}, \ \cdots \tag{47}$$

has zero as a limit point, and zero does not belong to the set.

Since every open interval includes rational points, if the set S consists of all the rational points of any open interval a,b, then all the points of the closed interval a,b will be limit points of S.

9. Bolzano-Weierstrass Theorem. Since every open interval including a limit point of S includes an infinite number of distinct points of S, it follows that a set containing only a finite number of points cannot have any limit points. A set may have an infinite number of points without having any limit points. An example is the set consisting of all the positive integers. That this situation cannot arise when all the points of the set can be included in some finite interval is the content of the Bolzano-Weierstrass theorem, which asserts that:

For every set of points lying in a finite interval and having infinitely many elements, at least one point of the interval is a limit point.

To prove this, consider a·set S containing an infinite number of points all of which are included in some finite interval, say the closed interval a,b. Define a cut in the real number system in the following manner. To class A, we assign a and all other numbers x such that, at most, a finite number of points of S have coördinates less than x. To class B, we assign b and all other numbers x' such that there is an infinite number of points of S with coördinates less than x'.

This cut satisfies the properties R1, R2, R3 of section 6, and therefore, by Dedekind's theorem, is effected by a unique real number which we denote by y. If, now, x,x' is any open interval which includes y, then x is a number of class A and x' is a number of class B. Hence there are an infinite number of points of S with coördinates less than x', of which only a finite number can have coördinates less than x. Thus there must be an infinite number of points of S in the open interval x,x' and therefore at least one point of S distinct from y in this interval, as demanded by the definition of limit point. Hence y is a limit point of S.

The method of proof shows that no limit point of the set S can precede y. If we had begun by assigning to class A all numbers such that an infinite number of points of S had larger coördinates, and to class B all numbers such that at most a finite number of points of S had larger coördinates, we should have found a point y' (possibly identical with y) such that no limit point of the set could follow y'. This proves that:

For every set of points lying in a finite interval and having infinitely many elements, there is a first limit point and also a last limit point.

10. Bounds. If a point set on a finite interval has only a finite number of elements but has at least one element, there will necessarily be a first point and a last point. Since these are the points of the set with the least and the greatest coördinates, we also refer to them as the least and greatest elements of the set.

If a point set S on a finite interval contains an infinite number of elements, we must have a first limit point y and a last limit point y', as shown in the preceding section. The set of points S may, or may not, include elements to the left of y. If it does, and x_1 is a point of S which precedes y, there is at most a finite number of points of S less than, or equal to, x_1, and we denote the first of these by B_1. If there are no elements of S to the left of y, we put B_1 equal to y itself. In either case, the point B_1 is called the *greatest lower bound* of the set S.

If there are elements of S which precede y, or if B_1 is itself a member of S, then B_1 is the least element of S. When y is not a member of S, and there are no elements of S which precede y, the set has no least element. The greatest lower bound, B_1, always has the property that there are no points of S to the left of B_1, but any closed interval B_1,c with B_1 as its left-hand end point, contains at least one point of the set, say x. For, when B_1 is the least element of the set, we may take B_1 itself as the point x. If the set S has no least element, there are points of the set in B_1,c since B_1 is then a limit point of the set and there are no points of the set to the left of B_1.

The point B_1 is thus the point with greatest coördinate having no points of S to its left. This explains the term greatest lower bound.

It will help the student to keep its meaning clear if he notes that *lower* is the important word in the phrase and that greatest is merely a modifier.

We say that a point set S is bounded from below if there is some point on the line to the left of all points of the set. Any point not to the right of any point of the set is called a *lower bound* for the set. If a is any lower bound for the set S, and x_1 is any element of S, we may form a new set S' by taking all those points x' which are in S and also have $a \leqq x' \leqq x_1$. As S' is on a finite interval, we may find a greatest lower bound B_1 for it. This will be the greatest number not exceeding any number x', and hence the greatest number not exceeding any coördinate of a point of S.

We may restate these results in terms of the coördinates of the points.

A lower bound of a set of numbers is any number not exceeding any number of the set.

A set of numbers is said to be bounded from below if it has a lower bound.

A set of numbers which contains at least one number and is bounded from below has a greatest lower bound.

We define upper bounds in a similar way and may obtain a similar result for them. Thus:

An upper bound of a set of numbers is any number not exceeded by any number of the set.

A set of numbers is said to be bounded from above if it has an upper bound.

A set of numbers which contains at least one number and is bounded from above has a least upper bound.

11. Heine-Borel Covering Theorem. We proceed to discuss a theorem on sets of intervals. Let I denote a set of intervals on a line. These intervals may be infinite in number and may overlap one another. It is immaterial for our purposes whether these intervals include their end points or not, but for definiteness we shall think of them as open intervals.

Let C denote a particular closed interval a,b related to a set of intervals I in the following way: For each point x of C, that is, each x such that

$$a \leqq x \leqq b, \tag{48}$$

we may find some interval of the set I containing x as an interior point, say the interval

$$y < x < y'. \tag{49}$$

We may use any interval of I for several, or even for an infinite number, of its interior points. Again, it may be possible to find several, or even an infinite number, of intervals of I which will serve for a particular point x.   We describe the relation of C to I by saying that the set of intervals I *covers* the fundamental interval C.

The Heine-Borel covering theorem states that:

If an infinite set of intervals I covers a fundamental closed interval C, then a finite number of intervals may be selected from the set I, such that this finite subset of intervals covers the fundamental closed interval C.

To prove this theorem, we first define an accessible point of the interval C as a point of C, c, such that the closed interval a,c can be covered by a finite number of intervals selected from the set I.   There are some accessible points, for a is in some interval of I so that any point of this interval to the right of a is accessible.   If c is accessible, all points between a and c will also be accessible.

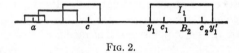

FIG. 2.

The set of accessible points is on a finite interval and therefore has a least upper bound, B_2.   Since b is an upper bound for all the points of C, it is an upper bound for the accessible points of C.   Thus either $B_2 < b$ or $B_2 = b$.

Suppose we had the first case, $B_2 < b$.   Then B_2, as a point of C, is in some interval of the set I, say I_1:

$$y_1 < x < y_1'. \tag{50}$$

From the properties of B_2 as a least upper bound of accessible points, there is at least one accessible point in I_1, say c_1, such that:

$$y_1 < c_1 \leqq B_2, \tag{51}$$

but any point c_2 such that

$$B_2 < c_2 < y_1', \tag{52}$$

is not accessible.

But this is an impossible situation.   For the finite set of intervals which cover the closed interval a,c_1 together with I_1, covers the closed interval a,c_2 so that c_2 is accessible.   This contradiction rules out the possibility $B_2 < b$.

Thus $B_2 = b$, and since the argument used for c_2 shows that B_2 is itself accessible, we can cover the whole interval a,b with a finite number of intervals of the set I, as stated in the theorem.

We may modify the meaning of the term cover by omitting all parts of intervals outside the fundamental interval and merely requiring a to be the left end and b to be the right end of some interval of I, in this case allowing some of the intervals of I to be closed. The proof proceeds exactly as before.

12. Closed Sets. The limit points of a set of points may, or may not be, points of the set. We define a *closed set of points* as a set of points which does contain all its limit points. Thus a closed interval is a simple example of a closed set.

Since the greatest lower bound of any set of points is either the first point of the set or the first limit point of the set, the greatest lower bound of a closed set necessarily belongs to the set and is the first point of the set. Thus *a closed set on a finite interval always has a first point and a last point.*

The theorem of the last section remains true if we replace the closed interval C by any closed set on a finite interval. If every point of a set S is an interior point of some interval of a set I, we say that the set of intervals I *covers* the set of points S. The modified theorem reads:

If an infinite set of intervals I covers a fundamental closed set of points S lying in a finite interval, then a finite number of intervals may be selected from the set I, such that this finite subset of intervals covers the fundamental closed set of points S.

Let a and b be the first and last points of the finite interval. If c is the mid-point of a,b, we may form two new closed sets S', the points of S in the closed interval a,c, and S'', the points of S in the closed interval c,b. If the conclusion of the theorem held for each of these sets, it would hold for S, since the two finite subsets of intervals, taken together with common intervals counted once, would form a new subset covering S. Thus, if the theorem is false for S, it must be false for S' or S'', or both. If both, take S'; otherwise, take the one for which it is false. Revise the notation, calling this set for which the theorem is false S_1, and relabel the end points of the interval of length $(b - a)/2$ on which it lies a_1 and b_1.

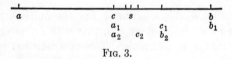

FIG. 3.

Now repeat the argument, using c_1, the mid-point of a_1, b_1, and so obtain a set S_2 on an interval a_2, b_2 of length $(b - a)/4$. Then continue in this way. We thus obtain a sequence of sets S_n on an interval a_n, b_n of length $(b - a)/2^n$, for each of which the theorem is false.

Since any finite number of points of S can be covered by a finite subset of intervals I, using a different interval for each point, each of the sets S_n must contain an infinite number of points. Thus we may select a point s_1 in S_1, s_2 a different point in S_2, and so on. The set of points $s_1, s_2, \cdots s_n \cdots$, being infinite in number and all on the finite interval a,b, have at least one limit point. Since all the s_n belong to S, and the set S is closed, this limit point belongs to S. Call it s. Then s is an interior point of some interval of the set I, say I_0:

$$y < s < y'. \tag{53}$$

If the point s were outside of any of the intervals a_n,b_n, an interval containing s and not containing the interval a_m,b_m would not contain any of the s_n with subscripts larger than m. Thus s could not be a limit point of the s_n. This proves that s is in every one of the intervals a_n,b_n so that

$$a_n \leqq s \leqq b_n. \tag{54}$$

From this and the relation (53) we may prove that

$$y < a_n < b_n < y' \tag{55}$$

if n is sufficiently large. For since

$$b_n - a_n = \frac{b - a}{2^n}, \tag{56}$$

it may be made smaller than any fixed number by taking n large enough. Thus, in particular, for some value of n we shall have

$$b_n - a_n < y' - s \quad \text{and} \quad b_n - a_n < s - y. \tag{57}$$

But, for this n the relation (54) holds, and it may be written:

$$a_n \leqq s \quad \text{and} \quad -b_n \leqq -s. \tag{58}$$

It follows from the last two relations, (57) and (58), that:

$$b_n < y' \quad \text{and} \quad -a_n < -y \quad \text{or} \quad y < a_n. \tag{59}$$

Since $b > a$, equation (56) shows that $b_n > a_n$, which may be combined with the relations (59) to give the relation (55).

But the relation (55) shows that the interval a_n,b_n is covered by the interval I. Thus the set S_n on this interval is covered by the single interval I, so that the assumed falsity of the theorem for S, which implied its falsity for S_n, leads to a contradiction.

Thus the theorem must be true for S, and we have proved the modified theorem.

13. Two Dimensions, Definitions. We associate points in a plane with pairs of real numbers by the use of two rectangular axes, an x-axis and a y-axis. We take the point of intersection of these axes as the origin of a real number scale on each of the lines. Then any point in the plane has a projection on each axis, determined by a line through the point perpendicular to the axis considered or parallel to the other axis. If these projected points have coördinates x and y in their respective scales, we speak of the point as having the coördinates (x,y), or briefly refer to it as the point (x,y). Each point determines such an ordered pair of real numbers, and conversely each such ordered pair determines a point in the plane, by our geometric assumption on the correspondence of numbers to points on a line.

We refer to the points whose coördinates satisfy the inequalities

$$a < x < b, \quad c < y < d \tag{60}$$

as the points of the *open two-dimensional interval a,b;c,d* and frequently omit the phrase two-dimensional if it is implied by the context.

If we wish to include the boundary points of such a rectangular region, we use the phrase *closed two-dimensional* interval $a,b;c,d$. Thus this means the points whose coördinates satisfy the relations

$$a \leqq x \leqq b, \quad c \leqq y \leqq d. \tag{61}$$

Any collection of points in the plane is called a *point set*. A point (x,y) is a *limit point* of a set S if every open two-dimensional interval of the plane which includes (x,y) includes at least one point of S different from (x,y). As in the one-dimensional case, it follows that the open interval must include an infinite number of points of S.

A set of points is said to be a *closed set* if its limit points all belong to the set.

14. Two Dimensions, Theorems. We may extend the Bolzano-Weierstrass theorem to two dimensions. The new form of the theorem is:

For every set of points lying in a finite two-dimensional interval and having infinitely many elements, at least one point of the interval is a limit point.

To prove this, let the two-dimensional interval $a,b;c,d$ be one which contains the set S. Divide this into four two-dimensional intervals by bisecting the two one-dimensional intervals a,b at e and c,d at f. The four new intervals are: $a,e;f,d$, $e,b;f,d$, $a,e;c,f$, and $e,b;c,f$. At least one of these must contain an infinite number of points of S. If more than one contains an infinite number of points, we take that one which occurs first in the order listed above. Revise the notation so that the selected infinite set of points is S_1 on R_1, the interval $a_1,b_1;c_1,d_1$ of dimensions $(b - a)/2$, $(d - c)/2$.

Now treat S_1 as we did the original set, thus obtaining a set S_2. Continuing in this way, we shall obtain an infinite succession of sets S_n on R_n, the interval $a_n,b_n;c_n,d_n$ of dimensions $(b - a)/2^n$, $(d - c)/2^n$.

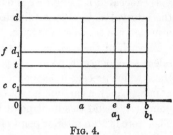

Fig. 4.

Next consider the points with co-ordinates a_n on the x-axis. If there is an infinite number of distinct points in this set, the argument used in section 12 shows that there is a limit point s which is contained in all the intervals a_n,b_n. If there is only a finite number of distinct points in this set, it follows from the method by which they were obtained that all the a_n from a certain point on will have a common value. If we call this s, all the intervals a_n,b_n will contain s.

Similarly we may find a point t on the y-axis which is either a limit point of the c_n or equal to all of them from some point on. In either case it will be in all the intervals c_n,d_n.

The point (s,t) is in all of the two-dimensional intervals R_n. But the dimensions of R_n are $(b - a)/2^n$ and $(d - c)/2^n$ and so may each be made less than any fixed number by taking n large enough. Consequently, any given open two-dimensional interval containing the point (s,t) will contain some one of the R_n, and thus the corresponding set of points S_n. As this includes an infinite number of points of S, at least one will be distinct from (s,t) and the point (s,t) is a limit point of S. This proves the theorem.

We may also extend the Heine-Borel covering theorem to two dimensions. In two dimensions, the phrase " the set of intervals I covers the set of points S " means that every point of S is an interior point of some two-dimensional interval of the set I.

We need only consider the extension of the modified covering theorem of section 12, since that theorem includes the theorem of section 11 as a special case. . The two-dimensional extension is as follows:

If an infinite set of two-dimensional intervals I covers a fundamental closed set of points S lying in a finite two-dimensional interval, then a finite number of intervals may be selected from the set I, such that this finite subset of intervals covers the fundamental closed set of points S.

To prove it, we select a two-dimensional interval $a,b;c,d$ which contains the set S and divide it into four two-dimensional intervals by bisecting the two one-dimensional intervals.   Then, if the theorem were false for the set S, we could select a set from among these four for which it was false.   With revised notation, this would be a set S_1 on R_1, the interval $a_1,b_1;c_1,d_1$ of dimensions $(b - a)/2$, $(d - c)/2$.

By repeated bisection we should obtain a sequence of sets S_n on R_n, the interval $a_n,b_n;c_n,d_n$ of dimensions $(b - a)/2^n$, $(d - c)/2^n$, for each of which the theorem was false.

As each of these S_n contains an infinite number of points, we could select a sequence of points (x_n,y_n) from S_n, each point distinct from all those which precede it, as for the earlier proof in this section.   The set of points (x_n,y_n), as an infinite set of points on a finite interval, has a limit point (x,y), and this limit point belongs to S, since the set S is closed. Therefore it is an interior point of some interval I_0 of I, since I covers S.

But since all except a finite number of points (x_n,y_n) are inside any interval R_n, the limit point (x,y) must be in all the R_n.   Since the dimensions of R_n, $(b - a)/2^n$ and $(d - c)/2^n$ can be made less than any fixed positive quantity by taking n large enough, for some value of n the interval I_0 will contain R_n.   Thus it will contain the corresponding set S_n.   Since the set S_n is covered by this single interval, this contradicts the assumption that the theorem was false for S, from which we deduced that the theorem was false for S_n.   Thus the theorem must be true for S, and we have proved the two-dimensional covering theorem.

15. Higher Dimensions.   We may consider any number, k, of one-dimensional scales as axes belonging to $x_1, x_2, \cdots , x_k$.   We continue to use geometric language, referring to $X = (x_1, x_2, \cdots , x_k)$ as a point in k dimensions, although we make no attempt to interpret our statements graphically when k is greater than 3.   The definitions of section 13 are easily extended to k dimensions.   Thus the inequalities

$$a_i < x_i < b_i, \quad i = 1, 2, \cdots , k \tag{62}$$

define an open k-dimensional interval, and

$$a_i \leqq x_i \leqq b_i, \quad i = 1, 2, \cdots , k \tag{63}$$

define a closed k-dimensional interval.

The definition of point set remains unchanged, and the definition of limit point and covering merely require us to read k-dimensional for two-dimensional.   There is no change in the definition of limit point.

The theorems of section 14 remain true when we replace two-dimensional by k-dimensional, and the methods of proof given there require only minor modifications.

Since the intervals we have used are bounded by $(k - 1)$-dimensional planes parallel to certain axes, our results seem to depend on the direction of the axes. However, we might use in place of a set of intervals I, a set of k-dimensional spheres K given by

$$\sum_{i=1}^{k} (x_i - c_i)^2 \leqq r^2. \tag{64}$$

That the covering theorem still holds follows from the fact that any sphere K containing X as an interior point includes some interval I containing X as an interior point. Similarly, any interval containing X as an interior point includes some sphere containing X as an interior point.

For any figure or point set in k-dimensional space, we define an interior point P as one for which all the points of some k-dimensional sphere with P as a center are points of the figure or set. An *open k-dimensional region* is a figure for which every point is an interior point. The covering theorem remains true if we use k-dimensional open regions of arbitrary shape in place of the covering intervals.

EXERCISES I

1. Using mathematical induction, prove the binomial theorem $(a + b)^n = a^n + na^{n-1}b + \cdots + {}^nC_r a^{n-r}b^r + \cdots + b^n$, for integral values of n, where

$$^nC_r = \frac{n(n - 1)(n - 2) \cdots (n - r + 1)}{1 \cdot 2 \cdot 3 \cdot \cdots r}.$$

2. Prove that

$$\sum_{p=1}^{n} p(p + 1)(p + 2) \cdots (p + m - 1) = \frac{n(n + 1)(n + 2) \cdots (n + m)}{m + 1}.$$

3. From problem 2, and an induction on m, prove that if $P(x)$ is a polynomial of the mth degree, the sum

$$P(1) + P(2) + P(3) + \cdots + P(n)$$

will be a polynomial in n of the $(m + 1)$st degree.

4. Prove the rule of cancellation for rational fractions

$$\frac{ma}{mb} = \frac{a}{b}.$$

5. Show that every positive rational fraction may be reduced to lowest terms or expressed as the quotient of two integers relatively prime, that is, without common factors other than unity.

6. If a, b, a', b', m, and n are all positive integers, and $ab' < a'b$, prove that $\dfrac{ma + na'}{mb + nb'}$ and $\dfrac{mab' + na'b}{(m + n)bb'}$ are each a rational number intermediate in value between $\dfrac{a}{b}$ and $\dfrac{a'}{b'}$.

7. Prove that the adopted law of signs for negative quantities is the only one consistent with the properties of zero and the distributive law for products. *Hint:* Use the relations $b - b = 0$, $a(b - b) = 0$, $ab + a(-b) = 0$, $a(-b) = -ab$.

8. Prove that, if $a \neq 0$, no value of x is defined by $\dfrac{a}{0}$, interpreted to mean $x \cdot 0 = a$; while if $a = 0$, any value of x satisfies the latter relation. This is why we do not define division by zero.

9. Prove that, if b and b' are both positive integers, $\dfrac{a}{b} < \dfrac{a'}{b'}$ if, and only if, $ab' < a'b$.

10. Prove that, if $a < b$ and $c < d$, $a + c < b + d$ and $a - d < b - c$.

11. Prove that, for any two positive rational numbers a and b, an integer N can be found such that $Na > b$.

12. If m and n take on all positive integral values, show that the set of values a_{mn} is enumerable.

13. If $a(n_1, n_2, \cdots, n_k)$ depends on a finite number of variables, each of which takes on all positive integral values, show that the set of values assumed is enumerable. *Hint:* Use mathematical induction and the preceding problem.

14. Assuming that no rational number has its square equal to 2, show that a cut with the properties P1, P2, and P3 of section 3 is defined by the following conditions: x is in class A if $x < 0$ or $x^2 < 2$, and x is in class B if $x > 0$ and also $x^2 > 2$.

15. Verify that 1, 1.4 are in class A and that 2, 1.5 are in class B for the cut defined in problem 14.

16. If p and q are relatively prime, show that the fraction p^2/q^2 is in its lowest terms as written. From this, show that no positive integer, not a perfect square, has a rational square root. Assume the theorem that every positive integer may be factored into prime factors in only one way.

17. State and prove a result similar to that of problem 16 for the nth root of a positive integer.

18. If the rational number x equals p/q when reduced to lowest terms and satisfies the equation

$$a_n x^n + a_{n-1} x^{n-1} + \cdots + a_1 x + a_0 = 0,$$

where the coefficients are all integers, and a_n and a_0 are both different from zero, prove that p is a divisor of a_0 and q is a divisor of a_n. (Gauss.)

19. Show that the equation $4x^3 - 12x^2 - x + 3 = 0$ has three rational roots, then find the roots. Also show that the equation $x^3 + 4x + 1 = 0$ has no rational roots. *Hint:* Use the result of problem 18.

20. If 0.9, 0.99, 0.999, $\cdots$ are all in class A, and 1.1, 1.01, 1.001, $\cdots$ are all in class B, show that the cut must be that which is identified with the rational number 1.

21. If 0.3, 0.33, 0.333, $\cdots$ are all in class A and 0.4, 0.34, 0.334, $\cdots$ are all in class B, show that the cut must be that which is identified with the rational number $1/3$.

22. For the cut which defines $\sqrt{2}$, find two rational numbers, a in class A and b in class B, which differ by not more than .01.

23. For the cut which defines $\sqrt{3}$, find two rational numbers, a in class A and b in class B, which differ by not more than 0.1.

24. Using the identity $bb' - aa' = a(b' - a') + b'(b - a)$, show that, if we take $b_1' - a_1' < \epsilon/2a_1$, where a_1 is any element of class A, and $b_1 - a_1 < \epsilon/2b_1'$, we shall have $b_1b_1' - a_1a_1' < \epsilon$. This proves that the cut for yy' defined in section 5 satisfies the property P3'. Assume y and y' positive, and take a_1 and a_1' positive.

25. Show that, if $y > 0$, and we take $b - a < \epsilon a^2$, where a is any positive element in A, we shall have $1/a - 1/b < \epsilon$. This proves that the cut for $1/y$ defined in section 5 satisfies the property P3'.

26. Prove from the definition that $y \cdot (1/y) = 1$.

27. Prove from the definition that $y + (-y) = 0$.

28. If $|y|$, the numerical value of y, is defined as y if $y \geqq 0$ and $-y$ if $y < 0$, prove that $|x + y| \leqq |x| + |y|$.

29. Let regular polygons of n sides be inscribed in and circumscribed to a circle of unit radius. Call I_n the perimeter of an inscribed polygon and C_n that of a circumscribed polygon. Prove that, if we let the numbers I_n be in class A, and the numbers C_n be in class B, the properties P1, P2, and P3' are satisfied. The number defined by this cut is 2π.

30. Show that 0 and 1 are the limit points of the set $\dfrac{1}{2} \pm \dfrac{n}{2n + 1}$, and that there are no others, where n takes on all positive integral values.

31. Show that every number x such that $0 \leqq x \leqq 1$ is a limit point of the set $b/2^n$, where n is any positive integer and b is any odd positive integer less than 2^n.

32. For any irrational number y let the fractional parts of the numbers ny, for all integral values of n, form a set. This set has every value of x, $0 \leqq x \leqq 1$ as a limit point. *Hint:* After $N + 1$ points have been plotted, some pair, say the fractional parts of $n'y$ and $n''y$, will be at distance from one another less than $1/N$. Then the set of values $k(n'' - n')y$, for integral values of k, yield a set of fractional parts on the interval 0,1 some one of which is nearer than $1/N$ to any point on this interval.

33. Show that 0 is the greatest lower bound and 1 is the least upper bound for each of the three sets described in problems 30, 31, and 32.

34. Show that the Heine-Borel theorem does not apply to the interval 0,1 if the intervals are $1/n < x < 2/n$, where n is a positive integer, but that the theorem becomes applicable if any one interval having zero as a left end point, e.g., $0 \leqq x < 1/N$ for any value of N, is added to the set of intervals.

CHAPTER II

LIMITS OF FUNCTIONS

We are now in a position to discuss the concept of functional dependence of one real variable on another. We shall develop certain results on the approach of a variable to a limit which are related to the notion of continuous function. We then proceed to study certain consequences of the property of continuity.

16. Function. We say that y is a *function* of x and write $y = f(x)$ if, for each of a certain set of values of x, there is determined one, or more than one, value of y. We refer to the values of x considered as the range of the variable x. If, for each x of the range, there is exactly one value of y, the function is *single-valued*. We call x the independent variable and y the dependent variable. In this chapter, the values of x and y will always be real numbers.

17. Limits. We wish now to consider certain special ranges for the independent variable, t, and several other variables a, b, etc., each of which is functionally dependent on t. The range of t will always include an infinite number of values, which we may consider successively.

These values, taken in order, may change abruptly. For example, the values of t may be: $1, 2, 3, \cdots$ or $1, \frac{1}{2}, \frac{1}{3}, \cdots$. In such cases the values form a discrete sequence. Or t may take on in order all the points of an open interval — for example, increasing from 0 to 1 through all the intermediate values. Or t may increase from 0 through all positive real values, or decrease from 0 through all negative real values. In these cases the values of t form a continuous sequence.

We write a_t in place of $a(t)$ to indicate that we are considering the single-valued variable a for a discrete or continuous sequence of values of t taken in order. We say that:

The variable a_t approaches a finite limit A if beyond a certain point in its succession of values the numerical value of the difference between a_t and A becomes and stays smaller than any fixed positive quantity.

We write in this case

$$\lim a_t = A. \tag{1}$$

If we denote the numerical value of any real number c by $|c|$, so that $|c| = c$ if $c \geqq 0$ and $|c| = -c$ if $c < 0$, the numerical value of the difference which occurs in the definition is $|A - a_t|$. We often use ϵ to indicate a positive quantity which may be taken arbitrarily small. With this symbolism we may restate the definition: $\lim a_t = A$ if for any positive ϵ,

$$|A - a_t| < \epsilon, \quad \text{for } t \text{ beyond } t_\epsilon. \tag{2}$$

Here t_ϵ means some t in the succession of values, usually dependent on the ϵ selected in the sense that the smaller ϵ we select, the further out we must go in the sequence of t values.

It follows at once from the definition that:

if $\lim a_t = A,$ $$\lim (A - a_t) = 0, \tag{3}$$

and conversely.

Since the condition for approach to a limit only involves the values beyond a certain point in the values of t, which may be taken arbitrarily far out, the values of t which precede any fixed t in the sequence, or the corresponding values of a_t, have no effect on the limit. They may be arbitrarily changed, or even discarded, without affecting the limit. As an example, consider the discrete sequence of values of t, 1, 2, 3, $\cdots$ and the corresponding sequence of values of a_t:

$$\frac{1}{1^2}, \frac{1}{2^2}, \frac{1}{3^2}, \cdots,$$

which approach the limit zero. We may derive from this such sequences as

$$10, \ 20, \ 30, \ \frac{1}{1^2}, \frac{1}{2^2}, \frac{1}{3^2}, \cdots,$$

obtained by adding terms at the beginning,

$$\frac{1}{6^2}, \frac{1}{7^2}, \frac{1}{8^2}, \cdots,$$

obtained by omitting terms at the beginning,

or $$4, \ 8, \ 12, \ \frac{1}{4^2}, \frac{1}{5^2}, \frac{1}{6^2}, \cdots,$$

obtained by changing terms at the beginning.

Similarly in the continuous case, if t varies from 0 to 1, the limit of $a_t = t^2$ is 1, and this limit is unchanged if we consider t as varying from -1 to 1, 0.9 to 1, or if we use any of these ranges with $a_t = 2t^3$ for t less than 0.99 and $a_t = t^2$ for t greater than, or equal to, 0.99.

If a_t is a constant for all the values of t under consideration, $a_t = k$, we may also write

$$\lim a_t = k, \tag{4}$$

since all the conditions of the definition are satisfied. That is, a constant is a special case of a variable approaching a limit. Variable here means a quantity which may, but does not necessarily, change.

18. Infinity. We say that:

The variable a_t becomes positively infinite if beyond a certain point in its succession of values the quantity a_t becomes, and stays, greater than any fixed positive quantity.

We write in this case

$$\lim a_t = +\infty. \tag{5}$$

If we indicate by N a positive quantity which may be taken arbitrarily large, the definition in symbols is: $\lim a_t = +\infty$ if for any positive N,

$$a_t > N, \quad \text{for } t \text{ beyond } t_N. \tag{6}$$

Note that, whereas, for a finite limit, $A - a_t$ becomes small, the corresponding expression for an infinite limit has no meaning. Even if we regarded $+\infty$ as a number subject to some of the arithmetic operations, the value assigned to $+\infty - a_t$ would be $+\infty$ which does not become small. Thus a_t does not " approach infinity as a limit," but it is often convenient to read the relation (5) " limit a_t equals plus infinity," instead of making the more precise statement " a_t becomes positively infinite."

The definition of a variable becoming negatively infinite is similar to the above. In this case we write:

$$\lim a_t = -\infty. \tag{7}$$

Or we may define this as being equivalent to $\lim (-a_t) = +\infty$.

19. Operations and Limits. If we perform any of the four fundamental arithmetic operations on variables approaching finite limits, we usually obtain new variables approaching finite limits, where the limits are obtained by the same operations. More specifically, if

$$\lim a_t = A \quad \text{and} \quad \lim b_t = B, \tag{8}$$

then it follows that:

$$\lim (a_t + b_t) = A + B, \tag{9}$$

$$\lim (a_t - b_t) = A - B, \tag{10}$$

$$\lim a_t b_t = AB, \tag{11}$$

and,

if $B \neq 0$,
$$\lim \frac{a_t}{b_t} = \frac{A}{B}. \tag{12}$$

To prove these equations, we note first that:

If α_t and β_t are two variables approaching zero and if p and q are each constants, or variables numerically less than some fixed quantity M, then $p\alpha_t + q\beta_t$ approaches zero.

For, if we select any positive quantity ϵ, α_t and β_t will each differ from zero by less than $\epsilon/(2M)$ beyond a certain stage, and thereafter we shall have:

$$|p\alpha_t + q\beta_t| \leq |p\alpha_t| + |q\beta_t| < 2M\epsilon/(2M) = \epsilon. \tag{13}$$

To prove the four relations, we put:

$$A - a_t = \alpha_t, \quad B - b_t = \beta_t. \tag{14}$$

Then, if $p = 1$, $q = 1$, we have:

$$p\alpha_t + q\beta_t = A - a_t + B - b_t = A + B - (a_t + b_t). \tag{15}$$

Since this approaches zero, the relation (9) follows.

If $p = 1$, $q = -1$, we have:

$$p\alpha_t + q\beta_t = A - a_t - (B - b_t) = A - B - (a_t - b_t). \tag{16}$$

Since this approaches zero, the relation (10) follows.

To prove the relation (11), we note that

$$AB - a_t b_t = A(B - b_t) + b_t(A - a_t) = A\beta_t + b_t\alpha_t. \tag{17}$$

But, for t beyond t', $|B - b_t| < \epsilon < 1$, so that $|b_t| < |B| + 1$. Thus, if we start with t', we may take M as the larger of $|A|$ and $|B| + 1$ and deduce the relation (11) from the fact that the right, and hence the left, member of equation (17) approaches zero.

To prove the relation (12), we note that

$$\frac{A}{B} - \frac{a_t}{b_t} = \frac{Ab_t - Ba_t}{Bb_t} = \frac{1}{b_t}(A - a_t) - \frac{A}{Bb_t}(B - b_t)$$

$$= \frac{1}{b_t}\alpha_t - \frac{A}{Bb_t}\beta_t. \tag{18}$$

But ultimately, say for t beyond t', $|B - b_t| < \epsilon < |B|/2$, and $|b_t| > |B|/2$. Consequently, if we start with t', we may take M as the greater of $2/|B|$ and $2|A|/|B|^2$, and so show that the final member of equation (18) approaches zero, which proves the relation (12).

Since, as remarked at the end of section 17, a constant is a special case of a variable approaching a limit, we have as a special case of the relations just proved,

$$\lim (a_t + k) = A + k, \quad \lim (ka_t) = kA,$$

if $k \neq 0$,
$$\lim \frac{a_t}{k} = \frac{A}{k},$$

and if $B \neq 0$,
$$\lim \frac{k}{b_t} = \frac{k}{B}. \tag{19}$$

By repeated application of the fundamental operations of this section, we may treat the case of a polynomial in any number of variables, each of which approaches a limit. The polynomial will approach a limit whose value may be obtained by replacing each variable in the polynomial by its limit. A similar result holds for the quotient of two polynomials unless the limit of the denominator is zero.

20. Determinate Operations on Variables Becoming Infinite. In certain cases where one of our variables becomes infinite and the other approaches a finite limit, the result of some of the operations on the variables leads to a new variable whose behavior may be predicted. Thus

if $\lim p_t = +\infty$, $\quad \lim a_t = A$, $\tag{20}$

we have:

$$\lim \frac{1}{p_t} = 0, \tag{21}$$

$$\lim (p_t + a_t) = +\infty, \quad \lim (p_t - a_t) = +\infty, \tag{22}$$

$$\lim (a_t - p_t) = -\infty. \tag{23}$$

Also,

if $A > 0$, $\quad \lim a_t p_t = +\infty \quad$ and $\quad \lim \frac{p_t}{a_t} = +\infty. \tag{24}$

These results follow directly from the definitions.

The correct behavior of the variable is obtained if we use the following operations with the symbols $+\infty$ and $-\infty$ in calculating the " limits ":

$$-(+\infty) = -\infty, \quad -(-\infty) = +\infty, \quad (+\infty) + A = +\infty,$$

$$\frac{1}{+\infty} = 0. \tag{25}$$

And,

if $A > 0$, $\quad A \cdot (+\infty) = +\infty. \tag{26}$

21. Indeterminate Operations. Such operations as

$$(+\infty) - (+\infty) = ? \quad \text{or} \quad \frac{+\infty}{+\infty} = ? \tag{27}$$

cannot be so simply treated, since, if $\lim p_t = +\infty$ and $\lim q_t = +\infty$, the variable $p_t - q_t$ may not approach any limit, may become positively infinite, negatively infinite, or may approach a finite limit. For example, as n takes on the values $1, 2, 3, \cdots$, all the quantities in brackets become positively infinite, but $[n^2 + (-1)^n n] - [n^2]$ takes on alternately increasingly large positive and negative values, $[n^2 + (-1)^n] - [n^2]$ is alternately 1 and -1, while $\lim \{[n^2] - [n]\} = +\infty$, $\lim \{[n] - [n^2]\} = -\infty$, and $\lim \{[n + 3] - [n]\} = 3$. Thus each case must be examined separately.

We note here that,

if $\qquad \lim a_t = A > 0, \quad \lim b_t = 0, \quad \text{and} \quad b_t > 0,$

then $\qquad \lim \dfrac{a_t}{b_t} = +\infty.$ $\qquad\qquad\qquad\qquad\qquad\qquad (28)$

If b_t does not have a fixed sign, the result may not follow, but

if $\lim a_t = A \neq 0, \quad \lim b_t = 0, \quad \text{and} \quad b_t \neq 0,$

$$\lim \frac{|a_t|}{|b_t|} = +\infty. \tag{29}$$

Some writers use $\lim a_t/b_t = \infty$ to indicate the last relation, and we shall find this notation convenient when dealing with complex quantities. When dealing with real numbers, we shall generally use ∞ as an alternative to $+\infty$. Whenever the context leaves the meaning in doubt, we shall use the more explicit notation.

As additional indeterminate operations, we have:

$$\frac{0}{0} = ? \quad \text{and} \quad 0 \cdot (+\infty) = ?. \tag{30}$$

That is, the quotient of two variables each approaching zero, or the product of two variables one of which approaches zero and the other of which becomes infinite, cannot be predicted in advance for all cases.

In arithmetic, the only undefined operation is division by zero. If we regarded $+\infty$ and $-\infty$ as numbers, this would enable us to define the operations of the preceding section, but we should still have all the operations mentioned in this section as indeterminate among the undefined operations. Also, in many theorems we would have to except infinity. Therefore it is more convenient not to regard infinity as a number and to regard it as being an exceptional situation when we can perform any of the arithmetic operations and so predict the behavior of combinations of variables becoming positively or negatively infinite.

22. Inequalities and Limits. If a_t is positive or zero for all values of t under consideration, its limit A cannot be negative. For, from

$$a_t \geqq 0, \quad A = -p < 0, \quad \text{or} \quad -A = p > 0, \tag{31.}$$

we deduce

$$a_t - A \geqq p > 0, \quad \text{so that} \quad |A - a_t| \geqq p, \tag{32}$$

and so cannot be made arbitrarily small.

Thus A must be positive or zero, and we have:

If $a_t \geqq 0$ and $\lim a_t = A$, $\qquad A \geqq 0$. $\tag{33}$

Even if a_t is always positive, no stronger conclusion can be drawn, since the limit may still be zero.

Next suppose that

$$a_t \geqq b_t, \quad \text{and} \quad \lim a_t = A, \quad \lim b_t = B. \tag{34}$$

Then we may deduce

from $a_t - b_t \geqq 0$,

$$A - B \geqq 0, \quad \text{hence} \quad A \geqq B. \tag{35}$$

Here again, even if we have strict inequality for all values of t, we may have equality in the limit. Thus

From inequalities in variables, we may deduce corresponding relations of inequality or equality for the limits.

These remarks still apply if numerical values are involved, an inequality in numerical values being completely equivalent to two inequalities, i.e.,

$$|x| < b \text{ is equivalent to } -b < x \quad \text{and} \quad x < b. \tag{36}$$

23. Upper and Lower Limits. Although we frequently make use of variables which approach limits, such variables are of a very special nature. We shall now study certain other ways in which a variable can act.

If there is no positive number M such that the values of a_t will ultimately be less than M, we say that a_t has the *upper limit plus infinity*, and write

$$\overline{\lim} \, a_t = +\infty. \tag{37}$$

Suppose that there are numbers M, positive or negative, such that the values of a_t are ultimately all less than M. Suppose further that not every real number has this property of the numbers M.   Then we may form a cut in the real number system by putting all numbers M into the class B and all other numbers into the class A.   The number which effects the separation, L_2, is called the *upper limit* of a_t, and we write:

$$\overline{\lim} \, a_t = L_2. \tag{38}$$

If every number has the property required of M, we say that a_t has the *upper limit minus infinity*, and we write:

$$\overline{\lim} \, a_t = -\infty. \tag{39}$$

Similarly to the above, by considering real numbers m such that the values of a_t are ultimately all greater than m, we define the concept of *lower limit*, and the expressions:

$$\underline{\lim} \, a_t = -\infty, \quad \underline{\lim} \, a_t = L_1, \quad \underline{\lim} \, a_t = +\infty. \tag{40}$$

Or, we may define

$$\underline{\lim} \, a_t = -\overline{\lim}(-a_t). \tag{41}$$

Any number M, which ultimately exceeds every a_t, is greater than any number m, which ultimately is less than every a_t.   Consequently, when the upper and lower limits are finite,

$$L_1 \leqq L_2. \tag{42}$$

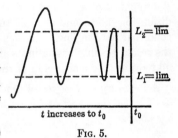

Fig. 5.

If the equality holds,

and if $L_1 = L_2 = A$, $\qquad \lim a_t = A.$ $\qquad\qquad$ (43)

To prove this, we note that for any positive ϵ, a_t is ultimately less than $L_2 + \epsilon$, and ultimately greater than $L_1 - \epsilon$, so that in the case under consideration we have, ultimately,

$$A - \epsilon < a_t < A + \epsilon, \quad \text{or} \quad |A - a_t| < \epsilon. \tag{44}$$

If a_t has the upper limit minus infinity, every number, and in particular every numerically large negative number, will ultimately exceed a_t. It follows that

if $\overline{\lim} \, a_t = -\infty$

$$\underline{\lim} \, a_t = -\infty \quad \text{and} \quad \lim a_t = -\infty. \tag{45}$$

Similarly,

if $\underline{\lim} \, a_t = +\infty$,

$$\overline{\lim} \, a_t = +\infty \quad \text{and} \quad \lim a_t = +\infty. \tag{46}$$

By reversing these arguments, we may show that if a_t approaches a finite limit, the upper limit and the lower limit are each equal to this limit. If a_t becomes positively infinite, a_t has the upper limit plus infinity and the lower limit plus infinity. If a_t becomes negatively infinite, a_t has the upper limit minus infinity, and the lower limit minus infinity.

Whenever the upper limit is different from the lower limit, the variable a_t cannot approach a limit, and it is said to oscillate.

If a first result implies a second one, we say that the first result is a *sufficient* condition for the second. Since it is also true that we cannot have the first result without the second, the second result is a *necessary* condition for the first. When one result not only implies but is itself implied by a second, we say that the first implies the second, and conversely. This form of expression is familiar to the reader from elementary geometry, where the two results were usually of equal interest. We might also say that the first result is a *necessary and sufficient* condition for the second or that the second is a necessary and sufficient condition for the first. In this form of statement, we generally take the result less interesting in itself as the condition. In these terms, we may restate the main result of this section as a theorem:

A necessary and sufficient condition for a variable to approach a finite limit is that the upper and lower limit of the variable be finite and equal to one another.

It follows from the definition of upper limit and lower limit that,

$$\text{if } b_t \leqq c_t, \qquad \overline{\lim} \, b_t \leqq \overline{\lim} \, c_t, \quad \text{and} \quad \underline{\lim} \, b_t \leqq \underline{\lim} \, c_t. \tag{47}$$

This fact may be combined with the theorem just stated to prove that:

If $a_t \leqq b_t \leqq c_t$ and if a_t and c_t approach the same limit L, then b_t also approaches the limit L.

It follows from the assumed inequalities that

$$\underline{\lim} \, a_t \leqq \underline{\lim} \, b_t \leqq \underline{\lim} \, c_t, \tag{48}$$

and

$$\overline{\lim} \, a_t \leqq \overline{\lim} \, b_t \leqq \overline{\lim} \, c_t. \tag{49}$$

But,

$$\text{since } \lim a_t = L, \qquad \underline{\lim} \, a_t = \overline{\lim} \, a_t = L, \tag{50}$$

and

$$\text{since } \lim c_t = L, \qquad \underline{\lim} \, c_t = \overline{\lim} \, c_t = L. \tag{51}$$

Thus we must have from the relations (48) and (49):

$$\underline{\lim} \, b_t = L \quad \text{and} \quad \overline{\lim} \, b_t = L, \quad \text{so that} \quad \lim b_t = L. \qquad (52)$$

This proves the result stated.

24. Greatest and Least Limits. The upper and lower limits of a variable a_t are sometimes called the greatest and least limits, for a reason which we shall proceed to study. Suppose that, from the continuous or discrete sequence of values of a_t, we have picked out some infinite, discrete set of values, a_i, where $i = t_1, t_2, \cdots, t_n \cdots$, such that:

$$\lim i = \lim t_n = \lim t, \qquad (53)$$

a condition which will automatically be fulfilled if the values of t form a discrete sequence. Let us suppose further that the subsequence a_i is such that

$$\lim a_i = A. \qquad (54)$$

Then, since we can find values of i arbitrarily far out in the sequence i, and hence by the condition (53) we can also find values which are arbitrarily far out in the sequence t, for which

$$a_i > A - \epsilon \qquad (55)$$

where ϵ is any positive number, it follows that any number M which ultimately exceeds the a_t must satisfy

$$M > A - \epsilon, \quad \text{or} \quad M \geqq A, \qquad (56)$$

since ϵ is arbitrary. Since this is true for all M, it will also be true for the lower bound of the M, or L_2, and so:

$$L_2 \geqq A. \qquad (57)$$

In a similar way we may show that

$$L_1 \leqq A. \qquad (58)$$

Thus, when L_1 and L_2 are finite, for any limit A satisfying the relations (53) and (54), we must have:

$$L_1 \leqq A \leqq L_2. \qquad (59)$$

Moreover, we may obtain each of the numbers L_1 and L_2 as a limit by using a suitable sequence. We illustrate for L_2. From the definition of L_2, all the values of a_t from a certain point in the sequence on are less than $L_2 + 1/n$, while some of them are in excess of $L_2 - 1/n$ beyond any point. Hence, if we take a particular discrete sequence of values of t, t_n', such that

$$\lim t_n' = \lim t, \qquad (60)$$

we may successively find values of a_i such that the nth value lies beyond the preceding value, beyond the value of t'_n for the particular sequence satisfying the condition (60), and such that

$$L_2 - \frac{1}{n} < a_i < L_2 + \frac{1}{n}. \qquad (61)$$

We shall then have

$$\lim i = \lim t, \quad \text{and} \quad \lim a_i = L_2. \qquad (62)$$

Thus we have found a sequence approaching L_2. In the same way we could find a sequence approaching L_1.

This shows that, when L_1 and L_2 are both finite, there are sequences satisfying the relations (53) and (54) and that L_1 and L_2 are among the values of A obtained. The inequality (59) shows that L_1 and L_2 are respectively the least and greatest of these limits.

A similar argument shows that, if $L_2 = +\infty$, a sequence a_i can be found with $\lim a_i = +\infty$, and likewise for the other infinite cases.

When $L_2 = -\infty$, all sequences a_i are such that $\lim a_i = -\infty$, while if $L_2 = +\infty$, the relation $A \leq L_2$ is satisfied in the sense that any finite number is $< +\infty$.

In this discussion, the number L_2 was ordinarily found by a cut and was replaced by $+\infty$ when the right-hand class was empty. Some of the operations with $+\infty$, such as the inequality just mentioned and those defined in section 20 are consistent with the interpretation of $+\infty$ as corresponding to a cut with the right-hand class empty.

25. Sequence Definition of Limit. The fact that L_1 and L_2 are the greatest and least limits obtained from discrete sequences, combined with the condition for approach to a limit which we obtained in section 23, leads to another interpretation of a variable approaching a finite limit. For, if every discrete sequence a_i such that $\lim t = \lim i$ approaches the same limit L, the greatest and least such limits L_1 and L_2 must each equal L, and the variable approaches the limit L. Conversely, when a variable approaches a limit L, since the greatest and least limits obtained from such a sequence a_i each equal L, the same is true of every discrete sequence obtained from it with $\lim i = \lim t$. Hence every such sequence approaches the same limit L. This leads to an alternative definition of approach to a limit, in terms of limit of a discrete sequence:

The variable a_t approaches a finite limit A, if for every discrete set of values of t, $i = t_n$, such that $\lim i = \lim t$, we have $\lim a_i = A$.

A similar statement reduces the definitions of $\lim a_t = +\infty$, $\lim a_t = -\infty$ to the corresponding situations for discrete sequences.

For a discrete sequence, we may define

The variable a_n approaches a finite limit A, if there are at most a finite number of values of n for which

$$|A - a_n| > \epsilon, \tag{63}$$

for any arbitrary positive number ϵ.

A similar definition may be made of $\lim a_n = +\infty$, where the inequality satisfied by at most a finite number of values is $a_n < M$, for any positive number M. We may also frame a definition of this type for $\lim a_n = -\infty$.

These definitions are taken as fundamental by some writers, who dislike the reference to time in the other definitions. It is useful for the student to appreciate both definitions of limit, as some arguments seem clearer with one and some with the other point of view.

26. The Cauchy Convergence Criterion. By using the upper and lower limits we may establish a second condition for a variable to approach a finite limit, known as the *Cauchy convergence criterion*. The theorem is:

A necessary and sufficient condition for a variable a_t to approach a finite limit is that for any positive quantity η, there is some point in the sequence of values of t, t_η, such that the difference of any two values of a_t, each with t beyond t_η, is numerically less than η.

In symbols, the condition is that for any positive η,

$$|a_u - a_v| < \eta, \quad \text{if } u,v \text{ follow } t_\eta \text{ in the sequence.} \tag{64}$$

To show that the condition is necessary, we assume that a_t approaches a finite limit A. Then

$$|A - a_t| < \frac{\eta}{2}, \quad \text{if } t \text{ follows } t_0 \text{ in the sequence,} \tag{65}$$

from the definition of a limit, where t_0 is t_ϵ for $\epsilon = \eta/2$.

In consequence of this, if u and v are any two values which follow t_0, we may write:

$$|A - a_u| < \frac{\eta}{2}, \quad \text{and} \quad |A - a_v| < \frac{\eta}{2}. \tag{66}$$

Hence

$$|a_u - a_v| = |(a_u - A) - (a_v - A)| < \eta. \tag{67}$$

Thus we may satisfy the condition of the theorem by taking $t_\eta = t_0$.

To show that the condition is sufficient, we start by assuming that the relation (64) holds. We keep η and u fixed and let v take on any value beyond u. Then, for any such v,

$$|a_u - a_v| < \eta, \quad \text{or} \quad a_u - \eta < a_v < a_u + \eta. \tag{68}$$

Thus, in the sense of section 23, $a_u - \eta$ is a possible value of m and $a_u + \eta$ is a possible value of M. Consequently, the upper and lower limits of a_t are both finite, and

$$a_u - \eta \leqq L_1 \leqq L_2 \leqq a_u + \eta. \tag{69}$$

From this it follows that

$$0 \leqq L_2 - L_1 \leqq 2\eta, \tag{70}$$

and, since η is arbitrary, we must have $L_1 = L_2$, and a limit is therefore approached.

27. Monotonic Variables. A variable a_t is increasing if each value is greater than any preceding value. If each value is merely greater than, or equal to, any preceding value, the variable is said to be monotonically increasing or never-decreasing. The behavior of a monotonically increasing variable is of a simpler nature than that of the unrestricted variable discussed in section 23. We shall show that:

A never-decreasing variable, and in particular an increasing variable, either approaches a finite limit or becomes positively infinite, according as its values have, or have not, a finite upper bound.

If the values of the variable a_t have no finite upper bound, any fixed positive number N will ultimately be exceeded by some a_t. But, since the a_t never decrease, all the a_t beyond this point will also exceed N. Hence, in this case we have

$$\lim a_t = +\infty. \tag{71}$$

If the values of the variable a_t admit a finite upper bound M, a_t will have a finite upper limit L_2. Hence, for any positive number ϵ, we have

$$a_t < L_2 + \epsilon, \quad \text{for } all \ t \text{ beyond a certain } t', \tag{72}$$

and

$$a_t > L_2 - \epsilon, \quad \text{for } some \ t'' \text{ beyond this } t', \tag{73}$$

since both of these relations are consequences of the definition of an upper limit.

But, since the a_t never decrease,

$$a_t > L_2 - \epsilon, \quad \text{for all } t \text{ beyond } t'' \tag{74}$$

so that, in view of the relation (72),

$$|L_2 - a_t| < \epsilon, \quad \text{for all } t \text{ beyond } t''. \tag{75}$$

As ϵ was arbitrary, we may take t'' as the t_ϵ in the original definition of a limit and conclude that a_t approaches the limit L_2.

In a similar manner, or by considering $-a_t$, we may define what is meant by a monotonically decreasing, or never-increasing, variable, and prove that:

A never-increasing variable, and in particular a decreasing variable, either approaches a finite limit or becomes negatively infinite, according as its values have, or have not, a finite lower bound.

28. Nested Intervals. Frequently we locate a point with desired properties by using a sequence of intervals, each of which is contained in the preceding. We made use of this process in section 12. Conditions under which this process leads to a unique point are given by the following theorem:

If a discrete, infinite sequence of closed intervals a_n, b_n is such that each includes the following, and the length of the nth interval approaches zero as we go out in the sequence, there is one, and only one, point which is a point of every one of the closed intervals.

Since the nth interval includes the $(n + 1)$st, we have

$$a_n \leqq a_{n+1} < b_{n+1} \leqq b_n. \tag{76}$$

Thus the left-hand end points, a_n, form a monotonically increasing sequence, with an upper bound b_1, and so approach a limit A. Similarly the right-hand end points, b_n, form a monotonically decreasing sequence, with a lower bound a_1, and so approach a limit B. Also, from repeated application of the inequality (76), we find:

$$a_n \leqq a_{n+m} < b_{n+m} \leqq b_n. \tag{77}$$

If we keep n fixed in this and let m increase, we may deduce from it that

$$a_n \leqq A \leqq B \leqq b_n, \tag{78}$$

and hence

$$0 \leqq B - A \leqq b_n - a_n. \tag{79}$$

But, since the limit of the right member is zero, this shows that $B - A = 0$, or $B = A$. This gives a point which is in all of the intervals because of the inequality (78).

That this is the only point in all of the intervals may be shown by assuming that C is in all the intervals. Then:

$$a_n \leqq C \leqq b_n, \tag{80}$$

and from this, on taking the limits,

$$A \leqq C \leqq B, \quad \text{or} \quad C = A, \quad \text{since} \quad B = A. \tag{81}$$

If we take one point from each of the intervals, c_n, these points will approach the point A as a limit. For, since

$$a_n \leqq c_n \leqq b_n, \quad \text{and} \quad B = A, \tag{82}$$

it follows that $\lim c_n = A$, by the last theorem of section 23.

29. Functions on Closed Intervals. The definition of a function already given — y is a function of x on a range if, for every value of x in the range, one or more values of y are determined — puts little restriction on the values of x or y. Thus, if $y = 1$ or -1 when $x = 0$ and if y equals any real number whatever when $x = 1$, we have a function defined for the range consisting of the two values 0 and 1. It is two-valued at 0 and infinitely many-valued at 1.

Let us restrict our attention to functions defined for all the values of x in some closed interval, $a \leqq x \leqq b$, and single-valued for these values of x. The requirement that the function be single-valued is not always a natural one from the standpoint of geometric applications, but may usually be met by suitable conventions. Thus, the equation $x^2 + y^2 = 1$ must be thought of as defining two single-valued functions in the interval $-1,1$, namely,

$$y = +\sqrt{1 - x^2} \quad \text{and} \quad y = -\sqrt{1 - x^2}. \tag{83}$$

As an additional example of a single-valued function on an interval, we may put

$$y = 1 \text{ for } x \text{ rational and } 0 \leqq x \leqq 1,$$
$$y = 0 \text{ for } x \text{ irrational and } 0 < x < 1. \tag{84}$$

A simpler example is given by

$$y = x, \quad 0 \leqq x \leqq \tfrac{1}{2}, \quad \text{and} \quad y = 1 - x, \quad \tfrac{1}{2} \leqq x \leqq 1. \tag{85}$$

Again, $y = x^2$ defines y as a function of x. This last function — like the two defined by equation (83) and the one defined by (85), and, in fact, like most of the functions met in elementary mathematics — have graphs which can be drawn without lifting our pencil from the paper. We proceed to give a more precise definition of this property.

30. Continuity. If $y = f(x)$ is a single-valued function of x defined for all x in the closed interval a,b, i.e., $a \leqq x \leqq b$, and x_0 is a value of x in this interval, by

$$\lim_{x \to x_0} f(x) = A, \tag{86}$$

we mean that, for any positive ϵ, there exists a second positive quantity δ_ϵ, such that

$$|A - f(x)| < \epsilon \quad \text{for all } x \neq x_0, \quad \text{such that } |x - x_0| < \delta_\epsilon. \quad (87)$$

We read $x \to x_0$ as " x tends to x_0," or " x approaches x_0," and shall sometimes use the notation $x \to x_0$ by itself.

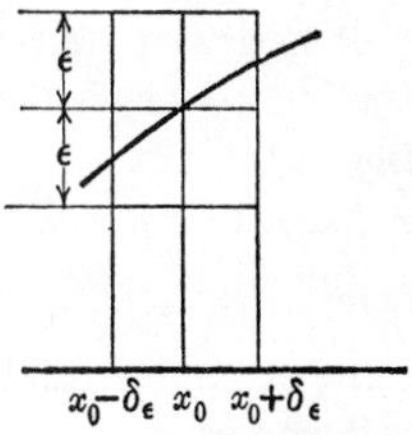

If we wish to consider only values of x greater than x_0, we write

$$\lim_{x \to x_0+} f(x) = A, \quad (88)$$

to mean that, for any positive ϵ, there exists a second positive quantity δ_ϵ, such that

Fig. 6.

$$|A - f(x)| < \epsilon \quad \text{for all } x > x_0, \text{ such that } x - x_0 < \delta_\epsilon. \quad (89)$$

This is a limit on the right.

Similarly we may denote a limit on the left by

$$\lim_{x \to x_0-} f(x) = A, \quad (90)$$

meaning that, for any positive ϵ, there exists a second positive quantity δ_ϵ, such that

$$|A - f(x)| < \epsilon \quad \text{for all } x < x_0, \quad \text{such that } x_0 - x < \delta_\epsilon. \quad (91)$$

If the function approaches a limit A at x_0 in the sense of equation (86), both the right-hand limit given by equation (88) and the left-hand limit given by equation (90) exist and equal A. Conversely, if both these last limits exist and are equal, the limit exists in the first sense.

The limit on the right is analogous to our earlier definition for a continuous sequence, x here decreasing from b to x_0, the range being open at the left as the number x_0 itself is excluded. This suggests that we define

$$\lim_{x \to x_0+} f(x) = +\infty \quad (92)$$

to mean that, for any positive N, there exists a second positive quantity δ_N, such that

$$f(x) > N, \quad \text{for all } x > x_0, \quad \text{such that } x - x_0 < \delta_N. \quad (93)$$

The definitions of

$$\lim_{x \to x_0-} f(x) = +\infty \quad \text{and} \quad \lim_{x \to x_0} f(x) = +\infty \quad (94)$$

are quite similar, and we do not bother to state them explicitly.

The corresponding relations for $-\infty$ are also defined in an entirely similar manner.

The *Cauchy convergence criterion* for a function approaching a limit may be formulated as follows:

A necessary and sufficient condition for the existence of a finite limit for $f(x)$ *as* $x \to x_0$ *is that, for any positive number* ϵ, *there exists a corresponding positive number* δ_ϵ *such that* $|f(x') - f(x'')| < \epsilon$, *for any two values of* x *distinct from* x_0 *and such that* $|x' - x_0| \leqq \delta_\epsilon$ *and* $|x'' - x_0| \leqq \delta_\epsilon$.

The necessity of the condition, where x' and x'' are on either the same or opposite sides of x_0, is proved exactly as in section 26. For the sufficiency, we note that, if the condition holds for x' and x'' when both are to the right of x_0, the limit on the right exists by the theorem of section 26. Call this limit B. Similarly the limit on the left exists by the same theorem. Call it A. Then, since $|f(x') - f(x'')| < \epsilon$, for all x' and x'' such that

$$|x' - x_0| < \delta_\epsilon \quad \text{and} \quad |x'' - x_0| < \delta_\epsilon, \tag{95}$$

we may take x' on the left and x'' on the right and let them each approach x_0. We thus deduce that

$$|A - B| \leqq \epsilon, \quad \text{and hence} \quad B = A, \tag{96}$$

since ϵ is arbitrary. Thus the limit exists, as the right- and left-hand limits exist and are equal.

We may now define continuity in terms of the notion of limit of a function. A function, defined as having a finite value, $f(x_0)$, for a value x_0, is said to be *continuous at the point* x_0 if

$$\lim_{x \to x_0} f(x) = f(x_0). \tag{97}$$

A function, defined and finite at each point of the closed interval $a \leqq x \leqq b$ is *continuous throughout the closed interval* a,b if the relation (97) holds at all interior points of the interval and at the end points:

$$\lim_{x \to a+} f(x) = f(a), \quad \lim_{x \to b-} f(x) = f(b). \tag{98}$$

Using the convergence criterion just established, and the definition of continuity just given, we may show that:

A necessary and sufficient condition for $f(x)$ *to be continuous at the point* x_0 *is that, for any positive number* ϵ, *there exists a corresponding positive number* δ_ϵ *such that* $|f(x') - f(x'')| < \epsilon$, *for any two values of* x *such that* $|x' - x_0| \leqq \delta_\epsilon$, *and* $|x'' - x_0| \leqq \delta_\epsilon$.

In this condition we have not excluded x_0 itself as a possible value of x' and x''. In this respect the situation differs from our previous definitions and results concerning limits, which were all independent of the value at the place approached.

31. Bounded Functions, Oscillations. Let the function $y = f(x)$ be defined on the interval a,b which may be open or closed. The function is said to be *bounded* on this interval, if the corresponding values of $f(x)$ all lie on some finite interval $c \leqq y \leqq d$. By the theorems of section 10, these values of y have a least upper bound M and a greatest lower bound m. The difference $M - m$ is called the *oscillation* of the function in the interval.

If, for any fixed number c, there are values of x in the interval a,b for which $f(x) < c$, the function has no lower bound. We indicate this by writing $m = -\infty$. Similarly, if for any fixed number d, there are values of x in the interval a,b for which $f(x) > d$, the function has no upper bound. In this case we write $M = +\infty$. In either of these cases the function is said to be unbounded, and we say that the oscillation of the function is infinite. This is natural since, for $m = -\infty$, M finite; m finite, $M = +\infty$; or $m = -\infty$, $M = +\infty$, $M - m$ is an operation of the type described in section 20, and $M - m = +\infty$.

Let x' and x'' be any two points of the interval a,b. Then

$$m \leqq f(x') \leqq M \quad \text{and} \quad m \leqq f(x'') \leqq M. \tag{99}$$

From this it follows that:

$$|f(x') - f(x'')| \leqq M - m. \tag{100}$$

Again, suppose that for all pairs of points x' and x'' in the interval a,b we have

$$|f(x') - f(x'')| \leqq k. \tag{101}$$

Then

$$f(x'') - k \leqq f(x') \leqq f(x'') + k. \tag{102}$$

Thus, if we keep x'' fixed and vary x', we see that $f(x)$ is bounded on the interval and so has both bounds, M and m, finite. But, as M is a least upper bound, for any positive ϵ, there is some x' in the interval for which

$$f(x') > M - \epsilon. \tag{103}$$

Similarly, since m is a greatest lower bound, for some x'',

$$f(x'') < m + \epsilon. \tag{104}$$

It follows that

$$M - m - 2\epsilon < f(x') - f(x'') \leqq k, \tag{105}$$

and, since ϵ is arbitrary,

$$M - m \leqq k. \tag{106}$$

The inequalities (100) and (106) show that a restriction on the size of $|f(x') - f(x'')|$ leads to a restriction on the oscillation and conversely. Consequently, we may formulate as an alternative to the condition for continuity given at the end of the last section:

A necessary and sufficient condition for $f(x)$ to be continuous at x_0 is that, for any positive number ϵ, there exists a corresponding positive number δ_ϵ such that the oscillation of $f(x)$ in the interval $|x - x_0| \leqq \delta_\epsilon$ is less than ϵ.

32. Uniform Continuity. Let $f(x)$ be continuous at all points of an open interval. Then, for each point x_0 of the interval and any positive ϵ, we may find a δ such that the oscillation of the function in the interval $|x - x_0| < \delta$ is less than ϵ, in accordance with the theorem just proved. The possible values of δ will usually depend on ϵ and x_0. We may indicate this by writing $\delta(\epsilon,x_0)$. This is an infinitely many-valued function of the two variables, since if we have any value, any smaller positive number will also serve. It may not be possible to find any value of δ which will serve for a given ϵ for all x_0 of the open interval. Thus, if $f(x) = 1/x$ and the interval is $0 < x < 1$, the function is continuous at all points of the interval. However, the oscillation of $f(x)$ for the interval $0 < x < x_0$ is infinite. Hence for any ϵ, the value of $\delta(\epsilon,x_0)$ cannot be as large as x_0. Thus for a particular ϵ, no one value of δ will serve for all x. For, no matter what δ_1 we attempt to use, there are values of x_0 in the interval $0 < x < 1$ with $x_0 < \delta_1$.

On the other hand, if $f(x) = 2x$, $0 < x < 1$, we may take any value less than $\epsilon/4$ as a $\delta(\epsilon,x_0)$ for all x_0 in the interval 0,1. If, as in this case, a value of δ may be found for any ϵ, which does not depend on x_0, the continuity is said to be *uniform* with respect to x for the range under consideration.

If $f(x)$ is continuous at all points of the closed interval a,b the relations (98) hold at the end points. It is easy to deduce from these one-sided relations results similar to those of sections 30 and 31. In particular, for any ϵ there exists a δ_ϵ such that the oscillation of $f(x)$ in the interval $a \leqq x \leqq a + \delta_\epsilon$ is less than ϵ. Similarly, there exists a δ_ϵ such that the oscillation of $f(x)$ in the interval $b - \delta_\epsilon \leqq x \leqq b$ is less than ϵ.

We shall now prove that:

A function, $y = f(x)$, continuous at all points of the closed interval $a \leqq x \leqq b$, is uniformly continuous in that interval.

By the theorem of section 31, for any positive number η, each interior point of the interval $a \leqq x \leqq b$ is in some closed interval $x_0 - \delta_0 \leqq x \leqq x_0 + \delta_0$, in which the oscillation is less than η. And, as just pointed out, the ends a and b are end points of intervals in which the oscillation is less than η. Hence, by the form of the Heine-Borel covering theorem mentioned in the remark at the end of section 11, a finite number of intervals can be selected from these which cover the closed interval a,b. Let all the end points p_i of these covering intervals be marked, and consider all the distances between two distinct end points, corresponding to the same or different intervals. As these distances are finite in number, there is a least such distance, say δ_m. Now consider any interval I of width less than δ_m, consisting entirely of points of the closed interval a,b. Such an interval can include at most one end point of the covering intervals, say p_1. Then, if x' and x'' are any two points of I, since x' and p_1 are in the same covering interval,

$$|f(x') - f(p_1)| < \eta, \tag{107}$$

and similarly

$$|f(p_1) - f(x'')| < \eta. \tag{108}$$

Thus

$$|f(x') - f(x'')| < 2\eta, \tag{109}$$

and, by the inequality (106),

$$M - m \leqq 2\eta. \tag{110}$$

Thus for any given positive quantity ϵ, we may take $\eta < \epsilon/2$, and by the above process find a δ_m, and hence a δ_0, $0 < \delta_0 < \delta_m$, such that the oscillation of $f(x)$ in any interval of length at most δ_0 is less than ϵ. In particular, we may use this δ_0 as a $\delta(\epsilon,x_0)$ for all x_0 of the closed interval a,b. This establishes the uniform continuity.

33. Maximum and Minimum of a Continuous Function. A function continuous at all points of an open interval need not be bounded, as the example $y = 1/x$, $0 < x < 1$, discussed in the preceding section, shows. However,

A function, continuous at all points of a closed interval, is bounded on that interval.

We prove this by noting that, since the function is uniformly continuous we may find a δ such that the oscillation of $f(x)$ in any interval of width less than δ is less than ϵ. We take $\epsilon = 1$ and select N so large that $1/N < \delta$. We then divide the interval a,b into N equal parts, by points

$$a = p_0 < p_1 < \cdots < p_{N-1} < p_N = b. \tag{111}$$

Then, from the choice of δ and N, we have

$$|f(p_{i+1}) - f(p_i)| < 1, \tag{112}$$

and for any x and the greatest p_i less than x, we have:

$$|f(x) - f(p_i)| < 1. \tag{113}$$

It follows from the relations (112) and (113) that:

$$|f(x) - f(a)| < N, \tag{114}$$

or

$$f(a) - N < f(x) < f(a) + N, \tag{115}$$

for all x in the closed interval. Thus the function is bounded in that interval.

A bounded function on an interval always has a least upper bound M and a greatest lower bound m, as shown in section 31. However, for a discontinuous function, there may not be any values of x in a closed interval where these bounds are taken on. Thus, if $f(x)$ is 1 at 0 and 1, and $2x$ for $0 < x < 1$, the function is defined for the closed interval $0 \leqq x \leqq 1$. For this interval $M = 2$ and $m = 0$, but these values do not correspond to any values of x in the closed interval.

The same situation may arise for a function which is continuous in an open interval, as the example $f(x) = 2x$ for $0 < x < 1$ shows, since the values of $M = 2$ and $m = 0$ do not correspond to any values of x in the open interval.

However, for a function which is continuous on a closed interval, the case is different. In fact, since the least upper bound of a function on an interval, M, is the least upper bound of the values of $f(x)$, by section 10, it is either one of these values or a limit point of these values. In the first case, there is a value x_0 such that

$$f(x_0) = M, \tag{116}$$

and the upper bound is taken on.

In the second case, we can find an infinite discrete sequence of points x_i such that

$$\lim f(x_i) = M. \tag{117}$$

Since the points x_i are infinite in number and on a finite interval, they have at least one limit point x_0. Let x_j be any subset of the x_i — renumbered if necessary — approaching x_0 as a limit as j increases. Then

$$\lim x_j = x_0 \quad \text{and} \quad \lim f(x_j) = M. \tag{118}$$

So far, the argument has not made any reference either to the continuity of the function or to the fact that the interval was closed. In fact, in both examples of bounded functions given above, we can find a set of values approaching a limit value (any set of values approaching 1) so that the limit of the values of $f(x)$ on these values is M (here 2).

However, let us return to the case of a function continuous on a closed interval. Since the interval is closed and all the x_j belong to it, so does the limiting value x_0. Again, since the function is continuous at x_0,

$$\lim_{x \to x_0} f(x) = f(x_0), \tag{119}$$

or the corresponding one-sided relation if x_0 is an end point.

From the relations (118) and (119), we have

$$f(x_0) = M, \tag{120}$$

and the least upper bound is taken on.

When the least upper bound is taken on, it is a value of the function greater than, or equal to, all other values, and is called a *maximum*. Similarly, when the greatest lower bound is taken on, it is called a *minimum*. By reasoning as above, or by considering the function $-f(x)$, we may deduce results for lower bounds similar to those just proved for upper bounds. This leads to the theorem:

A function, continuous at all points of a closed interval, takes on its maximum value at least once at some point of the interval and also takes on its minimum value at least once at some point of the interval.

34. Intermediate Values. If a function is continuous throughout the closed interval a,b and is positive at one end, say $f(a) > 0$, and negative at the other end of the interval, $f(b) < 0$, then we must have $f(x) = 0$ at some point x of the open interval a,b. For, consider the points x' such that

$$f(x) > 0, \quad a \leqq x \leqq x', \tag{121}$$

and denote their least upper bound by x_0. Then every interval I_i, including x_0 as an interior point has a point x_i to the left of x_0, for which $f(x) > 0$. Hence for a sequence of I_i with lengths decreasing to zero,

$$f(x_0) = \lim f(x_i) \geqq 0. \tag{122}$$

But every interval I_i also has a point x_j such that $x_j \geqq x_0$, for which $f(x) \leqq 0$. Hence

$$f(x_0) = \lim f(x_j) \leqq 0. \tag{123}$$

It follows from the relations (122) and (123) that

$$f(x_0) = 0, \tag{124}$$

which proves our contention.

We may readily extend this to a general intermediate value property:

A function, continuous at all points of a closed interval, $a \leqq x \leqq b$, takes on every value between $f(a)$ and $f(b)$ at some point of the interval between a and b.

If, for example, h is an intermediate value and $f(a)$ is less than $f(b)$, so that:

$$f(a) < h < f(b), \tag{125}$$

the function

$$F(x) = h - f(x) \tag{126}$$

is positive at a and negative at b, so that at some point x_0 between a and b it is zero. Thus

$$0 = F(x_0) = h - f(x_0), \quad \text{and} \quad f(x_0) = h, \tag{127}$$

as we set out to prove.

The intermediate value may be taken on several times, or even an infinite number of times. The method of proof shows that there is a smallest value of x_0 on the interval. A similar argument would show that there is a greatest value of x_0 on the interval.

35. Functions of Several Variables. Many of the definitions and theorems of this chapter may be extended to functions of more than one variable. If we have k variables and use the geometric language of section 15, our set of k independent variables may be referred to as a point in k dimensions, $X = (x_1, x_2, \cdots, x_k)$.

Thus, we say that y is a single-valued function of k variables and write $y = f(x_1, x_2, \cdots, x_k)$ if there is one value of y associated with each X, or set of values of the x_i in the range under consideration. When the number of variables is implied by the context, we write $y = f(x_i)$ or $y = f(X)$.

Let the function be defined in a k-dimensional interval including $A = (a_1, a_2, \cdots, a_k)$ as an interior point. Let $X_n = (x_{n1}, x_{n2}, \cdots, x_{nk})$ be a discrete sequence of points such that:

$$\lim x_{n1} = a_1, \quad \lim x_{n2} = a_2, \cdots, \quad \lim a_{nk} = a_k. \tag{128}$$

We briefly describe this situation by saying that the points X_n approach the point A as a limit, and we write

$$\lim X_n = A, \tag{129}$$

as an abbreviation for the relations (128). Then, from some n on, all the points X_n will be in the interval in which the function is defined.

The function $y = f(X)$ is continuous at A, if $\lim f(X_n) = f(A)$ for every discrete sequence X_n such that $X_n \to A$.

This definition is analogous to that given in section 25.

An equivalent definition is:

The function $y = f(X)$ is continuous at A if for every positive number ϵ there is a corresponding positive number δ_ϵ, such that

$$|f(A) - f(X)| < \epsilon, \quad if \quad |x_i - a_i| < \delta_\epsilon, \ i = 1, 2, \cdots, k. \quad (130)$$

To see the equivalence, we note that, if the second definition holds, for any sequence X_n such that $X_n \to A$, from some n on, we shall have $|x_{ni} - a_i| < \delta_\epsilon$, for all the i, so that for this sequence $|f(A) - f(X)| < \epsilon$ from a certain point on. Hence $\lim f(X_n) = f(A)$.

On the other hand, suppose the second definition failed to hold for a limit A. Then for some ϵ, we should have $|f(A) - f(X)| \geqq \epsilon$, for some X with $|x_i - a_i| < 1/n$, for all values of n. Let X_1 be one such point for $n = 1$, and take n_2 such that $1/n_2$ is less than the largest value of $|x_{1i} - a_i|$. Let X_2 be one point for n_2 for which $|f(A) - f(X)| \geqq \epsilon$, and repeat the process successively to form a sequence $X_1, X_2, \cdots$.

Then, we have

$$\lim X_n = A, \quad and \quad |f(A) - f(X_n)| \geqq \epsilon, \quad (131)$$

so that we cannot have $\lim f(X_n) = f(A)$. Thus the first definition also fails to hold for this A.

Since the first definition cannot apply when the second one fails to apply, if the first definition applies, the second does also. Thus each definition implies the other, and the two are equivalent.

The two definitions apply as they stand to interior points A of any open region of definition of the function. If the region of definition of the function includes boundary points B, which are at the same time limit points of sequences of points of the region, and also of some sequences of points not belonging to the region, the definitions do not directly apply to such points. In considering such boundary points, we modify the definition by considering only points X_n or X which either belong to the interior of the region or are boundary points.

If we consider the δ_ϵ of the second definition for different points A, it will presumably be necessary to select different δ for different points A, and, for some regions of definition, it may not be possible to find any δ which will serve for a given ϵ for all the points of the region.

However, for a closed region, that is, one which includes all its limit points, and hence all the boundary points, we may prove that a δ may be selected independent of A. The proof is similar to that for one dimension, where the k-dimensional Heine-Borel theorem is used in place of that for one dimension. That is:

A function of k variables, continuous in a closed k-dimensional region, is uniformly continuous in that region.

From this we may deduce that such a function is *bounded* and *takes on its maximum and minimum values in the region.*

There is no simple extension of the intermediate value property to more than one dimension.

It follows from either definition of continuity that a function of $k = m + n$ variables, continuous in all the k variables as a set, becomes a continuous function of the n remaining variables if m of the variables are kept fixed. In particular, if all except one of the variables are kept fixed, the function is a continuous function of the remaining variable. Thus,

A continuous function of k variables is continuous in each of the variables, considered one at a time.

The converse of this is *not* true. Thus $f(x,y) = 2xy/(x^2 + y^2)$, for $(x,y) \neq (0,0)$ and $f(0,0) = 0$, is continuous in x for each value of y and continuous in y for each value of x, but, since the function equals 1 for $x = y$, we may find points arbitrarily close to $(0,0)$ for which $f(x,y) - f(0,0) = 1$, and so the function is not continuous in the two variables at $(0,0)$.

A second interesting example is $f(x,y) = 2xy^2/(x^2 + y^4)$, for $(x,y) \neq (0,0)$ and $f(0,0) = 0$. This function is zero on the x-axis and also on the y-axis, and on any oblique straight line through the origin, $y = mx$, $f(x,y) = 2m^2x/(1 + m^4x^2)$. Thus the function approaches zero as we approach the origin on any straight line through it. However, the function is not continuous at $(0,0)$, as we see by approaching the origin along the parabola $x = y^2$, for which $f(x,y) = 1$. This illustrates the difficulty of using the definition of continuity in terms of sequences as a test, since we must examine all possible sequences.

36. Composite Functions. Let $y = f(x)$ be a single-valued function of x, continuous at $x = a$, and let $f(a) = b$. Again, let $u = g(y)$ be a single-valued function of y, continuous at $y = b$. Then we have:

$$\lim_{x \to a} g[f(x)] = \lim_{y \to b} g(y) = g(b) = g[f(a)]. \tag{132}$$

Thus
$$u(x) = g[f(x)] \tag{133}$$

is continuous at a. That is,

A continuous function of a continuous function is continuous.

This remains true, regardless of the number of variables.   That is, if $y_i = f_i(x_1, x_2, \cdots, x_m)$ is continuous at $x_j = a_j$, $j = 1, 2, \cdots, m$; for $i = 1, 2, \cdots, n$ and $f_i(a_j) = b_i$; while $u = g(y_1, y_2, \cdots, y_n)$ is continuous at $y_i = b_i$; then u is a continuous function of the m variables x_j at $x_j = a_j$.

37. Inverse Functions.   Consider the equation $y = f(x)$, where $f(x)$ is a single-valued continuous function of x and, for some interval $a \leqq x \leqq b$, is increasing with x.   That is, for any two values of x in the interval, x_1 and x_2,

$$f(x_2) > f(x_1) \quad \text{if} \quad x_2 > x_1. \tag{134}$$

Then, in the interval on the y-axis,

$$f(a) \leqq y \leqq f(b), \tag{135}$$

the relation between x and y defines x as a function of y,

$$x = f^{-1}(y), \tag{136}$$

which is also single-valued, continuous, and increasing.

We first note that if y_1 is any value satisfying the relation (135), by the intermediate value property of section 34, there is some x_1 such that

$$y_1 = f(x_1) \quad \text{and} \quad a \leqq x_1 \leqq b. \tag{137}$$

There cannot be two such values, since y increases with x.   We put $x_1 = f^{-1}(y_1)$, thus defining the function $f^{-1}(y)$.   This function is increasing, since by the relation (134),

$$\text{if } x_1 \geqq x_2, \qquad\qquad y_1 \geqq y_2. \tag{138}$$

Consequently,

$$\text{if } y_1 < y_2, \qquad x_1 < x_2 \quad \text{or} \quad f^{-1}(y_1) < f^{-1}(y_2). \tag{139}$$

Since the values of x all lie between a and b, they are bounded, and, by the theorem of section 27,

$$\lim_{y \to y_1-} f^{-1}(y) \quad \text{and} \quad \lim_{y \to y_1+} f^{-1}(y) \tag{140}$$

each exists as the limit of a bounded monotonic variable.

Let the first limit be c and the second d.   Then, since $y = f(x)$ corresponds to $x = f^{-1}(y)$, and since in the last relation $x \to c-$ as $y \to y_1-$, we have in consequence of the continuity of the function $f(x)$:

$$y_1 = \lim_{y \to y_1-} y = \lim_{x \to c-} f(x) = f(c). \tag{141}$$

Similarly,

$$y_1 = \lim_{y \to y_1+} y = \lim_{x \to d+} f(x) = f(d). \tag{142}$$

This shows that $f(c) = f(d) = y_1 = f(x_1)$, so that, from the relation (134), we must have $c = d = x_1$. Thus

$$\lim_{y \to y_1-} f^{-1}(y) = \lim_{y \to y_1+} f^{-1}(y) = x_1 = f^{-1}(y_1), \qquad (143)$$

which shows that the function $f^{-1}(y)$ is continuous at y_1.

The function $x = f^{-1}(y)$ is called the *inverse* of the function $y = f(x)$, and we have just proved that:

An equation $y = f(x)$, in any interval in which the function $f(x)$ is continuous and increasing, defines a single-valued inverse function, $x = f^{-1}(y)$ which is also continuous and increasing.

38. Implicit Functions. Let y and x be connected by an equation $f(x,y) = 0$. If this equation defines y as a function of x which would be written explicitly as $y = F(x)$, then the function $F(x)$ is said to be defined implicitly by $f(x,y) = 0$. Thus, in the preceding section we proved that for a certain type of function $f(x)$, the equation $y = f(x)$ implicitly defines an inverse function, which we may write explicitly as $x = f^{-1}(y)$. A more general theorem on the existence of implicit functions is the following:

Hypothesis: a) *The function $f(x,y)$ is a continuous function of the two variables x and y in some two-dimensional region, R, including the point (x_0, y_0) as an interior point.*

b) *At a particular point (x_0, y_0), $f(x_0, y_0) = 0$.*

c) *For each fixed $x = x_1$ in the interval $a \leqq x_1 \leqq b$ and for y a variable in the interval $c \leqq y \leqq d$, the function $f(x_1, y)$ is an increasing function of y. Here $a, b; c, d$ is some particular two-dimensional interval I lying entirely in the region R and including the point (x_0, y_0) as an interior point.*

Conclusion: a) *There is a function $y = F(x)$, defined in some interval*

$$x_0 - h \leqq x \leqq x_0 + h, \qquad (144)$$

for which $y_0 = F(x_0)$, and $f[x, F(x)]$ is identically zero.

b) *The function $y = F(x)$ is continuous at all points of the interval (144).*

c) *The function $F(x)$ is uniquely defined in the sense that, for values of x such that $x, F_1(x)$ and $x, F_2(x)$ each lie in the interval I, any two functions $F_1(x)$ and $F_2(x)$ satisfying the conditions in (a) of the conclusion must be equal.*

To prove this theorem, we begin by observing that $f(x_0, y)$ is an increasing function of y, so that,

since $\qquad\qquad c < y_0 < d, \quad$ and $\quad f(x_0, y_0) = 0, \qquad\qquad (145)$

we must have:

$$f(x_0,c) = f_1 < 0 \quad \text{and} \quad f(x_0,d) = f_2 > 0. \tag{146}$$

We next consider $f(x,c)$ as a function of x, continuous at x_0. We may find a δ_1, taking $\epsilon = -f_1/2$ such that,

$$\text{if } |x - x_0| < \delta_1, \qquad |f(x,c) - f(x_0,c)| < \frac{-f_1}{2}, \tag{147}$$

which implies that

$$f(x,c) = [f(x,c) - f(x_0,c)] + f(x_0,c) < \frac{f_1}{2} < 0. \tag{148}$$

Similarly, we may find a δ_2, such that,

$$\text{if } |x - x_0| < \delta_2, \qquad f(x,d) > \frac{f_2}{2} > 0.$$

We now take any positive number less than δ_1 and δ_2, $x_0 - a$ and $b - x_0$ as the h which defines the interval

$$x_0 - h \le x \le x_0 + h. \tag{149}$$

Then, for any fixed $x = x_1$ in the interval (149), we have $f(x_1,y)$ a continuous function of y which is negative at $y = c$, and positive for $y = d$. Hence by the intermediate value property it is zero for some value of y, say y_1, between c and d. Moreover, by part (c) of the hypothesis, $f(x_1,y)$ cannot take the same value for two distinct values of y, so that the value of y_1 is uniquely determined.

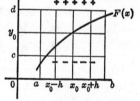

FIG. 7.

When applied to x_0, the process used to obtain y leads to y_0, by part (b) of the hypothesis.

Thus there is a function $y_1 = F(x_1)$, or $y = F(x)$, defined in the interval (149), for which $y_0 = F(x_0)$ and $f(x_1,y_1)$ or $f[x,F(x)] = 0$, so that part (a) of the conclusion is established.

To prove the continuity of $y = F(x)$ at any point x' of the interval (149), suppose that

$$\overline{\lim_{x \to x'}} F(x) = L_2 \quad \text{and} \quad \underline{\lim_{x \to x'}} F(x) = L_1. \tag{150}$$

Since all the values of y or $F(x)$ lie in the closed interval c,d, the limits L_1 and L_2 also lie in this interval, and both are finite. Next select any infinite discrete sequence of points x_i distinct from x', in the interval

(149) such that

$$\lim x_i = x' \quad \text{and} \quad \lim F(x_i) = L_2, \tag{151}$$

by the method used in section 24.

Now consider $f[x_i, F(x_i)]$. From the way in which $F(x)$ was obtained, this is zero for all x_i. But $f(x,y)$ is continuous at the point (x', L_2) which belongs to the two-dimensional interval I, or $a,b;c,d$. Consequently we have:

$$f(x', L_2) = \lim f[x_i, F(x_i)] = 0. \tag{152}$$

But

$$f[x', F(x')] = 0, \tag{153}$$

and since $F(x')$ and L_2 each lie in the interval c,d in which $f(x',y)$ is increasing, we must have

$$L_2 = F(x'). \tag{154}$$

In the same way we may show that

$$L_1 = F(x'), \tag{155}$$

and it follows from the equality of L_1 and L_2 that

$$\lim_{x \to x'} F(x) = F(x'), \tag{156}$$

so that we have proved part (b) of the conclusion.

Finally, part (c) follows from the fact that, if $[x', F_1(x')]$ and $[x', F_2(x')]$ each lie in I, then $F_1(x')$ and $F_2(x')$ each lie in the interval c,d in which $f(x',y)$ is increasing, so that

$$f[x', F_1(x')] = f[x', F_2(x')] \text{ implies } F_1(x') = F_2(x'). \tag{157}$$

This completes the proof of the theorem.

A similar theorem may be formulated for an implicit function of k variables, $y = F(x_1, x_2, \cdots, x_k)$ defined by a relation $f(y, x_1, x_2, \cdots, x_k) = 0$ for values of $X = (x_1, x_2, \cdots, x_k)$ near $X_0 = (x_{01}, x_{02}, \cdots, x_{0k})$ where $f(y,X)$ is continuous in the set of $k + 1$ variables in some $(k + 1)$-dimensional region including the point y,X as an interior point, $f(y_0, X_0) = 0$ and in some $(k + 1)$-dimensional interval, for y,X the function $f(y,X)$ for fixed X is an increasing function of y. The conclusion is that, in some k-dimensional interval including X_0 as an interior point, an implicit function $y = F(X)$ for which $y_0 = F(X_0)$ is defined in a unique way and that the implicit function is continuous in its set of k variables.

The proof is similar to that just given for $k = 1$.

The theorems still apply if we replace *increasing* by *decreasing* throughout.

EXERCISES II

1. Prove that, as $n \to +\infty$, $\lim 1/n = 0$, and find a value of N such that for $n > N$, the variable differs from its limit by less than 0.001.

2. Prove that, as $n \to +\infty$, $\lim (1 + 2^{-n}) = 1$, and find a value of N such that for $n > N$, the variable differs from its limit by less than 0.01.

3. Prove that, as $n \to +\infty$, $\lim 3^n = +\infty$, and find a value of N such that, for $n > N$, the variable exceeds 1,000.

4. Prove directly from the definition that, if $\lim a_t = +\infty$ and $\lim b_t = +\infty$ and if $s_t = a_t + b_t$ and $p_t = a_t b_t$, $\lim s_t = +\infty$, $\lim p_t = +\infty$, and $\lim s_t/p_t = 0$.

5. Find the limit, as $n \to +\infty$, of each of the following:

$$\text{(a)} \quad \frac{n^2 + 2n + 4}{2n^2 + 1}, \qquad \text{(b)} \quad \frac{3n^3 + 2n}{4n^3 - 3}, \qquad \text{(c)} \quad \frac{2n}{3n^2 + 4n + 1}.$$

Hint: Factor out the highest power of n from each polynomial.

6. As a generalization of problem 5, show that, if $b_m \neq 0$,

$$\lim_{n \to +\infty} \frac{a_m n^m + a_{m-1} n^{m-1} + \cdots + a_1 n + a_0}{b_m n^m + b_{m-1} n^{m-1} + \cdots + b_1 n + b_0} = \frac{a_m}{b_m}.$$

7. If, in problem 6, $a_m \neq 0$, and $b_m = 0$, so that the polynomial in the numerator is of higher degree than that in the denominator, show that the limit is $+\infty$ if the leading non-zero terms in the numerator and denominator have the same sign, and $-\infty$ if they have opposite signs.

8. If $R(n)$ is any rational function of n, that is the quotient of two polynomials, prove that $\lim\limits_{n \to +\infty} R(n + k)/R(n) = 1$.

9. If, as $n \to +\infty$, $\lim a_n = L$, prove that $\lim (a_1 + a_2 + a_3 + \cdots + a_n)/n = L$. *Hint:* Choose k so that $|L - a_n| < \epsilon$ for $n > k$, let s_p be the sum of the first p a_n, and put $n = k + m$. Then show that $s_k + mL - m\epsilon < s_{k+m} < s_k + mL + m\epsilon$. Now divide by $n = k + m$, and let $m \to +\infty$.

10. In each of the following cases, determine the upper limit and the lower limit as $n \to +\infty$:

(a) n,   (b) $(-1)^n$,   (c) $(-1)^n n$,   (d) $1 + (-1)^n n$,   (e) $-1 + (-1)^n n$,

11. Prove that $\overline{\lim} \, (a_t - b_t) \leqq \overline{\lim} \, a_t - \underline{\lim} \, b_t$.

12. Prove that $\overline{\lim} \, a_t + \underline{\lim} \, b_t \leqq \overline{\lim} \, (a_t + b_t) \leqq \overline{\lim} \, a_t + \overline{\lim} \, b_t$.

13. Prove that if $a_1, a_2, \cdots$ are any sequence of digits, each of which is 0, 1, 2, 3, 4, 5, 6, 7, 8, or 9, the decimal to n places $0.a_1 a_2 \cdots a_n$ is an increasing bounded function, and so approaches a limit. We indicate the limit by the infinite decimal $0.a_1 a_2 a_3 \cdots$.

Conversely, show that any real number y, between 0 and 1 may be represented by such a sequence. The sequence is uniquely determined unless $10^n y$ is an integer for some integral value of n, in which case there are two sequences, one ending in all zeros, and the other in all nines, after the nth place.

14. Show that any integer greater than one may be used in place of 10 in the discussion of problem 13. In particular, if the base is 2, b_i is either 0 or 1, and we have a binary representation

$$\frac{b_1}{2} + \frac{b_2}{2^2} + \cdots \frac{b_n}{2^n} + \cdots = 0._2 b_1 b_2 b_3 \cdots,$$

where the subscript after the point indicates the base.

15. Show that, if the nested intervals of section 28 which determine the point A in all of them are obtained by repeated bisection, as in section 12, and the first interval is taken as unity for the coördinate scale, the first n steps of the process, or the end points of the nth interval determine the first n digits b_i of the binary expansion of problem 14 for the coördinate of the point A. If the coördinate has two expansions, one ending in zeros and the other in ones, the latter may have to be used.

16. If $y = x^2$, $0 \leqq x \leqq 1$, find a δ such that $|f(x'') - f(x')| \leqq 0.1$ if $|x'' - x'| \leqq \delta$.

17. If $y = 1/x$, $x_0 \leqq x \leqq 1$, find a $\delta(x_0)$ such that $|f(x'') - f(x')| \leqq 0.1$ if $|x'' - x'| \leqq \delta$. Show that any $\delta(x_0)$ must approach zero as x_0 approaches zero.

18. Prove that a polynomial in one variable is continuous for all values of x.

19. Prove that a rational function or quotient of two polynomials is continous for all values of x which do not make the denominator zero.

20. For any real number p, let $[p]$, read " bracket p," denote the algebraically largest integer not exceeding p. In this problem integer means positive integer, negative integer, or zero. Show that the function $[x]$ and hence $x - [x]$ is continuous for all non-integral values of x, but that each function has an oscillation of unity at all the integral points.

21. Show that the function $x - [x]$ defined in problem 20 has a minimum value 0 but no maximum since its least upper bound, 1, is not taken on.

22. Let $f(x)$ be defined on the closed interval 0,1 as zero at all irrational points, 1 at the end points, and at any other rational value, p/q in its lowest terms, let $f(p/q) = 1/q$. Show that this function has its oscillation at any point equal to the value of the function, so that it is continuous at all the irrational points. See section 150.

23. Prove that, if $f(x)$ is any polynomial and has opposite signs at the ends of an interval, the equation $f(x) = 0$ has at least one real root inside the interval.

24. If $f(x)$ is any polynomial of odd degree, prove that the equation $f(x) = 0$ has at least one real root.

25. If $f(x)$ is a polynomial of even degree, with leading term positive, show that there is a value of x, x_0, for which $f(x_0) = m$ is a minimum value of the polynomial, that is $m \leqq f(x)$ for all real values of x. Hence, show that the equation $f(x) = k$ will have a real root if, and only if, $k \geqq m$.

26. A (real) number x, such that

$$a_n x^n + a_{n-1} x^{n-1} + \cdots + a_1 x + a_0 = 0, \quad a_n \neq 0,$$

for some positive integral value of n and for some integral values of a_k in the sense of problem 20, is called a (real) *algebraic number*. Thus, at least for integral coefficients (but see problem 30), the numbers obtained as roots in problems 24 and 25 are algebraic numbers. The least value of n which can be used for a given algebraic number is called its *degree*. Show that every algebraic number has a degree, and that the degree is one if, and only if, the number is rational.

27. If x, the b_k and the c_k are any real numbers, and

$$b_2 x^2 + b_1 x + b_0 = 0 \quad \text{and} \quad c_2 x^2 + c_1 x + c_0 = 0,$$

it follows that

$$b_2 x^3 + b_1 x^2 + b_0 x = 0 \quad \text{and} \quad c_2 x^3 + c_1 x^2 + c_0 x = 0.$$

Since these are linear homogeneous equations in the four variables $y_4 = x^3$, $y_3 = x^2$, $y_2 = x$, $y_1 = 1$, of which the last is not zero, the coefficients must have their determinant zero and

$$
\begin{vmatrix}
b_2 & b_1 & b_0 & 0 \\
0 & b_2 & b_1 & b_0 \\
c_2 & c_1 & c_0 & 0 \\
0 & c_2 & c_1 & c_0
\end{vmatrix} = 0,
$$

which is a polynomial in the coefficients. Discuss the generalization of this process (Sylvester's dialytic method) of elimination to two equations, one of the mth and one of the nth degree.

28. Prove that, if y is a polynomial in x with rational coefficients, and x is an algebraic number, then y is an algebraic number. *Hint:* Eliminate x by the method of problem 27.

29. By the method of problem 28, or otherwise, find an algebraic equation with integral coefficients satisfied by $y = 1 + 2^{1/3} + 4^{1/3}$.

30. Prove that, if a real number x satisfies an equation

$$y_n x^n + y_{n-1} x^{n-1} + \cdots + y_1 x + y_0 = 0, \quad y_n \neq 0,$$

with algebraic numbers for coefficients, then x is an algebraic number. *Hint:* Write the equation satisfied by y_0 with integral coefficients and eliminate y_0 as in problem 27. Similarly, eliminate the other coefficients in turn.

31. If x and y are algebraic numbers, then $x + y$, $x - y$, x/y, and xy are all algebraic numbers. *Hint:* Use problem 30 for the first three, and for the last after proving that $1/y$ is algebraic if y is an algebraic number.

32. Find equations with integral coefficients satisfied by

$$\sqrt{3} - \sqrt{2}, \frac{\sqrt{2}}{\sqrt{3} + 1}, x \quad \text{where} \quad x^2 - \sqrt{3}x + \sqrt{2} = 0,$$

by the method of problems 30 and 31 or otherwise.

33. With each algebraic equation with integral coefficients we may associate a number N, the height, where $N = n + |a_n| + |a_{n-1}| + \cdots + |a_1| + |a_0|$, the degree plus the sum of the numerical value of the coefficients. Show that there is only a finite number of algebraic equations of the type considered with a given height, and use this fact to show that the set of real algebraic numbers are enumerable. Compare problem 13 of Exercises I.

34. Suppose that the algebraic numbers between 0 and 1 are enumerated, and the nth number has a decimal representation $0.a_{n1}a_{n2}a_{n3}\cdots$ as in problem 13. Now form a number $0.c_1c_2c_3\cdots$, where $c_n = 5$ if $a_{nn} = 4$ and $c_n = 4$ if $a_{nn} \neq 4$. Since this number contains no zeros or nines, it is not a second representation of any terminating decimal in the list. And, since it differs from the nth number in the nth place, it is not a number in the list. Thus there are real numbers which are not algebraic. Such numbers are called *transcendental*. Extend this argument to show that no enumerated list can contain all the numbers between 0 and 1, so that this set of real numbers can not be enumerated. (Cantor.)

35. *Peano's Space-filling Arc.* Let t be a parameter and x and y the coördinates of a point of the unit square. As in problem 14, with the base 3, let us find infinite expressions for these numbers: $t = 0._3a_1a_2a_3\cdots$, $x = 0._3b_1b_2b_3\cdots$, and $y = 0._3c_1c_2c_3\cdots$, where, for example, the first expression means $a_1/3 + a_2/3^2 + a_3/3^3 + \cdots$. Thus all the a_k, b_k, and c_k are 0, 1, or 2. Let these numbers be associated in the following manner. We put $b_1 = a_1$, $b_2 = a_3$ or $2 - a_3$, according as a_2 is even or odd; $b_3 = a_5$ or $2 - a_5$, according as $a_2 + a_4$ is even or odd; and so on, $b_n = a_{2n-1}$ or $2 - a_{2n-1}$, according as $a_2 + a_4 + \cdots + a_{2n-2}$ is even or odd. Similarly, let $c_1 = a_2$ or $2 - a_2$, according as a_1 is even or odd; $c_2 = a_4$ or $2 - a_4$, according as $a_1 + a_3$ is even or odd; and so on, $c_n = a_{2n}$ or $2 - a_{2n}$ according as $a_1 + a_3 + \cdots + a_{2n-1}$ is even or odd.

Show that this defines x and y as continuous functions of t, for $0 \leqq t \leqq 1$. Also, show that, for any two values of x and y each between 0 and 1, their expressions in the base three uniquely determine the digits $a_1, a_2, a_3 \cdots$ in succession and so a value of t. When the value of one or both coördinates is a terminating expression, the expression ending in twos and that ending in zeros, will not lead to the same value of t.

The functions $x(t)$ and $y(t)$ of this problem, being continuous functions, may be thought of as the parametric equations of an arc, which passes through every point of the unit square. (Peano.)

CHAPTER III

EXPONENTIAL, LOGARITHMIC, AND TRIGONOMETRIC FUNCTIONS

The basic elementary functions are x^u, p^x and its inverse function $\log_p x$, and the trigonometric functions and their inverse functions. We give here a constructive arithmetic approach to these functions.

We show that the constants in certain fundamental relations involving limits are simplified if we take a special number e as our exponential base and as the base to which we take logarithms. We give a simple set of properties which characterize the exponential function e^x and a simple set of properties which characterize the logarithmic function $\log x$, when we take e as our base.

Similarly, we show that a fundamental limiting relation involving the sine function is simplified by a system of units, radian measure, related to the special number π. We give a simple set of properties which characterize the sine and cosine functions, $\sin x$ and $\cos x$, when x is measured in radians.

We then briefly discuss the other direct trigonometric functions and the inverse trigonometric functions.

39. Integral Powers and Roots. For any integral value of n, the function $y = x^n$ for any real value of x is obtained by starting with unity, and then multiplying by x n times.

Let us restrict x to the range $0 \leqq x \leqq N$. For any two distinct values in this range, x_1 and x_2, we have:

$$x_2^n - x_1^n = (x_2 - x_1)(x_2^{n-1} + x_1 x_2^{n-2} + x_1^2 x_2^{n-3} + \cdots + x_1^{n-1}). \quad (1)$$

All the terms of the last parenthesis are positive or zero, and if $x_2 > x_1$ the first term is greater than zero so that this last parenthesis is positive. It follows that,

$$\text{if } x_2 > x_1, \qquad\qquad x_2^n > x_1^n, \qquad\qquad (2)$$

and the function $y = x^n$ is increasing in the range considered.

Again, let x_1 be positive and fixed, and x_2 any value such that:

$$|x_2 - x_1| < \delta, \quad \text{where} \quad \delta < x_1 \quad \text{and} \quad \delta < 1. \quad (3)$$

Then,

$$\text{if } K = x_1 + 1, \qquad 0 < x_1 < K, \quad 0 < x_2 < K. \quad (4)$$

From the increasing character of the integral power, each of the powers in the last parenthesis of equation (1) will be increased if we replace x_1 and x_2 by K. This shows that:

$$|x_2^n - x_1^n| < |x_2 - x_1| nK^n < \delta nK^n. \tag{5}$$

Thus if we take

$$\delta_\epsilon < \frac{\epsilon}{nK^n}, \quad \delta_\epsilon < x_1, \quad \delta_\epsilon < 1, \tag{6}$$

we shall have:

$$|x_2^n - x_1^n| < \epsilon, \quad \text{if} \quad |x_2 - x_1| < \delta_\epsilon, \tag{7}$$

so that the function $y = x^n$ is continuous for all positive values of x in accordance with the definition in section 30.

For $x_1 = 0$, and any x_2 such that:

$$0 < x_2 < \delta < 1, \tag{8}$$

we have

$$|x_2^n - x_1^n| = x_2^n < x_2. \tag{9}$$

Thus, when we consider values only to the right of zero, we may take $\delta_\epsilon = \epsilon$ for $x_1 = 0$.

Since the function x^n is continuous and increasing in the closed interval $0, N$, by section 37 the equation $y = x^n$ defines a single-valued inverse function $x = f^{-1}(y)$ which is also continuous and increasing, for $0 \leqq y \leqq N^n$.

Since $N^n > N$, if $N > 1$, we may take the y interval arbitrarily large by taking N sufficiently large.

We use $y^{1/n}$ to denote the function inverse to x^n. Thus if $y = x^n$, $x = y^{1/n}$. We note that $y = x^n$ is zero for $x = 0$, and $\lim\limits_{x \to +\infty} x^n = +\infty$. Also $x = y^{1/n}$ is zero for $y = 0$ and $\lim\limits_{y \to +\infty} y^{1/n} = +\infty$.

For any positive real number p, the function $x = y^{1/n}$ defines a number $p^{1/n} = q$, the positive nth root of p. From the inverse relation of $x = y^{1/n}$ and $y = x^n$, we have $q^n = p$.

If we use the root function by itself, we write $y = x^{1/n}$, equivalent to $x = y^n$.

40. Rational Powers. As in elementary algebra, we may now define rational powers of a positive real number p in terms of roots of p. We write

$$p^{\frac{m}{n}} = \left(p^{\frac{1}{n}}\right)^m, \, p^0 = 1, \quad p^{-r} = \left(\frac{1}{p}\right)^r, \tag{10}$$

where m and n are any positive integers and r is any rational number. The relations

$$(p^r)^s = p^{rs}, \quad p^r p'^r = (pp')^r, \quad \text{and} \quad p^r p^s = p^{r+s}, \tag{11}$$

where p and p' are positive real numbers, may be proved for positive integral values of r and s directly from the definition of an integral power as repeated multiplication. They may then be proved for any rational values of r and s by reducing this case to that for integers, by means of the definitions (10).

Suppose that the rational number r has an odd denominator. Then we may write $r = N/D$, where N is integral and D is an odd integer. If N is even for one such representation of r, it will be even for all and we write:

$$(-p)^r = p^r, \quad r = \frac{N}{D}, \quad D \text{ odd}, \quad N \text{ even} \tag{12}$$

and

$$(-p)^r = -p^r, \quad r = \frac{N}{D}, \quad D \text{ odd}, \quad N \text{ odd}. \tag{13}$$

Then with this extended definition the relations (11) continue to hold when p and p' are positive or negative, if all the exponents which occur have odd denominators.

41. The Exponential Function for Rational Values. Let p be any positive real number greater than unity. Then, for all rational values of x, $x = r$, the function p^x is defined by equation (10) of the preceding section. We prove next that:

As r increases through rational values, the function $p^r (p > 1)$ increases, and

$$\lim_{r \to -\infty} p^r = 0, \quad \lim_{r \to 0} p^r = 1, \quad \text{and} \quad \lim_{r \to +\infty} p^r = +\infty. \tag{14}$$

For any two rational numbers r and s, we have:

$$p^s - p^r = p^r(p^{s-r} - 1). \tag{15}$$

But, since $p > 1$, any rational power of p is positive, and any positive rational power of p is greater than unity. Consequently, if $s > r$, the right member of equation (15) is positive. This proves that the function p^r increases, since $p^s > p^r$ if $s > r$.

Let us write

$$p = 1 + d, \quad \text{where} \quad d > 0, \quad \text{since} \quad p > 1. \tag{16}$$

Then, for any positive integer n, we have:

$$p^n = (1 + d)^n > 1 + nd, \tag{17}$$

from the binomial theorem, since the omitted terms are positive.

Since the function p^r increases,

if $r > n$, $p^r > p^n$.   (18)

Consequently, if, for any positive number N, we select an integer n such that

$$n > \frac{N-1}{d}, \quad \text{or} \quad 1 + nd > N,$$ (19)

we may deduce from the last three relations that:

if $r > n$, $p^r > N$.   (20)

This proves that

$$\lim_{x \to +\infty} p^r = +\infty.$$ (21)

We easily deduce from this that:

$$\lim_{r \to -\infty} p^r = \lim_{r \to +\infty} p^{-r} = \lim_{r \to +\infty} \frac{1}{p^r} = 0.$$ (22)

Let us next write, for any positive integer n,

$$p^{\frac{1}{n}} = 1 + d_n$$ (23)

where $d_n > 0$, since $p^{1/n} > 1$ when $p > 1$.   Then, as in equation (17), we have:

$$1 + d = p = (1 + d_n)^n > 1 + nd_n.$$ (24)

It follows that

$$d > nd_n \quad \text{so that} \quad 0 < d_n < \frac{d}{n}.$$ (25)

Thus

$$\lim_{n \to +\infty} d_n = 0, \quad \text{and} \quad \lim_{n \to +\infty} p^{\frac{1}{n}} = 1.$$ (26)

And we may further conclude that:

$$\lim_{n \to +\infty} p^{-\frac{1}{n}} = \lim_{n \to +\infty} \frac{1}{p^{\frac{1}{n}}} = 1.$$ (27)

Now, if $r \to 0$, we may find a sequence of positive integers n, such that

$$-\frac{1}{n} < r < \frac{1}{n}, \quad n \to +\infty \quad \text{as} \quad r \to 0.$$ (28)

Since the function p^r increases, this implies that

$$p^{-\frac{1}{n}} < p^r < p^{\frac{1}{n}}, \tag{29}$$

and we conclude from the last four relations that:

$$\lim_{r \to 0} p^r = 1. \tag{30}$$

This completes the proof of our statement concerning the behavior of the function p^r for rational values of r.

42. The Exponential Function for Real Values. If a sequence of rational values of x, $x = r$, approaches a limit c, then p^x or p^r approaches a limit, as we shall now prove. The limit c may be any real number, and the limit of p^x depends only on c, and not on the special rational sequence used. Let d denote any rational number greater than c.

If r and s are any two numbers of the sequence, $\lim r = c$, $\lim s = c$, then

$$\lim (s - r) = 0, \tag{31}$$

so that from equation (30):

$$\lim p^{s-r} = 1. \tag{32}$$

Also, beyond a certain point in the sequence, $r < d + 1$ so that

$$p^r < p^{d+1}. \tag{33}$$

But we have:

$$p^s - p^r = p^r(p^{s-r} - 1), \tag{34}$$

and as the first factor on the right is bounded by equation (33), and the second factor approaches zero by equation (32), we deduce that:

$$\lim |p^s - p^r| = 0 \quad \text{as} \quad r \to c \quad \text{and} \quad s - r \to 0. \tag{35}$$

If we interpret this relation in terms of the fundamental definition of a limit, we see by the Cauchy convergence criterion of section 26 that p^r approaches a limit as x runs through the rational sequence. We also see that the same limit is approached, regardless of the rational sequence r used, so long as $r \to c$.

If the limit c is rational, we have:

$$\lim_{r \to c} p^r = p^c, \tag{36}$$

since we may then take r constantly equal to c as a sequence of rational values approaching c.

If the limit c is irrational, we define p^c as the uniquely defined limit given by equation (36). Thus this equation then holds for all real values of c.

Now let c and $c' > c$ be any two real numbers. We may find two rational numbers s and s' such that $c < s < s' < c'$. We may also find two sequences of rational values, r and r', such that:

$$r \to c, \quad r' \to c' \quad \text{and} \quad r < s, \quad r' > s'. \tag{37}$$

Then, since p^r is an increasing function for rational values, we have:

$$p^r < p^s, \quad p^s < p^{s'}, \quad \text{and} \quad p^{s'} < p^{r'}. \tag{38}$$

On letting r and r' approach their limits, we may deduce from this that:

$$p^c \leqq p^s, \quad p^{s'} \leqq p^{c'} \quad \text{so that} \quad p^c < p^{c'}. \tag{39}$$

Since this is true for any two real numbers $c < c'$, it follows that p^x is an increasing function for all real values of x.

Next, let $x \to c$ through any sequence of real values. We may then find two sequences of rational values, r and s, such that

$$r < x < s, \quad \text{and} \quad r \to c, \, s \to c \text{ as } x \to c. \tag{40}$$

Then, from the increasing character of p^x for real values, we have

$$p^r < p^x < p^s. \tag{41}$$

But, in view of equations (40) and (36),

$$\lim p^r = p^c \quad \text{and} \quad \lim p^s = p^c. \tag{42}$$

Hence, by the last theorem of section 23,

$$\lim_{x \to c} p^x = p^c. \tag{43}$$

This proves that the function p^x is continuous for all real values x. We may now replace the rational value r by x in equations (18) through (22), reasoning exactly as before, and so conclude that

$$\lim_{x \to -\infty} p^x = 0, \quad \lim_{x \to +\infty} p^x = +\infty. \tag{44}$$

Finally, by using rational sequences approaching irrational limits, we may extend the relations (11) so that they apply when r and s are any two real numbers.

We may summarize the results of this section as follows:

If p is any positive real number greater than unity, the single-valued function p^x is positive and continuous for all real values of x. As $x \to -\infty$, $p^x \to 0$; as $x \to +\infty$, $p^x \to +\infty$. The function is increasing for all values of x.

We may remove the restriction $p > 1$. We define $1^x = 1$, for all values of x. If $q < 1$, $1/q > 1$, and we define:

$$q^x = \left(\frac{1}{q}\right)^{-x}, \quad \text{if} \quad q < 1. \tag{45}$$

Thus the first statement in the theorem applies unchanged for all positive real values of p. For values $q < 1$, the function q^x decreases for all real values of x, and as $x \to -\infty$, $q^x \to +\infty$, while as $x \to +\infty$, $q^x \to 0$.

Finally, analogous to equation (11), we have:

$$(p^x)^u = p^{xu}, \quad p^x p'^x = (pp')^x \quad \text{and} \quad p^x p^u = p^{x+u}, \tag{46}$$

where p and p' are any positive real numbers, and x and u are any real numbers.

43. The Logarithmic Function. If p is any positive real number greater than unity, the function p^x is continuous and increasing in the closed interval $-N, N$. Hence, by the theorem of section 37, the equation $y = f(x) = p^x$ defines a single-valued inverse function $x = f^{-1}(y)$, which is continuous and increasing in the closed interval $p^{-N} \leqq y \leqq p^N$. In view of equation (44) this interval will include any given positive value if N is taken sufficiently large. We use $\log_p y$, read "logarithm of y to the base p," to denote the function inverse to p^x. Thus

$$y = p^x \quad \text{and} \quad x = \log_p y \tag{47}$$

are equivalent equations.

We note that, in consequence of equation (44),

$$\lim_{y \to 0+} \log_p y = -\infty \quad \text{and} \quad \lim_{y \to +\infty} \log_p y = +\infty, \quad (p > 1). \tag{48}$$

The relation (47) enables us to deduce the properties of logarithms from those for exponential functions given by equation (46). Thus,

if $\qquad\qquad x_1 = \log_p y_1 \quad \text{and} \quad x_2 = \log_p y_2, \tag{49}$

we have:

$$y_1 y_2 = p^{x_1} p^{x_2} = p^{x_1+x_2} \quad \text{and} \quad x_1 + x_2 = \log_p (y_1 y_2). \tag{50}$$

That is:

$$\log_p (y_1 y_2) = \log_p y_1 + \log_p y_2. \tag{51}$$

Also

$$y^u = (p^x)^u = p^{ux} \quad \text{and} \quad ux = \log_p y^u. \tag{52}$$

That is:

$$\log_p (y^u) = u \log_p y. \tag{53}$$

In particular, from equation (53) with $u = -1$ and from equation (51):

$$\log_p \frac{1}{y} = - \log_p y \quad \text{and} \quad \log_p \frac{y_1}{y_2} = \log_p y_1 - \log_p y_2. \tag{54}$$

Finally, if we take the logarithm of y to a new base P,

$$X = \log_P y \quad \text{so that} \quad y = P^X, \tag{55}$$

where

$$P = p^v \quad \text{so that} \quad v = \log_p P, \tag{56}$$

we have:

$$y = P^X = (p^v)^X = p^{vX} \quad \text{and} \quad vX = \log_p y. \tag{57}$$

Thus:

$$\log_p y = \log_p P \log_P y \quad \text{or} \quad \log_P y = \frac{\log_p y}{\log_p P}. \tag{58}$$

In particular, if $y = p$,

$$\log_P p = \frac{1}{\log_p P}. \tag{59}$$

The last two equations are easily remembered by their analogy with

$$\frac{y}{p} = \frac{P}{p} \frac{y}{P}, \quad \frac{y}{P} = \frac{\dfrac{y}{p}}{\dfrac{P}{p}}, \quad \frac{p}{P} = \frac{1}{\dfrac{P}{p}}. \tag{60}$$

We could take a base less than unity and carry through all our arguments, merely replacing increasing by decreasing and suitably changing equation (48). All the other results still hold. Thus any positive number except unity may be used as the base of a logarithmic function.

When considering a logarithmic function of the independent variable x, we write

$$y = \log_p x \quad \text{equivalent to} \quad x = p^y \tag{61}$$

and interchange x and y in all the equations of this section.

44. The General Power Function. For any real value of u, a power function x^u may be defined for values of $x > 0$ in terms of the exponential and logarithmic functions, since

$$x^u = (p^{\log_p x})^u = p^{u \log_p x}. \tag{62}$$

Since the last expression increases with $u \log_p x$, we see that x^u increases with x if u is positive and decreases for increasing x if u is negative. By using equations (48) and (44), we may deduce from equation (62) that:

$$\lim_{x \to 0+} x^u = 0, \quad \text{if} \quad u > 0 \tag{63}$$

and

$$\lim_{x \to 0+} x^u = +\infty, \quad \text{if} \quad u < 0. \tag{64}$$

This makes it natural to define $0^u = 0$ if $u > 0$ and to regard this expression as undefined when $u < 0$ or $u = 0$.

In certain limiting relations, when u is fixed and negative, the relation (64) may enable us to evaluate the limit. Again, if u and x are related in such a way that $u \to 0$ when $x \to 0$, the expression x^u may not approach a limit, finite or infinite. But, by placing suitable restrictions on u and x, we may make the expression x^u approach a, any positive value whatever, as $x \to 0, u \to 0$. For example,

$$\text{if} \quad u = (\log_p a)/\log_p x, \quad u \to 0 \quad \text{when} \quad x \to 0 \tag{65}$$

and

$$x^u = a \quad \text{so that} \quad \lim_{x \to 0+} x^u = a. \tag{66}$$

45. The Derivative. The derivative of a function of x, $f(x)$, for a particular value of x is the number given by the limit, as $h \to 0$, of $[f(x + h) - f(x)]/h$, provided that this limit exists. We denote the derivative of $f(x)$ at x by $f'(x)$, so that:

$$f'(x) = \lim_{h \to 0} \frac{f(x + h) - f(x)}{h}. \tag{67}$$

While we shall postpone a detailed study of the properties of the derivative until the next chapter, we introduce the definition at this point in order to explain why we are interested in certain limiting relations.

In the case of the function $\log_p x$, the derivative is given by

$$f'(x) = \lim_{h \to 0} \frac{\log_p (x + h) - \log_p (x)}{h}, \tag{68}$$

if the limit exists.

For any $x > 0$, we may write:

$$\log_p (x + h) - \log_p x = \log_p \left(1 + \frac{h}{x}\right) = \frac{h}{x} \log_p \left(1 + \frac{h}{x}\right)^{\frac{x}{h}}, \tag{69}$$

in view of the properties expressed by equations (53) and (54).

Thus we have

$$\frac{\log_p (x + h) - \log_p x}{h} = \frac{1}{x} \log_p \left(1 + \frac{h}{x}\right)^{\frac{x}{h}}. \tag{70}$$

Since the logarithm is a continuous function, the calculation of the limit is reduced to the calculation of the following:

$$\lim_{h \to 0} \left(1 + \frac{h}{x}\right)^{\frac{x}{h}}, \quad x > 0. \tag{71}$$

This limit does not depend on x, since if we put $h = ux$, the limit becomes:

$$\lim_{u \to 0} (1 + u)^{\frac{1}{u}}. \tag{72}$$

46. The Number e. To study this limit (72) further, we put $u = 1/U$, and consider

$$\lim_{|U| \to \infty} \left(1 + \frac{1}{U}\right)^{U}. \tag{73}$$

For positive integral values of U, we may show that there is a limit by means of the theorem of section 27. We first observe that, if n is a positive integer, by the binomial theorem:

$$\left(1 + \frac{1}{n}\right)^{n} = 1 + n\frac{1}{n} + \frac{n(n-1)}{1 \cdot 2} \frac{1}{n^2} + \cdots + \frac{n(n-1) \cdots 1}{1 \cdot 2 \cdots n} \frac{1}{n^n} \tag{74}$$

$$= 1 + 1 + \frac{1\left(1 - \frac{1}{n}\right)}{2!} + \cdots + \frac{1\left(1 - \frac{1}{n}\right) \cdots \left(1 - \frac{n-1}{n}\right)}{n!}. \tag{75}$$

As n increases, the terms of this expression increase individually. Also their number increases. Thus the function increases with n. But the terms written in the expression (75) are less than

$$1 + 1 + \frac{1}{2} + \frac{1}{2^2} + \cdots + \frac{1}{2^{n-1}} = 3 - \frac{1}{2^{n-1}} < 3, \tag{76}$$

so that

$$\left(1 + \frac{1}{n}\right)^{n} < 3, \tag{77}$$

for all integral values of n, and 3 is an upper bound for the function. Thus, by the theorem on increasing variables of section 27, the function approaches a limit. We denote this limit by e and write:

$$\lim_{n \to +\infty} \left(1 + \frac{1}{n}\right)^n = e. \tag{78}$$

As the first two terms in the expression (75) add up to 2, and the rest are positive, we have:

$$2 < \left(1 + \frac{1}{n}\right)^n < 3 \quad \text{and} \quad 2 \leqq e \leqq 3. \tag{79}$$

The expression (75) suggests the sum:

$$s_n = 1 + 1 + \frac{1}{2!} + \frac{1}{3!} + \cdots + \frac{1}{n!}. \tag{80}$$

This sum s_n increases with n and has an upper bound 3, since after the first three each of its terms is less than the corresponding term of the sum (76). Thus s_n approaches a limit L, as $n \to +\infty$. Since each term of the sum (80) is greater than, or equal to, the corresponding term of the sum (75), we have

$$s_n > \left(1 + \frac{1}{n}\right)^n \quad \text{and} \quad \lim_{n \to +\infty} s_n \geqq e, \quad \text{or} \quad L \geqq e. \tag{81}$$

But, since s_n approaches L, for any positive ϵ we may find an N such that

$$s_N > L - \epsilon. \tag{82}$$

And, as each term of the sum (75) increases and approaches the corresponding term of the sum (80), when $n \to +\infty$, we may find an $N' > N$ such that, for n greater than N',

$$\frac{1\left(1 - \frac{1}{n}\right) \cdots \left(1 - \frac{r-1}{n}\right)}{r!} > \frac{1}{r!} - \frac{\epsilon}{N}, \quad r = 1, 2, \cdots, N. \tag{83}$$

Then, for any n exceeding N', as all the terms of the sum (75) are positive, the sum will exceed the sum of the first $N + 1$ terms, so that in view of equations (82) and (83) we shall have

$$\left(1 + \frac{1}{n}\right)^n > s_n - N\left(\frac{\epsilon}{N}\right) > L - 2\epsilon, \quad \text{if} \quad N > N'. \tag{84}$$

This shows that

$$e > L - 2\epsilon, \quad \text{or} \quad e \geqq L, \tag{85}$$

since ϵ is arbitrary. Equations (81) and (85) combined show that

$$L = e, \quad \text{and} \quad e = \lim_{n \to +\infty} s_n. \tag{86}$$

To estimate how much we shall add to the sum s_n by using $n + k$ in place of n, we note that for any positive integer n:

$$\frac{1}{(n+1)!} + \frac{1}{(n+2)!} + \cdots \frac{1}{(n+k)!} <$$

$$\frac{2}{(n+1)!}\left(\frac{1}{2} + \frac{1}{2^2} + \cdots + \frac{1}{2^k}\right) \qquad (87)$$

and

$$\frac{1}{2} + \frac{1}{2^2} + \cdots + \frac{1}{2^k} = 1 - \frac{1}{2^k} < 1. \qquad (88)$$

Thus

$$s_{n+k} < s_n + \frac{2}{(n+1)!}. \qquad (89)$$

Since this is true for all k, we may let k become infinite, keeping n fixed, and so find:

$$e = \lim_{k \to +\infty} s_{n+k} \leqq s_n + \frac{2}{(n+1)!}. \qquad (90)$$

Since the sum s_n increases to e, we deduce from this that

$$s_n < e < s_n + \frac{1}{n!}, \quad n > 1, \qquad (91)$$

where

$$s_n = 1 + 1 + \frac{1}{2!} + \frac{1}{3!} + \cdots + \frac{1}{n!}. \qquad (92)$$

As the sum s_n may be computed easily and as this sum approximates e to within $1/n!$, which decreases rapidly with n, the last relation enables us to find e numerically to any desired number of decimal places. Its value is $2.71828\cdots$.

47. Other Sequences. We have shown that for any sequence of positive integral values of n, such that $n \to +\infty$, $\lim (1 + 1/n)^n = e$.

Let us consider next a sequence of numbers U, integral or not, such that $U \to +\infty$. For each number of the sequence, there is an integer n such that

$$n \leqq U < n + 1, \qquad (93)$$

and,
since $U \to +\infty$,

$$n \to +\infty. \qquad (94)$$

We deduce from the relations (93) that:

$$1 + \frac{1}{n+1} < 1 + \frac{1}{U} \leqq 1 + \frac{1}{n}, \qquad (95)$$

and since x^u increases with x for fixed positive u and also increases with u for fixed x greater than one, we may further conclude from equations (93) and (95) that:

$$\left(1 + \frac{1}{n+1}\right)^n < \left(1 + \frac{1}{U}\right)^U < \left(1 + \frac{1}{n}\right)^{n+1} \tag{96}$$

But we have:

$$\lim \left(1 + \frac{1}{n}\right)^{n+1} = \lim \left(1 + \frac{1}{n}\right)^n \cdot \left(1 + \frac{1}{n}\right) = e \cdot 1 = e, \tag{97}$$

and

$$\lim \left(1 + \frac{1}{n+1}\right)^n = \lim \left(1 + \frac{1}{n+1}\right)^{n+1} \cdot \left(1 + \frac{1}{n+1}\right)^{-1}$$
$$= e \cdot 1 = e, \tag{98}$$

when n and hence $n + 1$ become infinite through any sequence of integers, and in particular through the sequence defined by the relation (93). Hence, from the last three relations we have

$$\lim_{U \to +\infty} \left(1 + \frac{1}{U}\right)^U = e, \tag{99}$$

in accordance with the theorem of section 23.

Finally, consider any sequence of real values U, such that $U \to -\infty$. We put $U = -V$, so that $V \to +\infty$, and write:

$$\left(1 + \frac{1}{U}\right)^U = \left(1 - \frac{1}{V}\right)^{-V} = \left(\frac{V}{V-1}\right)^V = \left(1 + \frac{1}{V-1}\right)^V. \tag{100}$$

But, from the relation (99), we have:

$$\lim \left(1 + \frac{1}{V-1}\right)^V = \lim \left(1 + \frac{1}{V-1}\right)^{V-1} \cdot \left(1 + \frac{1}{V-1}\right)$$
$$= e \cdot 1 = e, \tag{101}$$

when V and hence $V - 1 \to +\infty$. Thus we may conclude from equation (100) that

$$\lim_{U \to -\infty} \left(1 + \frac{1}{U}\right)^U = e. \tag{102}$$

Since every sequence of values of U for which $|U| \to \infty$ may be regarded as a combination of sequences for which $U \to +\infty$ or $U \to -\infty$, it follows from equations (99) and (102) that:

$$\lim_{|U| \to \infty} \left(1 + \frac{1}{U}\right)^U = e. \tag{103}$$

On putting $U = 1/u$, we deduce that

$$\lim_{u \to 0} (1 + u)^{\frac{1}{u}} = e. \tag{104}$$

48. The Derivative of the Logarithmic Function. Let us now return to the calculation of the derivative $f'(x)$, when $f(x) = \log_p x$, discussed in section 45. We showed there that

$$\frac{\log_p (x + h) - \log_p x}{h} = \frac{1}{x} \log_p \left(1 + \frac{h}{x}\right)^{\frac{x}{h}}. \tag{105}$$

As before, on putting $h = ux$, we have:

$$\lim_{h \to 0} \left(1 + \frac{h}{x}\right)^{\frac{x}{h}} = \lim_{u \to 0} (1 + u)^{\frac{1}{u}} = e, \tag{106}$$

by equation (104). From this and the fact that the logarithm is continuous, we deduce from equation (105) that

$$\lim_{h \to 0} \frac{\log_p (x + h) - \log_p x}{h} = \frac{1}{x} \log_p e. \tag{107}$$

This proves that,

if $f(x) = \log_p x$, $f'(x) = \dfrac{1}{x} \log_p e.$ \hfill (108)

49. Natural Logarithms. When we use logarithms to simplify computation, we generally take 10 as the base. Logarithms to the base 10, known as denary or common logarithms, have the useful property that the logarithm is only changed by the addition of an integer when the decimal point is shifted to the right. Thus we only need tables for the range $1 \leqq x < 10$.

In mathematical work, where the limiting relation (107) occurs quite often, it is advantageous to make this equation as simple as we can. Consequently, we generally take e as the base, since this makes $\log_p e = \log_e e = 1$, and we may omit the factor $\log_p e$. Logarithms to the base e are known as natural logarithms. In computations the notation $\ln x$ for $\log_e x$ is sometimes used. Since in the sequel we shall almost always be using natural logarithms, we write simply $\log x$ in place of $\log_e x$. In this notation, the relations of the preceding section may be written:

$$\lim_{h \to 0} \frac{\log (x + h) - \log x}{h} = \frac{1}{x}, \tag{109}$$

and,

if $f(x) = \log x$, $\qquad\qquad f'(x) = \dfrac{1}{x}$. $\qquad\qquad$ (110)

50. Characterization of the Logarithmic Function. Using the results of the preceding discussion, which, though lengthy, has included a constructive approach to the logarithmic function, we may now formulate a brief characterization of the function $\log x$.

The function $\log x$ *is a function having the property:*

$$\log x + \log x' = \log xx', \qquad\qquad (111)$$

for all positive real values of x *and* x', *and also having the special property:*

$$\lim_{x \to 0} \frac{\log (1 + x)}{x} = 1. \qquad\qquad (112)$$

These properties intrinsically define the logarithmic function, in the sense that it is possible to define a function having these properties, and this can only be done in one way.

We observe that the natural logarithm of x, $\log x$ as defined in the preceding section, has the property (111). Also, if we replace x by 1 and h by x in equation (109), it reduces to equation (112), so that the second property is also satisfied. This shows that the definition is possible.

Suppose next that the function $L(x)$ satisfies the equation

$$L(x) + L(x') = L(xx') \qquad\qquad (113)$$

analogous to equation (111) and

$$\lim_{x \to 0} \frac{L(1 + x)}{x} = 1, \qquad\qquad (114)$$

analogous to equation (112). Then on putting $x' = 1$ in equation (113), we have:

$$L(x) + L(1) = L(x) \quad \text{and} \quad L(1) = 0. \qquad\qquad (115)$$

Again, by putting $x' = 1 + h/x$, $xx' = x + h$ and we find from equation (113) that

$$L(x + h) - L(x) = L\left(1 + \frac{h}{x}\right). \qquad\qquad (116)$$

But, from the equation (114), we see that

$$\lim_{x \to 0} L(1 + x) = 0. \qquad\qquad (117)$$

This shows that, when $h \to 0$, the right member of equation (116) approaches zero, and hence the function $L(x)$ is continuous for all positive values of x.

By putting $x' = x$ and then $x' = x^n$ in equation (113), we may show by mathematical induction that for any positive integer n:

$$L(x^n) = nL(x). \tag{118}$$

It follows in particular that

$$L\left(1 + \frac{1}{n}\right)^n = nL\left(1 + \frac{1}{n}\right) = \frac{L\left(1 + \frac{1}{n}\right)}{\frac{1}{n}}. \tag{119}$$

As $n \to +\infty$ the limit of the first term written may be found from equation (78) and the fact that $L(x)$ is continuous. The limit of the last term in equation (119), as $n \to +\infty$ may be found by putting $x = 1/n$ in equation (114). We thus obtain the result:

$$L(e) = 1. \tag{120}$$

From the equation (118), we deduce that

$$L(x^{\frac{1}{q}}) = \frac{1}{q} L(x), \quad L(x^{\frac{p}{q}}) = \frac{p}{q} L(x), \tag{121}$$

for p and q positive integers and hence, from equation (120),

$$L(e^r) = r = \log (e^r), \tag{122}$$

so that $L(x)$ has the same value as $\log x$ whenever x has a positive rational logarithm. Since any number greater than 1 is the limit of a sequence of such special values and since both functions are continuous, it follows that

$$L(x) = \log x \tag{123}$$

for all real values of x greater than unity. Finally, by putting $x' = 1/x$ in equation (113), and recalling that $L(1) = 0$, we have

$$L\left(\frac{1}{x}\right) = -L(x). \tag{124}$$

This shows that, for any positive number less than unity,

$$L(x) = -L\left(\frac{1}{x}\right) = -\log\left(\frac{1}{x}\right) = \log x. \tag{125}$$

Since $L(1) = 0 = \log 1$, it follows that any function $L(x)$ having the properties (113) and (114) must agree with $\log x$ for all positive values.

51. Characterization of the Exponential Function. We may formulate a similar brief characterization of the exponential function.

The function e^x is a function having the property:

$$e^x e^{x'} = e^{x+x'}, \tag{126}$$

for all real values of x and x', and also having the special property:

$$\lim_{x \to 0} \frac{e^x - 1}{x} = 1. \tag{127}$$

These properties intrinsically define the exponential function.

We observe that the function p^x defined in section 42, with $p = e$ has the property (126). If we write:

$$e^x = 1 + u, \ \log(1 + u) = x \ \text{ and } \ u \to 0 \ \text{ as } \ x \to 0. \tag{128}$$

Hence,

$$\lim_{x \to 0} \frac{e^x - 1}{x} = \lim_{u \to 0} \frac{u}{\log(1 + u)} = 1, \tag{129}$$

by equation (112). This shows that it is possible to define a function having the two properties.

Suppose next that the function $E(x)$ satisfies the equation

$$E(x) \, E(x') = E(x + x'), \tag{130}$$

analogous to equation (126) and

$$\lim_{x \to 0} \frac{E(x) - 1}{x} = 1, \tag{131}$$

analogous to equation (127).

The first relation, with $x' = h$ shows that:

$$E(x + h) - E(x) = E(x)[E(h) - 1]. \tag{132}$$

But, from the second relation, we see that:

$$\lim_{x \to 0} [E(x) - 1] = 0, \tag{133}$$

which shows that when $h \to 0$, the right member of equation (132) approaches zero, and hence the function $E(x)$ is continuous for all real values of x.

In particular, from equation (133) and the continuity for $x = 0$, we see that

$$E(0) = 1. \tag{134}$$

Using mathematical induction as in the preceding section, we may deduce from equation (130) that for n a positive integer:

$$E(nx) = [E(x)]^n. \tag{135}$$

From this we find:

$$E\left(\frac{x}{q}\right) = [E(x)]^{\frac{1}{q}} \quad \text{and} \quad E\left(\frac{px}{q}\right) = [E(x)]^{\frac{p}{q}}, \tag{136}$$

for p and q positive integers.

Again, by putting $x' = -x$ in equation (130) and using equation (134), we find that:

$$E(-x) = [E(x)]^{-1} \tag{137}$$

The equations (136) and (137) show that for any rational number r we have:

$$E(rx) = [E(x)]^r. \tag{138}$$

This shows that if we put

$$p = E(1), \quad \text{then} \quad E(r) = p^r. \tag{139}$$

The number p must be greater than unity, since equation (131) shows that $E(r) = p^r$ is greater than unity for sufficiently small positive values of r. Since the functions $E(x)$ and p^x agree for all rational values of x and are both continuous functions, it follows that

$$E(x) = p^x \tag{140}$$

for all real values of x.

Now put:

$$p^x = 1 + u, \quad \log(1+u) = x \log p, \quad \text{and} \quad u \to 0 \quad \text{as} \quad x \to 0. \tag{141}$$

Then:

$$\frac{E(x) - 1}{x} = \frac{p^x - 1}{x} = \frac{u \log p}{\log(1+u)}, \tag{142}$$

so that:

$$1 = \lim_{x \to 0} \frac{E(x) - 1}{x} = \log p \lim_{u \to 0} \frac{u}{\log(1+u)} = \log p. \tag{143}$$

This shows that $\log p = 1$ and $p = e$, so that the function $E(x) = p^x$ is identified with the exponential function e^x. This proves that any function having the properties (130) and (131) must agree with e^x for all real values of x.

It is an interesting fact that the equations (113) and (114), and (130) and (131) do not explicitly involve the number e. However, this number is determined from the first pair by $L(e) = 1$, and from the second pair by $E(1) = e$.

52. Trigonometric Functions. The reader is familiar with definitions of the six trigonometric functions and a derivation of their properties based on geometrical considerations. Such a treatment is satisfactory provided that it is permissible to base the definitions of functions used in analysis on geometrical arguments, and that the geometrical results used are themselves derived by sound reasoning about concepts which have been precisely defined. The geometrical arguments in elementary texts are often not of this character. In many cases the length of an arc of a circle not a rational part of a complete circumference or the number of degrees in the corresponding central angle is not defined at all.

As it is aesthetically desirable to develop the foundations of analysis arithmetically, we avoid the necessity of a precise geometrical definition by giving a constructive arithmetic definition of the trigonometric functions.

The definitions:

$$\tan x = \frac{\sin x}{\cos x}, \quad \cot x = \frac{\cos x}{\sin x}, \quad \sec x = \frac{1}{\cos x}, \quad \csc x = \frac{1}{\sin x} \quad (144)$$

enable us to define these four functions in terms of the sine and cosine and to reduce all theorems involving any of the six functions to theorems involving the sine and cosine alone.

Accordingly, we first consider the sine and cosine, although even in this discussion we sometimes find it convenient to use $\tan x$ as an abbreviation for $\sin x/\cos x$.

53. Determination of Values for the First Quadrant. To prepare for our final definition, we outline one method of assigning numbers to the functions $\sin x$ and $\cos x$, for values of x in the range $0 \leqq x \leqq 90$.

The geometric development suggests that the numbers may be assigned in such a way that, for any two values of a and b in the range, for which $a + b$ is also in the range:

$$\sin (a + b) = \sin a \cos b + \cos a \sin b, \quad (145)$$

$$\cos (a + b) = \cos a \cos b - \sin a \sin b, \quad (146)$$

$$1 = \cos^2 a + \sin^2 a. \quad (147)$$

We shall use these equations as our guide, but shall only consider them proved for particular values if we can deduce this from our definitions.

We begin by arbitrarily defining

$$\sin 90 = 1, \quad \cos 90 = 0, \quad (148)$$

and
$$\sin 0 = 0, \quad \cos 0 = 1. \quad (149)$$

We then consider values of x of the special form $90/2^n$, where n is a positive integer. We indicate a particular value of this kind by writing:

$$s_n = \frac{90}{2^n}. \tag{150}$$

We shall use s and speak of a value s to mean any one of these. We determine the functions of the s_n by repeated use of

$$\sin \frac{s}{2} = +\sqrt{\frac{1 - \cos s}{2}}, \quad \cos \frac{s}{2} = +\sqrt{\frac{1 + \cos s}{2}} \tag{151}$$

to obtain the values of the left members. Starting with s_0, or 90 in place of s, we determine the functions of s_1, s_2, $\cdots$ in succession in this way.

The equations (148), (149), and (151) are all such that the relation (147) is automatically satisfied for the values so far considered. For the equations (145) and (146) we can only have a, b, and $a + b$ all among the values s by taking a and b equal or by taking one of them as zero. If we take $a = 0$, the equations (145) and (146) reduce to identities in view of equation (149). If we take $a = b = s/2$, the equation (146) is satisfied because of equation (151), while equation (145) is satisfied because of equation (151) combined with the relation (147) which we established for all values of s.

Let us next consider the function

$$\frac{\tan s_n}{s_n} \quad \text{or} \quad \frac{\sin s_n}{s_n \cos s_n}. \tag{152}$$

To see how this function varies with n, we first deduce from the relations (151) with $s/2 = s_n$, $s = 2s_n = s_{n-1}$, that

$$\cos^2 s_n + \sin^2 s_n = 1, \tag{153}$$

$$2 \sin s_n \cos s_n = \sqrt{1 - \cos^2 s_{n-1}} = \sin s_{n-1}, \tag{154}$$

$$\cos s_{n-1} = \cos^2 s_n - \sin^2 s_n < \cos^2 s_n. \tag{155}$$

It follows from these relations that:

$$\frac{\tan s_{n-1}}{s_{n-1}} = \frac{\sin s_{n-1}}{s_{n-1} \cos s_{n-1}} = \frac{2 \sin s_n \cos s_n}{2s_n \cos s_{n-1}}$$

$$= \frac{\tan s_n}{s_n} \cdot \frac{\cos^2 s_n}{\cos s_{n-1}} > \frac{\tan s_n}{s_n}. \tag{156}$$

This shows that the function (152) decreases as n increases. Since it is positive, it has zero as a lower bound. Hence, by section 27, it approaches a limit as n becomes infinite, and we have:

$$\lim_{n \to +\infty} \frac{\tan s_n}{s_n} = L. \tag{157}$$

Since, as $n \to +\infty$, $s_n \to 0$, it follows that:

$$\lim_{n \to +\infty} \tan s_n = 0, \tag{158}$$

and hence that:

$$\lim_{n \to +\infty} \sin s_n = \lim_{n \to +\infty} (\tan s_n \cos s_n) = 0, \tag{159}$$

since the values of the $\cos s_n$ are all at most one by equation (153).

Using equation (153) and the fact that the $\cos s_n$ is always positive, we may deduce from the last equation that:

$$\lim_{n \to +\infty} \cos s_n = 1, \tag{160}$$

which may be combined with equation (157) to show that:

$$\lim_{n \to +\infty} \frac{\sin s_n}{s_n} = L. \tag{161}$$

From equation (154) we have:

$$\frac{\sin s_{n-1}}{s_{n-1}} = \frac{2 \sin s_n \cos s_n}{2s_n} < \frac{\sin s_n}{s_n}, \tag{162}$$

since the $\cos s_n$ is less than unity. This shows that $(\sin s_n)/s_n$ increases as n increases and therefore is always less than its limit, L. Since $(\tan s_n)/s_n$ decreased to its limit, it is always greater than that limit. That is:

$$\frac{\sin s_n}{s_n} < L < \frac{\tan s_n}{s_n}, \tag{163}$$

or

$$\sin s_n < L s_n < \tan s_n, \quad n > 0. \tag{164}$$

We next extend our determination to values of the special form ms_n or $90m/2^n$, where m is any positive integer less than 2^n. We shall speak of any one of these as a value t. Thus, every value s is a value t. Since any positive integer is a sum of powers of 2, we have

$$m = \sum_{i=1}^{n} a_i \, 2^{n-i}, \; a_i = 0 \text{ or } 1, \tag{165}$$

and it follows from this that:

$$t = \frac{90m}{2^n} = \sum_{i=1}^{n} \frac{a_i \, 90}{2^i} = \sum_{i=1}^{n} a_i s_i. \tag{166}$$

This decomposition enables us to determine the functions sine and cosine for all the values t by a repeated use of the formulas (145) and (146). Each t is the sum of a number of distinct s, as the a_i are zero or one, which may be arranged in a definite order, that of increasing subscript. This enables us to prescribe a particular order of application for the formulas (145) and (146), for example, first for the first two terms, then these plus the third, and so on.

However, the result obtained does not depend on the order. For, if the formulas (145) and (146) hold for

$$(a + b) = a + b \quad \text{and} \quad (a + b + c) = (a + b) + c, \tag{167}$$

we find:

$$\sin (a + b + c) = \sin a \cos b \cos c + \sin b \cos c \cos a$$
$$+ \sin c \cos a \cos b - \sin a \sin b \sin c, \tag{168}$$

and

$$\cos (a + b + c) = \cos a \cos b \cos c - \cos a \sin b \sin c$$
$$- \cos b \sin c \sin a - \cos c \sin a \sin b. \tag{169}$$

The symmetrical form of the results shows that the functions of $(a + b + c)$ as computed by two applications of the formulas (145) and (146) will be the same regardless of the way in which we order or group the three terms. It follows from this that the values as computed for a sum of any finite number of terms will not depend on the way in which we order or group them. If, now, we have three different values of t, $t_1 + t_2 = t_3$ and we decompose t_1 and t_2 into sums of s_n, the functions of $(t_1 + t_2)$, as computed from formulas (145) and (146) with $a = t_1$ and $b = t_2$ will be the same as that obtained from the combined sum of the s_n with any other grouping. By first combining any two s_n of the same order which occur in t_1 and t_2 and by repeating this until all the s_n left are of distinct order, we finally come to a grouping of the sum which may be rearranged to give that used to determine the functions of t_3. This shows that the equations (145) and (146) are satisfied if a, b, and $a + b$ are all among the values t.

It is now possible to extend some of our properties to the functions of t. Since the equations (145) and (146) imply that:

$$\cos^2 (a + b) + \sin^2 (a + b) = (\cos^2 a + \sin^2 a)(\cos^2 b + \sin^2 b), \tag{170}$$

it follows from our method of determination that

$$1 = \cos^2 t + \sin^2 t, \tag{171}$$

since this relation held for the s_n.

We wish to show next that, in the range $0 < t < 90$, $\sin t$ and $\cos t$ are always positive.

The equations (145), (146) and (147) imply that

$$\sin (a + b) \cos a - \cos (a + b) \sin a = \sin b, \tag{172}$$

and

$$\cos (a + b) \cos a + \sin (a + b) \sin a = \cos b, \tag{173}$$

so that these equations are satisfied if a, b, and $a + b$ are all among the values t.

In particular, if we put $a = t$, $b = 90 - t$ in equation (172), we find:

$$\cos t = \sin (90 - t). \tag{174}$$

Let us next denote by a t of order n, a value of t which can be written in the form $90m/2^n$, with m an odd integer, $0 < m < 2^n$. Then the t of order $n + 1$ which are not of order n are values halfway between two consecutive t of order n, which differ by $90/2^n$, or s_n. The first such value of t is s_{n+1} whose sine and cosine are known to be positive. The rest can be obtained by adding s_{n+1} to some t of order n, that is, as the sum of a t of order n and s_{n+1}. Thus, if the functions sine and cosine are positive for all t of order n, by equation (145) the sine will be positive for all t of order $n + 1$. Hence, since $90 - t$ is a t of order $n + 1$ if t is of this order, it follows from equation (174) that the cosine will be positive for all t of order $n + 1$. But the only t of the first order is s_1, whose sine and cosine are known to be positive. Thus, by mathematical induction, it follows that the sine and cosine are positive for t of any integral order, that is for all values of t in the range $0 < t < 90$.

From this fact and equation (171) we have:

$$0 < \sin t < 1 \quad \text{and} \quad 0 < \cos t < 1. \quad (0 < t < 90). \tag{175}$$

We may now prove that $\sin t$ increases with t. Let t_1 and t_2 be two distinct values of t so that:

$$0 \leqq t_1 < t_2 \leqq 90. \tag{176}$$

Then $(t_2 + t_1)/2$ and $(t_2 - t_1)/2$ are both values t in the range $0 < t < 90$.

If we use these as a and b, we find from equation (145) that

$$\sin t_2 = \sin \left(\frac{t_2 + t_1}{2} \right) \cos \left(\frac{t_2 - t_1}{2} \right) + \cos \left(\frac{t_2 + t_1}{2} \right) \sin \left(\frac{t_2 - t_1}{2} \right). \tag{177}$$

Again, if we put $a = (t_2 - t_1)/2$ and $b = t_1$, we find from equation (172) that:

$$\sin t_1 = \sin\left(\frac{t_2 + t_1}{2}\right)\cos\left(\frac{t_2 - t_1}{2}\right) - \cos\left(\frac{t_2 + t_1}{2}\right)\sin\left(\frac{t_2 - t_1}{2}\right). \quad (178)$$

It follows from the last two equations that:

$$\sin t_2 - \sin t_1 = 2\cos\left(\frac{t_2 + t_1}{2}\right)\sin\left(\frac{t_2 - t_1}{2}\right). \quad (179)$$

The cosine and sine in the right member are both positive, since their arguments are in the range $0 < t < 90$. This shows that, if the relations (176) hold, then $\sin t_2 > \sin t_1$ and $\sin t$ increases with t in the range $0 < t < 90$.

We next consider some limiting relations. Suppose that we have a sequence of values t, whose limit is zero. We may associate with each t of the sequence an s_n, such that

$$t < s_n, \quad \text{and} \quad \lim_{t \to 0} n = +\infty. \quad (180)$$

It follows that:

$$0 < \sin t < \sin s_n, \quad (181)$$

and from this and equation (159) we conclude that

$$\lim_{t \to 0+} \sin t = 0. \quad (182)$$

Now let t' and t'' be any two values, each in the range $0 < t < 90$. Then we have:

$$|\sin t'' - \sin t'| = 2\cos\left(\frac{t'' + t'}{2}\right)\sin\left|\frac{t'' - t'}{2}\right|, \quad (183)$$

since both sides are zero if $t' = t''$, and if t' and t'' are unequal, this equation reduces to equation (179) with t_2 as the larger and t_1 as the smaller of t' and t''. Since the cosine factor in this equation has a lower bound zero and an upper bound one, it follows from the last two equations that:

$$\lim |\sin t'' - \sin t'| = 0, \quad \text{if} \quad |t'' - t'| \to 0. \quad (184)$$

The last equation enables us to determine values of $\sin x$ for any real value of x, in the range $0 \leq x \leq 90$. We note that, since we may find a t of order n which differs from any real number x by at most s_n, and $s_n \to 0$ for $n \to +\infty$, there are sequences of values t for any real number x such that $x = \lim t$. If t' and t'' are any two terms of such a sequence, each beyond the variable term t, we have two new sequences such that:

$$\lim |t'' - t'| = 0, \quad \text{if} \quad \lim t = x. \tag{185}$$

It follows from the last two equations, and the Cauchy convergence criterion, that $\sin t$ approaches a limit, as $t \to x$. By taking the t' and t'' in equation (184) from two different sequences, we see that the limit is the same for all sequences approaching x. In particular, if x is itself a value t, we may take $t'' = x$ in equation (184) and conclude that

$$\lim_{t \to x} \sin t = \sin x. \tag{186}$$

For values of x which are not values t, we consider the value of $\sin x$ to be determined by equation (186).

From equation (174), we see that if we put

$$\cos x = \sin (90 - x), \tag{187}$$

then we shall have

$$\lim_{t \to x} \cos t = \cos x, \tag{188}$$

for any sequence t such that $t \to x$.

By using a sequence of values t_1 approaching a real value x_1, and a sequence of values t_2 approaching a real value x_2, we may show by means of equations (186) and (188) that all the equations previously established for values t continue to hold for all real values of x in the range $0 \leq x \leq 90$. In particular, we may establish equation (179) and use it to show that $\sin x$ increases, and equation (184) and use it to show that $\sin x$ is continuous. It then follows from equation (187) that $\cos x$ is continuous and decreases as x increases in the range $0 \leq x \leq 90$.

The functions $\sin x$ and $\cos x$, as determined by the method of this section for values of x between 0 and 90, are both continuous in this closed range. The sine increases from 0 to 1, and the cosine decreases from 1 to 0, as x increases from 0 to 90.

54. The Number π. We may extend the limit relations (157) and (161) to other values of x as follows. Let a, b and $a + b$ be in the range $0 < x < 90$, and suppose that:

$$\sin a \leq La \leq \tan a, \tag{189}$$

and

$$\sin b < Lb < \tan b. \tag{190}$$

Then, since

$$0 < \cos a < 1 \quad \text{and} \quad 0 < \cos b < 1, \tag{191}$$

we may conclude from equation (145) that:

$$\sin (a + b) < \sin a + \sin b < L(a + b). \tag{192}$$

Again, since

$$0 < \cos (a + b) < 1, \tag{193}$$

we may conclude from equation (146) that:

$$\cos a \cos b > \sin a \sin b. \tag{194}$$

It follows from this and equation (191) that:

$$1 > \tan a \tan b. \tag{195}$$

Also,

$$\tan a \tan b > 0, \tag{196}$$

since $\sin a$, $\cos a$, $\sin b$, $\cos b$ are all positive. In consequence of the last two relations, we have:

$$1 > 1 - \tan a \tan b > 0. \tag{197}$$

But, we may deduce from equations (145) and (146) that:

$$\tan (a + b) = \frac{\tan a + \tan b}{1 - \tan a \tan b}. \tag{198}$$

We may conclude from this, and the relations (197), (189) and (190) that:

$$\tan (a + b) > \tan a + \tan b > L(a + b). \tag{199}$$

We may combine the result of relations (192) and (199) into:

$$\sin (a + b) < L(a + b) < \tan (a + b). \tag{200}$$

Since the equation (164) shows that the inequality (190) holds when b is an s_n, the argument just given shows that if it holds for all t of order n, it holds for all t of order $n + 1$. Thus starting with s_1, the only t of the first order, we may apply mathematical induction to show that, for all values of t,

$$\sin t < Lt < \tan t. \tag{201}$$

By taking a sequence of values t approaching any real value x, we deduce from this that:

$$\sin x \leqq Lx \leqq \tan x. \quad (0 < x < 90). \tag{202}$$

If we take the relations (202) and (201) in place of the relations (189) and (190), we find by the reasoning used to derive equation (200) that

$$\sin (x + t) < L(x + t) < \tan (x + t). \tag{203}$$

Since any real number in the range 0,90 may be written as the sum of another real number and a value t in this range, it follows from the last relation that we may omit the equality signs in equation (202). Thus we have, for any real x,

$$\sin x < Lx < \tan x, \quad \text{if} \quad 0 < x < 90. \tag{204}$$

This relation implies that

$$L \cos x < \frac{\sin x}{x} < L. \tag{205}$$

Since the $\cos x$ is continuous, when $x \to 0+$, $\cos x \to 1$, and we may deduce from this equation that:

$$\lim_{x \to 0+} \frac{\sin x}{x} = L, \tag{206}$$

and

$$\lim_{x \to 0+} \frac{\tan x}{x} = \lim_{x \to 0+} \frac{\sin x}{x} \frac{1}{\cos x} = L. \tag{207}$$

The numerical value of L could be computed to any desired accuracy by using a sufficiently large value of n in the relation:

$$\frac{\sin s_n}{s_n} < L < \frac{\tan s_n}{s_n}, \tag{208}$$

and, in fact, was computed in practically this way by Archimedes.

The geometric interpretation of the limit L may be seen by noting that, if $x = 360/(2n)$, the perimeter of a regular polygon of n sides inscribed in a unit circle is

$$p_n = 2n \sin x = 360 \frac{\sin x}{x}, \tag{209}$$

while that of a circumscribed regular polygon of n sides is:

$$P_n = 2n \tan x = 360 \frac{\tan x}{x}. \tag{210}$$

The limit of either of these expressions as n becomes infinite is $360L$. As the length of the unit circle, defined to be equal to this common limit, is denoted by 2π, we have:

$$360L = 2\pi, \quad \text{or} \quad L = \frac{\pi}{180}, \quad \text{where } \pi = 3.14159 \cdots \tag{211}$$

55. Values for Other Ranges. If we wish to have equations (145) and (146) hold for the values $a = x, b = 90$ we must have:

$$\sin (x + 90) = \cos x, \quad \cos (x + 90) = -\sin x. \tag{212}$$

On the other hand, if these equations hold, we may deduce that the relations (145), (146), and (147) hold for $a = x + 90,b$ if they hold for a,b. Thus we may use the equations (212) to extend the definition to values of x in the range $90 < x \leqq 180$, and the relations (145), (146) and (147) will continue to hold in the extended range $0 \leqq x \leqq 180$. We may repeat this any number of times, and so define the functions $\sin x$ and $\cos x$ for all positive values of x.

The equations (172) and (173), which we deduced from the three fundamental relations, will also hold for all positive values. If we wish these to hold for the values $a = x, b = -x$, we must have

$$\sin (-x) = -\sin x, \quad \text{and} \quad \cos (-x) = \cos x. \tag{213}$$

Again, if these equations hold, equation (147) holds for $a = -x$, if it holds for $a = x$. Also, in view of the relations (213), equations (145) and (146) for $a = y, b = -x$ reduce to equations (172) and (173) for $(a + b) = y, a = x$. Thus we may use the equations (213) to extend the definition to negative values of x, and the three fundamental relations will continue to hold in this extended range.

Since $(\sin x)/x$ does not change when we change the sign of x, in view of equation (213), we have for the extended functions:

$$\lim_{x \to 0} \frac{\sin x}{x} = L = \frac{\pi}{180}. \tag{214}$$

56. Radian Measure. The functions $\sin x$ and $\cos x$, which we determined in sections 53 and 55, depended on the initial choice of 90 as the smallest positive value of x for which $\sin x = 1$. This choice, based on the measurement of angles in degrees, is convenient for practical trigonometric computations, and is traditional in such work.

However, any other choice would have done as well. If we had used the positive number q in place of 90, we could have carried through the entire discussion as before, and would have found the functions $S_q(x)$ and $C_q(x)$ related to those in the preceding section by the equations:

$$S_q(x) = \sin \left(90 \frac{x}{q} \right) \quad \text{and} \quad C_q(x) = \cos \left(90 \frac{x}{q} \right). \tag{215}$$

For these functions, the relation (214) would be replaced by:

$$\lim_{x \to 0} \frac{S_q(x)}{x} = \lim_{y \to 0} \frac{\sin y}{\dfrac{qy}{90}} = \frac{\pi}{2q}. \tag{216}$$

Since the limiting relation (214) occurs quite often in mathematical analysis, it becomes worth while to simplify it by a suitable choice of q.

We do this by taking $q = \pi/2$, which reduces the right member of equation (216) to unity.

Since $\pi/2$ is the length of a quadrant of a unit circle, this choice corresponds to the geometrical measure of central angles by the arcs they subtend on a unit circle, or by the arcs they subtend on any circle measured in terms of the radius. Hence this is called *radian measure*. From now on we shall use radian measure exclusively, and use sin x to mean $S_q(x)$, with $q = \pi/2$. When we wish to use $S_q(x)$ with $q = 90$, the function determined in section 55, we shall write sin $x°$. Thus, we have with this notation:

$$\sin x = \sin \left(\frac{180x}{\pi}\right)^°, \tag{217}$$

from which we can obtain the function of x for radian measure if we have tables of these functions for x in degrees.

With the new notation, the limiting relation is:

$$\lim_{x \to 0} \frac{\sin x}{x} = 1. \tag{218}$$

The inequality (204) may now be written:

$$\sin x < x < \tan x, \quad \text{if} \quad 0 < x < \frac{\pi}{2}. \tag{219}$$

57. Characterization of the Functions sin x and cos x. Using the results of the preceding constructive discussion, we may now formulate a brief arithmetic characterization of the functions sin x and cos x.

The functions sin x *and* cos x *are two functions having the following properties:*

$$\sin (x + x') = \sin x \cos x' + \cos x \sin x', \tag{220}$$

$$\cos (x + x') = \cos x \cos x' - \sin x \sin x', \tag{221}$$

$$\cos^2 x + \sin^2 x = 1, \tag{222}$$

for all real values of x and x', and the special property:

$$\lim_{x \to 0} \frac{\sin x}{x} = 1. \tag{223}$$

It is possible to define the functions for all values of x so that these properties are satisfied, and there is only one way of doing this.

The functions sin x and cos x of the preceding section have these four properties. We shall now show that any other pair of functions having the four properties must be identical with sin x and cos x. Accordingly we consider two functions $S(x)$ and $C(x)$ which are defined for all real values of x, and which satisfy the relations:

$$S(x + x') = S(x)\, C(x') + C(x)\, S(x'), \tag{224}$$

$$C(x + x') = C(x)\, C(x') - S(x)\, S(x'), \tag{225}$$

$$C^2(x) + S^2(x) = 1, \tag{226}$$

and

$$\lim_{x \to 0} \frac{S(x)}{x} = 1. \tag{227}$$

From the last relation, $S(x)$ must be different from zero for some value of x. Let x have such a value, and put $x' = 0$ in equations (224) and (225). The result is:

$$S(x) = S(x)\, C(0) + C(x)\, S(0), \tag{228}$$

$$C(x) = C(x)\, C(0) - S(x)\, S(0). \tag{229}$$

It follows from these equations that

$$S(x)\, \{[C(0) - 1]^2 + S^2(0)\} = 0, \tag{230}$$

or, since $S(x)$ is different from zero,

$$C(0) = 1 \quad \text{and} \quad S(0) = 0. \tag{231}$$

Again, from the relation (227), $S(x)$ must be distinct from zero for sufficiently small values of x, $0 < |x| < h_1$, so that

$$\lim_{x \to 0} S(x) = \lim_{x \to 0} \frac{S(x)}{x}\, x = 0. \tag{232}$$

By reasoning from equations (224), (225) and (226) as we did in the derivation of equation (179), we may prove that:

$$S(x_2) - S(x_1) = 2C\left(\frac{x_2 + x_1}{2}\right) S\left(\frac{x_2 - x_1}{2}\right). \tag{233}$$

Since the values of $C(x)$ never exceed 1 numerically, by equation (226), the right member of equation (233) approaches zero if $x_2 - x_1$ approaches zero, in view of the relation (232). Thus, if x_1 is fixed, and $x_2 \to x_1$, $S(x_2) \to S(x_1)$ and the function $S(x)$ is continuous for all values of x.

We may also deduce from equations (224), (225) and (226) by a similar argument that:

$$C(x_2) - C(x_1) = -2S\left(\frac{x_2 + x_1}{2}\right) S\left(\frac{x_2 - x_1}{2}\right), \tag{234}$$

from which we may infer that the function $C(x)$ is continuous for all values of x.

Since $C(0) = 1$, there is some interval $0 < x \leqq h_2$ throughout which the functions $S(x)$ and $C(x)$ are both positive, in view of the continuity at zero, and the relation (227).   Put

$$r_n = \frac{\pi}{2^{n+1}}, \quad \text{so that} \quad \frac{180}{\pi} r_n = \frac{90}{2^n} = s_n, \tag{235}$$

and r_n radians corresponds to s_n degrees.   Since r_n is positive, and when n becomes infinite $r_n \to 0$ and hence $\sin r_n \to 0$, we may find a value of n, say N, such that

$$0 < \sin r_N < S(h_2). \tag{236}$$

Also, since the function $S(x)$ is continuous in the closed interval $0, h_2$ and $\sin r_N$ is an intermediate value, it is taken on.   Thus there is some value, h, in the interval $0, h_2$ for which

$$S(h) = \sin r_N. \tag{237}$$

Since $C(h)$ is positive, and satisfies equation (226), we must have:

$$C(h) = \cos r_N. \tag{238}$$

But it follows from equations (224) and (225), with $x = x'$, that

$$S(2x) = 2S(x) \, C(x) \quad \text{and} \quad C(2x) = C^2(x) - S^2(x). \tag{239}$$

Since the functions $\sin x$ and $\cos x$ satisfy similar equations, it follows that

$$S(2^N h) = \sin (2^N r_N) = \sin \frac{\pi}{2} = 1, \tag{240}$$

and

$$C(2^N h) = \cos (2^N r_N) = \cos \frac{\pi}{2} = 0. \tag{241}$$

Again, from the second equation (239) and equation (226) we may deduce that:

$$S^2 \left(\frac{x}{2} \right) = \frac{1 - C(x)}{2}, \quad C^2 \left(\frac{x}{2} \right) = \frac{1 + C(x)}{2}. \tag{242}$$

Since these are similar in form to the equations (151), and the values of $S(x)$ and $C(x)$ are positive for all x between 0 and h, it follows that

$$S \left(\frac{h}{2^k} \right) = \sin \left(\frac{r_N}{2^k} \right) = \sin s_{N+k}^{\circ}, \quad \text{and} \quad C \left(\frac{h}{2^k} \right) = \cos s_{N+k}^{\circ}. \tag{243}$$

Hence

$$S\left(\frac{2^N hx}{90}\right) = \sin x° \quad \text{and} \quad C\left(\frac{2^N hx}{90}\right) = \cos x°, \qquad (244)$$

whenever x is of the form s_n. And, since the addition theorems (224) and (225) hold, the equations continue to be valid whenever x is a value t. Finally, since all the functions involved are continuous, the equations must hold for all real values, at least in the range $0 \leqq x \leqq 90$.

It follows from the addition theorems and equations (240) and (241) that

$$S(x + 2^N h) = C(x) \quad \text{and} \quad C(x + 2^N h) = -S(x). \qquad (245)$$

By comparing these equations with equation (212), we see that equation (244) is valid for all positive values of x.

From the equation (231) and the three fundamental relations we may deduce that

$$S(-x) = -S(x) \quad \text{and} \quad C(-x) = C(x), \qquad (246)$$

by reasoning analogous to that used in connection with equation (213). Since equation (246) has the same form as equation (213), it follows that the equations (244) are valid for all values of x.

From the limiting relation (214), we have:

$$\lim_{x \to 0} \frac{S\left(\dfrac{2^N hx}{90}\right)}{x} = \lim_{x \to 0} \frac{\sin x°}{x} = \frac{\pi}{180}. \qquad (247)$$

But, if we put $u = 2^N hx/90$ and use the relation (227), we find:

$$\lim_{x \to 0} \frac{S\left(\dfrac{2^N hx}{90}\right)}{x} = \lim_{x \to 0} \frac{2^N h}{90} \frac{S(u)}{u} = \frac{2^N h}{90}. \qquad (248)$$

A comparison of these last two relations gives:

$$2^N h = \frac{\pi}{2}, \quad \text{so that} \quad u = \frac{2^N hx}{90} = \frac{\pi x}{180}, \qquad (249)$$

and hence by equations (217) and (244):

$$S(u) = \sin\left(\frac{180u}{\pi}\right)° = \sin u, \quad \text{and} \quad C(u) = \cos u. \qquad (250)$$

This proves our contention that any pair of functions satisfying the four stated relation must be identical with $\sin x$ and $\cos x$ for all real values of x.

It is an interesting fact that the original conditions made no explicit reference to the number π, but that these conditions determine $\pi/2$ as the smallest positive number for which

$$S\left(\frac{\pi}{2}\right) = 1 \quad \text{and} \quad C\left(\frac{\pi}{2}\right) = 0. \tag{251}$$

58. Properties of the Trigonometric Functions. From our present point of view, all the formulas involving functions of the sum or difference of x and an integral multiple of $\pi/2$ follow from the addition and subtraction theorems, and the fact that:

$$\sin\frac{\pi}{2} = 1, \quad \cos\frac{\pi}{2} = 0. \tag{252}$$

In addition to the relations:

$$\sin 0 = 0, \cos 0 = 1, \sin(-x) = -\sin x, \cos(-x) = \cos x \tag{253}$$

and

$$\sin\left(x + \frac{\pi}{2}\right) = \cos x, \quad \cos\left(x + \frac{\pi}{2}\right) = -\sin x, \tag{254}$$

which are essentially those already used to extend the range of definition beyond the first quadrant, we note that

$$\cos x = \sin\left(\frac{\pi}{2} - x\right). \tag{255}$$

We easily find from equation (252) and the addition theorems that:

$$\sin \pi = 0, \cos \pi = -1; \quad \sin 2\pi = 0, \cos 2\pi = 1. \tag{256}$$

Since the functions of 2π are the same as those of 0, the addition theorems show that $x + 2\pi$ has the same functions as $x + 0$, or x. Thus the sine and cosine each admit the period 2π. It is the smallest period for the cosine, since no value between 0 and 2π has $\cos x = 1$. It is the smallest for the sine, since the only value between 0 and 2π which makes $\sin x = 0$ is π, which is not a period since $\sin(x + \pi) = -\sin x$.

Similar reasoning shows that the tangent and cotangent each admit π as their smallest period.

We have shown that many of the identities involving the sine and cosine derived in elementary trigonometry hold for the functions as defined in section 56. Since all the remaining identities involving the sine and cosine can be derived from those here proved by algebraic means, we shall feel free to use any of their elementary properties in the sequel.

Identities involving the other functions may be considered identities in the sine and cosine, in view of equations (144).

59. The Derivative of the Sine and Cosine. The derivative of the function $\sin x$, in accordance with the definition (67) of section 45 is

$$\lim_{h \to 0} \frac{\sin (x + h) - \sin x}{h}, \tag{257}$$

if this limit exists.

But from equation (179) or (233),

$$\sin (x + h) - \sin x = 2 \cos \left(x + \frac{h}{2} \right) \sin \frac{h}{2}, \tag{258}$$

so that:

$$\frac{\sin (x + h) - \sin x}{h} = \cos \left(x + \frac{h}{2} \right) \frac{\sin \frac{h}{2}}{\frac{h}{2}}. \tag{259}$$

Since the cosine is continuous, the first factor approaches $\cos x$ when $h \to 0$. The second factor approaches unity, by equation (218). Thus the limit is $\cos x$, and we have:

If $f(x) = \sin x$, then $\qquad f'(x) = \cos x.$ (260)

In a similar way, using the equation

$$\cos (x + h) - \cos x = -2 \sin \left(x + \frac{h}{2} \right) \sin \frac{h}{2}, \tag{261}$$

we may show that

$$\lim_{h \to 0} \frac{\cos (x + h) - \cos x}{h} = -\sin x, \tag{262}$$

so that:

If $f(x) = \cos x$, then $\qquad f'(x) = -\sin x.$ (263)

60. Inverse Trigonometric Functions. Since the continuous function $y = \sin x$ increases from -1 to 1 as x increases from $-\pi/2$ to $\pi/2$, the inverse function $x = \sin^{-1} y$ is continuous, and increases from $-\pi/2$ to $\pi/2$ as y increases from -1 to 1. This is the principal branch of the function $x = \sin^{-1} y$. Other branches are obtained by taking other intervals, $(n - 1/2)\pi$ to $(n + 1/2)\pi$, where n is a positive or negative integer, in which the $\sin x$ either increases from -1 to 1, or decreases from 1 to -1. Collectively, the branches make up an infinitely many-valued function $\sin^{-1} y$.

In any application where y varies in one sense within the range $-1,1$ we may restrict ourselves to one branch, and usually find it convenient to use the principal branch. Where y varies in some other way, for example increasing to 1 and then decreasing, we may either use intervals in which y varies in one sense, and treat these intervals separately; or we may regard the relation $x = \sin^{-1} y$ as equivalent to the relation $y = \sin x$, and use such branches for the different intervals that x varies in one sense as y increases to 1 and then decreases.

Similar reasoning shows that the functions $\cos^{-1} y$, $\tan^{-1} y$, $\cot^{-1} y$, $\sec^{-1} y$ and $\csc^{-1} y$ are continuous and monotonic in certain restricted ranges.

The values of the principal branch of the $\csc^{-1} y$ are those in the range $-\pi/2 \leqq x \leqq \pi/2$. In fact $\csc^{-1} y = \sin^{-1} (1/y)$.

For $\cos^{-1} y$ and $\sec^{-1} y = \cos^{-1} (1/y)$ the values of the principal branch are those in the range $0 \leqq x \leqq \pi$.

For the functions $\tan^{-1} y$ and $\cot^{-1} y = \tan^{-1} (1/y)$ the values of the principal branch are those in the range $-\pi/2 \leqq x \leqq \pi/2$.

We note that for this branch,

$$\tan^{-1}(-\infty) = -\frac{\pi}{2} \quad \text{and} \quad \tan^{-1}(+\infty) = \frac{\pi}{2}, \qquad (264)$$

in the sense that if

$$x = \tan y \quad \text{and} \quad y = \tan^{-1} x, \quad \text{and} \quad -\frac{\pi}{2} < x < \frac{\pi}{2}, \qquad (265)$$

then

$$x \to -\infty \text{ as } y \to -\frac{\pi}{2}+, \quad \text{and} \quad x \to +\infty \text{ as } y \to \frac{\pi}{2}- \qquad (266)$$

Since

$$\lim_{x \to \frac{\pi}{2}-} \tan x = +\infty \quad \text{and} \quad \lim_{x \to \frac{\pi}{2}+} \tan x = -\infty, \qquad (267)$$

we can only write

$$\lim_{x \to \frac{\pi}{2}} |\tan x| = \infty, \qquad (268)$$

and the notation sometimes used, $\tan \pi/2 = \infty$ or $\tan \pi/2 = \pm\infty$, must be interpreted as meaning no more than the last two equations.

Similar remarks apply to the notation $\csc 0 = \infty$ and $\sec \pi/2 = \infty$.

61. Polar Coördinates. Let x and y be the Cartesian coördinates of a point in a plane, as in section 13. The *polar coördinates* of the point may be defined as any pair of values r, θ satisfying the relations:

$$r \geqq 0 \quad \text{and} \quad x = r \cos \theta, \ y = r \sin \theta. \qquad (269)$$

We proceed to discuss the solutions of this system of equations. The equations imply that

$$x^2 + y^2 = r^2, \quad \text{and} \quad r = +\sqrt{x^2 + y^2}. \tag{270}$$

Thus the value of r is uniquely determined. Geometrically it is the distance from the point to the origin.

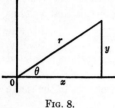

FIG. 8.

If x and y are both zero, r is zero and θ is unrestricted, since if $x = y = r = 0$, any value of θ will satisfy the equations (269).

For x and y not both zero, r is positive, and the value of θ must then satisfy

$$\cos \theta = \frac{x}{r}, \quad \sin \theta = \frac{y}{r}. \tag{271}$$

If $x = 0$, since $r \neq 0$, $y \neq 0$. If $y > 0$, $\theta = \pi/2$ will be a solution, while if $y < 0$, $\theta = -\pi/2$ will be a solution.

If $x \neq 0$, then θ must satisfy the relation:

$$\tan \theta = \frac{y}{x} \quad \text{or} \quad \theta = \tan^{-1} \frac{y}{x}. \tag{272}$$

This relation determines a unique value of θ_0 in the interval $-\pi/2 < \theta < \pi/2$, the value for the principal branch of the preceding section. This value θ_0 will either satisfy the equations (271) and (269), or will be such that $\theta_0 + \pi$ will satisfy them. Thus the equations (269) have a unique solution in the interval $-\pi/2 \leqq \theta < 3\pi/2$, whenever $r \neq 0$.

Since $\cos \theta$ and $\sin \theta$ each admit the period 2π, there will be a unique solution, if $r \neq 0$, in every interval

$$a \leqq \theta < a + 2\pi \quad \text{or} \quad b < \theta \leqq b + 2\pi, \tag{273}$$

and if θ_1 is one solution, all the solutions will be given by $\theta = \theta_1 + 2k\pi$, where k is zero or a positive or negative integer.

Geometrically, r is the length of the radius vector, and θ is the angle measured from the positive x-axis to the radius vector. We shall refer to (r,θ) as the polar coördinates of the point with Cartesian coördinates (x,y). We have thus proved:

If a point has Cartesian coördinates (x,y) distinct from $(0,0)$, the relations

$$x = r \cos \theta \quad \text{and} \quad y = r \sin \theta, \, r > 0 \tag{274}$$

determine uniquely a pair of polar coördinates r,θ in the range

$$a \leqq \theta < a + 2\pi, \tag{275}$$

determined by a.

EXERCISES III

1. For what real values of x does x^x define a real number?   For what values is this function continuous?   For what values of x and y is x^y a continuous function of the two variables?   Similarly for $(x^2)^{y/2}$?

2. An explicit algebraic expression is one built up of one or more variables and constants by the four fundamental operations, together with root extractions.   Prove that such an expression is continuous for any set of values of the variables which does not make a denominator zero, or an expression whose even root is taken zero or negative.

3. Prove that $\lim\limits_{n \to +\infty} (1 + x/n)^n = e^x$.   *Hint:* Put $n = x/h$, when $x \neq 0$.

4. Show that if $x > 0$, the function

$$s_n(x) = 1 + x + \frac{x^2}{2!} + \cdots + \frac{x^n}{n!}$$

for fixed x increases with n, and approaches a limit as $n \to +\infty$.   *Hint:* To obtain an upper bound, note that if $m > 2x$, the terms from the $(m+1)$th to the $(m+k+1)$th do not exceed

$$\frac{x^m}{m!}\left(1 + \frac{1}{2} + \frac{1}{2^2} + \cdots + \frac{1}{2^k}\right) < \frac{3x^m}{m!}.$$

5. Prove that $e^x = \lim\limits_{n \to +\infty} (1 + x + x^2/2! + \cdots x^n/n!)$, if $x > 0$.   *Hint:* Use problems 3, 4 and argue as in section 46.

6. Prove that, if $\lim\limits_{x \to +\infty} [f(x+1) - f(x)] = L$, then $\lim\limits_{x \to +\infty} f(x)/x = L$, if $f(x)$ is bounded on every finite interval.   *Hint:* If $a < f(x+1) - f(x) < b$, for $x > x'$, $an < f(x+n) - f(x) < bn$, and $\dfrac{an + f(x)}{x+n} < \dfrac{f(x+n)}{x+n} < \dfrac{bn + f(x)}{x+n}$.

For $x' < x \leq x' + 1$, $|f(x)| < M$,   and   hence,   for $n > n'$, $a - \epsilon < f(x+n)/(x+n) < b + \epsilon$.   Now find x' for $a = L - \epsilon$, $b = L + \epsilon$, so that for any $y > x' + n' + 1$, $y = x + n$ with $n > n'$ and $x' < x \leq x' + 1$. Hence $\lim f(y)/y = L$.

7. Show that the boundedness condition of problem 6 is necessary by considering $f(x) = \cot \pi x$, $x \neq n$ an integer, and $f(x) = 0$, x an integer or zero.

8. Prove that if $\lim\limits_{x \to +\infty} [f(x+1) - f(x)] = +\infty$, and $f(x)$ is bounded from below on every finite interval, $\lim\limits_{x \to +\infty} f(x)/x = +\infty$.

9. If $f(x)$ is bounded on every finite interval, and as $x \to +\infty$, the upper and lower limits of $f(x+1) - f(x)$ are B and A respectively, while those of $f(x)/x$ are B' and A', show that $A \leq A' \leq B' \leq B$.   Consider $\sin 2\pi x$ as an example.

10. Show that problem 9, Exercises II is a special case of problem 6, and formulate extensions of that problem analogous to problems 8 and 9.

11. Prove that, if $f(x)$ is positive and together with $1/f(x)$ is bounded on every finite interval, and $\lim\limits_{x \to +\infty} f(x+1)/f(x) = L > 0$, then $\lim\limits_{x \to +\infty} f(x)^{1/x} = L$. *Hint:* Apply problem 6 to $F(x) = \log f(x)$.

12. Formulate extensions of problem 11, based on problems 8 and 9.

13. Prove that, if $f(x)$ is positive and bounded on every finite interval, and $\lim\limits_{x \to +\infty} f(x+1)/f(x) = 0$, then $\lim\limits_{x \to +\infty} f(x)^{1/x} = 0$. This is an extension of problem 11.

14. Prove that $e^x > x^n/n\,!$, for any $x > 0$, and n a positive integer. Deduce that $\lim e^x x^{-m} = +\infty$, as $x \to +\infty$. *Hint:* Use problem 5. Take $n = m + k$.

15. Prove that $\lim\limits_{x \to +\infty} x^u e^{-x} = 0$ for any real u. *Hint:* Use problem 14, or problem 13 for the case $u > 0$.

16. Prove that if u is any real number, and $p > 1$, that $\lim\limits_{x \to +\infty} x^u p^{-x} = 0$. Also that $\lim\limits_{y \to +\infty} (\log y)^u /y = 0$. *Hint:* Put $y = e^x$ and use problem 15.

17. Prove that for any real value of u and any positive value of m,
$$\lim_{y \to +\infty} (\log y)^u/y^m = 0, \quad \text{and} \quad \lim_{y \to 0+} (\log y)^u y^m = 0. \quad \textit{Hint: Use problem 16.}$$

18. Prove that $\lim\limits_{x \to +\infty} \sqrt[x]{x} = 1$, and hence that $\lim\limits_{x \to 0+} x^x = 1$. *Hint:* Take logarithms and use problem 16.

19. Prove that $\lim\limits_{n \to +\infty} \sqrt[n]{n\,!} = +\infty$. *Hint:* By problem 14, $\sqrt[n]{n\,!} > x e^{-x/n} = n/e$ if $x = n$.

20. Prove that $\lim\limits_{n \to +\infty} n(x^{1/n} - 1) = \log x$, if $x > 0$. *Hint:* Put $n = (\log x)/h$, and use equation (127).

21. Prove that $\lim\limits_{n \to +\infty} \dfrac{f(x)e^{nx} + g(x)}{e^{nx} + 1}$ is $f(x)$ if $x > 0$, $g(x)$ if $x < 0$ and $[f(0) + g(0)]/2$ if $x = 0$.

22. The function sgn x, read " signum x," is defined to be 1 if x is positive, -1 if x is negative, and sgn $0 = 0$. Prove that $\lim\limits_{n \to +\infty} \dfrac{e^{nx} - 1}{e^{nx} + 1} = $ sgn x. Also prove that $\lim\limits_{n \to +\infty} \dfrac{2}{\pi} \tan^{-1} nx = $ sgn x, if the principal branch is used.

23. Prove that $\overline{\lim} \sin n\pi x = 1$, and $\underline{\lim} \sin n\pi x = -1$, if x is irrational and $n \to +\infty$ through integral values. *Hint:* Use problem 32, Exercises I.

24. Show that if $f(x) = \lim\limits_{n \to +\infty} \lim\limits_{m \to +\infty} \dfrac{2}{\pi} \tan^{-1} [m \sin^2 (n\,!\,\pi x)]$, then $f(x) = 1$ when x is irrational, and 0 when x is rational.

25. Show that if $f(x) = \lim\limits_{n \to +\infty} \lim\limits_{m \to +\infty} \cos^{2m} (n\,!\,\pi x)$, then $f(x) = 0$ when x is irrational, and 1 when x is rational.

26. Show that the function $\sin (1/x)$ has its oscillation equal to 2 for $x = 0$. See section 150.

27. Prove that for any real value of u and any positive value of m, the function $(x^2)^m \sin (x^2)^u$ is continuous at $x = 0$ if, for $u < 0$, we define the value of the function to be 0 when $x = 0$.

28. Suppose the function $f(r)$ is defined for all rational values on a finite interval, and is uniformly continuous in the sense that, for any two rational values on the interval, $|f(r'') - f(r')| < \epsilon$, any positive quantity, if $|r'' - r'| < \delta$ depending on ϵ. Prove that there is one and only one function $f(x)$, continuous for all values on the interval, and such that $f(x) = f(r)$ when x is a rational number r.

29. Show that $f(r) = 3r$, $0 \leqq r \leqq 2$, is an example to which the preceding problem applies to give $f(x) = 3x$, but that the function $f(r) = \dfrac{1}{\sin \dfrac{\pi}{r - \sqrt{2}}}$ may not be extended to a function continuous for all real values between 0 and 2, even though it is continuous at all the values r, in the sense that $\lim_{r \to r'} f(r) = f(r')$.

30. Prove that the result of problem 28 remains valid if the values r are replaced by any set of points on the interval such that every point of the interval is a limit point of the set. As examples of such sets we have that in problem 32, Exercises I, and the set $90m/2^n$ used in section 53.

31. If $f(x)$ is defined for all real values of x, is continuous at one point, and satisfies $f(x + y) = f(x) + f(y)$, then $f(x) = kx$. *Hint:* Since $f(x + h) - f(x) = f(h)$, which does not depend on x, continuity at one point implies continuity at all points. But if p and q are positive integers, it follows by induction from the original equation that $f(p) = pf(1)$, and $qf(p/q) = f(p)$. Hence, if $f(1) = k$, $f(r) = kr$ for r a positive rational. The equation also shows that $f(0) = 0$ and $f(-x) = -f(x)$, so that r may be zero or a negative rational number. Finally, by problem 28, $f(x) = kx$.

32. If $f(x)$ is defined for all positive values of x, is continuous at one point, and $f(xy) = f(x) + f(y)$, then $f(x) = k \log x$. *Hint:* Apply problem 31 to $F(u) = f(e^u)$. If $u = \log x$ and $v = \log y$ then $F(u + v) = f(xy)$.

33. If $f(x)$ is defined for all values of x, is continuous at one point, and $f(x + y) = f(x)f(y)$, then $f(x) = A^x$. *Hint:* If $f(x)$ is zero for one value it is always zero. If not, since $f(x) = [f(x/2)]^2$, all the values are positive, and we may put $F(x) = \log f(x)$ and use problem 31.

34. Prove that none of the expressions:

$$\frac{\sin \pi x}{\sin \pi x}, \quad \frac{1}{1 + x \sin \pi x}, \quad \frac{1 + x \sin \pi x}{x + x \sin \pi x}$$

approach limits as $x \to +\infty$, but that on any sequence including no integral values of x, the limit of the first is 1.

35. Prove that as $x \to 0$, $\dfrac{\sin ax}{x}$ and $\dfrac{\tan ax}{x}$ each $\to a$.

36. Prove that as $x \to 0$, $\dfrac{\sin^{-1} ax}{x}$ and $\dfrac{\tan^{-1} ax}{x}$ each $\to a$. *Hint:* Put $ax = \sin y$; $ax = \tan y$.

37. Prove that $\lim\limits_{x \to 0} \dfrac{1 - \cos x}{x^2} = \dfrac{1}{2}$. *Hint:* Use either $(1 - \cos x) = \dfrac{\sin^2 x}{1 + \cos x}$, or $1 - \cos x = 2 \sin^2 \left(\dfrac{x}{2} \right)$.

38. Prove that $\lim\limits_{x \to \pi/2} \dfrac{\cos x}{\pi/2 - x} = 1$.

CHAPTER IV

DIFFERENTIATION

In this chapter we shall study the special limit process, differentiation, which plays a central rôle in the differential calculus. We outline the fundamental theorems on differentiation, with particular emphasis on those points which are apt to be inadequately treated in a first course.

We then proceed to the mean value theorem, and various theorems about derivatives and applications of differentiation related to it.

62. Definitions. If $y = f(x)$ is a function of x, the *derivative* of the function for a particular value of x, is defined by

$$f'(x) = \lim_{h \to 0} \frac{f(x + h) - f(x)}{h}, \tag{1}$$

as we stated in section 45.

As the denominator of the fraction, h, is an increment of x, it is frequently denoted by Δx, and the numerator, being an increment of y is denoted by Δy. This leads to the more condensed form of the definition:

$$f'(x) = \lim_{\Delta x \to 0} \frac{\Delta y}{\Delta x}. \tag{2}$$

This does not indicate which value x is being considered, unless supplemented by

$$\Delta y = f(x + \Delta x) - f(x). \tag{3}$$

The alternative notation for a derivative,

$$\frac{dy}{dx} \quad \text{or} \quad \frac{d}{dx}(y) \quad \text{in place of } f'(x), \tag{4}$$

is intended to suggest the defining relation (2).

We recall that the notation $h \to 0$ or $\Delta x \to 0$ implies that h or Δx may approach zero through any sequence of values, each of which may be positive or negative but may not be zero.

To say that the function $f(x)$ has a derivative at x usually means that for this x, the difference quotient which appears in equation (1) approaches a finite limit. In this case the difference in the numerator must approach zero with h, so that the function $f(x)$ must be continuous for the value of x considered.

However, if the function $f(x)$ is continuous at x, and for this value the limit in equation (1) is plus infinity, we say that $f(x)$ has the derivative $+\infty$. Similarly, if the limit is $-\infty$, we say that $f'(x) = -\infty$. Whenever we wish to include these cases, we shall use the phrase, $f(x)$ has a finite or infinite derivative. Note that, in all cases where $f(x)$ has a derivative, finite or infinite, $f(x)$ is continuous by our definition.

The interpretation of derivative as a slope makes it desirable to include infinite derivatives, as here defined, since the question of a function having a derivative is then related to the question of its graph having a tangent. Geometrically, an infinite derivative merely means a vertical tangent, and so may be introduced by a mere rotation of axes.

If h is restricted to be positive and if the limit in equation (1) is obtained, this limit is called a right-hand derivative. Similarly, if h is restricted to be negative, the limit is a left-hand derivative. For example, if $y = |x|$, for $x = 0$, the function has a right-hand derivative equal to $+1$, and a left-hand derivative equal to -1. In the original sense, this function does not have a derivative at $x = 0$.

The process of finding the derivative of a function is called *differentiation*. We say that a function may be differentiated in a closed interval $a \leqq x \leqq b$, if the function has a derivative at all interior points, a right-hand derivative at a, and a left-hand derivative at b. The function $f'(x)$, obtained from a function by differentiation, is sometimes called the derived function.

63. Combinations of Functions. In view of the results of section 19, the definition of a derivative implies that the operation of differentiation is linear. That is, if u and v have finite derivatives, and k is a constant, then

$$\frac{d}{dx}(ku) = k\frac{du}{dx} \tag{5}$$

and

$$\frac{d}{dx}(u + v) = \frac{du}{dx} + \frac{dv}{dx}. \tag{6}$$

It may be deduced directly from the definition that

$$\frac{d}{dx}(uv) = u\frac{dv}{dx} + v\frac{du}{dx}, \tag{7}$$

and

$$\frac{d}{dx}\left(\frac{u}{v}\right) = \frac{v\dfrac{du}{dx} - u\dfrac{dv}{dx}}{v^2}, \quad \text{if} \quad v \neq 0. \tag{8}$$

It also follows immediately from the definition of a derivative that

$$\frac{dx}{dx} = 1 \quad \text{and} \quad \frac{dk}{dx} = 0, \tag{9}$$

where k is a constant.

The equations of this section enable us to derive the familiar formula for differentiating any polynomial:

$$\text{If} \qquad f(x) = \sum_{p=0}^{n} a_p x^p, \quad f'(x) = \sum_{p=1}^{n} p a_p x^{p-1}. \tag{10}$$

By using equations (8) and (10) we may find the derivative of any rational function for a value of x which makes the polynomial in the denominator different from zero.

64. Inverse Functions. We proved in section 37 that, if $y = f(x)$ is a continuous increasing function in some open interval including x_0, there is an inverse function $x = f^{-1}(y)$, which is continuous at y_0, where $y_0 = f(x_0)$. Let us assume in addition that $f(x)$ has a derivative at x_0, finite and distinct from zero. Then

$$f'(x_0) = \frac{dy}{dx} = \lim_{\Delta x \to 0} \frac{\Delta y}{\Delta x}, \tag{11}$$

where Δx is the increment of x at x_0, and Δy is the corresponding increment of y at y_0.

Since the inverse function $f^{-1}(y)$ is continuous at y_0, when Δy approaches zero, Δx also approaches zero. Also since the function is increasing, Δy is distinct from zero if and only if Δx is. Hence:

$$\lim_{\Delta y \to 0} \frac{\Delta x}{\Delta y} = \lim_{\Delta x \to 0} \frac{1}{\dfrac{\Delta y}{\Delta x}} = \frac{1}{\lim\limits_{\Delta x \to 0} \dfrac{\Delta y}{\Delta x}} = \frac{1}{\dfrac{dy}{dx}}. \tag{12}$$

This shows that $x = f^{-1}(y)$ has a derivative, and

$$\frac{dx}{dy} = \frac{1}{\dfrac{dy}{dx}}. \tag{13}$$

If $f(x)$ has the derivative equal to zero, then $f^{-1}(y)$ has the derivative $+\infty$, while if $f(x)$ has the derivative $+\infty$, then $f^{-1}(y)$ has its derivative equal to zero. These facts follow from the relations (12) and the remarks in section 20, since Δx and Δy have the same sign.

A similar discussion applies to decreasing functions. Here the inverse function has the derivative $-\infty$, if the original function has its derivative zero.

65. Composite Functions. Suppose that $u = f(x)$ has a finite derivative at x_0, and that $y = g(u)$ has a finite derivative at u_0, where $u_0 = f(x_0)$.   Then the function

$$y = g[f(x)] = F(x) \tag{14}$$

has a derivative at x_0, given by

$$F'(x_0) = g'(u_0)f'(x_0) \quad \text{or} \quad \frac{dy}{dx} = \frac{dy}{du}\frac{du}{dx}. \tag{15}$$

To prove this, we first consider the case in which for all $\Delta x \neq 0$ the corresponding values of Δu are never zero.   In this case we have:

$$\frac{\Delta y}{\Delta x} = \frac{\Delta y}{\Delta u}\frac{\Delta u}{\Delta x}, \tag{16}$$

and the relation (15) follows by taking limits, after noting that when $\Delta x \to 0$, then $\Delta u \to 0$, so that

$$\lim_{\Delta x \to 0} \frac{\Delta y}{\Delta u} = \lim_{\Delta u \to 0} \frac{\Delta y}{\Delta u} = \frac{dy}{du}. \tag{17}$$

This proof also applies if there are not arbitrarily small values of Δx, say $\Delta_1 x$, distinct from zero, for which $\Delta u = 0$, since in this case the Δu will be different from zero when Δx is different from zero and sufficiently small.

Now consider the special case in which there are arbitrarily small values of Δx, $\Delta_1 x \neq 0$, for which $\Delta u = 0$.   Then, on letting Δx approach zero through such values, we find

$$\lim \frac{\Delta u}{\Delta_1 x} = 0. \tag{18}$$

But, since u has a derivative, the limit must be the same for all methods of approach of x to zero, and

$$\frac{du}{dx} = \lim \frac{\Delta u}{\Delta x} = 0. \tag{19}$$

If we let Δx approach zero through values $\Delta_1 x$, we have $\Delta u = 0$, so that $\Delta y = 0$, and hence:

$$\lim \frac{\Delta y}{\Delta_1 x} = 0. \tag{20}$$

On the other hand, if we let Δx approach zero through values of Δx not of the type $\Delta_1 x$, say $\Delta_2 x$, we have:

$$\frac{\Delta y}{\Delta_2 x} = \frac{\Delta y}{\Delta u}\frac{\Delta u}{\Delta_2 x}, \tag{21}$$

so that, in view of equation (19),

$$\lim \frac{\Delta y}{\Delta_2 x} = \frac{dy}{du} \cdot 0 = 0. \tag{22}$$

Thus, in the special case where there are sequences $\Delta_1 x$,

$$\lim \frac{\Delta y}{\Delta x} = 0, \tag{23}$$

whether Δx approaches zero through sequences $\Delta_1 x$ or $\Delta_2 x$, and hence through sequences composed partly of one type and partly of the other. That is, the limit is zero for all methods of approach.

Finally, since in the special case,

$$\frac{dy}{dx} = 0 \quad \text{and} \quad \frac{du}{dx} = 0, \tag{24}$$

while dy/du is finite, we have

$$\frac{dy}{dx} = 0 = \frac{dy}{du}\frac{du}{dx}, \tag{25}$$

so that the relation (15) also holds in the special case.

A trivial example of the special case, where all values of Δx are $\Delta_1 x$, is the case where $f(x) = k$, a constant. A better example is given by $f(x) = x^2 \sin(1/x)$ if $x \neq 0$, and $f(0) = 0$; $g(u) = 2u$ with $u_0 = x_0 = 0$. Here the values $\Delta_1 x$ are $1/(n\pi)$, where n is a positive or negative integer. Compare equation (70) in section 69.

66. Logarithmic and Exponential Functions. We showed in section 49 that

$$\frac{d}{dx}(\log x) = \frac{1}{x}. \tag{26}$$

Since the function $y = \log x$ is increasing, we may find the derivative of its inverse function $x = e^y$ by equation (13), and

$$\frac{d}{dy}(e^y) = \frac{1}{\dfrac{d}{dx}(\log x)} = x = e^y. \tag{27}$$

If we now interchange x and y, this becomes:

$$\frac{d}{dx}(e^x) = e^x. \tag{28}$$

We may write

$$v^u = e^{u \log v}, \quad \text{if } v > 0. \tag{29}$$

If u and v are functions of x with finite derivatives, we find from this and equations (28), (16), (7), and (26) that:

$$\frac{d}{dx}\left(v^u\right) = v^u \log v \frac{du}{dx} + uv^{u-1}\frac{dv}{dx}. \tag{30}$$

As particular cases of this, we have:

$$\frac{d}{dx}\left(p^x\right) = p^x \log p, \quad p > 0, \tag{31}$$

where p is any positive real number, and

$$\frac{d}{dx}\left(x^k\right) = kx^{k-1}, \quad x > 0, \tag{32}$$

where k is any real number and x is any positive number. This formula remains valid for negative values of x if k is a rational number with an odd denominator, as we may show by using the equations (12) and (13) of section 40. For any value of $k > 1$, the function x^k has a right-hand derivative 0 at $x = 0$, as a direct application of equation (1) shows. Thus whenever the right member of equation (32) is finite for $x = 0$, it equals the value of the right-hand derivative.

The special result

$$\frac{d}{dx}\left(x^{-1}\right) = -\frac{1}{x^2}, \quad x \neq 0, \tag{33}$$

may be combined with equations (15) and (7) to give an alternative derivation of equation (8), since $u/v = uv^{-1}$. This point of view is sometimes convenient in differentiating a fraction.

The method of *logarithmic differentiation* consists in taking the logarithm of a function before differentiating. The derivation of equation (30) from the relation (29) was equivalent to this method. For example consider the product:

$$y = u_1 u_2 u_3 \cdots u_n. \tag{34}$$

We find:

$$\log y = \sum_{i=1}^{n} \log u_i, \quad \frac{1}{y}\frac{dy}{dx} = \sum_{i=1}^{n} \frac{1}{u_i}\frac{du_i}{dx}, \tag{35}$$

so that:

$$\frac{dy}{dx} = \sum_{i=1}^{n} \frac{y}{u_i}\frac{du_i}{dx}. \tag{36}$$

Since the last expression, with the u_i cancelled out, must agree with that obtained by repeated use of equation (7), it must hold in this form even when some of the u_i are zero or negative.

For the sake of completeness, we note that since

$$\log_p x = \frac{\log x}{\log p}, \quad \frac{d}{dx}(\log_p x) = \frac{1}{\log p}\frac{1}{x}. \tag{37}$$

This is essentially equation (108) of section 48, which was our reason for introducing natural logarithms.

67. Trigonometric and Inverse Trigonometric Functions. We showed in section 59 that

$$\frac{d}{dx}(\sin x) = \cos x, \quad \frac{d}{dx}(\cos x) = -\sin x. \tag{38}$$

It follows from their definitions in terms of the sine and cosine that:

$$\frac{d}{dx}(\tan x) = \sec^2 x, \quad \frac{d}{dx}(\cot x) = -\csc^2 x, \tag{39}$$

and

$$\frac{d}{dx}(\sec x) = \tan x \sec x, \quad \frac{d}{dx}(\csc x) = -\cot x \csc x. \tag{40}$$

For the principal branch of $x = \sin^{-1} y$, as defined in section 60, $-\pi/2 < x < \pi/2$, $\cos x$ is positive. Hence we have from section 64:

$$\frac{d}{dy}(\sin^{-1} y) = \frac{1}{\cos x} = \frac{1}{\sqrt{1 - y^2}}. \tag{41}$$

Interchanging x and y, we find

$$\frac{d}{dx}(\sin^{-1} x) = \frac{1}{\sqrt{1 - x^2}}, \quad -\frac{\pi}{2} < \sin^{-1} x < \frac{\pi}{2}. \tag{42}$$

By similar reasoning, we find, for values of y in the first quadrant, $0 < y < \pi/2$,

$$\frac{d}{dx}(\cos^{-1} x) = \frac{-1}{\sqrt{1 - x^2}}, \quad \frac{d}{dx}(\sec^{-1} x) = \frac{1}{x\sqrt{x^2 - 1}},$$

$$\frac{d}{dx}(\csc^{-1} x) = \frac{-1}{x\sqrt{x^2 - 1}}, \quad \frac{d}{dx}(\tan^{-1} x) = -\frac{d}{dx}(\cot^{-1} x) = \frac{1}{1 + x^2}. \tag{43}$$

These formulas may be modified to extend to all branches of the functions, by the use of

$$\frac{d}{dx}(\sin^{-1} x) = \frac{-1}{\sqrt{1 - x^2}} \quad \text{when } \cos y \text{ is negative,} \tag{44}$$

$$\frac{d}{dx}(\cos^{-1} x) = \frac{1}{\sqrt{1 - x^2}} \quad \text{when } \sin y \text{ is negative,} \tag{45}$$

$$\frac{d}{dx}(\sec^{-1} x) = \frac{-1}{x\sqrt{x^2 - 1}} \quad \text{when } \tan y \text{ is negative,} \qquad (46)$$

$$\frac{d}{dx}(\csc^{-1} x) = \frac{1}{x\sqrt{x^2 - 1}} \quad \text{when } \cot y \text{ is negative.} \qquad (47)$$

In each case y is the value of the inverse function, and the earlier formulas (42) and (43), which have the opposite sign, are to be used whenever the functions of y explicitly mentioned in each case as negative are positive.

To illustrate the necessity for care, consider the differentiation:

$$u = \cos^{-1}\left(\frac{1}{x}\right), \quad \frac{du}{dx} = \frac{-1}{\sqrt{1 - (1/x)^2}} \cdot \frac{-1}{x^2} = \frac{1}{x\sqrt{x^2 - 1}} \cdot \qquad (48)$$

The sign used in the differentiation must be changed if $\sin u$ is negative, and the multiplying in of x, or use of $x = \sqrt{x^2}$, is correct if x is positive, and requires an additional change of sign if x is negative. As $x = \sec u$, the result as given is correct if $\sin u$ and $\sec u$ have the same sign, that is when $\tan u$ is positive. Otherwise the sign should be changed. This is in accord with equation (46), since $u = \cos^{-1}(1/x) = \sec^{-1} x$.

68. Hyperbolic Functions and their Inverse Functions. The hyperbolic sine and cosine are defined in terms of the exponential functions:

$$\sinh x = \frac{e^x - e^{-x}}{2} \quad \text{and} \quad \cosh x = \frac{e^x + e^{-x}}{2} \cdot \qquad (49)$$

The other four hyperbolic functions are defined by equations analogous to those for the trigonometric functions:

$$\tanh x = \frac{\sinh x}{\cosh x}, \quad \coth x = \frac{\cosh x}{\sinh x}, \qquad (50)$$

$$\operatorname{sech} x = \frac{1}{\cosh x}, \quad \operatorname{csch} x = \frac{1}{\sinh x} \cdot \qquad (51)$$

The properties of these functions may all be deduced from these equations and from the properties of the exponential function.

In particular:

$$\cosh^2 x - \sinh^2 x = 1, \qquad (52)$$

and

$$\coth^2 x - \operatorname{csch}^2 x = 1, \quad \tanh^2 x + \operatorname{sech}^2 x = 1. \qquad (53)$$

Recalling equation (28), we find:

$$\frac{d}{dx}(\sinh x) = \cosh x, \quad \frac{d}{dx}(\cosh x) = \sinh x. \qquad (54)$$

By using equation (8), and the equations of this section, we find:

$$\frac{d}{dx}\,(\tanh x) = \operatorname{sech}^2 x, \quad \frac{d}{dx}\,(\coth x) = -\operatorname{csch}^2 x, \quad (55)$$

$$\frac{d}{dx}\,(\operatorname{sech} x) = -\tanh x \operatorname{sech} x, \quad \frac{d}{dx}\,(\operatorname{csch} x) = -\coth x \operatorname{csch} x. \quad (56)$$

It may be seen from equations (49) that $\cosh x$ is always positive, while $\sinh x$ is positive for positive x and negative for negative x. Also that:

$$\sinh(-x) = -\sinh x \quad \text{and} \quad \cosh(-x) = \cosh x. \quad (57)$$

While a simple method of systematically obtaining identities in hyperbolic functions from the corresponding ones in trigonometric functions will be given in section 106, we note here that the addition theorems are:

$$\sinh(a + b) = \sinh a \cosh b + \cosh a \sinh b, \quad (58)$$

$$\cosh(a + b) = \cosh a \cosh b + \sinh a \sinh b. \quad (59)$$

They may be verified by using equation (49) to reduce each side to a combination of exponentials. The subtraction theorems may be found by replacing b by $-b$ and using equations (57). We may then deduce that:

$$\sinh(x + h) - \sinh x = 2 \cosh\left(x + \frac{h}{2}\right) \sinh\frac{h}{2}, \quad (60)$$

and

$$\cosh(x + h) - \cosh x = 2 \sinh\left(x + \frac{h}{2}\right) \sinh\frac{h}{2}, \quad (61)$$

by a procedure analogous to that used for the corresponding trigonometric equations. It follows from equation (60) that $\sinh x$ increases for all values of x, and from equation (61) that $\cosh x$ increases for all positive values of x. Thus we may define the inverse functions $x = \sinh^{-1} y$, and $x = \cosh^{-1} y$. The latter is only defined for $y \geqq 1$, and has two branches, a positive and a negative branch. The increasing or decreasing character of the remaining functions may then be inferred from equations (51) and (53). Thus we may define $\tanh^{-1} y$, $\coth^{-1} y$ and $\operatorname{csch}^{-1} y$ which have only one branch, and $\operatorname{sech}^{-1} y$ which has two branches, one positive and one negative. We may find the derivatives of these functions as we did for the inverse trigonometric functions. The results, with x and y interchanged, are:

$$\frac{d}{dx}\,(\sinh^{-1} x) = \frac{1}{\sqrt{1 + x^2}}, \quad \frac{d}{dx}\,(\operatorname{csch}^{-1} x) = \frac{-1}{|x|\sqrt{1 + x^2}}, \quad (62)$$

$$\frac{d}{dx}(\tanh^{-1} x) = \frac{1}{1 - x^2}, \quad \frac{d}{dx}(\coth^{-1} x) = \frac{1}{1 - x^2}, \tag{63}$$

and, for the positive branch:

$$\frac{d}{dx}(\cosh^{-1} x) = \frac{1}{\sqrt{x^2 - 1}}, \quad \frac{d}{dx}(\operatorname{sech}^{-1} x) = \frac{-1}{x\sqrt{1 - x^2}}. \tag{64}$$

The signs must be reversed in these last two equations if we use the negative branch, that is the branch for which y and hence $\sinh y$ are negative.

We observe that the inverse hyperbolic functions may be expressed in terms of logarithms by such formulas as

$$\tanh^{-1} x = \frac{1}{2}\log\frac{1 + x}{1 - x}, \tag{65}$$

and

$$\sinh^{-1} x = \log (x + \sqrt{x^2 + 1}). \tag{66}$$

69. Elementary Functions. An elementary function is one which can be explicitly represented in terms of constants and the independent variable by means of the four fundamental operations and the basic elementary functions discussed in Chapter III, using at most a finite number of operations and a finite number of basic functions. For example, the hyperbolic functions and their inverses are elementary functions. While it is convenient to use fundamental formulas involving the power, x^a, logarithms and exponential functions to any base, the six trigonometric functions and their inverses, as well as the six hyperbolic functions and their inverses, we only need to take the functions e^x, $\log x$, $\sin x$ and $\sin^{-1} x$ as fundamental. For all the remaining functions can be expressed in terms of these, at least in a limited range of the variable. For example, we have:

$$v^u = e^{u \log v}, \; v > 0, \; \cos x = \sin\left(\frac{\pi}{2} - x\right), \tag{67}$$

and, for suitable branches of the inverse functions:

$$\tan^{-1} x = \sin^{-1} \frac{x}{\sqrt{1 + x^2}}. \tag{68}$$

By using the principles of sections 63 and 65, in combination with the special formulas of sections 66 and 67, we may determine the derivative of any elementary function for all values of x in suitably restricted ranges. Whenever the calculation of the expression which represents the derivative for a particular value of x does not introduce the division

by, or taking of the logarithm of, an expression which reduces to zero
for this value, or the even root, irrational power or logarithm of a negative quantity, the expression gives the derivative.

When the calculation does not lead to a definite result which is real
and finite, the principles involved are no longer applicable. Frequently,
the expression will fail to have a derivative for the excepted values of x.
For example $y = \sqrt{x}$ for $x = 0$ or x negative. In some cases the function will have a derivative, as we may show by a direct appeal to the
definition. For example, if $y = x^2 \sin (1/x)$ and $x \neq 0$, the rules show
that

$$\frac{dy}{dx} = 2x \sin \frac{1}{x} - \cos \frac{1}{x}. \tag{69}$$

If $x = 0$, this expression contains a vanishing denominator. Moreover,
as $x \to 0$, the expression oscillates. The function itself, $x^2 \sin (1/x)$,
defines no value directly when $x = 0$, since it contains a vanishing
denominator. However, as $x \to 0$, it approaches 0, so that it is natural
to define $y = 0$ when $x = 0$, since this is the only value that will make
the function continuous at zero. If we do this, so that $f(0) = 0$,
$f(x) = x^2 \sin (1/x)$, $x \neq 0$, then

$$\frac{f(0 + h) - f(0)}{h} = \frac{h^2 \sin \dfrac{1}{h} - 0}{h} = h \sin \frac{1}{h}, \tag{70}$$

which approaches zero when $h \to 0$, since the sine factor is never numerically greater than unity. Thus, the function $f(x)$ has a derivative at
zero, and $f'(0) = 0$.

We note that, as defined in this section, the inverse of an elementary
function is not necessarily an elementary function. An example is
$y = 2x + \sin x$.

70. Differentials. Let the function $y = f(x)$ have a derivative
$f'(x)$ at the point x. Then the *differential* of the independent variable,
dx, is any number, selected arbitrarily. It may be either fixed throughout the discussion, or dx itself may be regarded as an independent variable. The *differential* of the dependent variable, dy, is then defined by
the equation

$$dy = f'(x) \, dx. \tag{71}$$

In particular, if $y = x$, $f'(x) = 1$, so that

$$dy = dx. \tag{72}$$

Thus the differential of a dependent variable equal to x is equal to the
differential of the independent variable x.

Again, if a third variable t is taken as the independent variable, where $x = F(t)$ and $y = G(t)$ have derivatives, we have in accordance with the equation (71), with x replaced by t,

$$dx = F'(t)\, dt \quad \text{and} \quad dy = G'(t)\, dt. \tag{73}$$

But, by equation (15),

$$\frac{dy}{dt} = \frac{dy}{dx}\frac{dx}{dt} \quad \text{or} \quad G'(t) = f'(x)F'(t). \tag{74}$$

In view of this equation, the equations (73) together lead to $dy = f'(x)\, dx$. Thus the relation (71) holds whether x, or some other variable t is the independent variable.

Having defined differentials satisfying the relation

$$dy \div dx = f'(x) = \frac{dy}{dx}, \tag{75}$$

we may now think of this last notation as an actual fraction, and when $du \neq 0$, regard equation (15) as equivalent to ordinary cancellation of common factors from a fraction.

If we give x an increment, Δx, equal to the number selected for dx, we shall have:

$$dx = \Delta x, \quad dy = f'(x)\, \Delta x. \tag{76}$$

Again, if we put

$$\frac{\Delta y}{\Delta x} = f'(x) + \alpha, \tag{77}$$

then

$$f'(x) = \lim_{\Delta x \to 0} \frac{\Delta y}{\Delta x} \quad \text{implies} \quad \lim_{\Delta x \to 0} \alpha = 0. \tag{78}$$

That is,

$$\Delta y = f'(x)\, \Delta x + \alpha\, \Delta x, \quad \text{where} \quad \alpha \to 0 \text{ as } \Delta x \to 0. \tag{79}$$

This shows that dy and Δy differ by a term $\alpha\, \Delta x$, so that, if we take a sequence of values Δx approaching zero, the difference between dy and Δy for these values will not only approach zero, but will approach zero even when divided by Δx. Hence, when Δx is sufficiently small, dy and Δy will differ by a small fraction of Δx. In precise form:

For any positive quantity ϵ, there is a δ_ϵ, such that if

$$|\Delta x| < \delta_\epsilon, \quad \text{then} \quad \left| \frac{dy - \Delta y}{\Delta x} \right| < \epsilon. \tag{80}$$

If the increment Δy, corresponding to an increment Δx, at the point x for a functional relation $y = f(x)$ is such that for some A independent of Δx,

$$\Delta y = A \, \Delta x + \alpha \, \Delta x, \quad \text{where} \quad \alpha \to 0 \quad \text{as} \quad \Delta x \to 0, \tag{81}$$

the function $f(x)$ is said to be *differentiable*. From the relation (79) it follows that, if $f(x)$ has a derivative, the function is differentiable, with $A = f'(x)$.

Conversely, if a function is differentiable it has a derivative, since from the condition (81) we have:

$$\lim_{\Delta x \to 0} \frac{\Delta y}{\Delta x} = \lim_{\Delta x \to 0} (A + \alpha) = A, \tag{82}$$

so that $f(x)$ has a derivative, and $f'(x) = A$.

71. Higher Derivatives. If we start with a function $f(x)$, we may obtain from it by differentiation the derived function $f'(x)$. We may now take $f'(x)$ and apply the process of differentiation to it. The result is:

$$[f'(x)]' = \frac{d}{dx} \frac{d}{dx} y = \lim_{h \to 0} \frac{f'(x + h) - f'(x)}{h}, \tag{83}$$

if the fraction on the right approaches a limit. This derivative of the derived function is called the *second derivative*, or derivative of the second order, and is indicated by

$$f''(x) \quad \text{or} \quad \frac{d^2y}{dx^2}, \tag{84}$$

a contraction for the first two expressions in equation (83). The function $f''(x)$ is called the *second derived function*.

Similarly, we may repeat the process of differentiation n times, and so obtain the nth derivative, or nth derived function:

$$f^{(n)}(x) \quad \text{or} \quad \frac{d^ny}{dx^n}. \tag{85}$$

The derivative $f'(x)$ is sometimes called the first derivative, when derivatives of different orders are under consideration.

By restricting the increment h to be positive for each limiting process, we obtain right-hand derivatives of the nth order. Similarly, by restricting h to be negative, we obtain left-hand derivatives of the nth order. One application of these is to the higher derivatives of a function at the end points of a closed interval, outside of which the function is not defined.

If $u = f(x)$ and $y = g(u)$, as in section 65, we have

$$y = g[f(x)] = F(x), \tag{86}$$

and from equation (15)

$$\frac{dy}{dx} = \frac{dy}{du}\frac{du}{dx} \quad \text{or} \quad F'(x) = g'(u)f'(x). \tag{87}$$

If we differentiate this by using equations (7) and (15), we find:

$$\frac{d^2y}{dx^2} = \frac{d^2y}{du^2}\left(\frac{du}{dx}\right)^2 + \frac{dy}{du}\frac{d^2u}{dx^2}, \tag{88}$$

or
$$F''(x) = g''(u)[f'(x)]^2 + g'(u)f''(x). \tag{89}$$

By using this result we may find out how second differentials depend on our choice of independent variable. Let us indicate the independent variable by a subscript and define second differentials by the equations:

$$(d^2y)_x = \left(\frac{d^2y}{dx^2}\right)(dx)^2 = F''(x)(dx)^2, \tag{90}$$

and similarly

$$(d^2y)_u = \left(\frac{d^2y}{du^2}\right)(du)^2 = g''(u)(du)^2, \tag{91}$$

and

$$(d^2u)_x = \left(\frac{d^2u}{dx^2}\right)(dx)^2 = f''(x)(dx)^2. \tag{92}$$

Then, on multiplying equation (88) by $(dx)^2$ we find:

$$(d^2y)_x = (d^2y)_u + (d^2u)_x\frac{dy}{du}. \tag{93}$$

Since the last term in this equation is

$$g'(u)f''(x)(dx)^2, \tag{94}$$

it will be zero only in exceptional cases. Thus the second differential of y when x is the independent variable given by equation (90) will usually differ from the second differential of y when u is the independent variable given by equation (91).

While second, and higher, differentials may be introduced, since they depend on the choice of independent variable, and are of little help in making a change of independent variable, they have few of the advantages of the first differentials introduced in section 70. Consequently it is usually preferable to avoid them, regarding d^ny/dx^n not as an actual quotient of two differentials, but simply as a suggestive notation for n repetitions of the operation of differentiation, $(d/dx)^ny$.

72. The Rule of Leibniz. The formula for the differentiation of a product may be extended to higher derivatives, and is known as the *Leibniz rule*. If we denote differentiation of the factors of a product involving u by D_u, and of those involving v by D_v, then we may write:

$$\frac{d}{dx}(uv) = (D_u + D_v)uv = \frac{du}{dx}v + u\frac{dv}{dx}, \qquad (95)$$

since this agrees with equation (7). Since the operators D_u and D_v combine like algebraic quantities, with respect to addition, multiplication, and multiplication by constants, it follows that:

$$\frac{d^n}{dx^n}(uv) = (D_u + D_v)^n uv$$

$$= \left(D_u^n + nD_u^{n-1}D_v + \frac{n(n-1)}{1\cdot 2}D_u^{n-2}D_v^2 + \cdots + D_v^n \right)uv$$

$$= \frac{d^n u}{dx^n}v + n\frac{d^{n-1}u}{dx^{n-1}}\frac{dv}{dx} + \frac{n(n-1)}{1\cdot 2}\frac{d^{n-2}u}{dx^{n-2}}\frac{d^2 v}{dx^2} + \cdots + u\frac{d^n v}{dx^n},$$

$$(96)$$

where the coefficients are the binomial coefficients.

In particular, when the factor v is x^r, or a polynomial in x of the rth degree, where r is an integer, the expansion will contain at most $r + 1$ terms, since if n exceeds r, all the terms after the $(r + 1)$st will contain a derivative of v of at least the $(r + 1)$st order, and hence will vanish.

A similar rule could be developed for the nth derivative of a product of any number of terms,

$$\frac{d^n}{dx^n}(u_1 u_2 \cdots u_m) = (D_1 + D_2 + \cdots + D_m)^n u_1 u_2 \cdots u_m. \quad (97)$$

Here D_k denotes the differentiation of those factors of a product which involve u_k, and the product on the right may be expanded by the multinomial theorem.

73. Rolle's Theorem. This theorem states that:

If $f(x)$ has a derivative, finite or infinite, at all the points of an open interval, $a < x < b$, and if

$$\lim_{x\to a+}f(x) = 0 \quad \text{and} \quad \lim_{x\to b-}f(x) = 0, \qquad (98)$$

then at some point ξ of the open interval, $a < \xi < b$, the derivative is zero, $f'(\xi) = 0$.

To prove this theorem, we define a function in the closed interval $a \leqq x \leqq b$, by putting

$$F(x) = f(x),\ a < x < b;\quad F(a) = 0,\ F(b) = 0. \qquad (99)$$

This function is continuous, in view of the condition (98), throughout the closed interval. Hence, by section 33, there is a point of the closed interval a,b at which the function actually takes on its maximum value, and a point at which the function takes on its minimum value. If both these points were end points, the function $F(x)$, having its maximum and minimum values each equal to zero, would be zero throughout.

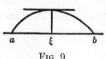

FIG. 9.

Hence $f(x)$ would be zero in the open interval, and $f'(x)$ would be zero at all points of this interval, so that we could take any point of the interval as the point ξ of the theorem.

Suppose then that one of the two points mentioned, say the maximum, is an interior point. If this point is ξ, from the nature of a maximum, we have:

$$F(\xi) \geqq F(x), \quad \text{or} \quad f(\xi) \geqq f(x). \tag{100}$$

Hence, for the derivative at ξ, we have:

$$f'(\xi) = \lim_{h \to 0+} \frac{f(\xi + h) - f(\xi)}{h} \leqq 0 \tag{101}$$

and also

$$f'(\xi) = \lim_{h \to 0-} \frac{f(\xi + h) - f(\xi)}{h} \geqq 0. \tag{102}$$

Thus we must have $f'(\xi) = 0$, and the theorem is proved.

If the minimum is taken on at an interior point, the maximum being only reached at an end point, we may prove the theorem in a similar manner. Or we may consider $-f(x)$.

We call attention to the fact that the theorem does not require the function $f(x)$ to be differentiable, or even to be defined, at the end points a and b. If it is differentiable at these points, it will be continuous at a and b. In this case, or whenever the function is continuous at a and b, we may replace the condition (98) by the requirement

$$f(a) = f(b) = 0. \tag{103}$$

In any case, the theorem shows that we may always take the point ξ as an interior point of the interval.

74. The Mean Value Theorem. This theorem is the analytic expression of the fact that on any smooth arc of a curve joining the points P and Q, there is at least one intermediate point T, such that the tangent to the curve at T is parallel to the chord joining P and Q.

If the curve is the graph of a single-valued function, $y = f(x)$, it will be smooth if the function is differentiable. If the end points of the arc are $P = [a, f(a)]$ and $Q = [b, f(b)]$, the slope of the chord will be $\dfrac{f(b) - f(a)}{b - a}$. As the slope of the tangent to the curve at any point x will be $f'(x)$, the analytic formulation of the theorem is:

If $f(x)$ has a derivative, finite or infinite, at all points of an open interval $a < x < b$, and is continuous at the end points of (and hence throughout) the closed interval $a \leqq x \leqq b$, then at some point ξ of the open interval, $a < \xi < b$,

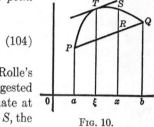

$$\frac{f(b) - f(a)}{b - a} = f'(\xi). \qquad (104)$$

FIG. 10.

We prove this theorem by applying Rolle's theorem to a function whose form is suggested by geometric considerations. If an ordinate at x meets the chord PQ in R and the curve in S, the part of the ordinate measured from R to S is:

$$F(x) = f(x) - \left[f(a) + \frac{f(b) - f(a)}{b - a} (x - a) \right]. \qquad (105)$$

Since $f(x)$ is continuous in the closed interval a,b and has a finite or infinite derivative at all points of the open interval a,b, the function $F(x)$ also has these properties. Moreover, a direct calculation shows that

$$F(a) = F(b) = 0. \qquad (106)$$

Hence $F(x)$ satisfies all the conditions of Rolle's theorem, and there is a point ξ in the open interval $a < x < b$ at which

$$F'(\xi) = f'(\xi) - \frac{f(b) - f(a)}{b - a} = 0, \qquad (107)$$

which is equivalent to the equation (104).

Since twice the area of the triangle PQS equals $(b - a) \, RS$, we might have proved the theorem by applying Rolle's theorem to this doubled area, which in determinant form is:

$$\begin{vmatrix} x & f(x) & 1 \\ a & f(a) & 1 \\ b & f(b) & 1 \end{vmatrix} = 2A(x) = (b - a) \, F(x). \qquad (108)$$

It follows from Rolle's theorem that:

$$\begin{vmatrix} 1 & f'(\xi) & 0 \\ a & f(a) & 1 \\ b & f(b) & 1 \end{vmatrix} = 2A'(\xi) = 0, \qquad (109)$$

which is equivalent to equation (104). The vanishing for $x = a$ and $x = b$ is seen from the fact that for these values the determinant in equation (108) has two rows identical. In differentiating the determinant, we may either consider the expansion or use the result of problem 6 of Exercises IV.

If we put $b = a + h$, we may write $\xi = a + \theta h$, where

$$0 < \theta < 1. \tag{110}$$

We shall frequently use the symbol θ for a suitably chosen number satisfying this restriction. With this notation, the conclusion of the mean value theorem may be written

$$\frac{f(a + h) - f(a)}{h} = f'(a + \theta h), \tag{111}$$

or

$$f(a + h) = f(a) + hf'(a + \theta h). \tag{112}$$

Since the left member of equation (104) is unchanged if we interchange a and b, the equation is equally true if $a > b$, the condition here holding in the interval b,a. Thus we may take h negative, as well as positive, in the equations (111) and (112).

Either of the results (104) and (111) is sometimes called the *Law of the Mean* for the differential calculus. The term *Law of finite increments* is also used for equation (112), or its equivalents:

$$f(b) - f(a) = (b - a) f'(\xi) \tag{113}$$

and

$$f(b) = f(a) + (b - a) f'(\xi). \tag{114}$$

As a particular result of equation (111), we note that for a finite h the difference quotient, whose limit as $h \to 0$ is the derivative at a, is equal to the value of the derivative at $a + \theta h$, a suitably chosen point between a and $a + h$.

75. Increasing Functions. In any interval throughout which $f'(x) > 0$, the function $f(x)$ is increasing. For, if x_1 and x_2 are any two points in such an interval, we see from the law of finite increments that

$$f(x_2) - f(x_1) = (x_2 - x_1) f'(\xi). \tag{115}$$

Thus, since $f'(\xi) > 0$, the differences $f(x_2) - f(x_1)$ and $x_2 - x_1$ necessarily have the same algebraic sign, and

$$f(x_2) > f(x_1) \quad \text{if} \quad x_2 > x_1. \tag{116}$$

As the statement that there is a derivative implies that the function is continuous, if $f(x)$ has a positive derivative throughout an interval,

$y = f(x)$ is a continuous increasing function in this interval, and there is an inverse function $x = f^{-1}(y)$. Hence the discussion of section 64 is applicable, and in particular the equation (13) holds.

A similar argument may be used if $f(x)$ has a negative derivative throughout an interval.

Whenever $f'(x)$ is continuous at x_0, and not zero there, there is some interval including x_0 in which $f'(x)$ preserves its sign, so that the equation (13) may be used at any point where the derivative is continuous and different from zero.

If $f'(x)$ is zero throughout an interval, the function $f(x)$ must be constant in that interval. For in this case, for a particular value a in the interval, and any x, we have:

$$f(x) - f(a) = (x - a) f'(\xi) = 0. \tag{117}$$

This shows that for all points x in the interval the function $f(x) = f(a)$, and so has a constant value.

Let us next suppose that the function $f(x)$ has a derivative $f'(x) > 0$ for all points of an interval a,b with the exception of a finite number of points p_i. Then these points p_i will divide the interval a,b into a set of subintervals. In the open interval corresponding to any one of these subintervals, the function $f(x)$ will be increasing. We may use the closed intervals if the function $f(x)$ is continuous at the points p_i. Thus, if the function is continuous at the points p_i, and hence throughout the interval a,b, it will be increasing in the interval a,b. The same argument applies if $f'(x) > 0$ for all values of x, all greater than a, or all less than b, except for a set of points p_i at which $f(x)$ is continuous. Here the p_i may be infinite in number so long as they are isolated, that is, have no limit point.

If we merely know that $f'(x) \geqq 0$ throughout an interval, we can only conclude from the equation (115) that

$$f(x_2) \geqq f(x_1) \quad \text{if} \quad x_2 > x_1, \tag{118}$$

so that while the function is monotonic, it is not necessarily actually increasing.

While we may draw conclusions as to the behavior of a function from any restriction as to the sign of the derivative which holds throughout an interval, similar conclusions can not be drawn from such information at a single point. As an example, consider the function $y = f(x)$,

where $\qquad f(x) = x + 2x^2 \sin\dfrac{1}{x}, \quad x \neq 0, \quad \text{and} \quad f(0) = 0. \tag{119}$

This has a derivative $+1$ at the origin, obtained by a direct application of the definition or from equation (70). But, for values near zero though different from it we have:

$$f'(x) = 1 + 4x \sin \frac{1}{x} - 2 \cos \frac{1}{x}, \qquad (120)$$

which is negative in some points of every interval which has point $x = 0$ as an interior or end point.

Thus, although the derivative is positive at $x = 0$, the function is not monotonic in any interval including 0. This follows from the fact, a direct consequence of the definition of a derivative, that if $f(x)$ is monotonically increasing throughout an interval, the derivative $f'(x)$ cannot be negative at any point of the interval.

76. Relative Maxima and Minima. The term maximum, as used in section 33, referred to the absolute maximum (maximum maximorum) for the interval considered. A point at which the value of a function is greater than or equal to all values considered in the immediate neighborhood of the point, that is, in a sufficiently small interval having the point in its interior, is a relative maximum. Thus a relative maximum for the original interval is an absolute maximum for some sufficiently small subinterval. At the end points of a closed interval a,b we only consider values on one side.

If $f(x)$ is considered for the interval $a < x < b$, and ξ is an interior point of this interval at which $f(x)$ has a relative maximum, and at which $f(x)$ has a derivative, $f'(\xi)$, then we may argue as in section 73 and deduce from equations (101) and (102) that $f'(\xi) = 0$. Similar reasoning applies to the relative minima. This proves that:

The relative maxima and minima of a function $f(x)$ for the closed interval $a \leqq x \leqq b$ can only occur at the end points a and b, at points where $f(x)$ fails to have a derivative, finite or infinite, or at points where $f'(x) = 0$.

In the examples treated in elementary calculus, the functions usually had derivatives at all the points considered. Either there were no end points, as when we considered a polynomial for all values of x, or the values taken on at the end points were not the maxima or minima wanted. Thus the desired points corresponded to $f'(x) = 0$.

Even in simple algebraic cases we sometimes need to consider the points where there is no derivative. Thus, if $y = x^{2/3}$, $-1 \leqq x \leqq 1$, the minimum occurs at the point $x = 0$, and is zero. There is no derivative at this point, since the right-hand derivative is $+ \infty$, while the left-hand derivative is $- \infty$.

A sufficient condition for a relative maximum is given by:

A point c, at which $f(x)$ is continuous, and such that $f'(x) > 0$ for some interval $c - h < x < c$ while $f'(x) < 0$ for some interval $c < x < c + k$, is a relative maximum.

This statement follows from the preceding section, since as x increases through c, $f(x)$ increases to $f(c)$ and then decreases.

Similarly:

A point c, at which $f(x)$ is continuous, and such that $f'(x) < 0$ for some interval $c - h < x < c$ while $f'(x) > 0$ for some interval $c < x < c + k$, is a relative minimum.

For functions with continuous derivatives, in these cases, $f'(c) = 0$. A less general test, in terms of higher derivatives, is given in problem 42, Exercises IV.

77. Intermediate Values of the Derivative. A function may be continuous at a point without having a derivative at the point. An example is $y = f(x)$, where

$$f(x) = x \sin \frac{1}{x}, \quad x \neq 0, \quad f(0) = 0, \tag{121}$$

which is continuous at $x = 0$, but has no derivative there, since the difference quotient $\sin (1/h)$ oscillates between 1 and -1 as $h \to 0$. In problem 10, Exercises IV, a function is given with no derivative at any point of an interval, throughout which it is continuous.

Even if a function has a derivative at all points of an interval, the derivative need not be continuous at all points of the interval. Thus the function defined by equation (119) has a derivative for all values of x, but this derivative is not continuous at $x = 0$. Nevertheless, the derived function has in common with continuous functions the intermediate value property we proved in section 34. Specifically:

If $f(x)$ has a derivative $f'(x)$, finite or infinite, at all points of a closed interval $a \leq x \leq b$, then $f'(x)$ takes on every value between $f'(a)$ and $f'(b)$ at some point of the interval between a and b.

Suppose, for definiteness, that $f'(a) < f'(b)$, so that the intermediate value in question, k, satisfies:

$$f'(a) < k < f'(b). \tag{122}$$

Then, from the definition of a derivative as a limit, we can find a positive number h such that:

$$\frac{f(a + h) - f(a)}{h} < k \quad \text{and} \quad \frac{f(b - h) - f(b)}{-h} > k. \tag{123}$$

Thus the function

$$F(x) = \frac{f(x + h) - f(x)}{h} \qquad (124)$$

is $<k$ at $x = a$, and $>k$ at $x = b - h$, so that k is an intermediate value of this function for the interval $a \leqq x \leqq b - h$. But, as $f(x)$ has a derivative throughout this interval, it is continuous in the closed interval, and the same is true of $F(x)$. Hence, by the intermediate value property of continuous functions, there is a point x_0 such that

$$a < x_0 < b - h, \qquad (125)$$

for which

$$F(x_0) = \frac{f(x_0 + h) - f(x_0)}{h} = k. \qquad (126)$$

But, by the mean value theorem,

$$\frac{f(x_0 + h) - f(x_0)}{h} = f'(\xi), \qquad (127)$$

where

$$x_0 < \xi < x_0 + h. \qquad (128)$$

From the relations (125) and (128) we see that

$$a < \xi < b, \qquad (129)$$

while from the equations (126) and (127) we have

$$f'(\xi) = k, \qquad (130)$$

so that we have proved the theorem.

78. Limiting Values of the Derived Function. A function may have a derivative at a even though the derived function $f'(x)$ approaches no limit as $x \to a$. The function defined by equation (119) is an example of this, with $a = 0$. However, we may show that:

If the derived function $f'(x)$ approaches a limit as $x \to a+$,

$$\lim_{x \to a+} f'(x) = L, \qquad (131)$$

then, if $f(x)$ is suitably defined at $x = a$, the function $f(x)$ will have a right-hand derivative at $x = a$.

We observe that the equation (131) implies that there is some open interval, $a < x < a + h_1$, in which the function $f(x)$ has a derivative. Consequently, we may apply the law of finite increments to obtain:

$$f(x_2) - f(x_1) = (x_2 - x_1) f'(\xi), \qquad (132)$$

where x_1 and x_2 are any two points of the open interval $a, a + h_1$, and ξ is a suitably determined value between x_1 and x_2.

Again, the condition (131) implies that we may find a δ_1 such that if $a < x < a + \delta_1$,

$$|f'(x) - L| < \epsilon < 1, \quad \text{so that} \quad |f'(x)| < |L| + 1. \tag{133}$$

Thus, if x_1 and x_2 are each in the interval

$$a < x < a + \delta_\epsilon, \tag{134}$$

where

$$\delta_\epsilon < \delta_1 \quad \text{and also} \quad \delta_\epsilon < \frac{\epsilon}{|L| + 1}, \tag{135}$$

we shall have

$$|f(x_2) - f(x_1)| < \epsilon. \tag{136}$$

Since this relation holds for arbitrarily small values of ϵ, when x_1 and x_2 are each in the interval (134), the Cauchy convergence criterion is satisfied, and $f(x)$ approaches a limit when $x \to a+$. Hence we may define

$$f(a) = \lim_{x \to a+} f(x). \tag{137}$$

With this definition of $f(a)$, and any positive h less than h_1, the function $f(x)$ is continuous in the closed interval $a, a + h$ and we may deduce from the mean value theorem that:

$$\frac{f(a + h) - f(a)}{h} = f'(a + \theta h), \quad 0 < \theta < 1. \tag{138}$$

It follows from this and equation (131) that

$$\lim_{h \to 0+} \frac{f(a + h) - f(a)}{h} = L, \tag{139}$$

which proves that the function has a right-hand derivative at a equal to L.

If

$$f(a) = \lim_{x \to a+} f(x), \quad \text{and} \quad \lim_{x \to a+} f'(x) = +\infty, \tag{140}$$

we may deduce from the second part of this argument that $f(x)$ has a right-hand derivative at a equal to $+\infty$. An example is $\sqrt{x}$, with $a = 0$.

However, we cannot conclude from the second part of equation (140) that the first part defines $f(a)$ as a finite limit. For example, if $f(x) = -1/x$, as $x \to 0+$, $f'(x) \to +\infty$, but $f(x) \to -\infty$, so that we cannot define $f(0)$ by equation (137).

In connection with this example, we prove that

If, for any finite value a, $|f(x)| \to \infty$ as $x \to a$, then $f'(x)$ cannot approach a finite limit as $x \to a$.

In fact, if $f'(x)$ approached a finite limit, it would be bounded in some open interval $a, a + h$, and for any two values x and x_1 each in this open interval we should have:

$$f(x) - f(x_1) = (x - x_1) f'(\xi). \tag{141}$$

But, from this in combination with

$$|f'(\xi)| < M, \quad \text{and} \quad |x - x_1| < h, \tag{142}$$

we may deduce that

$$|f(x) - f(x_1)| < Mh. \tag{143}$$

This shows that, if x_1 is fixed and $x \to a$, $f(x)$ remains bounded, which contradicts the hypothesis that $|f(x)| \to \infty$.

Note that this result need not hold if $x \to +\infty$, instead of a finite value a. For example if $f(x) = x$, as $x \to +\infty$, $f(x) \to +\infty$, but $f'(x) \to 1$. Also, if $f(x) = \sqrt{x}$, as $x \to +\infty$, $f(x) \to +\infty$, but $f'(x) \to 0$.

79. A Generalized Mean Value Theorem. Let us recall the geometric situation described at the beginning of section 74. Let us express the

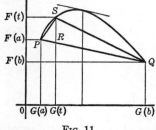

Fig. 11.

coördinates of any point S on the arc PQ in terms of a parameter t, so that $x = G(t)$, and $y = F(t)$ where the points of the arc correspond to the values of t, $a \leqq t \leqq b$. With this notation, the slope of the chord is $[F(b) - F(a)]/[G(b) - G(a)]$, while the slope of the curve at the point T corresponding to $t = \tau$, is $F'(\tau)/G'(\tau)$. This suggests the equation (145) below, and hence the theorem:

a) *If $F(t)$ and $G(t)$ each has a finite derivative at all the points of an open interval $a < t < b$, and are continuous at the end points (and hence throughout) the closed interval $a \leqq t \leqq b$, then at some point τ of the open interval, $a < \tau < b$,*

$$[F(b) - F(a)] G'(\tau) = [G(b) - G(a)] F'(\tau). \tag{144}$$

b) *If, in addition, $G(a) \neq G(b)$, and $F'(t)$ and $G'(t)$ are never both zero for the same value of t in the open interval, then*

$$\frac{F(b) - F(a)}{G(b) - G(a)} = \frac{F'(\tau)}{G'(\tau)}. \tag{145}$$

We prove part (a) of the theorem by applying Rolle's theorem to the doubled area of the triangle PQS.   With the present notation this is

$$\begin{vmatrix} G(t) & F(t) & 1 \\ G(a) & F(a) & 1 \\ G(b) & F(b) & 1 \end{vmatrix} = 2A(t). \tag{146}$$

Thus there is a τ for which:

$$\begin{vmatrix} G'(\tau) & F'(\tau) & 0 \\ G(a) & F(a) & 1 \\ G(b) & F(b) & 1 \end{vmatrix} = 2A'(\tau) = 0, \tag{147}$$

which is equivalent to equation (144).

Let us now assume that the additional hypotheses of part (b) hold. Then, if $F'(\tau) = 0$, it follows that $G'(\tau) \neq 0$.   On the other hand, if $F'(\tau) \neq 0$, since $G(b) - G(a) \neq 0$, the right member of equation (144) is not zero.   Therefore the left member is not zero, and again $G'(\tau) \neq 0$. Thus we may divide by $G'(\tau)$ and $[G(b) - G(a)]$ and so deduce equation (145).

We may replace the additional conditions (b) by:

c) *If $G'(t)$ is never zero throughout the open interval a,b the additional hypotheses (b) necessarily hold, so that equation (145) follows.*

For, if $G'(t) \neq 0$, $F'(t)$ and $G'(t)$ can never both vanish for the same t. And, from the law of finite increments,

$$G(b) - G(a) = (b - a) G'(\xi) \neq 0. \tag{148}$$

80. L'Hospital's Rule for the Indeterminate Form 0/0.   If, when $x \to a$, $f(x) \to 0$ and $g(x) \to 0$, the quotient $f(x)/g(x)$ may approach a limit as x approaches a.   As we remarked in section 21, whether this limit exists, and its value if it exists, cannot be predicted without further information about the functions.   The situation is briefly described as an indeterminate form 0/0.

For a continuous function $f(x)$, when $h \to 0$, $f(x + h) - f(x) \to 0$, so that $[f(x + h) - f(x)]/h$ is an indeterminate form 0/0 for $h = 0$. Thus every time we calculate a derivative we are evaluating a limit of the type now under consideration.

In some cases, where the indeterminate form approaches a limit, the value of the limit may be found by l'Hospital's rule, which states that:

If $f(x) \to 0$ and $g(x) \to 0$ as $x \to a+$,

and
$$\lim_{x \to a+} \frac{f'(x)}{g'(x)} = L, \tag{149}$$

then
$$\lim_{x \to a+} \frac{f(x)}{g(x)} = L. \tag{150}$$

In place of the finite limit L on the right of equations (149) *and* (150), *we may have* $+ \infty$ *or* $- \infty$.

Also, instead of taking all four limits in the theorem as $x \to a+$, *we may take them all as* $x \to a-$, *or simply as* $x \to a$.

This form of the rule is a consequence of the generalized mean value theorem. We note first that, from the condition (149), there must be some open interval $a < x < a + h$ throughout which the functions $f(x)$ and $g(x)$ each have finite derivatives, and in which $g'(x) \neq 0$. Let us define

$$F(x) = f(x) \quad \text{and} \quad G(x) = g(x) \quad \text{for} \quad a < x < a + h, \tag{151}$$

and
$$F(a) = 0 \quad \text{and} \quad G(a) = 0. \tag{152}$$

Then the functions $F(t)$ and $G(t)$ will satisfy all the original conditions of the generalized mean value theorem, as well as the additional hypothesis (c), in any closed interval $a \leqq t \leqq x$, where x is any value in the open interval $a < x < a + h$.

Thus, for some value, say x_0, in the open interval

$$a < x_0 < x, \tag{153}$$

we shall have, by equation (145):

$$\frac{f(x)}{g(x)} = \frac{F(x) - F(a)}{G(x) - G(a)} = \frac{F'(x_0)}{G'(x_0)} = \frac{f'(x_0)}{g'(x_0)}. \tag{154}$$

It follows from the relation (153) that to any sequence of values of x approaching $a+$, there corresponds a sequence of values of x_0 approaching $a+$. But, since the relation (149) holds, the limit of $f'(x_0)/g'(x_0)$ will be L, and hence, from equation (154), the limit of $f(x)/g(x)$ for the first sequence will be L. Since this is true for any sequence, the conclusion of the theorem, equation (150), follows.

Since all sequences x may correspond to a special set of sequences x_0, it is possible for $f(x)/g(x)$ to approach a limit, while $f'(x)/g'(x)$ does not. The rule does not permit us to draw any conclusion from the failure of $g'(x)/f'(x)$ to approach a limit.

From $\lim_{x \to a+} f'(x)/g'(x) = + \infty$, we may deduce that $\lim_{x \to a+} f(x)/g(x) = + \infty$, and similarly for $- \infty$. Also, from $\lim_{x \to a+} |f'(x)/g'(x)| = \infty$, we may deduce that $\lim_{x \to a+} |f(x)/g(x)| = \infty$, since in this case

$$\lim_{x \to a+} \frac{g(x)}{f(x)} = \lim_{x \to a+} \frac{g'(x)}{f'(x)} = 0. \tag{155}$$

The argument as given for $x \to a+$ requires only slight modification to apply to $x \to a-$, or to $x \to a$.

81. Infinitesimals. We define the term *infinitesimal* to mean any *variable whose limit is zero*. Thus, if x is approaching a, $h = x - a$ is an infinitesimal. We may think of any function of x which is infinitesimal as x approaches a as a function of this infinitesimal h. For example,

$$y = f(x) - f(a) = f(a + h) - f(a). \tag{156}$$

The particular infinitesimal in terms of which we express all the infinitesimals in a given limiting process is called the *principal infinitesimal*.

The principal infinitesimal is said to be of the *first order*. If h is the principal infinitesimal, and k is any other infinitesimal such that k/h approaches a finite limit distinct from zero; then k is also said to be of the first order. Similarly h^n, where n is any positive integer, or any infinitesimal k such that the limit of k/h^n is finite and different from zero, is said to be of the nth *order*.

If k_1 is an infinitesimal of order m, and k_2 an infinitesimal of order n, then the limit of k_1/k_2 will be finite and different from zero if $m = n$, and will be zero if $m > n$, since:

$$\frac{k_1}{k_2} = \frac{k_1}{h^m} \frac{h^n}{k_2} h^{m-n}. \tag{157}$$

By analogy, we say that any two infinitesimals k_1 and k_2 have the *same* order if the limit of k_1/k_2 is finite and different from zero, and that k_1 is of higher order than k_2, or k_2 is of lower order than k_1, if the limit of k_1/k_2 is zero.

We do not attempt to define non-integral orders. Thus we assign no order to $h^{3/2}$, although we can say that it is of higher order than h and of lower order than h^2. Again, the infinitesimal $h^2 \sin (1/h)$ is of higher order than h, but not of lower order than h^3 or than h^n with n any greater integer, since

$$\frac{h^3}{h^2 \sin \dfrac{1}{h}} \quad \text{or} \quad \frac{h^n}{h^2 \sin \dfrac{1}{h}} \tag{158}$$

each fails to approach the limit zero. In fact each is undefined when $1/h$ is an integral multiple of π; but for suitable sequences of values of h which approach 0, the upper limit is $+\infty$ and the lower limit is $-\infty$. Again, the infinitesimals

$$h \sin \frac{1}{h} \quad \text{and} \quad h \sin \frac{\sqrt{2}}{h} \tag{159}$$

are not of the same order, and neither is of higher order than the other. Our definitions thus serve to classify some but not all infinitesimals.

While the order assigned depends on the principal infinitesimal, it is unchanged if we replace h by any infinitesimal of the first order with respect to h. A relation of the form " k_1 is of higher order than k_2 " is independent of the choice of principal infinitesimal.

We write

$$k_1 = o(k_2), \tag{160}$$

read " k_1 is small o of k_2," if the limit of k_1/k_2 is zero. Thus, for any infinitesimal, k, we have $k = o(1)$, and, conversely, this implies that k is an infinitesimal. If k_1 and k_2 are both infinitesimal, then the equation (160) indicates that the infinitesimal k_1 is of higher order than k_2. For example,

$$h^{\frac{3}{2}} = o(h) \quad \text{and} \quad h^2 \sin \frac{1}{h} = o(h^{\frac{3}{2}}). \tag{161}$$

For an infinitesimal k of the nth order,

$$\text{since } \frac{k}{h^n} \to A, \qquad \frac{k - Ah^n}{h^n} \to 0, \tag{162}$$

and we may write:

$$k = Ah^n + o(h^n). \tag{163}$$

Whenever k may be expressed in this form, with $A \neq 0$, the term Ah^n is called the *principal part* of the infinitesimal k. The discussion of section 70 shows that, if $f'(a) \neq 0$ and Δx is the principal infinitesimal, then Δy is an infinitesimal of the first order, with $f'(a) \Delta x$, or the differential dy, as its principal part.

It follows from the definition and section 19 that if

$$s_1 = o(k_1) \quad \text{and} \quad s_2 = o(k_2), \tag{164}$$

then $s_1 s_2 = o(k_1 k_2)$. We abbreviate this result by writing

$$o(k_1)\, o(k_2) = o(k_1 k_2). \tag{165}$$

We interpret and prove

$$o(k_1) + o(k_2) = o(k_1 + k_2) \tag{166}$$

similarly. In particular,

$$Ao(h^n) = o(h^n) \quad \text{and} \quad o(h^n)\, o(h^m) = o(h^{m+n}). \tag{167}$$

Also,
if $m \geqq n$, $$\qquad o(h^n) + o(h^m) = o(h^n). \tag{168}$$

We may use these relations to prove that, if $m > n$ and k_1 has a principal part $A_1 h^m$, and k_2 has a principal part $A_2 h^n$, then $k_1 k_2$ has a principal part $A_1 A_2 h^{m+n}$, and $k_1 + k_2$ has a principal part $A_2 h^n$.

We shall occasionally use a notation somewhat similar to equation (160), and write

$$k_1 = O(k_2), \tag{169}$$

read " k_1 is large O of k_2," if there is some constant y such that

$$|k_1| \leqq y|k_2|, \tag{170}$$

beyond some stage of the limit process. Thus the relation (160) implies the relation (169), and in fact if k_1/k_2 approaches a finite limit, or even if k_1/k_2 has a finite upper limit the relation (169) holds. However the relation (170) also holds in other cases. For example,

$$h^2 \sin^2 \frac{1}{h} = O\left(h^2 \sin \frac{1}{h}\right). \tag{171}$$

Among the rules of operation for this symbol, we mention

$$O(k_1)\, O(k_2) = O(k_1 k_2), \quad AO(k_1) = O(k_1), \tag{172}$$

$$O(k_1) + O(k_2) = O(|k_1| + |k_2|),$$

and if $k_1 = O(k_2)$, $\qquad O(k_1) + O(k_2) = O(k_2)$. $\tag{173}$

82. Taylor's Theorem for Infinitesimal Increments. Let us consider a function $f(x)$, for values of x near a. As $x \to a$, $h = x - a$ is an infinitesimal. If it is possible to find a polynomial of the nth degree in h,

$$P(h) = A_0 + A_1 h + A_2 h^2 + \cdots + A_n h^n, \tag{174}$$

such that

$$f(x) = f(a + h) = P(h) + o(h^n), \tag{175}$$

then $P(h)$ is called a *Taylor's development* of the function $f(x)$ about the point a, of the nth order. We say that $P(h)$ approximates $f(a + h)$ to within terms of higher order than h^n.

We shall show that if the function $f(x)$ has an $(n + 1)$st derivative at the point a, $f^{(n+1)}(a)$, then it has a unique development of this type. As we need to know the values of the coefficients to carry out the proof, we shall begin by assuming that the function has a development of the form (175), and also that there is a derivative $f^{(n+1)}(a)$, and try to determine what the coefficients must be under these conditions.

Since $f^{(n+1)}(a)$ exists, $f^{(n)}(x)$ must exist throughout some closed interval $x - k \leqq a \leqq x + k$, and be continuous at a. Also, $f^{(n-1)}(x)$ and all the derivatives of lower order, as well as $f(x)$ itself, must exist and be continuous throughout this same closed interval.

The relation (175) implies that

$$\lim_{h \to 0} \frac{f(a + h) - P(h)}{h^n} = 0. \tag{176}$$

Since the denominator approaches zero, the numerator must also, and

$$\lim_{h \to 0} [f(a + h) - P(h)] = f(a) - A_0 = 0. \tag{177}$$

Thus the left member of equation (176) satisfies the first condition of l'Hospital's rule, and if

$$\lim_{h \to 0} \frac{f'(a + h) - P'(h)}{nh^{n-1}} \tag{178}$$

exists, it must be 0.   But the limit of the numerator is

$$f'(a) - A_1 \tag{179}$$

which would make the limit (178) $+ \infty$ or $- \infty$, and hence contradict the equation (176), unless

$$f'(a) - A_1 = 0. \tag{180}$$

In this case, we may apply l'Hospital's rule to the expression (178), and by the same argument deduce that:

$$\lim_{h \to 0} [f''(a + h) - P''(h)] = f''(a) - 2 \,!\, A_2 = 0. \tag{181}$$

A repetition of this argument shows that

$$f^{(i)}(a) = i \,!\, A_i, \text{ or } A_i = \frac{f^{(i)}(a)}{i \,!}, \quad \text{for} \quad i = 1, 2, \cdots, n. \tag{182}$$

Let us now consider any function $f(x)$, for which $f^{(n+1)}(a)$ exists and is finite.   We form the polynomial $P(h)$, defined by the equations (174) and (182).   Now consider

$$\lim_{h \to 0} \frac{f(a + h) - P(h)}{h^{n+1}} . \tag{183}$$

In view of the fact that $P(0) = A_0 = f(a)$, we may apply l'Hospital's rule if the limit of

$$\frac{f'(a + h) - P'(h)}{(n + 1)h^n} \tag{184}$$

exists.   Then, from the fact that $P'(0) = A_1 = f'(a)$, we may apply the rule again, if the limit of

$$\frac{f''(a + h) - P''(h)}{(n + 1)nh^{n-1}} \tag{185}$$

exists, and so on, until after n applications of the rule, we come to

$$\frac{f^{(n)}(a + h) - P^{(n)}(h)}{(n + 1)! h} = \frac{1}{(n + 1)!} \frac{f^{(n)}(a + h) - f^{(n)}(h)}{h}. \quad (186)$$

But, from the definition of the $(n + 1)$st derivative, the limit of the difference quotient just written as $h \to 0$ is $f^{(n+1)}(a)$. Thus we may justify each application of l'Hospital's rule in turn by working backwards, and so find that

$$\lim_{h \to 0} \frac{f(a + h) - P(h)}{h^{n+1}} = \frac{1}{(n + 1)!} f^{(n+1)}(a). \quad (187)$$

This proves that

$$f(a + h) - P(h) = O(h^{n+1}), \quad \text{and hence} = o(h^n). \quad (188)$$

We express our results in the following theorem:

If the function $f(x)$ has a finite derivative $f^{(n+1)}(a)$ for $x = a$, then the polynomial in the infinitesimal $h = x - a$,

$$P(h) = f(a) + f'(a)\frac{h}{1!} + f''(a)\frac{h^2}{2!} + \cdots + f^{(n)}(a)\frac{h^n}{n!} \quad (189)$$

differs from $f(a + h)$ by an infinitesimal of higher order than h^n, so that:

$$f(a + h) = P(h) + o(h^n). \quad (190)$$

There is no other polynomial of degree at most n which has this property. The behavior of $f(a + h) - P(h)$ is given more precisely by equation (187),

If the phrase $f^{(n+1)}(a) = +\infty$ means that $f^{(n)}(x)$ has its first derivative $+\infty$ for $x = a$, then the preceding argument proves that:

$$\lim_{h \to 0} \frac{f(a + h) - P(h)}{h^n} = 0, \quad (191)$$

so that the relation (190) still holds, but equation (187) must be replaced by

$$\lim_{h \to 0} \frac{f(a + h) - P(h)}{h^{n+1}} = +\infty. \quad (192)$$

Similar conclusions can be drawn if $f^{(n+1)}(a) = -\infty$.

It is to be noted, however, that we may have $\lim_{x \to a} f^{(n+1)}(x) = +\infty$ without having $f^{(n+1)}(a) = +\infty$, in the above sense. We illustrated **this** for the first derivative in connection with equation (140).

83. Taylor's Developments. The rules for operating with the symbols $o(h^n)$ and $O(h^n)$ given in section 81 show that Taylor's developments may be combined like polynomials in many respects. For example, let us start with

$$\sin x = x - \frac{x^3}{3!} + O(x^5), \tag{193}$$

$$\cos x = 1 - \frac{x^2}{2!} + \frac{x^4}{4!} + O(x^6), \tag{194}$$

$$e^x = 1 + x + \frac{x^2}{2!} + \frac{x^3}{3!} + O(x^4), \tag{195}$$

$$(1 + x)^m = 1 + mx + \frac{m(m-1)}{2!} x^2 + \frac{m(m-1)(m-2)}{3!} x^3 + O(x^4), \tag{196}$$

which may be derived from the equation (189) by direct differentiation. Then, operating as we would for polynomials, we may deduce:

$$\sin^2 x = x^2 - \frac{x^4}{3} + O(x^6), \quad \sin^3 x = x^3 - \frac{x^5}{2} + O(x^7), \tag{197}$$

$$e^{x^2} = 1 + x^2 + \frac{x^4}{2!} + \frac{x^6}{3!} + O(x^8), \tag{198}$$

$$\cos (\sin x) = 1 - \frac{x^2}{2} + \frac{5x^4}{24} + O(x^6), \tag{199}$$

$$\cos^m x = 1 - \frac{mx^2}{2} + \frac{m(3m-2)}{24} x^4 + O(x^6). \tag{200}$$

Here we obtain (197) by multiplying the expansion (193) by itself, and then by itself again. Replacing x by x^2 in the expansion (195) gives the expansion (198). Replacing x in the expansion (194) by the terms of the expansion (193) gives the expansion (199). Replacing x in the expansion (196) by the terms following the 1 in the expansion (194) gives the expansion (200).

For quotients, the special case of (196) with $m = -1$,

$$\frac{1}{1+x} = 1 - x + x^2 - x^3 + O(x^4), \tag{201}$$

may often be used to advantage. Thus we find from it and (194)

$$\sec x = \frac{1}{\cos x} = 1 + \frac{x^2}{2} + \frac{5}{24} x^4 + O(x^6). \tag{202}$$

This may also be found by long division, and checks with (200), if $m = -1$ there. Multiplication of (193) and (202) gives

$$\tan x = \sin x \cdot \frac{1}{\cos x} = x + \frac{x^3}{3} + O(x^5). \qquad (203)$$

Again, to find the development for $\sin^{-1} x$, we may put

$$y = \sin^{-1} x, \quad \text{so that} \quad x = \sin y = y - \frac{y^3}{3!} + O(y^5). \qquad (204)$$

We find from this, since x and y are of the same order,

$$y = x + \frac{y^3}{3!} + O(x^5), \quad y^3 = x^3 + O(x^5), \qquad (205)$$

and

$$y = x + \frac{x^3}{3!} + O(x^5). \qquad (206)$$

This may also be obtained by noting that if $f(x) = \sin^{-1}(x)$, then

$$F(x) = f'(x) = \frac{1}{\sqrt{1 - x^2}} = 1 + \frac{x^2}{2} + O(x^4), \qquad (207)$$

by putting $-1/2$ for m and $-x^2$ for x in (196). But, if $a_p x^p$ is a typical term of the expansion of $f(x)$, and $A_p x^p$ a term of the expansion of $F(x)$, $= f'(x)$, we have:

$$a_0 = f(0) \quad \text{and for} \quad p > 0,$$

$$a_p = \frac{f^{(p)}(0)}{p!} = \frac{F^{(p-1)}(0)}{(p-1)!\, p} = \frac{A_{p-1}}{p}. \qquad (208)$$

This relation enables us to derive (206) from (207).

In general, if we are expanding a function $g(x)$ in powers of the infinitesimal $h = x - a$, the expansion will start with $g(a)$, so that the infinitesimal $k = g(x) - g(a)$ will have an expansion in h with no constant term. Thus the expansions for the powers of k in terms of h may be obtained by the method used to deduce (197). If we then wish to expand $f[g(x)]$ in powers of h, we first expand $f(u)$ in powers of $u - b$, where $b = g(a)$ so that when $u = g(x)$, $u - b = g(x) - g(a) = k$, whose powers we have just discussed. For example, if $f(u) = 1/u$, we use:

$$\frac{1}{u} = \frac{1}{b + k} = \frac{1}{b} \frac{1}{1 + \dfrac{k}{b}} = \frac{1}{b} - \frac{k}{b^2} + \frac{k^2}{b^3} - \frac{k^3}{b^4} + O(k^4), \qquad (209)$$

an expansion which has (201) as a special case.

Since the combinations of elementary functions here under consideration have derivatives of all orders, we know that the expansions exist, so that we may use the method of undetermined coefficients. The ordinary process of long division for quotients, and the methods of finding an expansion from that of the inverse function, or from that of the derivative we illustrated for $\sin^{-1} x$, are equivalent to this method.

Since the expansions are uniquely determined, no matter what method we use, the development will be the same as that obtained by differentiation. The methods of this section are often preferable to a direct calculation of the higher derivatives which occur in equation (189).

84. Alternative Form of l'Hospital's Rule. The discussion of section 82 enables us to prove the following alternative form of l'Hospital's rule for the indeterminate form 0/0.

If the functions $f(x)$ and $g(x)$, as well as their derivatives of all orders from one up to n are zero for $x = a$, so that:

$$f(a) = f'(a) = f''(a) = \cdots = f^{(n)}(a) = 0, \tag{210}$$

$$g(a) = g'(a) = g''(a) = \cdots = g^{(n)}(a) = 0, \tag{211}$$

and each function has a derivative of the $(n + 1)$st order at a, with

$$g^{(n+1)}(a) \neq 0, \tag{212}$$

then

$$\lim_{x \to a} \frac{f(x)}{g(x)} = \frac{f^{(n+1)}(a)}{g^{(n+1)}(a)}. \tag{213}$$

If we apply equation (187) to each of our functions, noting that the polynomial $P(h)$ is zero in view of the conditions (210) and (211), we have:

$$\lim_{h \to 0} \frac{f(a + h)}{h^{n+1}} = \frac{f^{(n+1)}(a)}{(n + 1)!}, \tag{214}$$

and

$$\lim_{h \to 0} \frac{g(a + h)}{h^{n+1}} = \frac{g^{(n+1)}(a)}{(n + 1)!}. \tag{215}$$

It follows from these by division that

$$\lim_{h \to 0} \frac{f(a + h)}{g(a + h)} = \frac{f^{(n+1)}(a)}{g^{(n+1)}(a)}, \tag{216}$$

which is equivalent to equation (213), the conclusion of the theorem.

In this theorem, when $x \to a+$, we only need right-hand derivatives, and when $x \to a-$, we only need left-hand derivatives. If the derivatives are not restricted in this way, the theorem applies when $x \to a$.

Also if one, but not both, of the derivatives $f^{(n+1)}(a)$ and $g^{(n+1)}(a)$ is $+\infty$ or $-\infty$, we may deduce the behavior of $f(x)/g(x)$ from the equation (213) by the principles of section 20.

Whenever the functions $f(x)$ and $g(x)$ possess derivatives of the $(n+2)$nd order at a, and hence Taylor's developments of the $(n+1)$st order, we have:

$$f(a + h) = A_{n+1}h^{n+1} + O(h^{n+2}),   \tag{217}$$

and

$$g(a + h) = B_{n+1}h^{n+1} + O(h^{n+2}),   B_{n+1} \neq 0.   \tag{218}$$

It follows from these expansions that:

$$\lim_{x \to a} \frac{f(x)}{g(x)} = \frac{A_{n+1}}{B_{n+1}}.   \tag{219}$$

This is in accordance with equation (213), since the right member of equation (214) is A_{n+1}, while that of equation (215) is B_{n+1}. But, if the Taylor's developments for $f(x)$ and $g(x)$ are known, or can be easily found by the methods of section 83, it is simpler to verify equations (217) and (218), and apply equation (219), than to verify equations (210) and (211), and apply equation (213). For example, to evaluate

$$\lim_{x \to 0} \frac{\tan x - \sin x}{\sin^{-1} x - x},   \tag{220}$$

we deduce from equations (203) and (193) that

$$\tan x - \sin x = \frac{x^3}{2} + O(x^5),   \tag{221}$$

and from equation (206) that

$$\sin^{-1} x - x = \frac{x^3}{6} + O(x^5),   \tag{222}$$

so that the value of the limit (220) is 3.

Again, whenever the $(n+1)$st derivative is continuous at a, the equation (213) may be deduced by $(n+1)$ successive applications of the rule proved in section 80. In many cases such successive applications permit us to make simplifications at intermediate stages such as cancellation of factors, or replacing factors whose limits are known and different from zero by their limits. Thus, if we apply the earlier rule to evaluate the limit, as $x \to 0$, of $f(x)/g(x) = \sin^3 x / \sin x^3$, we find that:

$$\frac{f'(x)}{g'(x)} = \frac{3 \sin^2 x \cos x}{3x^2 \cos x^3} = \left(\frac{\sin x}{x}\right)^2 \frac{\cos x}{\cos x^3},   \tag{223}$$

so that the limit of $f(x)/g(x)$ is 1. This limit could also have been found by writing

$$\frac{f(x)}{g(x)} = \left(\frac{\sin x}{x}\right)^3 \left(\frac{x^3}{\sin x^3}\right) \quad \text{or} \quad \frac{f(x)}{g(x)} = \frac{x^3 + O(x^5)}{x^3 + O(x^9)}. \tag{224}$$

The theorem of this section does not apply to such cases as $\lim\limits_{x \to 0+} \dfrac{\sin x}{x^2}$, except to prove that its reciprocal approaches 0, so that its numerical value becomes infinite. However, the rule of section 80 shows that the expression $\to +\infty$.

When the $(n + 1)$st derivative is not continuous at a, the equation (213) may give a result, while the equation (149) does not hold. An example, with $n = 0$, is

$$\lim_{x \to 0} \frac{x^2 \sin \dfrac{1}{x}}{\sin x} = \frac{0}{1} = 0. \tag{225}$$

85. L'Hospital's Rule for the Indeterminate Form ∞/∞. If $\lim\limits_{x \to a} |f(x)| = \infty$, and $\lim\limits_{x \to a} |g(x)| = \infty$, the expression $f(x)/g(x)$ may approach a limit when $x \to a$. As this limit can not be predicted without further information about the functions, this situation is described as an indeterminate form ∞/∞. We shall now show that the rule given in section 80 for the indeterminate form $0/0$ applies also to the form ∞/∞. That is:

If $\lim\limits_{x \to a+} f(x) = \infty, \quad \lim\limits_{x \to a+} g(x) = \infty,$

and
$$\lim_{x \to a+} \frac{f'(x)}{g'(x)} = L, \tag{226}$$

then
$$\lim_{x \to a+} \frac{f(x)}{g(x)} = L. \tag{227}$$

The theorem remains valid if we replace L by $+\infty$, or by $-\infty$. Also we may replace $x \to a+$ by $x \to a-$, or by $x \to a$ in each of the places where it occurs.

To prove this, we select an open interval $a < x < a + h$, in which $f(x)$ and $g(x)$ each has finite derivatives. Then, for any two points x_1 and x in this interval, with $x_1 > x$, we have

$$\frac{f(x)}{g(x)} \frac{1 - \dfrac{f(x_1)}{f(x)}}{1 - \dfrac{g(x_1)}{g(x)}} = \frac{f(x) - f(x_1)}{g(x) - g(x_1)} = \frac{f'(x_0)}{g'(x_0)}, \tag{228}$$

where x_0 is a suitable point satisfying $x < x_0 < x_1$ by the generalized mean value theorem of section 79.

We may rewrite this equation in the form:

$$\frac{f(x)}{g(x)} = \frac{1 - \dfrac{g(x_1)}{g(x)}}{1 - \dfrac{f(x_1)}{f(x)}} \frac{f'(x_0)}{g'(x_0)}. \tag{229}$$

Next select a δ_1 such that

$$\left| \frac{f'(x)}{g'(x)} - L \right| < \epsilon, \quad \text{if} \quad 0 < x - a < \delta_1, \tag{230}$$

which we may do in view of the condition (226).

Then take a particular value of x_1, such that $a < x_1 < a + \delta_1$, and a number δ such that:

$$\left| \frac{f(x_1)}{f(x)} \right| < \epsilon, \quad \text{and} \quad \left| \frac{g(x_1)}{g(x)} \right| < \epsilon, \quad \text{if} \quad 0 < x - a < \delta, \tag{231}$$

which we may do since the numerators of these fractions are fixed, while the denominators become infinite as $x \to a$.

We then have:

$$\frac{f(x)}{g(x)} = \frac{1 - \alpha_2}{1 - \alpha_3}(L + \alpha_1), \quad \text{if} \quad 0 < x - a < \delta, \tag{232}$$

where $$|\alpha_1| < \epsilon, \ |\alpha_2| < \epsilon, \ |\alpha_3| < \epsilon. \tag{233}$$

Now take a sequence of values of ϵ approaching zero and a corresponding sequence of values of δ approaching zero. Then, for any sequence of values of $x \to a+$, we may write a series of equations (232) with ϵ and hence α_1, α_2 and α_3 all approaching zero. It follows from this that

$$\lim_{x \to a+} \frac{f(x)}{g(x)} = L, \tag{234}$$

so that we have proved equation (227).

When L is replaced by $+\infty$ in equation (226), we select δ_1 such that

$$\frac{f'(x)}{g'(x)} > \frac{1}{\epsilon}, \quad \text{if} \quad 0 < x - a < \delta_1, \tag{235}$$

so that if we put $f'(x)/g'(x) = 1/\alpha_1$, $0 < \alpha_1 < \epsilon$. We then have in place of equation (232),

$$\frac{f(x)}{g(x)} = \frac{1 - \alpha_2}{1 - \alpha_3}\frac{1}{\alpha_1}, \quad \alpha_1 > 0, \tag{236}$$

and we may deduce from this by the earlier argument that

$$\lim_{x \to a+} \frac{f(x)}{g(x)} = +\infty. \tag{237}$$

86. Indeterminate Forms for $x \to +\infty$. If

$$\lim_{x \to +\infty} f(x) = 0, \quad \text{and} \quad \lim_{x \to +\infty} g(x) = 0, \tag{238}$$

we may reduce this to the case discussed in section 80 by making the change of variables:

$$y = \frac{1}{x}, \quad \text{so that } y \to 0+, \text{ when } x \to +\infty. \tag{239}$$

If we define

$$F(y) = f\left(\frac{1}{y}\right) = f(x), \quad \text{and} \quad G(y) = g\left(\frac{1}{y}\right) = g(x), \tag{240}$$

we have:

$$F'(y) = -\frac{1}{y^2} f'\left(\frac{1}{y}\right) = -x^2 f'(x), \quad \text{and} \quad G'(y) = -x^2 g'(x), \tag{241}$$

so that:

$$\frac{F'(y)}{G'(y)} = \frac{f'(x)}{g'(x)}. \tag{242}$$

This shows that, if

$$\lim_{x \to +\infty} \frac{f'(x)}{g'(x)} = L, \tag{243}$$

we have:

$$\lim_{x \to +\infty} \frac{f(x)}{g(x)} = \lim_{y \to 0+} \frac{F(y)}{G(y)} = \lim_{y \to 0+} \frac{F'(y)}{G'(y)} = \lim_{x \to +\infty} \frac{f'(x)}{g'(x)} = L. \tag{244}$$

This proves that l'Hospital's rule as stated in the theorem of section **80** remains valid if we replace $x \to a+$ by $x \to +\infty$.

This is also true if we replace $x \to a+$ by $x \to -\infty$, or $|x| \to \infty$.

The same argument reduces the case in which

$$\lim_{x \to +\infty} |f(x)| = \infty, \quad \lim_{x \to +\infty} |g(x)| = \infty, \tag{245}$$

to the case discussed in section 85, and shows that the rule of that section may be similarly extended.

87. Other Indeterminate Forms. If $\lim f(x) = 0$ and if $\lim |g(x)| = \infty$, we speak of the limit of $f(x)g(x)$ as the indeterminate form $0 \cdot \infty$. We may sometimes evaluate this limit by the preceding rules, since

$$f(x)g(x) = \frac{f(x)}{\dfrac{1}{g(x)}} = \frac{g(x)}{\dfrac{1}{f(x)}}, \tag{246}$$

which are respectively indeterminate forms $0/0$ and ∞/∞.

Again, we speak of $f(x)^{g(x)}$ as an indeterminate form, when the limits of $f(x)$ and $g(x)$ are both 0, in which case we have the indeterminate form 0^0, or are those indicated by 1^∞ and ∞^0. These may be reduced to the discussion of an indeterminate product $0 \cdot \infty$ by taking logarithms, since in each of these cases the product $g(x) \log f(x)$ has the limit of one factor zero, while the other factor becomes infinite.

Similarly the form $f(x) - g(x)$, where $f(x)$ and $g(x)$ each become infinite, may be reduced by

$$f(x) - g(x) = \frac{\dfrac{1}{g(x)} - \dfrac{1}{f(x)}}{\dfrac{1}{f(x)g(x)}}, \tag{247}$$

or some similar transformation to a case to which l'Hospital's rule applies.

In all these cases, whenever the Taylor's developments are at hand, they may be used to shorten the calculation. As an example, consider the limit when $x \to 0$ of $f(x)^{g(x)}$, where

$$f(x) = 1 + ax + o(x) \quad \text{and} \quad xg(x) = b + o(1), \tag{248}$$

so that this is an indeterminate form 1^∞. From the Taylor's development

$$\log(1 + u) = u + O(u^2), \tag{249}$$

we deduce that

$$\log f(x) = ax + o(x), \; g(x) \log f(x) = ab + o(1), \tag{250}$$

so that

$$\lim_{x \to 0} f(x)^{g(x)} = e^{ab}. \tag{251}$$

88. Vanishing Factors. In the application of l'Hospital's rule, it is desirable to make algebraic simplifications of the fraction $f'(x)/g'(x)$, as we indicated in section 84.

But one must not cancel out a factor from $f'(x)$ and $g'(x)$ which vanishes in every neighborhood of a, the value at which the limit is taken. The presence of such a factor makes $f'(x)/g'(x)$ undefined for one sequence of values approaching a, and so the limit does not exist in the sense required to prove l'Hospital's rule.

In fact, it is possible for $f'(x)/g'(x)$ to approach a limit A for all sequences of values not including this one sequence of values, while $f(x)/g(x)$ either fails to approach a limit, or approaches a limit distinct from A.

Similar remarks apply when we take the limits as $x \to +\infty$, if there is a factor vanishing for arbitrarily large values of x.

An example is

$$f(x) = x - \sin x \cos x, \ g(x) = (x - \sin x \cos x)^p \, e^{\cos x}, \quad (252)$$

where $p > 0$, and we consider the limit of $f(x)/g(x)$ as $x \to +\infty$. By using the fact that

$$\lim_{x \to +\infty} \frac{x - \sin x \cos x}{x} = 1, \quad (253)$$

we see that

$$\frac{f(x)}{g(x)} = M_1 x^{1-p}, \quad (254)$$

where M_1 has a finite upper limit e and a lower limit greater than zero, $1/e$.

The derivatives of the functions are:

$$f'(x) = 2 \sin^2 x, \quad (255)$$

and

$$g'(x) = (-x + \sin x \cos x + 2p \sin x) \sin x \ (x - \sin x \cos x)^{p-1} \, e^{\cos x} \quad (256)$$

Thus we may write:

$$\frac{f'(x)}{g'(x)} = -M_2 x^{-p} \frac{\sin^2 x}{\sin x}, \quad (257)$$

where M_2 has its upper and lower limits finite and positive. This shows that $f'(x)/g'(x)$ is undefined for the sequence $x = n\pi$, for which $\sin x = 0$. If we avoid these values, we may cancel out the factor $\sin x$ and so have:

if $x' \neq n\pi$, $$\lim_{x' \to +\infty} \frac{f'(x)}{g'(x)} = 0. \quad (258)$$

But, if $p = 1$, $f(x)/g(x) = M_1$ oscillates between finite limits, and so fails to approach any limit. If $p < 1$, e.g., $2/3$, $f(x)/g(x)$ becomes positively infinite.

By considering

$$F(x) = Af(x) + Bg(x), \quad G(x) = f(x) + g(x), \tag{259}$$

derived from the functions of equation (252), we have:

$$\lim_{x' \to +\infty} \frac{F'(x)}{G'(x)} = B, \quad x' \neq n\pi, \tag{260}$$

while

$$\lim_{x \to +\infty} \frac{F(x)}{G(x)} = A, \quad \text{if} \quad p = \frac{2}{3}, \tag{261}$$

and $F(x)/G(x)$ oscillates, and so approaches no limit, if $p = 1$.

89. Taylor's Theorem for Finite Increments. The theorem of section 82 suggests that, for certain values of h, the polynomial $P(h)$ of equation (189) has a simple relation to the function $f(x)$, and we proceed to study this relation in more detail.

In section 82 we merely assumed the existence of the $(n + 1)$st derivative at the point a itself. We shall now assume that the function $f(x)$ has a finite $(n + 1)$st derivative at all points of the closed interval $a \leqq x \leqq a + h$. In this case we may apply the generalized mean value theorem to the functions

$$F(h) = f(a + h) - P(h), \quad G(h) = h^{n+1}, \tag{262}$$

to obtain:

$$\frac{F(h)}{G(h)} = \frac{F(h) - F(0)}{G(h) - G(0)} = \frac{F'(h_1)}{G'(h_1)}, \tag{263}$$

since $F(0)$ and $G(0)$ are each zero. But, since $F(h)$ and $G(h)$ each have their derivatives of the first n orders zero for $h = 0$, we may repeat this process n times more, and so find:

$$\frac{F'(h_1)}{G'(h_1)} = \frac{F''(h_2)}{G''(h_2)} = \cdots = \frac{F^{(n+1)}(h_{n+1})}{G^{(n+1)}(h_{n+1})}. \tag{264}$$

Since

$$0 < h_{n+1} < h_n < \cdots < h_2 < h_1 < h, \tag{265}$$

we may write

$$h_{n+1} = \theta h, \quad \text{where} \quad 0 < \theta < 1, \tag{266}$$

and conclude that:

$$\frac{f(a + h) - P(h)}{h^{n+1}} = \frac{f^{(n+1)}(a + \theta h)}{(n + 1)!}. \tag{267}$$

We have thus proved one form of *Taylor's theorem for finite increments*, which we formulate as follows:

If the function $f(x)$ has a finite $(n + 1)$st derivative at all points of the closed interval $a \leqq x \leqq a + h$, then there is a value of θ between zero and one, for which:

$$f(a + h) = f(a) + f'(a) \frac{h}{1!} + f''(a) \frac{h^2}{2!} + \cdots$$

$$+ f^{(n)}(a) \frac{h^n}{n!} + f^{(n+1)}(a + \theta h) \frac{h^{n+1}}{(n+1)!} \cdot \quad (268)$$

If we put $a + h = x$, $h = x - a$, the result may be written:

$$f(x) = f(a) + f'(a) \frac{(x - a)}{1!} + f''(a) \frac{(x - a)^2}{2!} + \cdots$$

$$+ f^{(n)}(a) \frac{(x - a)^n}{n!} + f^{(n+1)}(\xi) \frac{(x - a)^{n+1}}{(n+1)!}, \quad (269)$$

where ξ is a suitably chosen value between a and x. The equation just written will hold for any value of x in the closed interval $a \leqq x \leqq b$, if the function $f(x)$ has a finite $(n + 1)$st derivative throughout this interval, and if ξ is appropriate to this x.

The difference between the function $f(a + h)$ and its Taylor's development $P(h)$, the $F(h)$ of equation (262), is referred to as the *remainder* for the development. Thus the equation (267) determines one expression for the remainder. The theorem, as expressed in equations (268) or (269), is often called *Taylor's theorem with the remainder*. The special case with $a = 0$ is called *Maclaurin's theorem*.

If, throughout the closed interval a,b the numerical value of $f^{(n+1)}(x)$ admits the upper bound M, the numerical value of the remainder, or error made by using the first n terms of the Taylor's development, $P(h)$ or $P(x - a)$ in place of $f(x)$ will not exceed $M(b - a)^{n+1}/(n + 1)!$ at any point of the interval. This enables us to use the developments for computation, for which the first form, $P(h)$, is usually preferable; the error being numerically at most $Mh^{n+1}/(n + 1)!$

90. The Limiting Value of θ. While we can usually say little about the value of θ beyond the fact that it is between 0 and 1, we can determine its limiting value as h approaches zero, if the function has a derivative of order one higher than that used in the term involving $a + \theta h$, and this derivative is continuous and not zero at a.

Let us assume that $f^{(n+1)}(x)$ is continuous at a, and therefore finite in some closed interval $a \leqq x \leqq a + h$, and apply equation (268), both as written, and with n replaced by $n - 1$, and θ replaced by θ_n. Then, by equating the two expressions for $f(a + h)$ so obtained, we find:

$$f^{(n)}(a + \theta_n h)\, \frac{h^n}{n\,!} = f^{(n)}(a)\, \frac{h^n}{n\,!} + f^{(n+1)}(a + \theta h)\, \frac{h^{n+1}}{(n+1)\,!}, \quad (270)$$

or

$$f^{(n)}(a + \theta_n h) = f^{(n)}(a) + f^{(n+1)}(a + \theta h)\, \frac{h}{n+1}. \quad (271)$$

But, from the law of finite increments, applied to $f^{(n)}(x)$, we have:

$$f^{(n)}(a + \theta_n h) = f^{(n)}(a) + \theta_n h f^{(n+1)}(a + \theta_0 \theta_n h), \quad (272)$$

for a suitable choice of θ_0 between zero and one.

From the last two equations, we deduce that:

$$\theta_n = \frac{1}{n+1}\, \frac{f^{(n+1)}(a + \theta h)}{f^{(n+1)}(a + \theta_0 \theta_n h)}. \quad (273)$$

Finally, by taking the limit of this expression as h approaches zero, and recalling that $f^{(n+1)}(x)$ is continuous at a, while $f^{(n+1)}(a) \neq 0$, we deduce

$$\lim_{h \to 0+} \theta_n = \frac{1}{n+1}. \quad (274)$$

The same argument applies for negative values of h.

This proves the theorem, formulated with the n of the proof replaced by $n + 1$:

If the function $f(x)$ has an $(n + 2)$nd derivative, continuous and not zero at a, the θ in the remainder term of equation (268),

$$f^{(n+1)}(a + \theta h)\, \frac{h^{n+1}}{(n+1)\,!}, \quad \text{is such that} \quad \lim_{h \to 0} \theta = \frac{1}{n+2}. \quad (275)$$

91. Other Expressions for the Remainder. We may obtain the expression for the remainder term in Taylor's theorem given in equation (268), as well as some other expressions which are sometimes useful, by a shorter but less natural approach than that of section 89. As in that section, we assume that the function $f(x)$ has a finite $(n + 1)$st derivative throughout the closed interval $a \leq x \leq b$.

We next select some particular function $g(x)$, having a finite derivative $g'(x) \neq 0$ at all points of the open interval $0 < x < b - a$. The function $g(x)$ is to be continuous at the end points of the interval, 0 and $b - a$, and must have $g(0) = 0$.

The function $g(x)$ is otherwise arbitrary, and each choice of this function will lead to a special form for the remainder.

We note that we may apply the law of finite increments to $g(x)$ and so obtain:

$$g(b - a) = g(b - a) - g(0) = (b - a) g'(\xi) \neq 0. \qquad (276)$$

Since $g(b - a) \neq 0$, we may solve the equation:

$$f(b) = f(a) + f'(a) \frac{(b - a)}{1!} + f''(a) \frac{(b - a)^2}{2!} + \cdots$$
$$+ f^{(n)}(a) \frac{(b - a)^n}{n!} + Gg(b - a), \qquad (277)$$

for the value of G. Let G then be a constant, defined by this equation. Next define a function $F(x)$ by the equation:

$$F(x) = -f(b) + f(x) + f'(x) \frac{(b - x)}{1!} + f''(x) \frac{(b - x)^2}{2!} + \cdots$$
$$+ f^{(n)}(x) \frac{(b - x)^n}{n!} + Gg(b - x). \qquad (278)$$

While these definitions require no logical justification, the reader may find some motivation for them if he observes that, if the remainder term is expressed as a constant times $g(h)$, or $g(b - a)$, then the equation (277) follows, while the right member of equation (278) may be obtained from equation (277) by transposing the term $f(b)$ and then replacing a by x.

We now apply Rolle's theorem, section 73, to the function $F(x)$. The function $F(x)$ has a derivative for $a < x < b$, since $f(x)$ has an $(n + 1)$st derivative throughout this interval, while $g(b - x)$ has a first derivative in this interval. Also, our conditions on $f(x)$ and $g(x)$ make $F(x)$ continuous at the end points of this interval. Finally, $F(a) = 0$, by equation (277), while $F(b) = 0$, as we see from equation (278), if we recall that $g(0) = 0$. Thus, since all the conditions of Rolle's theorem are met, for some point between a and b,

$$F'(\xi) = 0. \qquad (279)$$

When we differentiate the right member of equation (278) most of the terms cancel in pairs, and we find:

$$F'(x) = f^{(n+1)}(x) \frac{(b - x)^n}{n!} - Gg'(b - x). \qquad (280)$$

But, since $F'(\xi) = 0$, we may deduce from this that:

$$G = \frac{(b - \xi)^n}{n!} \frac{f^{(n+1)}(\xi)}{g'(b - \xi)}, \qquad (281)$$

so that the remainder, $Gg(b - a)$, is given by

$$Gg(b - a) = \frac{(b - \xi)^n}{n!} f^{(n+1)}(\xi)\, \frac{g(b - a)}{g'(b - \xi)}. \tag{282}$$

If we put $b = a + h$, $\xi = a + \theta h$, and write

$$f(a + h) = P(h) + R(h), \tag{283}$$

we may express the remainder in terms of h:

$$R(h) = Gg(h) = \frac{h^n}{n!} (1 - \theta)^n f^{(n+1)}(a + \theta h) \frac{g(h)}{g'[(1 - \theta)h]}. \tag{284}$$

Since the equations (279) and (282) held for a suitable value of ξ, $a < \xi < b$, it follows that equation (284) will hold for a suitable value of θ with $0 < \theta < 1$.

If we now specialize the function $g(x)$ by putting $g(x) = x^p$, where p is any positive number, we find the expression:

$$R(h) = \frac{h^{n+1}}{pn!} (1 - \theta)^{n-p+1} f^{(n+1)}(a + \theta h), \tag{285}$$

a form due to Schloemilch.

If we further specialize this by putting $p = 1$, we obtain:

$$R(h) = \frac{h^{n+1}}{n!} (1 - \theta)^n f^{(n+1)}(a + \theta h), \tag{286}$$

or Cauchy's form of the remainder.

If we put $p = n + 1$ in equation (285), we find:

$$R(h) = \frac{h^{n+1}}{(n + 1)!} f^{(n+1)}(a + \theta h), \tag{287}$$

or Lagrange's form of the remainder, which we have already derived in section 89. This is generally the most useful form. However, in a few applications the Cauchy form is preferable.

92. Orders of Infinity. In section 81 we defined a series of infinitesimals of integral order with respect to a fundamental infinitesimal, h. In a similar way, we may select a particular quantity H which is becoming positively infinite, and refer other quantities becoming infinite to it. Thus H^n would be of the nth order, with respect to H.

As for infinitesimals, we say that K_1 and K_2 are of the same order of infinity if K_1/K_2 approaches a finite limit greater than zero. When $K_1/K_2 \to +\infty$, so that the limit of K_2/K_1 is zero, we say that K_1 is of a higher order of infinity than K_2, or that K_2 is a lower order of infinity than K_1. We may write in this case $K_2 = o(K_1)$, in accordance with the definition of equation (160). In this way we may indicate that a positive variable is becoming infinite by $1 = o(K)$.

We also use the notation of equation (169), defined by equation (170), for variables with any behavior. Thus $K_2 = O(K_1)$ if the order of infinity of K_1 is the same or higher than that of K_2.

The theory of quantities becoming positively infinite may be reduced to the theory of positive infinitesimals by putting $H = 1/h$, analogous to the use of equation (239) in section 86. This would lead us to think of positive orders of infinity being negative orders of infinitesimals, and conversely. However, it is better to have both points of view at our disposal.

The simplest quantities becoming infinite which are not comparable to powers of H, are exponentials. In fact, if we apply equation (268) with $a = 0$ and $h = x$ to $f(x) = e^x$, we find:

$$e^x = 1 + x + \frac{x^2}{2!} + \cdots + \frac{x^n}{n!} + \frac{x^{n+1}}{(n+1)!} e^{\theta x}. \tag{288}$$

If x is positive, all the terms of this expression are positive. Hence, for any integer n,

$$e^x > \frac{x^n}{n!}, \quad x > 0. \tag{289}$$

It follows that

$$\frac{1}{e^x} < \frac{n!}{x^n} \quad \text{and} \quad \frac{x^p}{e^x} < \frac{n!}{x^{n-p}}. \tag{290}$$

If we take $x = H$, a quantity becoming positively infinite, for any fixed number p we may take $n > p$ and deduce from this that:

$$\frac{H^p}{e^H} = o(1) \quad \text{or} \quad H^p = o(e^H), \tag{291}$$

which shows that e^H is a higher order of infinity than any (large) positive power of H.

If H is becoming positively infinite, $K = \log H$ also becomes positively infinite, as we showed in section 43, equation (48). However, $\log H$ is a lower order of infinity than H, or any (small) positive power of H. To see this, let q be any positive number and apply equation (291) with $p = 1/q$ to the variable K. Then:

$$\frac{K^{\frac{1}{q}}}{e^K} = o(1), \quad \text{and} \quad \frac{K}{e^{Kq}} = o(1), \tag{292}$$

since any positive power of an infinitesimal is an infinitesimal. Finally, put $K = \log H$ in the last relation, and so obtain:

$$\frac{\log H}{H^q} = o(1), \quad \text{or} \quad \log H = o(H^q). \tag{293}$$

By putting $H = 1/h$ in the equations (291) and (293) we find the corresponding relations for positive infinitesimals,

$$\left(\frac{1}{h}\right)^p e^{-\frac{1}{h}} = o(1), \quad \text{or} \quad e^{-\frac{1}{h}} = o(h^p), \quad \text{if} \quad h > 0, \tag{294}$$

and

$$\log\left(\frac{1}{h}\right) h^q = o(1), \quad \text{or} \quad h^q = o\left(\frac{1}{|\log h|}\right), \quad \text{if} \quad h > 0. \tag{295}$$

These relations may all be kept in mind by referring them to the following basic facts. If $H \to +\infty$, the exponential e^H is a higher order of infinity than the variable H, and the logarithm $\log H$ is a lower order of infinity than the variable H. Moreover, these relations are not disturbed by raising any of these quantities to positive powers, so that if p, q, and r are all positive, e^{pH} is of higher order than H^q, and H^q is of higher order than $(\log H)^r$. These principles often enable us to detect at once when certain combinations of simple functions become infinite or approach zero.

For example, $e^{ax}x^b (\log x)^c$, for $x \to +\infty$, becomes positively infinite if $a > 0$, and approaches 0 if $a < 0$, regardless of the values of b and c. If $a = 0$, the behavior depends on the sign of b, and if $a = b = 0$, on the sign of c. Similar remarks apply to $e^{a/x}x^b |\log x|^c$, for $x \to 0+$.

We may now appreciate to some extent the incompleteness of a scale of positive infinitesimals consisting only of positive powers of h, h^p. For an infinitesimal such as $|\log h|^q h^2$ is of higher order than any h^p with $p < 2$, and is of lower order than any h^p with $p \geqq 2$. If we admitted powers of $|\log h|$ such expressions as $\log |\log h| \, h^2$ would remain unclassified. This is why we defined only integral orders.

If P, Q, and R are any three polynomials, or other functions of x having the same order of infinity as some positive power of x, the behavior of $e^{aP}Q^b (\log R)^c$ as $x \to +\infty$ may be deduced from our basic principles.

The property of the exponential function expressed in equation (291) is not possessed by any function $y = f(x)$ which satisfies a polynomial relation $P(x,y) = 0$, that is by any *algebraic function*. For, let $x^p = o(y)$ as $x \to +\infty$ for all p and hence in particular for all the powers of x in the polynomial $P(x,y)$. Take $Ax^m y^n$ as the term in the polynomial such that $A \neq 0$: no higher power of y than y^n occurs, and no term in y^n with a higher power of x than x^m occurs. Then we may write:

$$P(x,y) = Ax^m y^n + o(x^m y^n). \tag{296}$$

This contradicts our assumption that when $y = f(x)$, $P(x,y) = 0$, since it makes $|P(x,y)| \to \infty$ as x, and hence $y \to +\infty$.

The considerations just mentioned prove that the exponential and logarithmic functions are not algebraic functions.

93. Finite Differences. If a function is tabulated for a series of values differing by the same positive quantity a, we may, by subtraction, form the first difference for any value of x used as an entry in the table; namely,

$$\Delta f(x) = f(x + a) - f(x). \tag{297}$$

The second difference is the first difference of the first difference; namely,

$$\Delta^2 f(x) = \Delta f(x + a) - \Delta f(x) = f(x + 2a) - 2f(x + a) + f(x). \tag{298}$$

The higher differences are defined by induction, the nth difference being the first difference of the $(n - 1)$st difference. The nth difference may be expressed directly in terms of the values of the function by a formula similar to equation (298) involving binomial coefficients. In fact, if A is a symbol of operation meaning that the argument is to be increased by a, then

$$\Delta f = (A - 1)f, \quad \text{and} \quad \Delta^n f = (A - 1)^n f, \tag{299}$$

and the formula in question may be obtained by expanding this by the binomial theorem and noting that A^m is the operator which means that the argument is to be increased by ma.

We shall prove that if the function $f(x)$ has an nth derivative throughout the open interval $x, x + na$, and the $(n - 1)$st derivative is continuous at the end points of this interval, then

$$\Delta^n f(x) = a^n f^{(n)}(x + \theta na), \tag{300}$$

where θ is a suitably chosen number between 0 and 1.

For n equal to 1, this is the law of finite increments. Thus we need merely prove that its truth for n follows from that for $1, 2, \cdots, n - 1$ to establish the result by mathematical induction.

But, if the nth and $(n - 1)$st derivatives of $f(x)$ satisfy the required conditions, the function:

$$\Delta f(x) = f(x + a) - f(x) \tag{301}$$

also does, so that, as a consequence, its $(n - 1)$st derivative exists in the open interval, and its $(n - 2)$nd derivative is continuous at the

end points. Hence, by the hypothesis of the induction, we may apply
the equation (300) to the function $\Delta f(x)$, with n replaced by $(n-1)$.
This gives

$$\Delta^n f(x) = a^{n-1} \{ f^{(n-1)}[x + a + \theta'(n-1)a] - f^{(n-1)}[x + \theta'(n-1)a] \}, \tag{302}$$

for a suitable value of θ' between 0 and 1.

The conditions on the derivatives of $f(x)$ show that the right member
of equation (302) has a first derivative in the open interval, and that the
function itself is continuous in the closed interval. Thus we may apply
the law of the mean to the difference in brackets to obtain the result:

$$a^n f^{(n)}[x + \theta''a + \theta'(n-1)a]. \tag{303}$$

Here θ'', like θ' is a suitably chosen number between 0 and 1. Consequently

$$\theta''a + \theta'(n-1)a = \theta na, \tag{304}$$

where θ is a suitably chosen number between 0 and 1.

By combining this equation with the expression (303), which was
obtained from $\Delta^n f(x)$, we find:

$$\Delta^n f(x) = a^n f^{(n)}(x + \theta na), \tag{305}$$

which is the result for n, and completes the proof by induction.

We note in particular that if the function $f(x)$ has an nth derivative
continuous in the closed interval, the conditions are satisfied, and equation (300) holds.

Next suppose that the function $f(x)$ has a finite nth derivative for a
particular value. Then, in some neighborhood of this value it has an
$(n-1)$st derivative, and hence a continuous $(n-2)$nd derivative.
Thus, for a sufficiently small value of a, we may deduce the equation
(302).

But, since the function $f(x)$ has an nth derivative at x, it follows that
$f^{(n-1)}(x)$ is differentiable at x, and we have:

$$f^{(n-1)}[x + a + \theta'(n-1)a] - f^{(n-1)}(x) =$$
$$[1 + \theta'(n-1)] a [f^{(n)}(x) + \alpha], \tag{306}$$

and

$$f^{(n-1)}[x + \theta'(n-1)a] - f^{(n-1)}(x) = \theta'(n-1)a [f^{(n)}(x) + \alpha'], \tag{307}$$

in which α and α' are infinitesimals, approaching zero with a.

It follows from these two equations, and equation (302), that

$$\Delta^n f(x) = a^n [f^{(n)}(x) + \beta], \tag{308}$$

where β is an infinitesimal.   If we put $a = \Delta x$, we may write

$$\lim_{\Delta x \to 0} \frac{\Delta^n f}{\Delta x^n} = f^{(n)}(x). \tag{309}$$

EXERCISES IV

1. Prove that the function defined by $f(x) = (x^2)^m \sin (x^{-2})^n$ if $x \neq 0$ and $f(0) = 0$ has a derivative for $x = 0$ if m exceeds $1/2$ and if n is positive.

2. Show that the derivative in problem 1 is continuous at 0 if $2m$ exceeds $2n + 1$.

3. If $f(x) = x \cot^{-1} x$ when $x \neq 0$, and $f(0) = 0$, find the right-hand derivative and the left-hand derivative for $x = 0$.   *Ans.* $\pi/2, -\pi/2$.

4. Find the right-hand and left-hand derivative at zero of the function $x/(1 + e^{1/x})$ with $f(0) = 0$.   *Ans.*   0,1.

5. Prove that, if $y = f(u)$ and $u = \cdot g(x)$ have derivatives for values of x near, but not equal to x_0, and values of u near, but not equal to $g(x_0)$, and $f'[g(x)]g'(x) \to L$ as $x \to x_0$, then $dy/dx = L$. An example is $y = u^m, u = x^n$ with m and n both positive and $mn = 1$, but one of them greater than $1, x_0 = 0$.

6. Prove that if all the elements of a determinant are differentiable functions of x, the derivative of the determinant is the sum of the n determinants obtained by replacing in succession each row (or each column) by the corresponding derivatives.

7. If $y_1, y_2, \cdots, y_n$ are n functions of x, the determinant

$$W = \begin{vmatrix} y_1, & y_2, & \cdots, & y_n \\ y'_1, & y'_2, & \cdots, & y'_n \\ \cdot & \cdot & & \cdot \\ \cdot & \cdot & & \cdot \\ \cdot & \cdot & & \cdot \\ y_1^{(n-1)}, & y_2^{(n-1)}, & \cdots, & y_n^{(n-1)} \end{vmatrix}$$

is called the Wronskian of the n functions.   Show that dW/dx may be obtained by replacing the elements of the last row, $y_k^{(n-1)}$ by $y_k^{(n)}$.   *Hint:* Use problem 6.

8. If the functions of problem 7 are each solutions of the linear differential equation

$$y^{(n)} = a_{n-1} y^{(n-1)} + \cdots + a_1 y' + a_0 y,$$

where the coefficients may be functions of x, prove that their Wronskian satisfies the differential equation $dW/dx = a_{n-1} W$.

9. If the Wronskian of two functions y_1 and y_2, $W = y_1 y'_2 - y_2 y'_1$ never vanishes, show that the zeros of y_1 separate those of y_2, in the sense that if $y_1(a) = y_1(b) = 0$, y_2 is not zero at a and b, and is zero at least once in the interval a,b.   *Hint:* Assume $y_2 \neq 0$ in the interval, and apply Rolle's theorem to y_1/y_2 to obtain a contradiction to the hypothesis $y_2 \neq 0$ for $a < x < b$.

10. Let $x(t)$ be the function defined in Exercises II, example 35.   Show that, for any t_0, if a_{2n-1} is replaced by a new digit differing from it by unity, to change t_0 to $t_0 + \Delta t$, with $\Delta t = \pm 1/3^{2n-1}$, then $|\Delta x/\Delta t| = 3^{n-1}$.   If, for t_0, a_{2n-2} is 0 or 2, and we replace it by 2 or 0, $\Delta x / \Delta t = 0$. If a_{2n-2} is 1, and $a_{2n} = 1$, and they are replaced by 0,0 or 2,2, $\Delta x / \Delta t$ will be zero if $a_{2n-1} = 1$, and otherwise will be $\pm 3^n / 5$. Combine these facts to show that for every t_0 of the interval 0,1 there are sequences of values of $\Delta_1 t$ approaching zero for which two of the three conditions $\Delta x / \Delta_1 t \rightarrow +\infty$, $\Delta x / \Delta_1 t \rightarrow -\infty$, or $\Delta x / \Delta_1 t \rightarrow 0$ can arise. This proves that the function has no finite or infinite derivative at any point of the interval, although it was proved continuous on this interval in the earlier problem. This example of a possibility first noted by Weierstrass is due to Peano.

11. If (x_0, y_0) is a point on the graph of $y = f(x)$, so that $y_0 = f(x_0)$, show that $y = y_0 + f'(x_0)(x - x_0)$ passes through the point x_0, y_0 and has the same derivative as $f(x)$ at that point, and that no other first degree expression in x has this property. It is the familiar tangent line.

12. Prove that, if dy is the differential, and Δy the increment corresponding to $dx = \Delta x$, then $\lim dy/\Delta y$ as $\Delta x \rightarrow 0$ is 1 if $dy/dx = f'(x) \neq 0$, but is 0 if $f'(x) = 0$.

13. Show that if x and y are the coördinates of a point on any second degree curve, or conic section, that $\dfrac{d^3}{dx^3}(y''^{-2/3}) = 0$. (Halphen) *Hint:* Find $y''^{-2/3}$ from $y = ax + b \pm \sqrt{cx^2 + dx + e}$.

14. If x and y are the coördinates of a point on any parabola, show that $\dfrac{d^2}{dx^2}(y''^{-2/3}) = 0$. (Halphen) *Hint:* Find $y''^{-2/3}$ from $y = ax + b \pm \sqrt{dx + e}$.

15. If the function y satisfies a differential equation $(ax^2 + bx + c)y'' + (dx + e)y' + fy = 0$, prove that each of the higher derivatives of y satisfies an equation of similar form. *Hint:* Use the rule of Leibniz to differentiate each part of the equation n times.

16. Prove that the higher derivatives of the function $x = f^{-1}(y)$ inverse to $y = f(x)$ may be found from

$$\frac{d^2 x}{dy^2} = \frac{-y''}{(y')^3} \quad \text{and} \quad \frac{d^3 x}{dy^3} = \frac{3(y'')^2 - y'''y'}{(y')^5}.$$

17. If $f(x)$ and $g(x)$ are differentiable in the closed interval a,b prove that, for a suitable intermediate value of x,

$$\frac{f'(x)}{g'(x)} = \frac{f(x) - f(a)}{g(b) - g(x)}.$$

Hint: Consider $f(x)g(x) - f(a)g(x) - g(b)f(x)$.

18. Use the derivatives to determine the increasing or decreasing character of the six hyperbolic functions, and in particular show that $\cosh 0 = 1$ is the only minimum, and $\operatorname{sech} 0 = 1$ the only maximum.

19. Show that the existence of a Taylor's development of higher order does not imply that any derivatives except the first exist, by considering $f(x) = 4 + x^2 + x^3 \sin(x^{-2})$ near 0.

20. If, as $x \rightarrow +\infty$, $f'(x) \rightarrow L$, then $f(x)/x \rightarrow L$. This also holds if L is replaced by $+\infty$, or $-\infty$. *Hint:* Use l'Hospital's rule.

21. If $f'(x) \rightarrow L$, $+\infty$ or $-\infty$, and $f(x) \rightarrow M$, as $x \rightarrow +\infty$, then $f'(x) \rightarrow 0$. *Hint:* Use problem 20.

22. If $f(x) + f'(x) \to L$ as $x \to +\infty$, then $f(x) \to L$. *Hint:* If $f'(x)$ ultimately preserves its sign, $f(x)$ ultimately is monotonic, and either becomes infinite or approaches a finite limit. In the first case $f'(x)$ becomes infinite with opposite sign, contrary to problem 20, and in the second $f'(x)$ approaches a limit, and we may apply problem 21. Otherwise there are maximum and minimum values, M_i and m_i, of $f(x)$ for arbitrarily large values of x_i, with $f'(x_i) = 0$. Hence $M_i \to L$, and $m_i \to L$, so that, since the other values of $f(x)$ are between the maximum and minimum, $f(x) \to L$.

23. If r_1 is an approximate value of one root of the equation $f(x) = 0$, where $f(x)$ has a continuous first derivative not zero in some interval including the root and r_1, a second approximation to the root may be obtained by *Newton's method.* If $r_1 + h$ is the root sought, then from

$$0 = f(r_1 + h) = f(r_1) + hf'(r_1 + \theta h), \quad h = \frac{-f(r_1)}{f'(r_1 + \theta h)},$$

and if we take $f'(r_1)$ as an approximation to $f'(r_1 + \theta h)$, the second approximation is given by $r_1 - f(r_1)/f'(r_1) = r_2$. The process may be repeated.

By applying the method to $f(x) = x^2 - a$, deduce the rule for improving the approximation to $\sqrt{a}$, by starting with r_1 and taking the average of r_1 and a/r_1 as the second approximation.

24. If the function $f(x)$ of problem 23 has higher derivatives, deduce from the Taylor's expansion of $f(r_1 + h)$ that $r_1 - f(r_1)/f'(r_1) - 1/2 \, [f(r_1)]^2 f''(r_1)/[f'(r_1)]^3$ differs from the root by a term $o(h^3)$. This may also be shown by writing $y = f(x)$ to define x in terms of y and expanding in a Taylor's series in powers of $y - h$, where $h = f(r_1)$. The derivatives are found from problem 16, and $y = 0$ gives the root sought.

25. If a is less than 0.1, the equation $\sin x = ax$ has a root near π. Show that $(1 - a)\pi$, and $(1 - a + a^2)\pi$ are improved approximations to this root.

26. Show that $e^x = 1 + x + x^2/2! + \cdots + x^n/n! + R_n$, where $|R_n| < |x|^{n+1}/(n + 1)!$ if $x < 0$, and $|R_n| < e^x x^{n+1}/(n + 1)!$ if $x > 0$. Hence show that $R_n \to 0$, if $n \to +\infty$.

27. Show that $\sin x = x - x^3/3! + \cdots + (-1)^{n+1} x^{2n-1}/(2n - 1)! + R_{2n}$, and $\cos x = 1 - x^2/2! + \cdots + (-1)^n x^{2n}/(2n)! + R_{2n+1}$, where for each $|R_m| \leq |x|^{m+1}/(m + 1)!$, so that $R_m \to 0$, as $m \to +\infty$.

28. Use the expansions of problem 27 to deduce that:

$$\tan x = x + \frac{1}{3}x^3 + \frac{2}{15}x^5 + O(x^7),$$

$$x \cot x = 1 - \frac{1}{3}x^2 - \frac{1}{45}x^4 + O(x^6),$$

and

$$x \csc x = 1 + \frac{1}{6}x^2 + \frac{7}{360}x^4 + O(x^6).$$

29. Prove the binomial theorem for all real m and all values of x with $|x| < 1$, namely,

$$(1 + x)^m = 1 + mx + \cdots + \frac{m(m - 1) \cdots (m - n + 1)}{n!} x^n + R_n,$$

with $R_n \to 0$ as $n \to +\infty$. *Hint:* Use the Cauchy form of the remainder to find
$R_n = \dfrac{m(m-1)\cdots(m-n)}{1\cdot 2\cdot\,\cdots\,\cdot n}\dfrac{(1-\theta)^n x^{n+1}}{(1+\theta x)^{n-m+1}}$, which may be written as the
product of a number of factors of the form $x(m-k)/k$, times a term independent of n, times $(1-\theta)^n/(1+\theta x)^n$. The last does not exceed unity, and the factors in numerical value approach $|x| < 1$, and so are ultimately less than $1 - \delta$, $\delta > 0$. Thus ultimately R_n is dominated by $K(1-\delta)^{n-n_0}$, which $\to 0$.

30. If we use equation (208) to deduce $f(x) = S_n(x) + R_n(x)$ from $f'(x) = S_n'(x) + R_n'(x)$, show that if as $n \to +\infty$, $R_n' \to 0$, for $|x| < a$, then $R_n \to 0$. *Hint:* Since $R_n(0) = 0$, $R_n(x) = R_n(x) - R_n(0) = xR_n'(\theta x)$.

31. Show that $\tan^{-1} x = x - x^3/3 + x^5/5 - \cdots + (-1)^{n+1}x^{2n-1}/(2n-1) + R_{2n}$, and $\sin^{-1} x = x + \dfrac{x^3}{2\cdot 3} + \cdots + \dfrac{1\cdot 3\cdot\,\cdots\,\cdot(2n-1)}{n!\,2^n(2n+1)}x^{2n+1} + R_{2n+2}$, where in each case, $R_m = O(x^{m+1})$, and, if $|x| < 1$, $R_m \to 0$ as $m \to +\infty$. *Hint:* Use problems 30 and 29.

32. Prove that $\pi/4 = \tan^{-1} 1 = 4\tan^{-1}(1/5) - \tan^{-1}(1/239)$. This may be combined with the first expansion of problem 31 to compute π conveniently.

33. Prove $\log(1+x) = x - x^2/2 + \cdots + (-1)^{n+1}x^n/n + R_n$, where $R_n = O(x^{n+1})$, and if $|x| < 1$, $R_n \to 0$ as $n \to +\infty$.

34. Show that, if $0 < x < 1$,

$$\log\left(\frac{1+x}{1-x}\right) = 2\left(x + \frac{x^3}{3} + \cdots + \frac{x^{2n-1}}{2n-1}\right) + R_{2n}, \quad \text{where}$$

$$|R_{2n}| < \frac{2x^{2n+1}}{(2n+1)(1-x)^{2n+1}}.$$

35. If in the preceding problem we put $x = 1/31,\ 1/49$ and $1/161$, we may compute the values of $P = \log 16/15$, $Q = \log 25/24$ and $R = \log 81/80$. Show that $\log 10 = (23P + 17Q + 10R)$. Such combinations are desirable to get the logarithms of small integers. After several of these are known, the difference between the logarithm of any integer sought, and of one known from its factors may be found directly from problem 34 with a small value of x.

36. Verify each of the following limits as $x \to 0$:

(a) $\lim \dfrac{a^x - b^x}{x} = \log\left(\dfrac{a}{b}\right)$; (b) $\lim \dfrac{x - \tan^{-1} x}{\sin^{-1} x - x} = 2$;

(c) $\lim \dfrac{\tan x - x}{x - \sin x} = 2$.

37. Show that, as $x \to 0$:

(a) $\dfrac{1}{x^2} - \cot^2 x \to \dfrac{2}{3}$, (b) $\dfrac{x\sin(\sin x) - \sin^2 x}{x^6} \to \dfrac{1}{18}$,

(c) $\dfrac{1 - \cos(1 - \cos x)}{x^4} \to \dfrac{1}{8}$.

38. Prove that when $x \to 0$,

(a) $|x|^x \to 1$, (b) $(\cos 2x)^{\csc^2 3x} \to e^{-\frac{2}{9}}$, (c) $\left(\dfrac{\sin x}{x}\right)^{\frac{1}{x^2}} \to e^{-\frac{1}{6}}$.

39. Verify that, as $|x| \to \infty$,

$$(a) \ (1 + x)^{\frac{1}{x}} \to 1, \quad (b) \ \left(\frac{2}{\pi} \tan^{-1} x\right)^x \to e^{-\frac{2}{\pi}},$$

$$(c) \ x \log\left(\frac{x - 2}{x + 2}\right) \to -4, \quad (d) \ \left|\frac{\pi}{2} - \tan^{-1} x\right|^{\frac{1}{x}} \to 1.$$

40. Prove that, if $f(x) \to 1$ and $g(x)[f(x) - 1] \to L$, then $f(x)^{g(x)} \to e^L$.

41. If $f(x) = e^{-1/x^2}$, $x \neq 0$, and $f(0) = 0$, show that $f(x)$ is continuous for $x = 0$, and has derivatives of all orders at $x = 0$, with $f^{(n)}(0) = 0$. Thus the Taylor's development to any order is zero, and $f(x) = o(x^n)$, for all n. Also, $f(x) = R_n(x)$, so that, in spite of its possessing continuous derivatives of all orders, we cannot compute the function from its Taylor's expansion.

42. Prove that $f(x)$ has a relative maximum at $x = a$ if $f'(a) = 0$ and $f''(a) < 0$. More generally, if $f'(a) = f''(a) = \cdots = f^{(m-1)}(a) = 0$, and $f^{(m)}(a) \neq 0$, $f(a)$ has a relative maximum if m is even and $f^{(m)}(a) < 0$, a relative minimum if m is even and $f^{(m)}(a) > 0$. If m is odd, there is neither a maximum nor a minimum. *Hint:* Use equation (187), noting that the conditions make $P(h) = f(a)$, if $n = m - 1$.

43. Assuming that the $(m + 1)$st derivative exists, deduce the rule of problem 42 from Taylor's development. If $A_m h^m$ is the first term with non-zero coefficient in any development of $f(a + h)$, we may infer the behavior at a from the parity of m and the sign of A_m. For example, from problem 37(b) we may deduce that $x \sin (\sin x) - \sin^2 x$ has a minimum at $x = 0$.

44. Use the test of section 76 to prove that the function of problem 41 has a minimum at 0. Note that the tests of problems 42 and 43 do not apply to this function.

45. Obtain the development:

$$(1 + x)^{\frac{1}{x}} = e\left[1 - \frac{x}{2} + \frac{11}{24} x^2 - \frac{21}{48} x^3 + O(x^4)\right].$$

Hint: Use $e^{[\log (1+x)]/x}$, and first develop the exponent. See problem 33 and section 83.

46. Prove that for $0 < x < \pi/2$,

$$\frac{2}{\pi} < \frac{\sin x}{x} < 1.$$

Hint: The derivative of $(\sin x)/x$ is $(x - \tan x)(\cos x)/x^2$. Since $\tan x > x$, this is negative and the function decreases for all x between 0 and $\pi/2$. Hence the values of the function lie between the limits approached as x approaches 0 and as x approaches $\pi/2$.

47. Prove that $a^x > x^a$ if $x > a \geq e$. *Hint:* The result follows from $x \log a > a \log x$, or $f(x) > 0$ if $f(x) = x \log a - a \log x$. But $f(a) = 0$, and $f'(x) = \log a - a/x > 0$, since $\log a \geq 1 > a/x$.

CHAPTER V

COMPLEX NUMBERS

The discussion of the elementary functions may be simplified by the introduction of complex numbers, even if the chief interest is in methods which lead to final results expressible in terms of real numbers. Therefore this chapter is devoted to the study of complex numbers.

We define such numbers and the four fundamental operations for them. We next enlarge the concepts of function, limit, and continuity so that they apply when the variables are complex, and we then define the basic elementary functions for complex values of the independent variable.

We prove the fundamental theorem of algebra and apply this to the decomposition of polynomials and rational functions.

94. Complex Numbers. A complex number is an expression of the form

$$a + bi, \tag{1}$$

where a and b are two real numbers, and i is the imaginary unit. Each distinct ordered pair of real numbers defines a different complex number. That is:

$$a + bi = a' + b'i \quad \text{implies} \quad a = a' \quad \text{and} \quad b = b'. \tag{2}$$

We include the real numbers by the convention that

$$a = a + 0i. \tag{3}$$

We also include i itself and its real multiples by putting:

$$i = 1i = 0 + 1i \quad \text{and} \quad bi = 0 + bi. \tag{4}$$

95. Operations on Complex Numbers. We define addition for complex numbers by the law:

$$(a + bi) + (a' + b'i) = (a + a') + (b + b')i, \tag{5}$$

and multiplication by the law:

$$(a + bi)(a' + b'i) = (aa' - bb') + (ab' + a'b)i. \tag{6}$$

The inverse operations of subtraction and division are defined by

$$(a + bi) - (a' + b'i) = (a - a') + (b - b')i, \tag{7}$$

and

$$\frac{a' + b'i}{a + bi} = \frac{aa' + bb'}{a^2 + b^2} + \frac{ab' - a'b}{a^2 + b^2} \, i. \tag{8}$$

These laws are easily remembered and practically applied by using the ordinary rules for real quantities, together with the special relation

$$i^2 = -1, \tag{9}$$

which follows from equations (4) and (6). The definitions given are consistent with the other laws of algebra, such as the commutative, associative, and distributive laws for multiplication and addition stated in section 2. In practice, we obtain the result of equation (8) by multiplying numerator and denominator by $a - bi$. Since the commutative law holds, it is immaterial whether we write $a + bi$ or $a + ib$.

96. Geometric Representation. We may match up the points in a plane with complex numbers by associating the point with Cartesian coördinates (x,y) with the complex number $x + iy$. It follows from equation (2) and the discussion of section 13 that there is one point for each complex number, and one complex number for each point. It is convenient to use a single letter z to denote the complex number $x + iy$, and to speak of the point z when referring to (x,y).

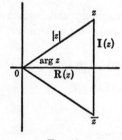

Fig. 12.

Each point (x,y) determines a vector drawn from the origin to the point, whose components are x and y. We may regard this vector, or any other vector with the same components, as a geometric representation of the complex number z. Thus, if (p,q) is any point, the vector from it to $(p + x, q + y)$ represents z. We refer to any such vector as a vector z. This leads us to denote the relation of x and y to z by calling x the real component of z, and y the imaginary component of z. We write:

$$x = \mathbf{R}(z) \text{ and } y = \mathbf{I}\,(z) \quad \text{when} \quad z = x + iy = \mathbf{R}(z) + i\mathbf{I}\,(z). \tag{10}$$

The vector representing the sum of two complex numbers $z_1 + z_2$ may be obtained by adding the vectors z_1 and z_2 in accordance with the parallelogram law.

The geometric interpretation of the product of two complex numbers $z_1 z_2$ is simplified if we introduce the polar coördinates of the points $z_1 = (x_1,y_1)$ and $z_2 = (x_2,y_2)$ as defined in section 61. We have:

$$z_1 = r_1 \, (\cos \theta_1 + i \sin \theta_1) \quad \text{and} \quad z_2 = r_2 \, (\cos \theta_2 + i \sin \theta_2). \tag{11}$$

The product of the factors involving θ_1 and θ_2 is:

$$(\cos \theta_1 \cos \theta_2 - \sin \theta_1 \sin \theta_2) + i (\sin \theta_1 \cos \theta_2 + \cos \theta_1 \sin \theta_2)$$
$$= \cos (\theta_1 + \theta_2) + i \sin (\theta_1 + \theta_2), \quad (12)$$

in view of the addition theorems for the sine and cosine. Thus

$$z_1 z_2 = r_1 r_2 [\cos (\theta_1 + \theta_2) + i \sin (\theta_1 + \theta_2)], \quad (13)$$

so that

$$r = r_1 r_2 \quad \text{and} \quad \theta = \theta_1 + \theta_2 \quad (14)$$

give a possible choice of polar coördinates for $z = z_1 z_2$. If we plot the origin $0 = (0,0)$ and the unit point $1 = (1,0)$, and construct the triangle with vertices 0, 1, z_1 and that with vertices 0, z_2, z, we may show from equation (14) that these triangles are similar since they have two sides proportional and the included angles equal. A geometric construction for the point or vector representing the product $z = z_1 z_2$ may be deduced from this fact.

Whenever

$$z = r (\cos \theta + i \sin \theta), \quad (15)$$

so that r and θ are polar coördinates of the point z, we call r the *absolute value* or modulus of z, and θ the *argument* or amplitude. We write:

$$r = |z| \quad \text{and} \quad \theta = \arg z. \quad (16)$$

The notation $|z|$ is consistent with $|x|$ to denote the numerical value of a real number x, since

$$|z| = \sqrt{x^2 + y^2} \quad (17)$$

reduces to $\sqrt{x^2}$, or the numerical value of x, when $y = 0$ and z is the real number x.

We recall from section 61 that $|z|$ is uniquely determined by equation (17), and that if $z \neq 0$, $\arg z$ is determined to within an integral multiple of 2π. If $z = 0$, $\arg z$ may have any value.

It follows from equation (13) that

$$|z_1 z_2| = |z_1| |z_2|. \quad (18)$$

This shows that a product can not be zero unless one of the factors is zero.

97. Conjugate Complex Numbers. If $z = x + iy$, the complex number

$$\bar{z} = x - iy, \quad (19)$$

is called the conjugate complex number to z. We note that z is the conjugate of $\bar{z}$, so that the relationship of a number to its conjugate is reciprocal. We note that

$$R(\bar{z}) = R(z) \quad \text{and} \quad I(\bar{z}) = -I(z). \tag{20}$$

Also $\qquad\qquad |z| = |\bar{z}|, \quad \text{and} \quad |z| = \sqrt{z\bar{z}}, \tag{21}$

while $-\arg z$ is a possible value of $\arg \bar{z}$. Geometrically the point $\bar{z}$ is the reflection of the point z in the x, or real axis. That is, the point $\bar{z}$ is so situated that the axis is the perpendicular bisector of the line joining the two points z and $\bar{z}$.

Suppose we start with two complex numbers z and z', and combine them by any one of the four fundamental operations to obtain a new complex number w. If we now start with the conjugates of these numbers, $\bar{z}$ and $\bar{z}'$, and use the same operation, we shall obtain as a result the number $\bar{w}$, conjugate to w. This follows from the rules given in section 95, and may be checked by the geometric interpretation.

We note that the sum and product of two conjugate complex numbers are both real numbers.

98. Inequalities for Absolute Values. We shall prove that:

The absolute value of the sum of two complex numbers is less than or equal to the sum of their absolute values.

If $z_1 = x_1 + iy_1$ and $z_2 = x_2 + iy_2$, we have:

$$|z_1| = \sqrt{x_1^2 + y_1^2}, \quad |z_2| = \sqrt{x_2^2 + y_2^2} \tag{22}$$

and $\qquad\qquad |z_1 + z_2|^2 = (x_1 + x_2)^2 + (y_1 + y_2)^2. \tag{23}$

Consequently,

$$[|z_1| + |z_2|]^2 - |z_1 + z_2|^2 =$$
$$2\sqrt{x_1^2 + y_1^2}\sqrt{x_2^2 + y_2^2} - 2x_1x_2 - 2y_1y_2. \tag{24}$$

This will be greater than or equal to zero if

$$\sqrt{x_1^2 + y_1^2}\sqrt{x_2^2 + y_2^2} \geqq x_1x_2 + y_1y_2, \tag{25}$$

or since the left member is positive or zero, if

$$x_1^2x_2^2 + x_1^2y_2^2 + y_1^2x_2^2 + y_1^2y_2^2 \geqq x_1^2x_2^2 + 2x_1x_2y_1y_2 + y_1^2y_2^2,$$

which may be written

$$(x_1y_2 - y_1x_2)^2 \geqq 0. \tag{26}$$

Since the left member is the square of a real number, this last inequality always holds, and this proves that

$$[|z_1| + |z_2|]^2 \geqq |z_1 + z_2|^2, \tag{27}$$

or

$$|z_1| + |z_2| \geqq |z_1 + z_2|, \tag{28}$$

since both members of this inequality are non-negative. This proves the theorem.

From the form of relation (26), we see that the equality can only occur if

$$x_1 y_2 - y_1 x_2 = \begin{vmatrix} x_1 & x_2 \\ y_1 & y_2 \end{vmatrix} = 0. \tag{29}$$

This is the condition that the numbers x_1, y_1 are proportional to the numbers x_2, y_2 since it implies either

$$x_1 = 0, \ y_1 = 0; \ x_2 = 0, \ y_2 = 0; \ y_1 = 0, \ y_2 = 0 \ \text{ or } \ \frac{x_1}{y_1} = \frac{x_2}{y_2}. \tag{30}$$

In the geometric representation, the sides of the triangle with vertices at 0, z_1 and $z_1 + z_2$ may be considered as vectors representing z_1, z_2 and $z_1 + z_2$. The corresponding absolute values are the lengths of the sides of the triangle, and the relation (28) states that two sides have a sum greater than the third side. The equality may occur if the triangle degenerates to one with all three vertices

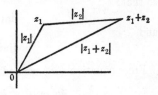

FIG. 13.

in the same line, or with zero area, in which case equation (29) holds.

The relation

$$|z_1 - z_2| \geqq ||z_1| - |z_2|| \tag{31}$$

follows from

$$|z_1 - z_2| + |z_2| \geqq |z_1|, \tag{32}$$

if $|z_1| \geqq |z_2|$, and from this by interchanging z_1 and z_2 if $|z_1| < |z_2|$. Here, again, we can only have the equality if the points representing 0, z_1, and z_2 are collinear.

By mathematical induction based on the relation (28), we may prove that for any integer n,

$$\sum_{k=1}^{n} |z_k| \geqq \left| \sum_{k=1}^{n} z_k \right|, \tag{33}$$

with strict inequality unless the points representing z_k and the origin are collinear. The relation (33) corresponds to the geometric fact that a straight line segment joining two points is shorter than a broken line joining the same two points.

99. Limits. If x_t and y_t are real variables approaching limits in the sense of section 17, we say that the complex variable $z_t = x_t + iy_t$ approaches $(\lim x_t) + i (\lim y_t)$ as a limit. That is:

For a complex variable, $z_t = x_t + iy_t$ whose values are determined by a continuous or discrete sequence of real numbers t, we define:

$$\lim z_t = Z = X + iY, \tag{34}$$

if, and only if,

$$\lim x_t = X \quad and \quad \lim y_t = Y. \tag{35}$$

These relations imply that:

$$\lim (X - x_t) = 0 \quad and \quad \lim (Y - y_t) = 0. \tag{36}$$

But,

$$Z - z_t = (X - x_t) + i(Y - y_t) \tag{37}$$

and

$$|Z - z_t| = \sqrt{(X - x_t)^2 + (Y - y_t)^2}, \tag{38}$$

so that:

$$\lim (Z - z_t) = 0, \tag{39}$$

and

$$\lim |Z - z_t| = 0. \tag{40}$$

From equation (38) we deduce that:

$$0 \leqq |X - x_t| \leqq |Z - z_t| \quad and \quad 0 \leqq |Y - y_t| \leqq |Z - z_t|. \tag{41}$$

From these relations we see that the equation (40) implies equation (36) and hence equation (35) and (34). That is:

A necessary and sufficient condition for the complex variable z_t to approach Z as a limit is that $\lim |Z - z_t| = 0$.

This reduces the problem of determining whether a complex variable depending on a real variable approaches a limit to that of determining whether a real variable approaches zero. Since $|Z - z_t|$ is the distance between the fixed point Z and the variable point z_t, the condition has a simple geometric meaning.

The Cauchy convergence criterion of section 26 applies to complex variables. We shall prove that:

A necessary and sufficient condition for z_t to approach a limit is that for any positive quantity ϵ, there is some point in the sequence of values of t, t_ϵ such that the absolute value of the difference of any two values of z_t, each with t beyond t_ϵ, is less than ϵ.

We first note that if $z_1 = x_1 + iy_1$ and $z_2 = x_2 + iy_2$ are any two complex numbers, we have:

$$0 \leqq |x_2 - x_1| \leqq |z_2 - z_1| \quad and \quad 0 \leqq |y_2 - y_1| \leqq |z_2 - z_1|, \tag{42}$$

analogous to the relation (41). Consequently,

if $|z_2 - z_1| < \epsilon$,

$$|x_2 - x_1| < \epsilon \quad \text{and} \quad |y_2 - y_1| < \epsilon. \tag{43}$$

Thus, if the condition of the theorem is satisfied, for $z_t = x_t + iy_t$, by the Cauchy convergence criterion for the real sequences x_t and y_t, we see that they each approach limits. Thus, by our first definition, z_t approaches a limit, and the sufficiency of the condition is proved.

Conversely, if z_t approaches a limit Z, equation (40) holds, so that for any arbitrary positive quantity,

$$|Z - z_t| < \frac{\epsilon}{2}, \quad \text{for} \quad t \text{ beyond } t_\epsilon. \tag{44}$$

Thus, if z' and z'' are any two values of z_t with t beyond t_ϵ,

$$|Z - z'| < \frac{\epsilon}{2} \quad \text{and} \quad |Z - z''| < \frac{\epsilon}{2}, \tag{45}$$

so that

$$|z' - z''| = |(z' - Z) + (Z - z'')| < \epsilon. \tag{46}$$

This proves that the condition is also necessary, and proves the theorem.

With only slight modifications the reasoning of section 19 applies to complex limits. Hence we may use the results of that section to determine the behavior of the sum, difference, product, and quotient of two complex variables.

100. Infinity. For a complex variable z_t, we write

$$\lim z_t = \infty, \tag{47}$$

to mean

$$\lim |z_t| = \infty. \tag{48}$$

It follows that:

$$\lim z_t = \infty \quad \text{if, and only if,} \quad \lim \frac{1}{z_t} = 0. \tag{49}$$

When dealing with a variable a_t restricted to real values, we shall generally continue to use the more explicit notation $\lim |a_t| = \infty$, since for real variables the distinction between $\lim a_t = +\infty$ and $\lim a_t = -\infty$ is important.

For complex variables, we generally reduce the study of a variable becoming infinite to the study of a variable approaching zero, by using equation (49).

101. Functions. If $z = x + iy$ and $w = u + iv$ are two variable complex numbers, there may be a relation between them. As for real numbers, we say that w is a function of z for a set of values if for each value of z in a certain range one or more values of w are determined. We write

$$w = f(z) \tag{50}$$

to indicate this.

Since x and y determine z, which in turn determines w, and hence u and v, we see that u and v are each functions of x and y, so that:

$$w = u(x,y) + iv(x,y), \tag{51}$$

and a single function of a complex variable determines two real functions of two real variables. Conversely, any two functions of x and y may be used in place of u and v to determine w as a function of z.

For the present we shall be interested in a very restricted class of functions of a complex variable, those which correspond to the elementary functions defined in section 69.

The range of z will usually be some two-dimensional open region as defined in section 15, or the corresponding closed region obtained from it by adding the boundary points as in section 35. If the functions $u(x,y)$ and $v(x,y)$ are each single-valued in the range, there will be just one value of w for each value of z, and we say that w is a single-valued function of z.

102. Continuity. Let $w = f(z)$ be a single-valued function of the complex variable $z = x + iy$ for values of (x,y) in some two-dimensional region. If z' is any interior point of this region, we say that:

The function $f(z)$ is continuous at z' if

$$\lim f(z_t) = f(z') \tag{52}$$

for every sequence z_t such that $z_t \rightarrow z'$.

This is analogous to the first definition of section 35 if we restrict ourselves to discrete sequences. By reasoning as in that section, we may show that if the property holds for discrete sequences, it holds for all sequences, and that the definition is equivalent to:

The function $f(z)$ is continuous at z' if, for every positive number ϵ there is a corresponding positive number δ_ϵ such that

$$|f(z) - f(z')| < \epsilon, \quad if \quad |z - z'| < \delta_\epsilon. \tag{53}$$

If we write $z' = x' + iy'$, and $z_t = x_t + iy_t$, it follows from the definition of section 99 that $\lim z_t = z'$ if, and only if, $\lim x_t = x'$ and $\lim y_t = y'$. Also $\lim f(z_t) = f(z')$ if, and only if, $\lim u(x_t,y_t) = u(x',y')$ and $\lim v(x_t,y_t) = v(x',y')$, where $f(z) = u(x,y) + iv(x,y)$. In view of these facts, a comparison of the first definition of this section with the first definition of section 35 shows that:

The function $f(z)$ of the complex variable $z = x + iy$ is continuous at $z' = x' + iy'$ if, and only if, the two real functions $u(x,y)$ and $v(x,y)$ such that $w(x + iy) = u(x,y) + iv(x,y)$ are each continuous at (x',y').

103. The Exponential Function. Since the properties

$$E(z)E(z') = E(z + z'), \tag{54}$$

and

$$\lim_{z \to 0} \frac{E(z) - 1}{z} = 1, \tag{55}$$

completely characterize the function $E(z)$ as the exponential function when z is restricted to real values, as we saw in section 51, it is natural to extend the definition to complex values by attempting to satisfy these relations for complex values of z. We shall see that this is possible and may be done in only one way.

Let us first suppose that there is a function satisfying these relations, and let us determine its properties on this assumption.

If $z = x + iy$, where x and y are real, we have from equation (54),

$$E(x + iy) = E(x)E(iy). \tag{56}$$

But, if we put $z = x$ in equations (54) and (55) they reduce to the equations (130) and (131) of section 51. This shows that we must have

$$E(x) = e^x. \tag{57}$$

The equations (54) and (55) are then satisfied, since

$$e^x e^{x'} = e^{x+x'}, \tag{58}$$

and

$$\lim_{x \to 0} \frac{e^x - 1}{x} = 1. \tag{59}$$

For any particular value of y, $E(iy)$ is a complex number which may be expressed in terms of two real numbers:

$$E(iy) = C(y) + iS(y), \tag{60}$$

so that the real and imaginary components of $E(iy)$ are each real functions of the real variable y.

If we put $z = iy$, $z' = iy'$ in equation (54), we have:

$$E(iy)E(iy') = E[i(y + y')], \tag{61}$$

or,

$$[C(y) + iS(y)][C(y') + iS(y')] = C(y + y') + iS(y + y'). \tag{62}$$

This is equivalent to

$$C(y + y') = C(y)C(y') - S(y)S(y'), \tag{63}$$

$$S(y + y') = S(y)C(y') + C(y)S(y'), \tag{64}$$

in view of equations (6) and (2).

For $z = iy$, the condition (55) becomes:

$$\lim_{iy \to 0} \frac{E(iy) - 1}{iy} = 1, \tag{65}$$

or, if we use equation (60),

$$\lim_{y \to 0} \frac{C(y) + iS(y) - 1}{iy} = 1. \tag{66}$$

But, by equation (35), this is equivalent to:

$$\lim_{y \to 0} \frac{S(y)}{y} = 1, \tag{67}$$

and

$$\lim_{y \to 0} \frac{C(y) - 1}{y} = 0. \tag{68}$$

From equation (63) we may deduce that

$$\frac{C(y + h) - C(y)}{h} = C(y) \frac{C(h) - 1}{h} - S(y) \frac{S(h)}{h}. \tag{69}$$

Again, from equation (64) we may deduce that

$$\frac{S(y + h) - S(y)}{h} = S(y) \frac{C(h) - 1}{h} + C(y) \frac{S(h)}{h}. \tag{70}$$

Since h only appears in these two equations in expressions similar to those in equations (67) and (68), the right members of these two equations will approach limits as $h \to 0$. Hence the left members will approach limits, and the functions $C(y)$ and $S(y)$ have derivatives for all values of y, given by:

$$\frac{d}{dy} C(y) = -S(y) \quad \text{and} \quad \frac{d}{dy} S(y) = C(y). \tag{71}$$

Now consider the function

$$F(y) = C^2(y) + S^2(y). \tag{72}$$

By using equation (71), we find that

$$\frac{d}{dy} F(y) = 2C(y)[-S(y)] + 2S(y)C(y) = 0, \tag{73}$$

so that by a theorem proved in section 75, the function $F(y)$ is a constant. But equations (67) and (68) show that $S(y) \to 0$ and $C(y) \to 1$ as $y \to 0$. Thus the right member of equation (72) approaches 1, and the value of the constant is 1. Hence:

$$C^2(y) + S^2(y) = 1. \tag{74}$$

Since the equations (64), (63), (74) and (67) only differ from equations (224), (225), (226) and (227) of section 57 in having x replaced by y, it follows from the theorem of that section that

$$C(y) = \cos y \quad \text{and} \quad S(y) = \sin y. \tag{75}$$

These functions satisfy equations (63) and (64), which are equivalent to equation (61) if equation (60) holds. Hence if we define

$$e^{iy} = \cos y + i \sin y, \tag{76}$$

we have:

$$e^{iy}e^{iy'} = e^{i(y+y')}. \tag{77}$$

We note that for any function $f(y)$ having a derivative for $y = 0$,

$$\lim_{y \to 0} \frac{f(y) - f(0)}{y} = f'(0). \tag{78}$$

In particular, for the sine and cosine this becomes:

$$\lim_{y \to 0} \frac{\sin y}{y} = 1 \quad \text{and} \quad \lim_{y \to 0} \frac{\cos y - 1}{y} = 0. \tag{79}$$

It follows that the functions as defined by equation (75) satisfy the equations (67) and (68), which together are equivalent to equation (65) if equation (60) holds. Thus we have for the function defined by equation (76):

$$\lim_{iy \to 0} \frac{e^{iy} - 1}{iy} = 1, \quad \text{or} \quad \lim_{y \to 0} \frac{e^{iy} - 1}{y} = i. \tag{80}$$

In accordance with equation (56) we now define

$$e^z = e^{x+iy} = e^x e^{iy} = e^x (\cos y + i \sin y). \tag{81}$$

Its continuity for all values of z follows from the continuity of its real and imaginary components by section 102.

The preceding argument has shown that no other function of z can satisfy the two conditions (54) and (55). We must next investigate whether the function given by equation (81) itself satisfies these conditions. We have:

$$e^z e^{z'} = e^x e^{iy} e^{x'} e^{iy'} = e^{x+x'} e^{i(y+y')} = e^{z+z'}, \tag{82}$$

as a consequence of equations (58) and (77). Thus the first condition is satisfied.

The second condition is satisfied when z is restricted to real values, in view of equation (59). In consequence of this and the fundamental definition of a limit, we may write

$$e^x = 1 + x + hx, \text{ where } |h| < \epsilon, \text{ if } |x| < \delta_1. \tag{83}$$

Similarly, the condition is satisfied when z is restricted to real multiples of i, in view of equation (80). From this and the property of a complex limit expressed in equation (40), we may write

$$e^{iy} = 1 + iy + ky, \text{ where } |k| < \epsilon, \text{ if } |y| < \delta_2. \tag{84}$$

We may deduce from the last two equations that:

$$e^z - 1 = e^x e^{iy} - 1 = x + iy + hx + ky + (i + hi + k + hk)xy. \tag{85}$$

Let us now take $0 < \epsilon < 1$, determine δ_1 and δ_2, and then take

$$0 < |z| < \delta, \text{ where } \delta < \min(\epsilon, \delta_1, \delta_2), \tag{86}$$

the minimum of the three numbers. Then, since

$$|x| \leqq |z| \quad \text{and} \quad |y| \leqq |z|, \tag{87}$$

for any complex number $z = x + iy$, we have:

$$|h| < \epsilon, |k| < \epsilon \text{ and } |i + hi + k + hk| < 4, \tag{88}$$

so that

$$|hx + ky + (i + hi + k + hk)xy| < \epsilon|z| + \epsilon|z| + 4\epsilon|z| \leqq 6\epsilon|z|. \tag{89}$$

It follows from this relation and equation (85) that

$$\left|\frac{e^z - 1}{z} - 1\right| < 6\epsilon, \text{ if } 0 < |z| < \delta. \tag{90}$$

Since ϵ is an arbitrary positive number less than unity, 6ϵ may be made arbitrarily small, and this equation is the condition that

$$\lim_{z \to 0} \left|\frac{e^z - 1}{z} - 1\right| = 0, \quad \text{or} \quad \lim_{z \to 0} \frac{e^z - 1}{z} = 1. \tag{91}$$

Thus the second condition is satisfied, and we have proved that:

The function of the complex number $z = x + iy$,

$$e^z = e^{x+iy} = e^x (\cos y + i \sin y), \tag{92}$$

has the property:

$$e^z e^{z'} = e^{z+z'}, \tag{93}$$

for all complex values of z and z′, and the special property

$$\lim_{z \to 0} \frac{e^z - 1}{z} = 1. \tag{94}$$

These two properties uniquely characterize the function.

104. The Trigonometric Functions, sin z and cos z. The properties

$$S(z + z') = S(z)C(z') + C(z)S(z'), \tag{95}$$

$$C(z + z') = C(z)C(z') - S(z)S(z'), \tag{96}$$

$$C^2(z) + S^2(z) = 1, \tag{97}$$

and

$$\lim_{z \to 0} \frac{S(z)}{z} = 1 \tag{98}$$

completely characterize the functions $S(x)$ and $C(x)$ when z is restricted to real values, x.   In fact, we showed in section 57 that these properties hold if and only if

$$S(x) = \sin x \quad \text{and} \quad C(x) = \cos x. \tag{99}$$

We shall accordingly use these properties to extend the definition of the trigonometric functions to complex values.

If the four fundamental equations hold for all complex values of z, they hold, in particular, for all real values.   For these values equation (99) holds, and hence

$$S(0) = 0 \quad \text{and} \quad C(0) = 1. \tag{100}$$

It follows from equation (98) that

$$\lim_{z \to 0} S(z) = 0. \tag{101}$$

Thus the function $S(z)$ is a continuous function of the complex variable z, at $z = 0$.

Since the equations (96) and (97) imply that

$$C(2z) = 1 - 2S^2(z), \tag{102}$$

it follows that the function $C(z)$ is a continuous function of the complex variable z, at $z = 0$.   Hence,

$$\lim_{z \to 0} [C(z) + 1] = C(0) + 1 = 2,$$

and from equations (97) and (98) we may conclude that:

$$\lim_{z \to 0} \frac{C(z) - 1}{z} = \lim_{z \to 0} \frac{-S(z)}{C(z) + 1} \frac{S(z)}{z} = 0. \tag{103}$$

The similarity in form of our equations with those used in the last section to determine $E(iy)$ suggests that we introduce a function $E(iz)$, defined by the equation:

$$E(iz) = C(z) + iS(z). \tag{104}$$

Then, since

$$[C(z) + iS(z)][C(z') + iS(z')] = C(z + z') + iS(z + z') \tag{105}$$

is a consequence of equations (95) and (96), we have

$$E(iz)E(iz') = E[i(z + z')]. \tag{106}$$

We also note from equation (104) that:

$$\frac{E(iz) - 1}{iz} = \frac{1}{i}\frac{C(z) - 1}{z} + \frac{S(z)}{z}. \tag{107}$$

It follows from this, equation (98) and equation (103) that:

$$\lim_{z \to 0} \frac{E(iz) - 1}{iz} = 1. \tag{108}$$

If we write

$$z = -iw, \quad w = iz, \tag{109}$$

the function $E(w)$ is defined for all complex values of w by equations (109) and (104). In terms of w, equation (106) is

$$E(w)E(w') = E(w + w'). \tag{110}$$

Also, since $z \to 0$ when $w \to 0$, equation (108) may be written:

$$\lim_{w \to 0} \frac{E(w) - 1}{w} = 1. \tag{111}$$

As these equations are identical in form with equations (54) and (55) of the last section, it follows that they will be satisfied if, and only if:

$$E(w) = e^w, \tag{112}$$

and

$$C(z) + iS(z) = E(iz) = e^{iz}. \tag{113}$$

This equation does not immediately determine $C(z)$ and $S(z)$, since they are not necessarily the real and imaginary components of the complex number on the right when z is not a real number.

However, we have:

$$e^{-iz} = \frac{1}{e^{iz}} = \frac{1}{C(z) + iS(z)} = \frac{C(z) - iS(z)}{C^2(z) + S^2(z)}. \tag{114}$$

It follows from this and equation (97) that:

$$C(z) - iS(z) = e^{-iz}. \tag{115}$$

We may now conclude from equations (113) and (115) that:

$$C(z) = \frac{e^{iz} + e^{-iz}}{2} \quad \text{and} \quad S(z) = \frac{e^{iz} - e^{-iz}}{2i} \cdot \tag{116}$$

It is a direct algebraic consequence of the fundamental property of the exponential function expressed in equation (93) that the functions defined by equation (116) satisfy the relations (95), (96), and (97), if, for the last, we recall that $e^0 = 1$. That these functions satisfy the fourth condition, equation (98), is a consequence of the second property of the exponential function given in equation (94).

We use the equations (116) as the definition of cos z and sin z for complex values of the variable. If we put:

$$z = x + iy, \quad iz = -y + ix, \quad -iz = y - ix, \tag{117}$$

we have from equation (92):

$$e^{iz} = e^{-y} (\cos x + i \sin x), \; e^{-iz} = e^{y} (\cos x - i \sin x). \tag{118}$$

These equations enable us to define sin z and cos z directly in terms of trigonometric functions of x and hyperbolic functions of y, as defined in section 68. We have:

$$\sin z = \frac{e^{iz} - e^{-iz}}{2i} = \sin x \cosh y + i \cos x \sinh y. \tag{119}$$

$$\cos z = \frac{e^{iz} + e^{-iz}}{2} = \cos x \cosh y - i \sin x \sinh y. \tag{120}$$

The discussion of this section has proved that:

The functions of the complex number $z = x + iy$ defined by equations (119) and (120) have the properties:

$$\sin (z + z') = \sin z \cos z' + \cos z \sin z', \tag{121}$$

$$\cos (z + z') = \cos z \cos z' - \sin z \sin z', \tag{122}$$

$$\cos^2 z + \sin^2 z = 1, \tag{123}$$

for all complex values of z, and also have the special property:

$$\lim_{z \to 0} \frac{\sin z}{z} = 1. \tag{124}$$

These four properties uniquely characterize the functions.

105. Properties of the Trigonometric Functions. All the identities involving the functions $\sin z$ and $\cos z$ derivable as consequences of the equations (121), (122), and (123), mentioned in section 58 for real values of the variable, hold when z is complex, since the algebraic processes by which they were proved for real values are still valid.

However, a direct proof of any such identity for complex values of z is always possible by using the formulas

$$\sin z = \frac{e^{iz} - e^{-iz}}{2i} \quad \text{and} \quad \cos z = \frac{e^{iz} + e^{-iz}}{2} \tag{125}$$

to reduce the trigonometric identity to an identity involving exponentials which is an algebraic consequence of equation (93). Such a proof is often simpler than a proof involving real quantities only.

It is often convenient to use also the formulas

$$e^{iz} = \cos z + i \sin z \quad \text{and} \quad e^{-iz} = \cos z - i \sin z. \tag{126}$$

For example, from

$$\sin nz = \frac{e^{inz} - e^{-inz}}{2i} = \frac{(\cos z + i \sin z)^n - (\cos z - i \sin z)^n}{2i} \tag{127}$$

we easily derive a formula expressing $\sin nz$ as a polynomial in $\sin z$ and $\cos z$, with real coefficients. Similarly, any polynomial involving sines and cosines of multiples of z may be expressed as a polynomial in $\sin z$ and $\cos z$.

Conversely, from

$$\sin^n z \cos^m z = \left(\frac{e^{iz} - e^{-iz}}{2i}\right)^n \left(\frac{e^{iz} + e^{-iz}}{2}\right)^m$$

$$= \sum_{k=-m-n}^{m+n} A_k e^{kiz} = \sum_{k=0}^{m+n} (a_k \cos kz + b_k \sin kz), \tag{128}$$

we may express any polynomial in $\sin z$ and $\cos z$ as a linear combination of sines and cosines of multiples of z. The final coefficients a_k and b_k will be real. For the values of the expressions in parentheses are unchanged if we replace i by $-i$, which shows that A_{-k} must be the complex number conjugate to A_k. Thus, if the original polynomial has real coefficients, the coefficients in the linear combination will also be real.

As in the case of real quantities, the remaining four trigonometric functions are defined by the equations:

$$\tan z = \frac{\sin z}{\cos z}, \quad \cot z = \frac{\cos z}{\sin z}, \tag{129}$$

$$\sec z = \frac{1}{\cos z}, \quad \csc z = \frac{1}{\sin z}. \tag{130}$$

Thus their properties may be deduced from those of the sine and cosine. It follows from the preceding discussion that all the algebraic identities involving any of the six trigonometric functions which hold for real values of the variable are valid when the variable is complex.

We note that inequalities derived for real values do not in general continue to be true. For example, when $\sin x$ and $\cos x$ are real, it follows from $\cos^2 x + \sin^2 x = 1$, that $|\sin x| \leqq 1$, but we cannot draw this conclusion, and the inequality does not necessarily hold, when the values are complex.

106. Hyperbolic Functions. The definitions of the hyperbolic functions given in section 68 may be used for complex values of the variable, and give:

$$\sinh z = \frac{e^z - e^{-z}}{2}, \quad \cosh z = \frac{e^z + e^{-z}}{2}. \tag{131}$$

It follows from this and equation (92) that if $z = x + iy$,

$$\sinh z = \sinh x \cos y + i \cosh x \sin y, \tag{132}$$

$$\cosh z = \cosh x \cos y + i \sinh x \sin y. \tag{133}$$

The four other functions are defined as before by:

$$\tanh z = \frac{\sinh z}{\cosh z}, \quad \coth z = \frac{\cosh z}{\sinh z}, \tag{134}$$

$$\operatorname{sech} z = \frac{1}{\cosh z}, \quad \operatorname{csch} z = \frac{1}{\sinh z} \tag{135}$$

A comparison of equations (131) and (125) shows that:

$$\sinh iz = i \sin z \quad \text{and} \quad \cosh iz = \cos z, \tag{136}$$

and also that

$$\sin iz = i \sinh z \quad \text{and} \quad \cos iz = \cosh z. \tag{137}$$

These and the relations of similar character derived from them combined with equations (134) and (135) are often convenient in deriving formulas for hyperbolic functions from the more familiar formulas for the trigonometric functions. For example:

$$\cosh (z + z') = \cos (iz + iz') = \cos iz \cos iz' - \sin iz \sin iz'$$
$$= \cosh z \cosh z' + \sinh z \sinh z'. \tag{138}$$

Identities in the hyperbolic functions may also be derived directly from equations (131) combined with

$$e^z = \cosh z + \sinh z \quad \text{and} \quad e^{-z} = \cosh z - \sinh z, \tag{139}$$

in a manner analogous to that illustrated for the trigonometric functions.

107. The Logarithmic Function.   For real values of the variables, the relations

$$w = \log z \quad \text{and} \quad z = e^{w} \tag{140}$$

are equivalent.   If $z = x + iy$ is a given complex number, and the complex number $w = u + iv$ satisfies this last equation, then

$$x + iy = e^{u} (\cos v + i \sin v). \tag{141}$$

This implies that

$$x = e^{u} \cos v, \quad y = e^{u} \sin v \tag{142}$$

so that

$$x^2 + y^2 = e^{2u} \quad \text{and} \quad e^{u} = |z|, \tag{143}$$

since e^{u} is positive for all real values of u.

If we assume that $z \neq 0$, this determines u as

$$u = \log |z| \tag{144}$$

and when combined with equation (142) leads to

$$\cos v = \frac{x}{|z|}, \quad \sin v = \frac{y}{|z|} \tag{145}$$

which determine v to within an integral multiple of 2π as we showed in section 61.   In fact,

$$v = \arg z, \tag{146}$$

as we might have noted directly by comparing equation (141) with equation (15), and identifying e^{u} and v with the polar coördinates $r = |z|$ and $\theta = \arg z$.

Since equation (141) follows from equations (144) and (146), we are led to define the logarithm of a complex number z by

$$\log z = \log |z| + i \arg z = \log r + i\theta. \tag{147}$$

This function is many valued, since arg z is not uniquely determined. For any real constant a, there is just one possible value of arg z or θ in the range

$$a \leqq \theta < a + 2\pi. \tag{148}$$

These values constitute a single-valued branch of the function arg z corresponding to a.   The values of the logarithm satisfying the restriction (148) constitute a single-valued branch of the logarithmic function corresponding to a.   Thus:

The branch of the logarithmic function corresponding to a is defined by

$$\log z = \log |z| + i \arg z, \quad \text{where} \quad a \leqq \arg z < a + 2\pi. \tag{149}$$

The function is uniquely defined for any value of z ≠ 0,

and if w = log z, $z = e^w$.   (150)

If θ is the value of arg z for any one branch and if θ′ is the value for the same z for any other branch, then θ − θ′ = 2kπ, where k is zero or a positive or negative integer.

While log z is not defined for z = 0, we may write

$$\lim_{z \to 0} \log z = \infty,$$ (151)

in accordance with the convention of section 100, since

$$|\log z| \geqq \log |z|, \quad \text{and} \quad \lim_{z \to 0} \log |z| = -\infty.$$ (152)

We note that for any one branch, if z ≠ 0 and θ ≠ a, the function θ, and hence the function log z, is continuous. If we start with a value of z ≠ 0, and then select a value of a not a possible value of arg z for this value, we shall obtain a branch of log z continuous for the value in question.

Thus, if z varies continuously, without passing through zero we may change the branch in such a way that log z varies continuously. However, if z traverses a circle with center at the origin, the final value of log z will differ from the initial value. For any range of z which excludes some radius drawn out from the origin, i.e., such that for some value of a none of the values

$$z = r \cos a + ir \sin a, \quad 0 \leqq r$$ (153)

belong to the region, we may find a branch of the function w = log z which is single-valued and continuous. We shall usually consider z restricted to such a range.

The properties used to characterize the logarithmic function for real values in section 50 apply with certain reservations to the function defined by equation (149). If w = log z and w′ = log z′, we have

$$z = e^w, \quad z' = e^{w'}, \quad zz' = e^{w+w'}.$$ (154)

Thus, if z and z′ are both distinct from zero, log z + log z′ or w + w′ is, for some branch, log (zz′). Thus we may write either

$$\log z + \log z' = \log (zz') \text{ for suitable branches,}$$ (155)

or

$$\log z + \log z' = \log zz' + 2k\pi i,$$ (156)

where we may take all three logarithms for the same branch, or for any branches, provided we use a suitable value of the integral multiple k.

That k is not necessarily zero when we use the same branch in all cases may be seen by taking $0 \leqq \theta < 2\pi$ for all the logarithms, and $\theta = 3\pi/2$ for log z and log z'.

The special relation (112) of section 50 can only hold for complex values if log $(1 + z) \to 0$ as $z \to 0$. Accordingly, we consider a branch with $-2\pi < a < 0$. We put:

$$w = \log (1 + z), \quad z = e^w - 1. \tag{157}$$

For the branch considered log $1 = 0$ and the logarithm is continuous in a region including 1, so that $w \to 0$ when $z \to 0$. Consequently we have:

$$\lim_{z \to 0} \frac{\log (1 + z)}{z} = \lim_{w \to 0} \frac{w}{e^w - 1} = 1, \tag{158}$$

by equation (94). Thus the special relation holds for any branch with $-2\pi < a < 0$, that is any branch which makes log z continuous for all real and positive values of z, and is such that for these values log z is identical with the function log x of section 50.

108. Power Functions. For any complex value of $A \neq 0$, and any complex value of B, we write:

$$A^B = e^{B \log A}, \tag{159}$$

which determines a value of the power for each choice of a particular branch of the function log z.

If α is the value of the argument of A for any one branch, for any other branch the value may be written $\alpha + 2k\pi$, where k is zero or a positive or negative integer. Thus, if a is the absolute value of A, we shall have for any branch:

$$\log A = \log a + i(\alpha + 2k\pi). \tag{160}$$

Consequently,

$$A^B = e^{B[\log a + i(\alpha + 2k\pi)]} = e^{B(\log a + i\alpha)} e^{2Bk\pi i}. \tag{161}$$

The value of the power for a branch with $k \neq 0$ will only agree with that for $k = 0$ if

$$e^{2Bk\pi i} = 1 \quad \text{and} \quad 2Bk\pi i = \log 1, \tag{162}$$

for some branch of the logarithm. But, since log 1 is 0 for one branch, for any other branch it will be an integral multiple of $2\pi i$, say $2K\pi i$, and we must have:

$$2Bk\pi i = 2K\pi i \quad \text{and} \quad Bk = K \quad \text{or} \quad B = \frac{K}{k}. \tag{163}$$

This shows that B is real and rational if equation (162) holds.

When B is not real and rational, each different value of k in equations (160) and (161) will give a different value to A^B, and this expression is infinitely many-valued. By restricting z to a region in which some branch of the logarithmic function is single-valued and continuous, we may obtain a single-valued and continuous branch of the function z^B for all values of B.

For the function A^z, since

$$A^z = e^{z \log A} = e^{z(\log a + i\alpha + 2k\pi i)}, \tag{164}$$

each choice of k determines a separate function, single-valued and continuous for all complex values of z. For real and positive values of A, $A = p$, one choice makes

$$p^z = e^{z \log p}. \tag{165}$$

When p is real and positive, unless the context indicates otherwise, we take this last equation as the definition of p^z. This convention justifies our use of e^z for the function defined in section 103, instead of for the infinitely many-valued function found by putting $A = e$ in equation (164).

The possibility of the second interpretation is occasionally convenient, for example in using a particular branch of z^B, and evaluating this function for $z = p$, or $z = e$.

Let us return to the consideration of A^B when B is real and rational. If $B = 0$, we have for all $A \neq 0$, $A^0 = 1$, regardless of the value of k in equation (161). For an integral value of B, Bk is an integer for all values of k, and the last exponential written in equation (161) is unity.

In fact, the value uniquely determined by putting $B = n$, a positive integer in equation (159) or (161), is the same as that obtained by repeated multiplication by A, as we see from equation (93). We also see from this equation that the value obtained by putting $B = -n$ is the reciprocal of that for $B = n$.

For p, a positive or negative integer, and a particular determination of $\log A$,

$$A^{Bp} = e^{Bp \log A} = (e^{B \log A})^p = (A^B)^p, \tag{166}$$

so that a rational power, p/q is uniquely determined from the value of the power $1/q$, and we may take q positive.

For $B = 1/q$, with q a positive integer, the equation (163) will be satisfied if $k = qK$, in which case k is an integral multiple of q. Thus, any two values of the logarithm which differ by $2k\pi i$ will give the same value of A^B if k is an integral multiple of q. If we take $k = 0, 1, 2, \cdots$, $q - 1$, in equation (161) we obtain q distinct values. Since any other integer differs from one of these by a multiple of q, the equation (159) gives q possible values to $A^{1/q}$. Each of these has its qth power equal to A, and these are the q roots of the equation $z^q - A = 0$. We sometimes write $\sqrt[q]{A}$ in place of $A^{1/q}$ or $\sqrt{A}$ for $A^{1/2}$. For A real and positive, one of these roots is real and positive. When q is even, there is a second real root which is negative. Also, when A is real and negative, and q is odd, there is a negative real root. For $q = 2$, and any complex value of A, the two square roots differ by a factor of -1.

109. Inverse Functions. By solving quadratic equations, and taking logarithms, we may express all the inverse trigonometric functions in terms of square roots and logarithms, so that these functions are single valued in suitably restricted regions. We have:

$$\sin^{-1} z = \csc^{-1} \frac{1}{z} = -i \log (iz + \sqrt{1 - z^2}) \tag{167}$$

$$\cos^{-1} z = \sec^{-1} \frac{1}{z} = -i \log (z + \sqrt{z^2 - 1}) \tag{168}$$

$$\tan^{-1} z = \cot^{-1} \frac{1}{z} = \frac{i}{2} \log \frac{1 - iz}{1 + iz}. \tag{169}$$

Similarly we find for the inverse hyperbolic functions:

$$\sinh^{-1} z = \operatorname{csch}^{-1} \frac{1}{z} = \log (z + \sqrt{1 + z^2}) \tag{170}$$

$$\cosh^{-1} z = \operatorname{sech}^{-1} \frac{1}{z} = \log (z + \sqrt{z^2 - 1}) \tag{171}$$

$$\tanh^{-1} z = \coth^{-1} \frac{1}{z} = \frac{1}{2} \log \frac{1 + z}{1 - z}. \tag{172}$$

110. Derivatives. If $w = f(z)$ and Δw and Δz denote corresponding complex increments of w and z, we define the derivative

$$f'(z) = \frac{dw}{dz} = \lim_{\Delta z \to 0} \frac{\Delta w}{\Delta z} = \lim_{h \to 0} \frac{f(z + h) - f(z)}{h}, \tag{173}$$

in case the last limit exists and has the same value for all sequences of complex values of h or Δz distinct from zero, and approaching zero as a limit.

As in the case of real variables, it follows from the definition that:

$$\frac{d}{dz} (kU) = k \frac{dU}{dz}, \tag{174}$$

$$\frac{d}{dz} (U + V) = \frac{dU}{dz} + \frac{dV}{dz}, \tag{175}$$

$$\frac{d}{dz}(UV) = U\frac{dV}{dz} + V\frac{dU}{dz},\tag{176}$$

$$\frac{d}{dz}\left(\frac{U}{V}\right) = \frac{V\dfrac{dU}{dz} - U\dfrac{dV}{dz}}{V^2}.\tag{177}$$

Also, the reasoning used in section 65 shows that, if $w = f(U)$ and $U = g(z)$, and for $U_0 = g(z_0)$, the function $f(U)$ has a finite derivative at U_0, while $g(z)$ has a finite derivative at z_0, then the function

$$w = f[g(z)] = F(z),\tag{178}$$

has a derivative, at z_0 given by

$$\frac{dw}{dz} = \frac{dw}{dU}\frac{dU}{dz} \quad\text{or}\quad F'(z_0) = f'(U_0)g'(z_0).\tag{179}$$

It also follows directly from the definition of a derivative that

$$\frac{dk}{dz} = 0, \quad\text{and}\quad \frac{dz}{dz} = 1,\tag{180}$$

so that polynomials and rational functions of a complex variable may be differentiated by the rules derived in section 63.

111. Special Functions. For the function e^z, we have:

$$\lim_{h\to 0}\frac{e^{z+h} - e^z}{h} = \lim_{h\to 0}e^z\frac{e^h - 1}{h} = e^z,\tag{181}$$

in view of equations (93) and (94). This proves that:

$$\frac{d}{dz}e^z = e^z.\tag{182}$$

Consider next the function $w = \log z$, at a point z interior to a region in which the branch used is continuous and single-valued. Then

$$z = e^w, \quad\text{and}\quad \frac{\log(z + \Delta z) - \log z}{\Delta z} = \frac{\Delta w}{e^{w+\Delta w} - e^w}.\tag{183}$$

As e^w is single-valued, $\Delta w \neq 0$ if $\Delta z \neq 0$, and since $w = \log z$ is continuous at z, $\Delta w \to 0$ when $\Delta z \to 0$. But

$$\lim_{\Delta w\to 0}\frac{e^{w+\Delta w} - e^w}{\Delta w} = \frac{d}{dw}e^w = e^w = z.\tag{184}$$

It follows from the last two equations that:

$$\frac{d}{dz}(\log z) = \lim_{h\to 0}\frac{\log(z + h) - \log z}{h} = \frac{1}{z}.\tag{185}$$

Again, from equations (125), (182) and the preceding section we find for the functions sin z and cos z that:

$$\frac{d}{dz}(\sin z) = \cos z \quad \text{and} \quad \frac{d}{dz}(\cos z) = -\sin z. \tag{186}$$

Thus all the formulas for differentiating trigonometric and inverse trigonometric functions for real values apply to complex values, with suitable restrictions on the regions and branches for the inverse functions.

Similarly, in consequence of equation (131) we find:

$$\frac{d}{dz}(\sinh z) = \cosh z \quad \text{and} \quad \frac{d}{dz}(\cosh z) = \sinh z, \tag{187}$$

and the formulas for differentiating hyperbolic functions and their inverse functions for real values may be extended to the case where the variable is complex.

112. Elementary Functions. The function sin z is expressed in terms of the exponential function by equation (125). The power function A^B is expressed in terms of the exponential and logarithmic function by equation (159). The function $\sin^{-1} z$ may be written

$$\sin^{-1} z = -i \log [iz + e^{\frac{1}{2}\log(1-z^2)}], \tag{188}$$

in view of equations (167) and (159). Consequently, when considering complex values of the variable, we need to consider only the functions e^z and log z as basic elementary functions. Thus we may define:

An elementary function of the complex variable z is a function which can be explicitly represented in terms of constants and the independent variable z, by means of the four fundamental operations and the exponential and logarithmic functions, using, at most, a finite number of operations and, at most, a finite number of basic functions. For any choice of branches of the logarithmic functions involved, if the explicit representation of an elementary function leads to a finite and determinate value for values of z in some two-dimensional region, we may find two-dimensional regions in which the representation leads to a single-valued and continuous function. We shall speak of such a function with its associated region as the single-valued branch of an elementary function, or simply as a single-valued elementary function.

A comparison of this definition with that given in section 69 shows that, at least in a limited range of the variable, every elementary function as there defined may be obtained from a single-valued elementary function by further restricting z to real values. The principles of the last two sections enable us to find the derivative of a single-valued elementary function for any value z interior to the region associated with the single-valued branch considered.   For any region composed entirely of such interior points, the derivative is again a single-valued elementary function.   The rules for differentiation are formally identical with the familiar rules for real functions.

113. The Fundamental Theorem of Algebra. The fundamental theorem of algebra asserts that *if $P(z)$ is a polynomial in z which is not identically a constant, then the equation*

$$P(z) = 0 \tag{189}$$

is satisfied by some complex number.   Since $|P(z)|$ is always positive or zero, any root of $P(z) = 0$ makes this a minimum, and our proof will be based on this minimum property.

We shall first prove that, *if $|P(z)|$ takes on its minimum value m for a region R at z_0, an interior point of R, then $m = 0$.*

Let us assume that the minimum m, taken on at z_0 is not zero.   If

$$P(z) = a_0 + a_1 z + \cdots + a_n z^n, \quad a_n \neq 0, \tag{190}$$

n, the highest power of z present with non-zero coefficient is called the *degree* of the polynomial.   Since $P(z)$ is not a constant, n is at least unity.   If we write $z = z_0 + h$, we have

$$P(z) = P(z_0 + h) = Q(h). \tag{191}$$

Here $Q(h)$ is a polynomial of the nth degree in h, as we see on multiplying out the powers and combining the terms.   The degree is n since the only term in h^n is $a_n h^n$ and since no higher power occurs.   Put

$$Q(h) = c_0 + c_1 h + \cdots + c_n h^n, \quad c_n \neq 0. \tag{192}$$

Let $c_r = c_1$ if $c_1 \neq 0$, and otherwise, the first coefficient following c_0 which is not zero.   It follows from our assumption that

$$c_0 \neq 0, \quad \text{since} \quad |c_0| = |Q(0)| = |P(z_0)| = m. \tag{193}$$

Thus there is a complex number $-c_r/c_0$ which is not zero, and, if one value of its logarithm is $b + iB$, we may write:

$$-\frac{c_r}{c_0} = e^b e^{iB} \quad \text{and} \quad c_r = -c_0 e^b e^{iB}. \tag{194}$$

Let p be a positive real number, and take

$$h_1 = pe^{-\frac{iB}{r}} \quad \text{so that} \quad h_1^r = p^r e^{-iB}. \tag{195}$$

Then the first two non-zero terms of $Q(h_1)$ may be written:

$$c_0 + c_r h_1^r = c_0 - c_0 e^b p^r, \tag{196}$$

and the absolute value of these terms will be

$$|c_0| \, |1 - e^b p^r|, \tag{197}$$

which will be less than $|c_0|$ if $p^r e^b < 1$,

or if

$$p < e^{-\frac{b}{r}}. \tag{198}$$

Let C be an upper bound for $|c_k|$. Then the terms of $Q(h_1)$ following c_r are less than n in number and each term contains a power of h_1 greater than r. Hence if we take

$$|h_1| < 1, \quad \text{that is,} \quad p < 1, \tag{199}$$

we shall have for each of these terms:

$$|c_k h_1^k| \leqq C p^k \leqq C p^{r+1}, \quad k > r, \tag{200}$$

and the absolute value of the sum of these terms will not exceed:

$$C n p^{r+1} \quad \text{or} \quad \frac{|c_0| e^b p^r}{2} \quad \text{if} \quad p < \frac{|c_0| e^b}{2Cn}. \tag{201}$$

Under these conditions, we shall have

$$|Q(h_1)| \leqq |c_0|(1 - e^b p^r) + \frac{|c_0| e^b p^r}{2}$$

$$\leqq |c_0|\left(1 - \frac{e^b p^r}{2}\right) < |c_0|. \tag{202}$$

Let us now take p so as to satisfy the relations (198), (199), (201), and also so small that $z_1 = z_0 + h_1$ is in R, which we may do since z_0 is an interior point of the region R. Then

$$P(z_1) = Q(h_1) \quad \text{and} \quad |P(z_1)| < |c_0| \quad \text{or} \quad m, \tag{203}$$

by equations (202) and (193). Since m is the minimum value of $|P(z)|$ for the region R, this relation cannot hold, so that the assumption that $m \neq 0$ leads to a contradiction. This proves that m must equal 0, as stated.

We shall now show that $|P(z)|$ *must take on its minimum value at an interior point of a circle with center at the origin and radius q, if q is sufficiently large.* On such a circle, $|z| = q$, and the numerical value of the term of highest degree in $P(z)$, equation (190), is:

$$|a_n z^n| = |a_n| q^n. \tag{204}$$

Let A be an upper bound for all the $|a_k|$. Then the remaining terms of $P(z)$ are n in number, and each term contains at most the $(n-1)$st power of z. Hence if we take

$$q > 1, \tag{205}$$

we shall have for each of these terms

$$|a_k z^k| \leqq A q^k \leqq A q^{n-1}, \quad k < n, \tag{206}$$

and the absolute value of the sum of these terms will not exceed:

$$A n q^{n-1} \quad \text{or} \quad \frac{|a_n| q^n}{2} \quad \text{if} \quad q > \frac{2An}{|a_n|}. \tag{207}$$

With these conditions, we shall have on the circle,

$$|P(z)| \geqq |a_n| q^n - \frac{|a_n| q^n}{2} \geqq \frac{|a_n| q^n}{2}. \tag{208}$$

This will exceed the value of $|P(z)|$ at the center of the circle, $|P(0)| = |a_0|$,

if $$\frac{|a_n| q^n}{2} > |a_0| \quad \text{or} \quad q > \left(\frac{2|a_0|}{|a_n|}\right)^{\frac{1}{n}}. \tag{209}$$

Let us now take a value of q so large that the relations (205), (207) and (209) are all satisfied. Then

$$|P(z)| > |P(0)|, \quad \text{if} \quad |z| = q. \tag{210}$$

This shows that $|P(z)|$ cannot take on a minimum value for the region R_q consisting of the interior and boundary points of the circle $|z| = q$ at any point of the boundary.

Let us now introduce the real coördinates (x,y) of the point z. Then $z = x + iy$, and $P(z) = u(x,y) + iv(x,y)$, where u and v are each polynomials in x and y with real coefficients. Hence

$$u^2 + v^2 \geqq 0, \quad \text{and} \quad |P(z)| = \sqrt{u^2 + v^2} \tag{211}$$

is a continuous function of the two real variables x,y by section 35 and section 39, for all values.

In particular, the function $|P(z)|$ is continuous in the closed region R_q consisting of the points for which

$$|z| \leqq q \quad \text{or} \quad x^2 + y^2 \leqq q^2. \tag{212}$$

Thus, by a theorem of section 35, there is some point z_0 of this closed region for which $|P(z)|$ takes on its minimum value.

As we have already deduced from equation (210) that z_0 is not a point of the bounding circle $|z| = q$, it must be an interior point.   This proves our second contention.

Let us now apply the first result to the region R_q and the minimum value of $|P(z)|$, $m = |P(z_0)|$.   This shows that

$$|P(z_0)| = m = 0, \quad \text{and} \quad P(z_0) = 0. \tag{213}$$

Thus we have shown the existence of a root of the equation (189) and proved the fundamental theorem of algebra.

114. Polynomials.   If $A(z)$ is any polynomial of degree m, and $B(z)$ is any polynomial of degree n, where $m \geqq n > 0$, the algebraic process of long division enables us to find a quotient polynomial $Q(z)$, of degree $m - n$, and a remainder polynomial $R(z)$ whose degree is lower than that of $B(z)$, such that:

$$A(z) = B(z)Q(z) + R(z), \tag{214}$$

or

$$\frac{A(z)}{B(z)} = Q(z) + \frac{R(z)}{B(z)}. \tag{215}$$

These are identities, in the sense that the right side may be simplified to an expression of the same form, with the same coefficients, as the left side.   Thus, in the first equation we may put z equal to any value, and in the second we may put z equal to any value for which $B(z) \neq 0$.

Now let us apply the identity (214) to the division of a polynomial $P(z)$ by $z - b$, where b is any complex number.   Then the remainder will be a constant, and we shall have:

$$P(z) = Q(z)(z - b) + c. \tag{216}$$

If we put $z = b$ in this identity, we find:

$$P(b) = c, \quad \text{and hence} \quad P(z) = Q(z)(z - b) + P(b). \tag{217}$$

Thus the remainder is $P(b)$ and will be zero if, and only if, $P(b) = 0$, that is, if b is a root of the polynomial.

We proved in the last section that every polynomial of positive degree has a root.   Let us start with $P(z)$, any polynomial of degree n, $n \geqq 1$, and let b_1 be a root.   Then we may write

$$P(z) = Q(z)(z - b_1), \tag{218}$$

where $Q(z)$ is of the $(n - 1)$st degree.   If we treat $Q(z)$ in the same way we treated $P(z)$ and continue with the new quotient, we shall find after n steps a quotient which is a constant, and thus have:

$$P(z) = k(z - b_1)(z - b_2)(z - b_3) \cdots (z - b_n), \quad k \neq 0. \tag{219}$$

Several of the b_j may be equal. If there are r and no more roots equal to b_1, b_1 is said to be of multiplicity r, or a multiple root of order r. In this case we see from equation (219) that

$$P(z) = (z - b_1)^r Q(z), \quad \text{where} \quad Q(b_1) \neq 0. \tag{220}$$

These facts may be summarized in the statement:

If we count a multiple root of order r, r times, every polynomial of the nth degree, $n \geq 1$, has n roots b_j. The polynomial may be written as the product of a constant and n first degree factors of the form $z - b_j$.

The b_j are uniquely determined by the polynomial, since no value of z distinct from the n b_j can make the product (219) vanish. The multiplicities are also determined. For, from equation (220):

$$\lim_{z \to b_1} \frac{P(z)}{(z - b_1)^r} = Q(b_1) \neq 0, \quad \text{and} \quad \lim_{z \to b_1} \frac{P(z)}{(z - b_1)^{r-1}} = 0, \tag{221}$$

and these properties define the multiplicity of b_1.

115. Rational Functions. A rational function is one obtained from z and a finite set of constants by a finite number of additions, multiplications, and divisions. Such a function may always be written as the quotient of two polynomials, by operations which are reversible except for those values of z for which certain polynomials are zero. If the two polynomials in the final simplified form have any common roots, these will lead to common factors, which may be cancelled out, except when z equals such a common root. When the rational function has been reduced to the quotient of two polynomials, without common roots, it is said to be reduced to lowest terms. The reduced form is defined for all values of z except those which make the reduced denominator zero. There may be other values of z for which the original form of the function is undefined. If these are finite in number, we generally find it convenient to define arbitrarily the value of the original function for these values as the value of the reduced form. With this convention, the original function equals the reduced function for all values for which the latter is defined.

If a rational function, reduced to lowest terms, is the quotient of two polynomials $A(z)/B(z)$, it is said to be a proper fraction if the degree of the denominator exceeds that of the numerator, and an improper fraction if the degree of the numerator is at least as high as that of the denominator.

By the division process used to obtain equation (215), we may replace any improper fraction by the sum of a polynomial and a proper fraction:

$$\frac{A(z)}{B(z)} = C(z) + \frac{D(z)}{B(z)}. \tag{222}$$

This corresponds to the identity

$$A(z) = C(z)B(z) + D(z), \tag{223}$$

which shows that for any value of z, b, which is a root of $B(z)$,

$$B(b) = 0, \quad A(b) = D(b). \tag{224}$$

If $A(z)/B(z)$ was reduced to its lowest terms, no root b is a root of $A(z)$. Hence if $B(b) = 0$, $A(b) \neq 0$, and $D(b) \neq 0$, so that the proper fraction $D(z)/B(z)$ is in its lowest terms.

Now let b be a root of $B(z)$ of multiplicity r, so that

$$B(z) = (z - b)^r E(z), \quad E(b) \neq 0. \tag{225}$$

Let us try to find a constant A_r such that

$$\frac{D(z)}{B(z)} = \frac{A_r}{(z - b)^r} + \frac{F(z)}{(z - b)^s E(z)}, \tag{226}$$

where $s < r$, and the last fraction written is a proper fraction. Such a constant will make equation (226) an identity for all values of z for which both sides are defined and will imply that

$$\frac{D(z)}{E(z)} = A_r + \frac{F(z)(z - b)^{r-s}}{E(z)} \tag{227}$$

holds for all such values. If we let $z \to b$, we find:

$$A_r = \frac{D(b)}{E(b)}. \tag{228}$$

To show that a relation of the form (226) may be found with this value of A_r, consider the identity:

$$\frac{D(z)}{B(z)} - \frac{A_r}{(z - b)^r} = \frac{D(z) - A_r E(z)}{(z - b)^r E(z)} \tag{229}$$

Since the numerator of this fraction is a polynomial which is zero for $z = b$, by equation (228), it is divisible by $(z - b)$. Thus, when the fraction is reduced to its lowest terms, the denominator will contain $(z - b)^s$ where s is less than r. This exponent will be $r - 1$, if b is a simple zero of the numerator. But it may be any lower value, including 0, if the numerator happens to be divisible by a higher power of $(z - b)$ than the first. On the other hand, if b' is any root of $E(z)$, the numerator reduces to $D(b')$ for $z = b'$, which is not zero since $B(b') = 0$ implies $D(b') \neq 0$. Thus no factors of $E(z)$ are canceled out in reducing the fraction to its lowest terms, and the reduced form is that given in equation (226). Unless $E(z)$ is a constant, there is a root b', and the function $F(z)$ is not identically zero. If $E(z)$ is a constant, and $D(z)$ is also a constant, then the right member of equation (229) is identically zero, and we may put $F(z) = 0$ in equation (226) or omit the last term.

Since the right member of equation (229) is a proper fraction, the last fraction in equation (226) is a proper fraction if $E(z)$ is not a constant. Thus it may be treated in the same way we treated $D(z)/B(z)$. If s is positive, we may again use the root b, if $s = 0$, we use another root of $B(z)$, that is, a root of $E(z)$. Since the process used yields a new fraction whose denominator is of lower degree than the one with which we started, after at most n steps we shall come to a fraction for which the equation (226) applies with $F(z) = 0$, or without the last term. This proves the possibility of decomposing any rational function into partial fractions of a kind described in the following theorem:

Any rational function may be decomposed into the sum of a polynomial, and terms of the form

$$\frac{A_{jk}}{(z - b_j)^k}, \quad j = 1, 2, \cdots, m; \quad k = 1, 2, \cdots, r_j \qquad (230)$$

where $b_1, b_2, \cdots, b_m$ are the distinct roots of the denominator of the function after it has been reduced to its lowest terms, and r_j is the multiplicity of the root b_j.

We may prove in the following way that the decomposition is unique. If $R(z)$ is the rational function and b is a particular root of multiplicity r, from any decomposition we may obtain:

$$R(z) = \frac{A_r}{(z - b)^r} + \frac{F(z)}{(z - b)^s E(z)}, \quad s < r, \ E(b) \neq 0, \qquad (231)$$

by adding the polynomial and all the fractions except that with denominator $(z - b)^r$ to obtain the second fraction. If we multiply by $(z - b)^r$ and let $z \to b$, we find:

$$A_r = \lim_{z \to b} R(z)(z - b)^r. \qquad (232)$$

Thus the coefficient A_r is determined by the function. If we now subtract the fraction with numerator A_r and apply the same argument to $R(z) - A_r/(z - b)^r$, we find that A_{r-1} is determined. Continuing in this way, we see that the coefficients for any root b_i are all determined by the function $R(z)$. The polynomial part is determined, since it must equal the remainder when all the fractions are subtracted. Thus the decomposition is independent of the order in which the roots are taken.

Since the sum of the fractions and polynomial of a decomposition gives $A(z)/B(z)$, the rational function $R(z)$ reduced to its lowest terms, this fraction is independent of the manner of reduction.

116. Taylor's Expansions of Rational Fractions. If $P(z)$ is any polynomial, and b is any complex number, we may divide the polynomial by $z - b$ and deduce the equation:

$$P(z) = (z - b)P_1(z) + c_0, \qquad (233)$$

analogous to equation (216). If $P_1(z)$ is not a constant, we may repeat the process to obtain

$$P_1(z) = (z - b)P_2(z) + c_1, \qquad (234)$$

and so on until we come to

$$P_{n-1}(z) = (z - b)P_n(z) + c_{n-1}. \qquad (235)$$

Since each polynomial $P_j(x)$ is of degree one lower than the preceding, if $P(z)$ is of the nth degree, $P_n(z)$ will be a constant, c_n. By eliminating the polynomials $P_j(z)$ from the series of equations, we deduce

$$P(z) = c_0 + c_1(z - b) + c_2(z - b)^2 + \cdots + c_n(z - b)^n. \quad (236)$$

The coefficients could be found by the process just indicated with less labor than the method used to obtain equation (192), equivalent to this with $b = z_0$ and $z - b = h$.

However, we may express the coefficients directly in terms of derivatives. In fact, by putting $z = b$ in equation (236), and in the equations derived from it by differentiation, we find:

$$c_0 = P(b), \quad c_j = \frac{P^{(j)}(b)}{j!}, \quad j = 1, 2, \cdots, n. \qquad (237)$$

Equations (236) and (237) are analogous to those of section 82, but here the expansion is in closed form, and is valid for complex values of the variables.

Let us consider next the decomposition of a rational fraction,

$$\frac{A(z)}{B(z)} \quad \text{where} \quad B(z) = (z - b)^r E(z), \quad E(b) \neq 0. \qquad (238)$$

By combining the polynomial and the partial fractions whose denominators are not powers of $(z - b)$, we find:

$$\frac{A(z)}{B(z)} = \sum_{k=1}^{r} \frac{A_k}{(z - b)^k} + \frac{H(z)}{E(z)}. \qquad (239)$$

Thus: $\dfrac{A(z)}{E(z)} = A_r + A_{r-1}(z - b) + A_{r-2}(z - b)^2 + \cdots$

$$+ A_1(z - b)^{r-1} + \frac{(z - b)^r H(z)}{E(z)}. \qquad (240)$$

Since $E(b) \neq 0$, the fraction $H(z)/E(z)$ will have its derivatives of all orders finite for $z = b$. Hence, if we apply the rule of Leibniz for differentiating a product of section 72 to the product of this fraction by $(z - b)^r$, the terms in the derivatives of the first $r - 1$ orders will all contain a factor $(z - b)$ and so will vanish for $z = b$. Consequently, we may put $z = b$ in equation (240) and the equations found from it by differentiating $1, 2, \cdots, r - 1$ times, and so obtain:

$$A_r = \frac{A(b)}{E(b)}, \quad A_k = \frac{1}{(r - k)!} \frac{d^{r-k}}{dz^{r-k}} \left[\frac{A(z)}{E(z)} \right]_{z=b} \qquad (241)$$

These formulas may be applied with $A(z)/E(z) = R(z)(z - b)^r$ replaced by $R_1(z)(z - b)^r$, where $R_1(z)$ is the function with the polynomial removed, or with any fractions removed whose denominators are not divisible by $(z - b)$.

If we differentiate the right member of

$$B(z) = (z - b)^r E(z), \qquad (242)$$

successively by the rule of Leibniz, we note that the first $r - 1$ derivatives will contain a factor $(z - b)$ and so vanish for $z = b$, while the rth derivative will contain only one term, $r!\,E(z)$ which does not vanish for $z = b$. Thus:

$$B(b) = B'(b) = \cdots = B^{(r-1)}(b) = 0, \quad B^{(r)}(b) = E(b) \neq 0. \quad (243)$$

These conditions are in accord with the fact that the Taylor's expansion of $B(z)$ in ascending powers of $(z - b)$ starts with $(z - b)^r$. They may sometimes be used practically to detect multiple roots of a polynomial $B(z)$ or the order of multiplicity of a given root.

In particular, if b is a root of $B(z)$, and $B'(b) \neq 0$, then b is a simple root, and from equations (241) and (243) we find as the term for this root:

$$\frac{A_1}{z - b} \quad \text{where} \quad A_1 = \frac{A(b)}{B'(b)}, \qquad (244)$$

a formula of practical use in finding the coefficients for simple roots, particularly when they are real.

If $A(z)/E(z)$ is any rational fraction, b any complex number such that $E(b) \neq 0$, and r any positive integer, we may form the fraction which satisfies equation (238), and deduce equations (240) and (241). Thus, with changed notation:

$$R(z) = c_0 + c_1(z - b) + c_2(z - b)^2 + \cdots \\ + c_n(z - b)^n + R_1(z)(z - b)^{n+1}, \quad (245)$$

where $$c_0 = R(b), \quad c_j = \frac{R^{(j)}(b)}{j!}, \tag{246}$$

and $$R_1(z)(z - b)^{n+1} = O[(z - b)^{n+1}], \quad \text{as} \quad z \to b. \tag{247}$$

This is a Taylor's development for any rational fraction for values near b, for which it has a finite value. The last result follows from the fact that $R_1(b)$ is finite, since $R_1(z)$ is a rational function with the same denominator as $R(z)$.

117. Real Polynomials. By a real polynomial $P(z)$ we mean one which has all its coefficients real. Let us replace z by $a + ib$, and so obtain the complex number:

$$P(a + bi) = A + Bi. \tag{248}$$

If we now replace z by the conjugate value $a - bi$, we shall find

$$P(a - bi) = A - Bi, \tag{249}$$

since the coefficients, being real, are their own conjugates, and addition and multiplication when applied to conjugate complex numbers yield conjugate results, as remarked in section 97.

In particular, this shows that, if $a + bi$ is a complex root of the real polynomial, so that $A + Bi$, and hence A and B, are zero, then $a - bi$ is also a root. That is, for a real polynomial, non-real roots occur in conjugate pairs. A pair of conjugate complex roots in the factorization (219) corresponds to two linear factors whose product

$$(z - a - bi)(z - a + bi) = z^2 - 2az + a^2 + b^2 \tag{250}$$

is a real quadratic factor. As division by such a factor yields a new real polynomial of lower degree, a real polynomial may always be factored into a number of real factors of the first or second degree, and two conjugate roots of a real polynomial will have the same multiplicity.

118. Real Rational Functions. A real rational function is one which, when reduced to its lowest terms, is the quotient of two real polynomials. If we start with such a function whose reduced form $A(z)/B(z)$ is an improper fraction, division will yield a real polynomial $C(z)$ and a real proper fraction $D(z)/B(z)$. If the polynomial $B(z)$ has the quadratic factor

$$z^2 + pz + q = (z - a - bi)(z - a + bi) \tag{251}$$

corresponding to a pair of conjugate complex roots, and each root is of multiplicity r, we may write

$$B(z) = (z^2 + pz + q)^r G(z), \tag{252}$$

with $G(z)$ a real polynomial. Thus for the first root, $a + bi$, the coefficient A_r of equation (228) will have the value

$$A_r = \frac{D(a + bi)}{(2bi)^r G(a + bi)}, \tag{253}$$

while the corresponding coefficient for the conjugate root, $a - bi$ will have the value

$$\bar{A}_r = \frac{D(a - bi)}{(-2bi)^r G(a - bi)}, \tag{254}$$

which is the conjugate of A_r. Thus the fraction may be decomposed as follows:

$$\frac{D(z)}{B(z)} = \frac{A_r}{(z - a - bi)^r} + \frac{\bar{A}_r}{(z - a + bi)^r} + \frac{F(z)}{(z^2 + pz + q)^s G(z)}, \tag{255}$$

where $s < r$. Since the left member is a real function, and the two conjugate fractions add up to a real function, the third member is also real. This shows that the next two coefficients, A_{r-1} and $\bar{A}_{r-1}$, will be conjugate, and continuing in this way we see that all the coefficients in the expansion of section 115, for conjugate complex factors will be conjugate complex numbers.

If we wish to keep the decomposition real, we may add up the two conjugate fractions in equation (255), and so obtain a fraction

$$\frac{H(z)}{(z^2 + pz + q)^r}. \tag{256}$$

By division, we may obtain

$$H(z) = J(z)(z^2 + pz + q) + P + Qz, \tag{257}$$

the remainder being of the first degree.

This enables us to write

$$\frac{A_r}{(z - a - bi)^r} + \frac{\bar{A}_r}{(z - a + bi)^r} = \frac{P + Qz}{(z^2 + pz + q)^r} + \frac{J(z)}{(z^2 + pz + q)^{r-1}}. \tag{258}$$

If we substitute this expression in equation (255), and combine the last fraction in equation (258) with the last fraction in equation (255), we shall be led to the decomposition

$$\frac{D(z)}{B(z)} = \frac{P + Qz}{(z^2 + pz + q)^r} + \frac{K(z)}{(z^2 + pz + q)^t G(z)}, \tag{259}$$

with $t < r$.

Equation (228) shows that A_r in equation (226) is real if b is real, and $D(x)$ and $B(x)$ are real polynomials.

We may use these facts to prove a unique decomposition in which all the coefficients are real:

Any real rational function may be decomposed into the sum of a polynomial, terms of the form:

$$\frac{A_j}{(z-b)^j}, \quad j = 1, 2, \cdots, r, \tag{260}$$

one series for each real root b of multiplicity r, and terms of the form

$$\frac{P + Qz}{(z^2 + pz + q)^j}, \quad j = 1, 2, \cdots, r. \tag{261}$$

one series for each real quadratic factor $z^2 + pz + q$, corresponding to a pair of conjugate complex roots of multiplicity r of the denominator after the function has been reduced to its lowest terms.

In this decomposition the coefficients are uniquely determined and will all be real.

119. The Derivative of a Complex Function of a Real Variable. If $s(x)$ and $t(x)$ are two real functions of the real variable x, defined for a certain range, the function

$$w(x) = s(x) + it(x) \tag{262}$$

is called a *complex function of the real variable x.* Any association of complex numbers with the real values of x in the range determines a complex function of x, with

$$s(x) = \mathbf{R}[w(x)] \quad \text{and} \quad t(x) = \mathbf{I}[w(x)], \tag{263}$$

the real and imaginary components of $w(x)$.

We say that the function $w(x)$ has a derivative for real increments if

$$\lim_{h \to 0} \frac{w(x+h) - w(x)}{h} \tag{264}$$

exists for all real sequences of values of h, $h \to 0$. We use dw/dx or $w'(x)$ to denote this derivative.

If $t(x)$ is zero, this definition agrees with that of section 62. Suppose next that $w(x)$ is obtained by putting $z = x$ in a function $w(z)$ defined for complex values, which has a derivative for complex increments, $F'(z)$ in the sense of section 110. Then, for $z = x$, the expression (264) will approach $w'(x)$ for all complex sequences h approaching zero, and hence in particular for all sequences of real values approaching zero. Thus whenever our previous definitions assign a meaning to $w'(x)$, the definition just given is consistent with it.

Of course $w'(x)$ may exist without $w'(z)$ existing for $z = x$, and Δz complex. This will cause no confusion, since we shall for the most part be concerned with elementary functions whose derivatives may be found by the methods of section 112.

Since

$$\frac{w(x+h) - w(x)}{h} = \frac{s(x+h) - s(x)}{h} + i\,\frac{t(x+h) - t(x)}{h}, \quad (265)$$

it follows from equation (35) that $w(x)$ will have a derivative for real increments if, and only if, $s(x)$ and $t(x)$ have derivatives. Also, in this case,

$$\mathbf{R}[w'(x)] = s'(x) \quad \text{and} \quad \mathbf{I}[w'(x)] = t'(x). \quad (266)$$

Thus, if a complex function $w(x)$ has a derivative for real increments,

$$\frac{d}{dx}\,\mathbf{R}[w(x)] = \mathbf{R}\left[\frac{dw}{dx}\right] \quad \text{and} \quad \frac{d}{dx}\,\mathbf{I}[w(x)] = \mathbf{I}\left[\frac{dw}{dx}\right]. \quad (267)$$

120. Higher Derivatives. We may now express the higher derivatives of certain real elementary functions in a simple form.

Consider first a rational function with real coefficients. By the theorem of section 115, and the discussion of section 118, such a function may be represented as a sum of terms of the form

$$cx^r \quad \text{and} \quad \frac{A}{(x-b)^r}, \quad (268)$$

where r is integral, c is real, and either b and A are real, or b is complex and the sum includes the corresponding conjugate fraction obtained by replacing b and A by their conjugates $\bar{b}$ and $\bar{A}$.

For the first form, we have for the nth derivative:

$$\frac{d^n}{dx^n}(cx^r) = r(r-1)(r-2) \cdots (r-n+1)cx^{r-n}, \quad (269)$$

so that the derivative is zero for $n > r$.

For the second term, the nth derivative is

$$\frac{d^n}{dx^n}\left[\frac{A}{(x-b)^r}\right] = (-1)^n r(r+1)(r+2) \cdots (r+n-1)\,\frac{A}{(x-b)^{r+n}}. \quad (270)$$

This is real as it stands, when b is real, and hence A real.

When b is not real, the sum of the fraction and its conjugate will give twice the real component of the fraction,

$$S = \frac{A}{(x-b)^r} + \frac{\bar{A}}{(x-\bar{b})^r} = 2\mathbf{R}\left[\frac{A}{(x-b)^r}\right], \qquad (271)$$

and by equation (267)

$$\frac{d^n S}{dx^n} = 2\mathbf{R}\left\{\frac{d^n}{dx^n}\left[\frac{A}{(x-b)^r}\right]\right\}, \qquad (272)$$

which may be found from equation (270).

Again, consider

$$e^{(p+qi)x} = e^{px}\cos qx + ie^{px}\sin qx. \qquad (273)$$

From equation (267), we find:

$$\frac{d^n}{dx^n}(e^{px}\cos qx) = \mathbf{R}[(p+qi)^n e^{(p+qi)x}], \qquad (274)$$

and

$$\frac{d^n}{dx^n}(e^{px}\sin qx) = \mathbf{I}[(p+qi)^n e^{(p+qi)x}]. \qquad (275)$$

EXERCISES V

1. Let P be the point on the line through P_1 and P_2 for which $P_1P/PP_2 = s_1/s_2$, any real ratio. Show that if P_1 and P_2 represent z_1 and z_2, then P represents $(s_2z_1 + s_1z_2)/(s_2 + s_1)$. We say P divides the segment in the ratio s_1/s_2, and include $s_2 = 0$, $s_1 \neq 0$ to mean $PP_2 = 0$.

2. Let us associate real numbers m_i with points P_i or z_i. By problem 1, the point dividing P_1P_2 in a ratio inverse to that of their numbers is P' or $(m_1z_1 + m_2z_2)/(m_1 + m_2)$. We may associate the number $m_1 + m_2$ with this point, and treat P' and P_3 as we did P_1 and P_2. Show that, if we continue until n points are used, we shall obtain a point G or $\sum_{k=1}^{n} m_i z_i \Big/ \sum_{k=1}^{n} m_i$, the weighted average or center of mass of the weighted points. The result shows that G is independent of the order in which the points are taken or grouped, and the construction shows it to be independent of the choice of axes or scale.

3. Prove that if z_1z_2 is real, and $z_1 + z_2$ is real, then either z_1 and z_2 are both real, or they are conjugate and $z_2 = \bar{z}_1$.

4. Prove that if $z = x + iy$, $(|x| + |y|)/\sqrt{2} \leq |z|$, and that the equality only holds if $|x| = |y|$.

5. Let 0, P_1, P_2 be three given points in a plane. We may fix a coördinate system by putting $0 = (0,0)$ and any point U distinct from 0 as the unit point $U = (1,0)$. In this system let z_1 and z_2 be the complex numbers for P_1 and P_2. Show that the point for the quotient z_1/z_2 does not depend on the choice of U, but that any point P distinct from 0 may be made to represent $z_1 z_2$ by an appropriate choice of U.

6. Prove the following geometric construction for the roots of the quadratic equation $az^2 + bz + c = 0$, with a, b, c real. If the circle with i and $-b/a + ic/a$ as diametral points cuts the real axis, these points give the real roots. If the circle with 0 and $-2c/b$ as diametral points cuts the line $x = -b/2a$, these points give the conjugate complex roots. Equal roots are given by the point of tangency in either case.

7. Prove that if $z = x + iy$, $|e^z| = e^x$, $|e^{-z}| = e^{-x}$.

8. If p is any real number, $|e^{ip}| = 1$.

9. De Moivre's theorem states that for real θ,

$$(\cos\theta + i\sin\theta)^n = \cos n\theta + i\sin n\theta,$$

where n is a positive or negative integer. Prove this.

10. Show that the identity of problem 9 holds if θ is complex, and for one value of the left side if n is any complex number.

11. Prove that the roots of $az^2 + bz + c = 0$ are

$$\sqrt{-\frac{c}{a}}\tan\frac{A}{2} \quad \text{and} \quad -\sqrt{-\frac{c}{a}}\cot\frac{A}{2} \quad \text{if} \quad \tan A = \frac{2}{b}\sqrt{-ac};$$

$$\sqrt{\frac{c}{a}}\tan\frac{A}{2} \quad \text{and} \quad \sqrt{\frac{c}{a}}\cot\frac{A}{2} \quad \text{if} \quad \sin A = -\frac{2}{b}\sqrt{ac};$$

and $\sqrt{\dfrac{c}{a}}(\cos A \pm i\sin A)$ if $\cos A = -\dfrac{b}{2\sqrt{ac}}$. If a, b and c are real, a real

value of A can be found from one of the conditions.

12. If $P(z) = az^2 + bz + c$ with a, b, c real, and $z = x + iy$, express $\mathbf{R}(P)$, $\mathbf{I}(P)$ and $|P(z)|^2$ as polynomials in x and y.

13. A pair of relations $u = u(x,y)$ and $v = v(x,y)$ may be geometrically interpreted as a *transformation* of points in the plane, which takes (x,y) into (u,v). Show that if $w = z + z_1$, the transformation is a translation, and that if $w = e^{i\alpha}z$, the transformation is a rotation about 0. Also that $w = e^{i\alpha}z + z_1$ may be made to represent any rigid displacement of the plane on itself.

14. If $A \neq 0$, interpret $w = Az$ as a similarity transformation, and hence interpret $w = Az + B$.

15. A geometrical *inversion* of the plane in the unit circle replaces the point P by P', where P' is on OP or OP produced beyond P and $OP \cdot OP' = 1$. Thus, in polar coördinates $\theta' = \theta$ and $r' = 1/r$. Hence $w = 1/\bar{z}$, a continuous function of z except when $z = 0$. Show that $u = x/(x^2 + y^2)$ and $v = y/(x^2 + y^2)$ and that the inverse of the curve $a(x^2 + y^2) + bx + cy + d = 0$ is the curve $d(u^2 + v^2) + bu + cv + a = 0$. If we complete the inversion plane by a "point at infinity" I, the inverse of 0, the transformation is single-valued for all points. It takes 0 into I and, since it is its own inverse, I into 0. An inversion takes "circles," including straight lines as a special case, into "circles." Show that the straight lines, or the only "circles" through I, go into "circles" through 0, and conversely.

16. Show that the equation of a straight line may be written $Sz + \overline{S}\overline{z} + t = 0$, with t real, while that of a circle may be written $|z - S|^2 = (z - S)(\overline{z} - \overline{S}) = t^2$. Hence, when the locus of $sz\overline{z} + Sz + \overline{S}\overline{z} + t = 0$, s, t real is more than one point, it is a " circle," with $tw\overline{w} + Sw + \overline{S}\overline{w} + s = 0$ as its inverse under $w = 1/\overline{z}$.

17. Interpret $w = 1/z$ as a combination of an inversion and a reflection, and show that it transforms the " circle " of the preceding problem into the " circle " with equation $tw\overline{w} + S\overline{w} + \overline{S}w + s = 0$.

18. The relation $w = \dfrac{Az + B}{Cz + D}$, where $AD - BC \neq 0$ defines a *bilinear* transformation. If $C = 0$ it reduces to that of problem 14. If $C \neq 0$ it may be represented as a combination of such transformations with one of the type $w' = 1/z'$, e.g., with $w = w' + A/C$ and $z' = \dfrac{C(Cz + D)}{BC - AD}$.

19. If we introduce the point I of problem 15, the bilinear transformation of problem 18 is single-valued. It takes I into I if $C = 0$ and if $C \neq 0$, it takes $-D/C$ into I, and I into A/C. Show that it takes " circles " into " circles," and state which ones go into straight lines or are the images of straight lines.

20. Find the equation of the image of the " circle " of problem 16, when $w = \dfrac{Az + B}{Cz + D}$. *Hint:* Use $\overline{w} = \dfrac{\overline{A}\overline{z} + \overline{B}}{\overline{C}\overline{z} + \overline{D}}$.

21. Show that the locus of $\arg \dfrac{z - z_1}{z - z_2} = \alpha$ is an arc of a " circle " through the points z_1 and z_2. The other arc of the same " circle " is given by replacing α by $\alpha - \pi$. The locus of $\left|\dfrac{z - z_1}{z - z_2}\right| = p$ is a circle intersecting all the arcs for varying α at right angles.

22. Show that a necessary and sufficient condition for four points to be concyclic, i.e., lie on a " circle," is that the cross-ratio of their complex values taken in any order, e.g., $\dfrac{z_3 - z_1}{z_3 - z_2} \dfrac{z_4 - z_2}{z_4 - z_1}$, be real. *Hint:* Use the first result of problem 21.

23. If the transformation of problem 18 takes z_1 into w_1 and z_2 into w_2, show that $\dfrac{w - w_1}{w - w_2} = \dfrac{Cz_2 + D}{Cz_1 + D} \cdot \dfrac{z - z_1}{z - z_2}$. Hence show that the cross-ratio of four points equals the corresponding cross-ratio of their images. This, with problem 22, proves that " circles " go into " circles." By using problem 21 directly, show that each of the families there mentioned for z_1 and z_2 go into corresponding families for w_1 and w_2:

24. If $z = x + iy$, prove that $|\sin z| = \sqrt{\sin^2 x + \sinh^2 y}$, $|\cos z| = \sqrt{\cos^2 x + \sinh^2 y}$, $|\sinh z| = \sqrt{\sin^2 y + \sinh^2 x}$, and $|\cosh z| = \sqrt{\cos^2 y + \sinh^2 x}$.

25. Using problem 24, or otherwise, show that

$$|\sinh y| \leqq |\sin z| \leqq \cosh y, \quad |\sinh y| \leqq |\cos z| \leqq \cosh y,$$
$$|\sinh x| \leqq |\sinh z| \leqq \cosh x \quad \text{and} \quad |\sinh x| \leqq |\cosh z| \leqq \cosh x.$$

26. Prove that the roots of the special cubic equation $4z^3 + 3z + p = 0$ are $\sinh A$, $-\frac{1}{2}\sinh A \pm \frac{1}{2}\sqrt{3}i \cosh A$ if $p = -\sinh 3A$; while for $4z^3 - 3z + p = 0$, the roots are $\cosh A, -\frac{1}{2}\cosh A \pm \frac{1}{2}\sqrt{3}\sinh A$ if $p = -\cosh 3A$; and $\sin A$, $\sin(A \pm 2\pi/3)$ if $p = \sin 3A$. If p is real, one value of $3A$ is real.

27. Let $z^3 + az^2 + bz + c = 0$. Show that if $z = z' - a/3, z'^3 + b'z' + c' = 0$, and if $z' = 2\sqrt{\dfrac{|b'|}{3}}\, z''$, then $4z''^3 \pm 3z'' + p = 0$. Combine this with the preceding problem to develop a method of solving any cubic with real coefficients.

28. If z is any complex number, and $w = 2\tan^{-1} e^z - \pi/2$, then w is called the *Gudermannian* of z, and we write $w = \text{gd } z$. Prove that $z = \log\tan\left(\dfrac{w}{2} + \dfrac{\pi}{4}\right)$ and that:

$$\sinh z = \tan w, \quad \cosh z = \sec w, \quad \tanh z = \sin w, \quad \coth z = \csc w,$$
$$\text{csch } z = \cot w, \quad \text{sech } z = \cos w.$$

29. Prove that the points representing the qth roots of any complex number are the vertices of a regular polygon with center of symmetry at the origin. Hence show that the vectorial sum of the lines drawn from the center to the vertices of any regular polygon is zero.

30. Let a_k be any complex constants, $a_n \neq 0$, and b_j be the roots of the polynomial $\sum_{k=0}^{n} a_k Z^k = P(Z)$. Show that if $L(w)$ denotes the corresponding differential operator $\sum_{k=0}^{n} a_k \left(\dfrac{d}{dz}\right)^k w$, where $\left(\dfrac{d}{dz}\right)^0 = 1$, then

$$L(w) = a_n\left(\frac{d}{dz} - b_n\right)\cdots\left(\frac{d}{dz} - b_2\right)\left(\frac{d}{dz} - b_1\right)w,$$

where the operators on the right may be taken with any order of the b_j.

31. From problem 30 and $\left(\dfrac{d}{dz} - b\right) z^k e^{bz} = kz^{k-1}e^{bz}$, deduce that Ce^{bz} is a solution of $L(w) = 0$ if b is a simple root of $P(Z)$, and $(C_1 + C_2 z + \cdots + C_r z^{r-1})e^{bz}$ is a solution if b is a multiple root of order r, where C and the C_j are any complex constants.

32. In the preceding problem, the sum of two solutions is a solution. Hence show that if $p \pm qi$ is a pair of conjugate complex roots, $C'e^{pz}\cos qz$ and $C''e^{pz}\sin qz$ are solutions, with C' and C'' replaced by $(r-1)$st degree polynomials if the roots are each of multiplicity r. If all the a_k are real, and z is real these solutions involve real functions only.

33. If we write for the $L(w)$ of problem 30, $L(w) = P(D)w$, and interpret $\dfrac{1}{P(D)}f(z)$ as any solution of $L(w) = f$, then in particular $1/(D-b)f$ is any solution of $(D-b)w = f$, or $dw/dz - bw = f$, and $1/(D-b)^n f$ is any solution of $(D-b)^n w = f$. Also $A\, 1/(D-b)f$ and $1/(D-b)\, Af$ have the same meaning for A a constant. Show that if $F(Z)$ denotes the partial fraction decomposition of $1/P(Z)$, any of the interpretations of $F(D)f$ is an interpretation of $1/P(D)f$.

This enables us to obtain solutions of $L(w) = f$ from those of equations of simpler type.

34. Deduce a rule for finding solutions of $\sum_{k=0}^{n} a_k z^k \left(\dfrac{d}{dz}\right)^k w = 0$ of the form $C (\log z)^s z^b$ in terms of the roots b_j of the equation $\sum_{k=1}^{n} Z(Z - 1) \cdots$ $(Z - k + 1)a_k + a_0 = 0$, with $s = 0$ for simple roots, and $s = 0, 1, 2, \cdots,$ or $r - 1$ for roots of order r. *Hint:* Put $z = \log z'$, and use problem 31.

35. Verify that for $f(z) = e^z, z_1 = 0$ and $z_2 = \pi i /2, \left| \dfrac{f(z_2) - f(z_1)}{z_2 - z_1} \right| = \dfrac{2\sqrt{2}}{\pi} < 1,$ while if z_3 is any point of the line segment joining z_1 and $z_2, |f'(z_3)| = 1$. This proves that the law of the mean does not hold for complex variables in the form valid for real quantities.

36. Decompose $\dfrac{1}{z^n - 1}$ into simple partial fractions, and also into the simplest fractions of real form. *Ans.* $\sum_{k=1}^{n} \dfrac{b_k}{n(z - b_k)},$ where $b_k = e^{2k\pi i/n}$. The real form includes a simple fraction $\dfrac{1}{n(z - 1)}$ in all cases, and $\dfrac{-1}{n(z + 1)}$ if n is even, together with $\dfrac{2[z \cos (2k\pi/n) - 1]}{n[z^2 - 2z \cos (2k\pi /n) + 1]}$ for $k = 1, 2, \cdots, \left[\dfrac{n - 1}{2} \right].$

37. Decompose $\dfrac{z^m}{z^n - 1}$ into simple partial fractions. *Ans.* $\sum_{k=1}^{n} \dfrac{b_k^{m+1}}{n(z - b_k)},$ where $b_k = e^{2k\pi i/n}$, if $m < n$; and if $m \geqq n$ the polynomial $z^{m-n} + z^{m-2n} + \cdots$ $+ z^{m-pn}, p = \left[\dfrac{m}{n} \right],$ must be added.

38. Let $A(z)$ be a polynomial of degree at most $q - 1$ and $B(z)$ a polynomial of the qth degree with $B(0) \neq 0$, so that there is a Taylor's expansion of $A(z)/B(z)$ about $z = 0$,

$$\frac{A(z)}{B(z)} = u_0 + u_1 z + u_2 z^2 + \cdots + u_m z^m + O(z^{m+1}). \qquad (1)$$

Show that if $B(z) = \sum_{k=0}^{q} a_k z^k, a_q \neq 0$ and $a_0 \neq 0$, then

$$0 = a_0 u_n + a_1 u_{n-1} + a_2 u_{n-2} + \cdots + a_q u_{n-q}, \quad n \geqq q. \qquad (2)$$

Conversely, show that if a sequence of numbers $u_0, u_1, u_2, \cdots$, satisfy (2), the first q values determine a polynomial $A(z)$ of degree less than q for which (1) is satisfied for any m.

39. Prove that the Taylor's development of $R'(z)$ the derivative of any rational function $R(z)$ may be obtained from that of $R(z)$ by termwise differentiation. Hence prove by induction the binomial expansion for integral r and $b \neq 0$:

$$\frac{1}{(z - b)^r} = \left(-\frac{1}{b} \right)^r \left(1 + r\frac{z}{b} + \cdots + \frac{(m + 1) \cdots (m + r - 1)}{(r - 1)\,!} \frac{z^m}{b^m} \right) + O(z^{m+1}).$$

40. Identify the Taylor's expansion of $A(z)/B(z)$ of equation (1) problem 38 with that of its partial fraction expansion obtained from problem 39. Hence show that u_m is a sum of terms of the form Cb^{-m}, for each simple root of $B(z)$, and $(C_1 + C_2 m + \cdots + C_r m^{r-1})b^{-m}$, for each multiple root of order r, where the C's are independent of m.

41. A relation similar to equation (2) of problem 38 is called a *linear difference equation* of the qth order with constant coefficients. From the preceding problems deduce a rule for expressing any sequence which solves such a relation in terms of q constants. Show that the constants can always be determined to make the first q u_n, u_0 to u_{q-1} take any given values. The solution for u_m will be a sum of terms of the form $(C_1 + C_2 m + \cdots + C_r m^{r-1})\beta^m$, if the β are the roots of $\sum_{k=0}^{q} a_{q-k} Z^k$, whose relation to (2) is easily recalled by replacing u_n in (2) by CZ^n.

42. Show that if $f(x + na) = u_n$, any linear relation with constant coefficients between the differences of section 93 of the first q orders and the function itself leads to a difference equation of the qth order, as defined in problem 41. In particular, show that if the qth difference is constant, u_n is a qth degree polynomial in n.

43. If $u_n - 2\cos A u_{n-1} + u_{n-2} = 0$, show that $u_n = c_1 \cos nA + c_2 \sin nA$ if $\sin A \neq 0$, $c_1 + c_2 n$ if $\cos A = 1$, and $c_1 + c_2(-1)^n n$ if $\cos A = -1$. *Hint:* Use problem 41.

44. If the roots β of problem 41 all have $|\beta| < 1$, then $\lim_{n \to +\infty} u_n = 0$. If one root equals 1 and the remaining $q - 1$ roots have $|\beta| < 1$, then any particular sequence approaches a limit. Show that this argument applies to any equation with $\sum_{k=1}^{q} |a_k| \geqq |a_0|$, and in particular to $qu_n - \sum_{k=1}^{q} u_{n-k} = 0$. Solve explicitly for $q = 1, 2, 3$.

45. If $z = x(t) + iy(t)$ is a function of the real variable t, the time, the velocity vector is $x'(t) + iy'(t) = z'(t)$, and the acceleration vector is $x''(t) + iy''(t) = z''(t)$. Write $z = re^{i\theta}$, where r and θ are functions of t, and hence verify that the velocity has a component r' along the radius vector and $r\theta'$ perpendicular to it, while the corresponding components for the acceleration are $(r'' - r\theta'^2)$ and $\frac{1}{r}(r^2\theta)'$.

46. By writing $z' = ve^{i\phi}$ in problem 45, show that the acceleration has a component v' parallel to the velocity vector, and $v\phi'$ perpendicular to it.

CHAPTER VI

INTEGRATION

We devote this chapter to the special limit process, integration, which plays a central rôle in the integral calculus. We define this limit process, and prove its applicability to continuous functions. We investigate some of the properties of integrals and, in particular, show that under certain conditions integration and differentiation are inverse operations.

We show that for each continuous function, the process of integration defines to within an additive constant an indefinite integral function which has the first function as its derivative. In fact, the definition of integration leads to a method by which the integral function could be computed.

We then discuss the problem of representing the integral of certain types of explicit expressions in terms of a small class of known functions. We show that the integral of any rational function can be expressed in terms of rational functions, logarithms, and inverse trigonometric functions, and we describe a number of other classes of expressions whose integrals can be found in terms of elementary functions.

We mention a few integrals not of this character, including the three standard forms of elliptic integrals, and prove that the integral of any rational function of x and the square root of a polynomial in x of at most the fourth degree can be expressed in terms of elementary functions and the three standard forms of elliptic integrals.

121. The Definite Integral. Let $y = f(x)$ be a single-valued function on the closed interval $a \leq x \leq b$, and bounded on this interval in the sense of section 31. In order to define the integral of the function $f(x)$, we divide the interval a,b into n subintervals by the points:

$$a = x_0 < x_1 < x_2 < \cdots < x_n = b, \tag{1}$$

which satisfy this relation but are otherwise arbitrary.

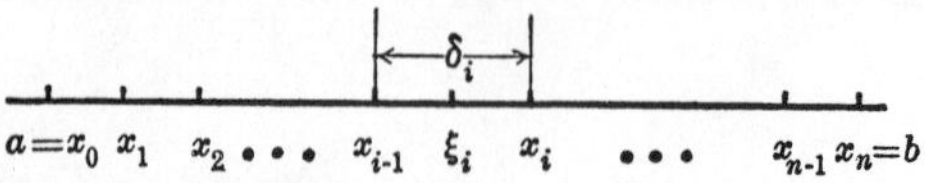

$$a = x_0 \quad x_1 \quad x_2 \bullet \bullet \bullet \quad x_{i-1} \quad \xi_i \quad x_i \quad \bullet \bullet \bullet \quad x_{n-1} x_n = b$$

FIG. 14.

Let ξ_i be any point in, and δ_i the length of, the ith subinterval so that:

$$x_{i-1} \leq \xi_i \leq x_i \quad \text{and} \quad \delta_i = x_i - x_{i-1}. \tag{2}$$

194

Now form the sum:

$$S = f(\xi_1)\delta_1 + f(\xi_2)\delta_2 + \cdots + f(\xi_n)\delta_n$$

$$= \sum_{i=1}^{n} f(\xi_i)\delta_i. \tag{3}$$

The sum S depends on the number n, the choice of the x_i, and the choice of the ξ_i.

Let us denote the maximum of the n positive quantities δ_i by δ_M,

$$\delta_M = \max (\delta_i), \tag{4}$$

and consider an infinite discrete sequence of sums S_t for which

$$\lim_{t \to +\infty} \delta_M = 0. \tag{5}$$

If, for any sequence of this type, the values of S_t approach a finite limit, and if this limit has the same value, I, for all such sequences, then I is called the *definite integral* of $f(x)$ for the interval a,b. We then say that the function $f(x)$ is *integrable* over this interval a,b, and we write:

$$\int_a^b f(x)\, dx = I = \lim S_t. \tag{6}$$

The process by which I was derived from $f(x)$ is called *Riemann integration*, or simply integration. In the expression for I just written, we call $f(x)$ the integrand, x the variable of integration, and a and b the limits of the integral.

122. Integrals of Continuous Functions. In order to show that there are some functions to which the process of integration as defined in the preceding section is applicable, we prove next that:

A function $f(x)$ is integrable over any closed interval throughout which it is continuous.

Let $f(x)$ be continuous over the closed interval a,b. Then, by section 32, it is uniformly continuous in the closed interval. Thus we may select a δ_0 such that, for any positive quantity η,

$$|f(x_2) - f(x_1)| < \epsilon, \quad \text{if} \quad |x_2 - x_1| < \delta_0, \tag{7}$$

where

$$\epsilon = \frac{\eta}{b-a}. \tag{8}$$

Now consider two sums:

$$S = \sum_{i=1}^{n} f(\xi_i)\delta_i \quad \text{and} \quad S' = \sum_{j=1}^{m} f(\xi_j')\delta_j', \tag{9}$$

such that:

$$\delta_M = \max \, (\delta_i) \quad \text{and} \quad \delta_M' = \max \, (\delta_j') \tag{10}$$

are each less than $\dfrac{\delta_0}{2}$,

$$\delta_M < \frac{\delta_0}{2}, \quad \delta_M' < \frac{\delta_0}{2}. \tag{11}$$

Next mark all the points of subdivision of each set, x_i and x_j', to form a new subdivision. Let these points, taken in order with a point in both sets counted only once, be called x_k'', so that

$$a = x_0'' < x_1'' < x_2'' < \cdots < x_p'' = b, \tag{12}$$

and let

$$\delta_k'' = x_k'' - x_{k-1}'' \tag{13}$$

denote the length of the kth interval. Then

$$\sum_{k=1}^{p} \delta_k'' = b - a. \tag{14}$$

The difference of the two sums S and S' may be written:

$$S - S' = \sum_{k=1}^{p} [f(\xi_i) - f(\xi_j')]\delta_k'', \tag{15}$$

where ξ_i is in that interval of the first subdivision which includes the points x_{k-1}'' and x_k'', and ξ_j' is in that interval of the second subdivision which includes these points x_{k-1}'' and x_k''. Thus ξ_i and ξ_j' lie in two intervals which overlap, since they each contain the kth interval of the third subdivision x_{k-1}'', x_k''. Hence we have:

$$|\xi_i - \xi_j'| \le \delta_i + \delta_j', \tag{16}$$

or, in view of the relations (10) and (11),

$$|\xi_i - \xi_j'| < \delta_0. \tag{17}$$

This, combined with the relation (7) shows that:

$$|f(\xi_i) - f(\xi_j')| < \epsilon, \tag{18}$$

and since this is true for each term of the sum in equation (15), we deduce that

$$|S - S'| = |\sum_{k=1}^{p} [f(\xi_i) - f(\xi_j')]\delta_k''| < \sum_{k=1}^{p} \epsilon \delta_k''. \tag{19}$$

Hence it follows from equations (14) and (8) that:

$$|S - S'| < \epsilon(b - a) \le \eta. \tag{20}$$

Let us now apply this to a sequence S_t. Since, for such a sequence, we have the relation (5), there will be a certain point in the sequence, t_0, beyond which $\delta_M < \delta_0/2$. Hence, the difference of any two values of S_t, with t beyond t_0, will be numerically less than η, since we may take these two sums S_t as the S and S' of the relation (20).

Thus the sequence S_t approaches a finite limit I_1 by the Cauchy convergence criterion of section 26.

Next, consider any second sequence S_t'. This approaches a finite limit I_2 by the argument just given. Thus

$$\lim (S_t - S_t') = I_1 - I_2. \tag{21}$$

But, if for the second sequence $\delta_M' < \delta_0/2$ for t beyond t_0', for all values of t beyond t_0 and t_0' we may take S_t and S_t' as the S and S' of the relation (20), so that:

$$|S_t - S_t'| < \eta, \quad \text{for} \quad t \text{ beyond } t_0,\, t_0'. \tag{22}$$

The relations (21) and (22) show that

$$|I_1 - I_2| < \eta, \tag{23}$$

and hence

$$I_1 - I_2 = 0, \tag{24}$$

since η is arbitrary.

Thus the limit I_2 is the same as I_1, and there is a common limit I for all sequences, as we set out to prove.

Let us return to the relation (20), with S any sum for which $\delta_M < \delta_0/2$ and with S' replaced by any value of S_t, with t beyond t_0. Then we have:

$$|S - S_t| < \eta, \quad \text{for} \quad t \text{ beyond } t_0. \tag{25}$$

If we let t become infinite in this relation, and recall that the limit of S_t is I_1, or I, we have:

$$|S - I| < \eta. \tag{26}$$

Thus any sum with $\delta_M < \delta_0/2$ approximates the value of the integral to within η.

123. Linear Properties of the Integral. The definition of $\int_a^b f(x)\, dx$ was made on the assumption that b, the upper limit of the integral, was greater than a, the lower limit of the integral.

The use of the word limit as applied to a and b, the end points of the interval over which the integral is taken, is well established but has little connection with the various technical meanings of limit defined in Chapter II.

We extend the meaning of the expression for an integral by *defining:*

$$\int_a^b f(x)\, dx = -\int_b^a f(x)\, dx, \quad \text{if} \quad a > b, \tag{27}$$

and

$$\int_a^a f(x)\, dx = 0. \tag{28}$$

Thus the equality in the relation (27) holds when $a = b$, and hence for all values of a and b.

If the values a, b, c are such that $a < b < c$, it follows from the original definition of the integral in section 121 that:

$$\int_a^b f(x)\, dx + \int_b^c f(x)\, dx = \int_a^c f(x)\, dx, \tag{29}$$

since we may evaluate the integral on the right by using a sequence of sums, for each of which the point b is one of the x_i.

If $a = b$ or $b = c$, equation (29) is an identity in view of equation (28). And, by equation (27), equation (29) may be written:

$$\int_a^b f(x)\, dx + \int_b^c f(x)\, dx + \int_c^a f(x)\, dx = 0. \tag{30}$$

This is symmetrical in a, b, and c and so holds without any restriction on the order of the three quantities.

The definitions (27) and (28) are motivated by the desire to have equation (29) hold for all values.

By a repeated application of equation (29) we may show that the integral of a function depends linearly on the interval of integration, in the sense that if a finite number of intervals are added or subtracted to form a new set of intervals, the integrals combine in the same way.

For a fixed interval of integration, the integral depends linearly on the function, in the sense that, if u and v are two functions of x, each integrable for the interval,

$$\int_a^b ku\, dx = k \int_a^b u\, dx, \tag{31}$$

and

$$\int_a^b (u + v)\, dx = \int_a^b u\, dx + \int_a^b v\, dx. \tag{32}$$

These relations follow from the linear character of the sum (3) from which the integral was obtained by a limiting process.

124. Inequalities. *If two functions,* $f(x)$ *and* $g(x)$, *are each integrable over the interval a,b, and throughout this interval*

$$f(x) \leqq g(x), \tag{33}$$

then it follows that:

$$\int_a^b f(x)\ dx \ \leqq \int_a^b g(x)\ dx. \tag{34}$$

For, if we use the same n, x_i and δ_i to form a sum S for each function, it follows from the relation (33) that

$$\sum_{i=1}^n f(\xi_i)\delta_i \leqq \sum_{i=1}^n g(\xi_i)\delta_i. \tag{35}$$

Thus, if we form two sequences of sums related in this way, and take the limit, we may deduce the relation (34).

We note next that, if $f(x)$ is a constant, k, each $f(\xi_i) = k$, and we have in place of equation (3):

$$S = \sum_{i=1}^n k\delta_i = k \sum_{i=1}^n \delta_i = k(b - a), \tag{36}$$

so that the limit of any sequence S_t is $k(b - a) = I$. Thus the integral of a constant is the product of the constant times the interval of integration when $a < b$. By equations (27) and (28), we have in all cases:

$$\int_a^b k\ dx = k(b - a). \tag{37}$$

If m is any lower bound and M any upper bound for the function $f(x)$ on the closed interval a,b, we have:

$$m \leqq f(x) \leqq M. \tag{38}$$

This implies that:

$$\int_a^b m\ dx \leqq \int_a^b f(x)\ dx \leqq \int_a^b M\ dx, \tag{39}$$

or, in view of formula (37):

$$m(b - a) \leqq \int_a^b f(x)\ dx \leqq M(b - a). \tag{40}$$

The number K defined by

$$K = \frac{1}{b - a} \int_a^b f(x)\ dx, \tag{41}$$

is called the average value of the function $f(x)$ for the interval a,b. It follows from the relation (40) that:

$$m \leqq K \leqq M. \tag{42}$$

Since m and M are any bounds for the function $f(x)$, we may in particular take m as the greatest lower bound, and M as the least upper bound, and express our result in the theorem:

The average value of a function integrable between a and b,

$$K = \frac{1}{b-a} \int_a^b f(x)\, dx, \tag{43}$$

lies in the closed interval whose end points are the greatest lower bound and least upper bound of the values of $f(x)$ between a and b.

In this form the result holds if $a > b$, in view of equation (27).

Again, if $g(x) \geqq 0$ throughout the closed interval a,b, and $f(x)g(x)$ as well as $g(x)$ is integrable for this interval, we may deduce from the relation (38) that:

$$mg(x) \leqq f(x)g(x) \leqq Mg(x). \tag{44}$$

This implies that:

$$\int_a^b mg(x)\, dx \leqq \int_a^b f(x)g(x)\, dx \leqq \int_a^b Mg(x)\, dx. \tag{45}$$

or, in view of equation (31):

$$m\int_a^b g(x)\, dx \leqq \int_a^b f(x)g(x)\, dx \leqq M \int_a^b g(x)\, dx. \tag{46}$$

It follows from the condition $g(x) \geqq 0$ that $\int_a^b g(x)\, dx \geqq 0$. If this integral is positive, there is a constant k uniquely defined by

$$\int_a^b f(x)g(x)\, dx = k\int_a^b g(x)\, dx. \tag{47}$$

From this and the relation (46) we may deduce that

$$m \leqq k \leqq M. \tag{48}$$

If the integral of $g(x)$ equals zero, the relation (46) shows that the integral of $f(x)g(x)$ is also zero, and then the equation (47) holds for all values of k.

If $a > b$, or if $g(x) \leqq 0$ throughout the interval, some of our inequalities are reversed, but a similar conclusion may be drawn. Thus we may formulate the theorem:

If $g(x)$ is never negative (or never positive) throughout the closed interval a,b, and $g(x)$ as well as $f(x)g(x)$ is integrable over this interval, we may write

$$\int_a^b f(x)g(x)\,dx = k\int_a^b g(x)\,dx, \tag{49}$$

where k is a suitably chosen value between the greatest lower bound and the least upper bound of $f(x)$ for the closed interval.

125. Mean Value Theorems. If the function $f(x)$ is continuous throughout the closed interval a,b there will be two points in this interval, x_1 and x_2, such that

$$f(x_1) = m \quad \text{and} \quad f(x_2) = M, \tag{50}$$

where m is the minimum and M the maximum value of the function for the interval, as we proved in section 33.   Hence we may take these as the m and M of equation (38).

But, any number K such that $m \leq K \leq M$ is either m, taken on at x_1; or M, taken on at x_2; or an intermediate value in the sense of section 34, and therefore taken on at some point between x_1 and x_2. Thus, there is a point ξ between a and b such that $K = f(\xi)$, and the first theorem of the preceding section becomes, for continuous integrands:

If the function $f(x)$ is continuous on the closed interval a,b there is a point ξ of this interval such that:

$$\int_a^b f(x)\,dx = f(\xi)(b-a). \tag{51}$$

This is known as the first mean value theorem for integrals.

Similarly, there is a point ξ', of the closed interval such that $k = f(\xi')$, and we may restate the second theorem of the preceding section:

If the function $f(x)$ is continuous on the closed interval a,b; if $g(x)$ is never negative (or never positive) throughout this interval; and if $g(x)$, as well as $f(x)g(x)$, is integrable over this interval: then there is a point ξ' of this interval such that

$$\int_a^b f(x)g(x)\,dx = f(\xi')\int_a^b g(x)\,dx. \tag{52}$$

126. Evaluation of the Integral. Suppose that $f(x)$ is a function integrable over the interval a,b and throughout this interval is known to be the derivative of a second function $F(x)$, so that

$$f(x) = F'(x). \tag{53}$$

Then we may apply the law of finite increments of section 74 to the function $F(x)$ for each of the subintervals used in section 121, and so find points ξ_i such that

$$F(x_i) - F(x_{i-1}) = F'(\xi_i)(x_i - x_{i-1}). \tag{54}$$

Now use these values as the ξ_i in the sum for S in equation (3). We shall then have:

$$f(\xi_i)\delta_i = F'(\xi_i)(x_i - x_{i-1}) = F(x_i) - F(x_{i-1}), \tag{55}$$

so that:

$$\begin{aligned} S &= f(\xi_1)\delta_1 + f(\xi_2)\delta_2 + \cdots + f(\xi_n)\delta_n \\ &= F(x_1) - F(x_0) + F(x_2) - F(x_1) + \cdots + F(x_n) - F(x_{n-1}) \\ &= F(x_n) - F(x_0) = F(b) - F(a). \end{aligned} \tag{56}$$

Thus we may form a particular sequence S_t for which the ξ_i are always chosen so that equation (54) is satisfied, and for this sequence the values of S_t are all equal, so that the limit is $F(b) - F(a)$.

Since $f(x)$ is integrable, the limit will be the same for all other sequences, and hence we shall have:

$$\int_a^b f(x)\, dx = F(b) - F(a). \tag{57}$$

We write $F(x)\Big|_a^b$ in place of $F(b) - F(a)$.

If $G(x)$ is any second function such that $f(x) = G'(x)$ throughout the interval a,b and we write $H(x) = G(x) - F(x)$, we shall have:

$$H'(x) = G'(x) - F'(x) = 0, \quad a \leqq x \leqq b. \tag{58}$$

Hence, by the theorem deduced from equation (117) of section 75, $H(x) = c$, a constant, and $G(x) = F(x) + c$.

Any function having $f(x)$ as its derivative is called an indefinite integral of $f(x)$. It is clear that if $F(x)$ is an indefinite integral of $f(x)$, then $F(x) + c$ is also an indefinite integral of $f(x)$, and we have just proved that all indefinite integrals are of this form. The symbol $\int f(x)\, dx$ or $\int^x f(x)\, dx$ is used to mean any indefinite integral.

We restate the main result of this section:

If $f(x)$ is an integrable function over the interval c,d and $F(x)$ is any indefinite integral of $f(x)$, so that $f(x) = F'(x)$ throughout the closed interval c,d, then

$$\int_a^b f(x)\, dx = F(x)\Big|_a^b = F(b) - F(a) \tag{59}$$

for a and b, any two points of the closed interval c,d.

That equation (59) holds when $a = b$ follows from equation (28), and that it holds for $b < a$ follows from equation (27).

127. Dummy Indices and Variables. In a finite summation, abbreviated by the symbol $\sum$ with an index of summation i, the precise letter used for the index of summation is of no importance, since it does not appear in the sum when written out in full. Thus:

$$\sum_{i=1}^{3} \delta_i = \sum_{j=1}^{3} \delta_j = \sum_{k=1}^{3} \delta_k, \tag{60}$$

since each is an abbreviation for $\delta_1 + \delta_2 + \delta_3$. We call such an index a dummy index. We may always replace a dummy index by some other letter, and to do so sometimes clarifies an argument and avoids confusion. This was the case in section 122, where we replaced i by j in the summation S'.

In the sum for S in equation (3), we may in particular take $\xi_i = x_i$, in which case the sum is

$$S = \sum_{i=1}^{n} f(x_i)\delta_i, \tag{61}$$

or, if we write Δx_i in place of $\delta_i = x_i - x_{i-1}$, a difference of two values of x,

$$S = \sum_{i=1}^{n} f(x_i)\,\Delta x_i. \tag{62}$$

This is the form which gave rise to the notation for an integral, $\int_a^b f(x)\,dx$, the sign of integration being a modified S, and the replacement of the Greek letters Σ and Δ by the Latin letters S and d indicating that we have performed a limiting process. This is analogous to replacing Δ by d to indicate that dy/dx is obtained from $\Delta y/\Delta x$ by a limiting process.

The limits a and b are analogous to the initial and final values of the index of summation. As we have replaced x_i by x, the index of summation i no longer appears, but the variable x itself plays an analogous rôle. In fact, if we considered the function $f(u)$ for values of u such that $a \leqq u \leqq b$, we could carry out the entire process of section 121, regarding the x_i as intermediate values of u. Thus we should find the same values for the sums S and S_t and the same limiting value I.

This shows that the variable of integration is a dummy variable and may be replaced by any other letter. That is:

$$I = \int_a^b f(x)\,dx = \int_a^b f(u)\,du = \int_a^b f(y)\,dy. \tag{63}$$

The value of the integral depends on the choice of the interval of integration, that is on the values of a and b. Hence for a fixed function $f(x)$, the integral is a function of the limits.

In particular, we may keep the limit a fixed and replace b by a variable quantity x. The integral then becomes a function of x:

$$A(x) = \int_a^x f(x)\, dx = \int_a^x f(u)\, du. \tag{64}$$

In the first integral written, x is used in two senses, both as a variable limit, and as the dummy variable of integration. When we replace the dummy variable x by u, we do not affect the x used as a variable limit.

We note that, since $f(x)$ is bounded, the function $A(x)$ is a continuous function of x. We have, in fact:

$$A(x + h) - A(x) = \int_x^{x+h} f(u)\, du = Kh, \tag{65}$$

where K lies between the upper and lower bounds of $f(x)$. Thus, if

$$|f(x)| \leq M, \quad -M \leq K \leq M, \quad \text{and} \quad |Kh| \leq M|h|. \tag{66}$$

It follows that when $h \to 0$, $Kh \to 0$, and $A(x + h) \to A(x)$, so that the function $A(x)$ is continuous at x.

128. Equal Subintervals. The expression (62) may be further specialized by taking all the Δx_i equal, so that $\Delta x_i = (b - a)/n$. This gives a particular sequence of sums S_n:

$$S_n = \sum_{i=1}^n f(x_i)\, \Delta x_i, \tag{67}$$

where

$$\Delta x_i = \frac{b - a}{n}, \quad x_i = a + \frac{i(b - a)}{n}. \tag{68}$$

For integrable functions, we have:

$$\int_a^b f(x)\, dx = \lim_{n \to +\infty} S_n. \tag{69}$$

This last equation, restricted in its application to continuous functions, and interpreted as expressing a property of the area under a curve, is sometimes used as a definition in elementary calculus. This approach enables one to confine his attention to a single specific sequence S_n.

The values of S_n are sometimes calculated in a specific case for a few values of n, to suggest that a limit is approached. We may form a precise estimate of the behavior of S_n, from the remark at the end of section 122, which shows that,

$$\text{if} \qquad \frac{b-a}{n} < \tfrac{1}{2}\delta_0, \quad \text{then} \quad |S_n - I| < \eta. \qquad (70)$$

In simple cases, we may determine δ_0 numerically. Thus, suppose that $f(x)$ has a derivative throughout the closed interval a,b and that M is any upper bound for $f'(x)$ in this interval. Then from the law of finite increments of section 74, we have

$$f(x_2) - f(x_1) = (x_2 - x_1)f'(\xi), \qquad (71)$$

so that,

$$\text{if} \qquad x_2 - x_1 \leqq \delta_0 \quad \text{and} \quad |f'(x)| \leqq M, \qquad (72)$$

we shall have:

$$|f(x_2) - f(x_1)| \leqq M\delta_0. \qquad (73)$$

Thus, we can satisfy the relations (7) and (8) by taking:

$$M\delta_0 < \epsilon \leqq \frac{\eta}{b-a}. \qquad (74)$$

If we take δ_0 to satisfy this inequality, and then take n to satisfy the inequality (70), we shall have:

$$n > \frac{2M(b-a)^2}{\eta}. \qquad (75)$$

This proves that:

If, throughout the closed interval a,b, the function $f(x)$ has a derivative $f'(x)$ and M is any upper bound for $|f'(x)|$ on the interval, then, for any n such that $n > 2M(b-a)^2/\eta$, the sum:

$$S_n = \sum_{i=1}^{n} f(x_i)\,\Delta x_i; \;\; \Delta x_i = \frac{b-a}{n}, \; x_i = a + \frac{i(b-a)}{n}, \qquad (76)$$

approximates the integral $I = \int_a^b f(x)\,dx$ to within η, so that $|S_n - I| < \eta$.

The conclusion still holds, whether $f(x)$ has a derivative or not, provided M is such that

$$|f(x_2) - f(x_1)| < M|x_2 - x_1|, \qquad (77)$$

for all values of x_1 and x_2 in the closed interval a,b.

The condition (77) is called a Lipschitz condition, and implies that the function is continuous and hence integrable.

129. Derivatives of Integrals. Let the function $f(x)$ be integrable on the closed interval a,b and continuous at x_0, a point of this interval. Then the integral of $f(x)$ over the interval a,x is a function of x, and we may write as in equation (64):

$$A(x) = \int_a^x f(x)\, dx = \int_a^x f(u)\, du, \tag{78}$$

where we have replaced the dummy variable of integration x by u so as to avoid confusion between the variable of integration and the variable upper limit.

Let us now calculate the derivative of $A(x)$ at x_0, using the fundamental definition. We have for any value of x and $x + h$ in the closed interval a,b:

$$A(x + h) - A(x) = \int_a^{x+h} f(u)\, du - \int_a^x f(u)\, du = \int_x^{x+h} f(u)\, du, \tag{79}$$

by equation (29). We next deduce from the first mean value theorem for integrals that for a suitable intermediate value ξ,

$$\xi \text{ between } x \text{ and } x + h, \text{ or } \xi = x + \theta h, \ 0 < \theta < 1, \tag{80}$$

$$\int_x^{x+h} f(u)\, du = hf(\xi) = hf(x + \theta h). \tag{81}$$

This shows that

$$\frac{A(x + h) - A(x)}{h} = f(x + \theta h), \tag{82}$$

so that

$$\lim_{h \to 0} \frac{A(x_0 + h) - A(x_0)}{h} = f(x_0), \tag{83}$$

since $f(x)$ is continuous at x_0.

Thus the function $A(x)$ has a derivative at x_0,

and
$$A'(x_0) = f(x_0). \tag{84}$$

We may formulate the result as a theorem:

If $f(x)$ is integrable in some closed interval a,b and if $f(x)$ is continuous at some point x_0 in the open interval a,b, then the function $A(x) = \int_a^x f(x)\, dx$ or $\int_a^x f(u)\, du$ has a derivative for $x = x_0$, and this derivative $A'(x_0) = f(x_0)$.

130. Existence of Indefinite Integrals. If the function $f(x)$ is continuous throughout the closed interval a,b, then the argument of the preceding section shows that the function

$$A(x) = \int_a^x f(u) \, du \qquad (85)$$

is an indefinite integral of $f(x)$ as defined in section 126,

since $\qquad\qquad A'(x) = f(x) \qquad\qquad (86)$

throughout the closed interval.

The function $A(x)$ is the particular indefinite integral which is zero when $x = a$. The indefinite integral similarly obtained by using any other value a' in place of a is $A(x) - A(a')$, by the reasoning of section 126.

Thus every continuous function has associated with it another function, its indefinite integral for a particular value of a. For a particular function $f(x)$ and a particular value of a, the function $A(x)$ could be computed and tabulated. We shall develop practical methods of doing this in section 145. Theoretically the values could be found to any desired degree of approximation by the method given in section 128.

131. Inverse Operations. The theorems of sections 126 and 129 show that differentiation and integration are to some extent inverse operations.

For, if we start with an integrable function $f(x)$, integrate it with lower limit fixed and upper limit the variable x, and then differentiate, we shall come back to the original function for any value at which the function $f(x)$ is continuous, by section 129.

Again, if we start with a function $F(x)$ having an integrable derivative, differentiate it, and then integrate it with lower limit fixed and upper limit the variable x, we shall come back to a function only differing by a constant from the original function, by section 126.

In particular, when we are dealing with simple explicit functions on restricted intervals, all of the functions which come into consideration have continuous derivatives. For such functions, integration followed by differentiation with respect to the upper limit leaves a function unchanged, while differentiation followed by integration with variable upper limit changes a function at most by an additive constant. This principle, or the more precise result expressed by the theorems of sections 129 and 126 paraphrased above, is sometimes referred to as the " fundamental theorem of the integral calculus."

In elementary work, where we are interested in explicit expressions, we think of differentiation as leading to a simpler result than integration, since the derivatives of the functions with which we deal can always be found explicitly with comparative ease, whereas the indefinite integrals of many of the functions we meet can not be found in terms of functions already known to us.

However, from another point of view, integration leads to a simpler result than differentiation. For, in all the theorems of Chapter IV, we had to assume that the functions could be differentiated to yield the derivatives involved. On the contrary, if we start with any continuous function and integrate it, we obtain a second function as shown in section 122, and this function has a derivative.

Or, if we start with an integrable function, not necessarily continuous, and integrate it, the result will be a continuous function, by section 127. In fact, equations (65) and (66) show that $A(x)$ satisfies a Lipschitz condition, as defined in equation (77).

Thus integration is a smoothing process, always leading to a function having at least as much in the way of continuity or differentiability properties as the original function.

132. Tables of Integrals. In some cases the indefinite integral of a simple explicit expression can be found as an algebraic expression, or can be expressed in terms of functions which are already tabulated. Every specific formula of differentiation leads to the determination of some indefinite integral. Thus, we obtain such results as

$$\int^x x^n \, dx = \frac{x^{n+1}}{n+1}, \quad n \neq -1, \tag{87}$$

$$\int^x x^{-1} \, dx = \log x, \text{ etc.} \tag{88}$$

Results of this kind are arranged in convenient form as tables of integrals and may always be checked by differentiation. The scope of such a table is greatly increased by certain general methods of reduction, to which we proceed.

133. General Reductions. The general rules for differentiation given in section 63 lead to corresponding rules for integrals. Throughout this section, we shall assume that all the derivatives used exist, and that any function used as an integrand, as u or $u \, dv/dx$, is continuous. With this assumption, we have:

$$\int^x ku \, dx = k \int^x u \, dx, \tag{89}$$

and $$\int^x (u + v) \, dx = \int^x u \, dx + \int^x v \, dx, \tag{90}$$

since both sides have the same derivatives with respect to x.

The rule of " integration by parts,"

$$\int^x u \frac{dv}{dx} dx = uv - \int^x v \frac{du}{dx} dx, \tag{91}$$

is proved similarly. This is useful when the integral on the right is simpler than that on the left.

Finally we have the rule of substitution,

$$A(x) = \int_{x_0}^x f(x) \, dx = \int_{t_0}^t f[g(t)]g'(t) \, dt, \tag{92}$$

where

$$x_0 = g(t_0), \quad x = g(t), \tag{93}$$

and the function $g(t)$ is a single-valued function for the closed interval t_0, t.

We prove this rule by differentiating both sides with respect to t.

For the left side, $A = \int_{x_0}^x f(u) \, du$, we find:

$$\frac{dA}{dt} = \frac{dA}{dx} \frac{dx}{dt} = f(x)g'(t), \tag{94}$$

and for the right side, $B = \int_{t_0}^t f[g(u)]g'(u) \, du$, we find:

$$\frac{dB}{dt} = f[g(t)]g'(t), \tag{95}$$

by section 129. But the expressions (94) and (95) are equal, in view of the equation (93).

That the integrals A and B do not differ by a constant follows from the circumstance that $x = x_0$ when $t = t_0$, so that both integrals in equation (92) are zero when $x = x_0$.

The rule of substitution for indefinite integrals may be written in the form:

$$\int^x f(x) \, dx = \int^t f[g(t)]g'(t) \, dt, \tag{96}$$

where the limit $x = g(t)$ and this function is single-valued for the range of t to which the equation is to be applied. This is a consequence of equation (92). It is easily remembered, since if $x = g(t)$, the differential $f(x) \, dx = f(g) \, dg = f(g) \frac{dg}{dt} \, dt$, and the value of t corresponding to x is such that $x = g(t)$.

134. Separable Differential Equations. A relation of the form

$$\frac{dy}{dx} = F(x,y) \tag{97}$$

is called a differential equation of the first order, and any function $y = f(x)$ is a solution of this equation

if $$f'(x) = F[x,f(x)]. \tag{98}$$

The differential equation is said to be separable if the function $F(x,y)$ may be written as the quotient of a function of x alone by a function of y alone, so that

$$\frac{dy}{dx} = \frac{p(x)}{q(y)} \quad \text{and} \quad q(y)\,dy = p(x)\,dx, \tag{99}$$

an equation involving differentials in which the variables are separated. We assume that $q(y)$ and $p(x)$ are continuous.

Let us next assume that the equation (99) has a solution $y = f(x)$, for x in a certain range $x_0 \leqq x \leqq x_1$, and that for x in this range $q[f(x)]$ is never zero. Then, if $y_0 = f(x_0)$, and $y = f(x)$, the rule of substitution in the form of equation (92) shows that

$$\int_{y_0}^{y} q(y)\,dy = \int_{x_0}^{x} p(x)\,d. \tag{100}$$

But, if we define

$$A(y) = \int_{y_0}^{y} q(y)\,dy, \tag{101}$$

in the range considered this function has a derivative $q(y)$ which is never zero. Hence, by section 75, it has a uniquely determined inverse function, and the equation

$$f_1(x) = A^{-1}\left[\int_{x_0}^{x} p(x)\,dx\right] \tag{102}$$

defines a function $f_1(x)$.

If, then, we start with the equation (99) with $p(x)$ and $q(y)$ continuous functions, restrict y so that in the range y_0, y the function $q(y)$ is never zero, and form the equation (100), this equation will determine y as a function of x, $y = f_1(x)$.

Since this function is given by equation (102), by sections 75 and 129 we have:

$$\frac{dy}{dx} = f_1'(x) = \frac{p(x)}{\dfrac{dA}{dy}} = \frac{p(x)}{q(y)}. \tag{103}$$

Moreover, we see from equation (102) that when $x = x_0$, $y = y_0$, so that $f_1(x_0) = y_0$. This shows that $y = f_1(x)$ is a solution of the differential equation (99), which is y_0 when $x = x_0$. Since this function was uniquely determined by equation (100), and any solution of this kind necessarily satisfied equation (100), it is the only solution. That is:

If the functions $p(x)$ and $q(y)$ are continuous, the solution of the separable differential equation

$$\frac{dy}{dx} = \frac{p(x)}{q(y)} \tag{104}$$

which equals y_0 when $x = x_0$, is uniquely determined by:

$$\int_{y_0}^{y} q(y)\, dy = \int_{x_0}^{x} p(x)\, dx, \tag{105}$$

provided that $q(y)$ is never zero in the closed interval y_0, y.

This justifies the solution of separable differential equations by separating the variables and integrating between corresponding limits.

135. Complex Notation. If $W(x)$ is a complex function of a real variable, as defined in section 119, whose derivative for real increments is $w(x)$, we call $W(x)$ an indefinite integral of $w(x)$ and write:

$$\int^{x} w(x)\, dx = W(x). \tag{106}$$

By section 119, $dW(x)/dx = w(x)$ if, and only if,

$$\frac{d}{dx} \mathbf{R}W(x) = \mathbf{R}w(x) \quad \text{and} \quad \frac{d}{dx} \mathbf{I}W(x) = \mathbf{I}w(x). \tag{107}$$

Thus the equation (106) is completely equivalent to the two real equations:

$$\int^{x} \mathbf{R}w(x)\, dx = \mathbf{R}W(x) \quad \text{and} \quad \int^{x} \mathbf{I}w(x)\, dx = \mathbf{I}W(x). \tag{108}$$

The integration of certain functions is simplified by regarding them as the real or imaginary part of a complex function of a real variable. For example, from

$$e^{(a+bi)x} = e^{ax} \cos bx + i e^{ax} \sin bx, \tag{109}$$

and

$$\int^{x} e^{(a+bi)x}\, dx = \frac{e^{(a+bi)x}}{a + bi}, \tag{110}$$

we may deduce:

$$\int^{x} e^{ax} \cos bx\, dx = \frac{e^{ax}(a \cos bx + b \sin bx)}{a^2 + b^2}, \tag{111}$$

and
$$\int^x e^{ax} \sin bx \, dx = \frac{e^{ax}(a \sin bx - b \cos bx)}{a^2 + b^2}.$$ (112)

136. Known Integrals. We may use the rule of substitution of section 133 to show how the ease or difficulty of evaluating an integral depends on our previous knowledge. Thus, suppose that for any function $f(x)$, continuous and positive on the closed interval a,b, we have already calculated and tabulated the function

$$A(x) = \int_a^x f(x) \, dx$$ (113)

of section 129 for a large number of values of x on this interval. Then this function, $A(x)$, will be a known function in the sense that the function $\log_{10} x$ is known for values of x on the interval 1,10.

As we have assumed that $f(x)$ is positive, by section 129, $A'(x) = f(x)$ is positive. Hence, by section 75 the function $y = A(x)$ has an inverse function $x = A^{-1}(y)$ whose derivative is

$$\frac{d}{dy} A^{-1}(y) = \frac{1}{A'(x)} = \frac{1}{f(x)},$$ (114)

so that

$$[A^{-1}(y)]' = \frac{1}{f[A^{-1}(y)]}.$$ (115)

The inverse function $x = A^{-1}(y)$ may be read from our table for $A(x)$ if y is in the interval $A(a), A(b)$, just as we read the values of 10^y, the number whose logarithm is y, from a table of logarithms for values of y in the interval 0,1.

Now suppose that we have either forgotten the origin of the function $A(x)$ which appears in equation (114), or that we have derived this property of the function from some other definition. In any case we recall the function and the equation (115), and try to use it to evaluate the indefinite integral $\int^x f(x) \, dx$. Let us transform this by the rule of substitution, equation (96), with

$$x = g(t) = A^{-1}(t), \quad \text{so that} \quad t = g^{-1}(x) = A(x).$$ (116)

Then, from this and equation (115),

$$g'(t) = [A^{-1}(t)]' = \frac{1}{f[A^{-1}(t)]} = \frac{1}{f[g(t)]},$$ (117)

so that

$$f[g(t)]g'(t) = 1.$$ (118)

As this is the second integrand in equation (96), we have:

$$\int^x f(x)\, dx = \int^t dt = t = g^{-1}(x) = A(x). \tag{119}$$

We have thus reduced the indefinite integral $\int^x f(x)\, dx$ to a known function, $A(x)$.

While this process seems unnecessarily roundabout and highly artificial when stated in general terms, it is essentially the process used to reduce

$$\int^x \frac{dx}{x} = \log x \quad \text{and} \quad \int^x \frac{dx}{1+x^2} = \tan^{-1} x \tag{120}$$

to known functions in elementary calculus. In fact, the best methods of computing tables of these functions are based on expansions directly derived from the properties:

$$\frac{d}{dx} \log x = \frac{1}{x}, \quad \frac{d}{dx} \tan^{-1} x = \frac{1}{1+x^2}, \tag{121}$$

analogous to the property $A'(x) = f(x)$. Compare problems 31 to 35 of Exercises IV.

137. Rational Functions. To integrate a rational function with real coefficients, we use the decomposition of section 115. We showed there that any rational function of x could be reduced to the quotient of two polynomials in x, $A(x)/B(x)$, where $A(x)$ and $B(x)$ have no common factors. Furthermore, the function could be expressed as the sum of a polynomial and terms of the form $A_n(x - b)^{-n}$, there being a series of such terms with $n = 1, 2, \cdots, r$ for each real or complex root b of the denominator $B(x)$, where r is the multiplicity of the root. A rational function with real coefficients may be reduced to the quotient of two real polynomials. Since any common complex roots will occur in conjugate pairs, they may be removed by dividing by real factors, and we may assume that $A(x)$ and $B(x)$ have real coefficients. Thus the function is a real rational function as defined in section 118, and in the decomposition the coefficients of the polynomial, as well as the A_n for any real root b, will be real. Conjugate complex roots will have the same multiplicity, and will give rise to terms with conjugate coefficients.

The integration of the rational function is deduced from the integrals of the separate terms of the decomposition by equation (90). For the terms of the polynomial we use:

$$\int^x k\, dx = kx \quad \text{and} \quad \int^x kx^m\, dx = \frac{kx^{m+1}}{m+1}, \quad m = 1, 2, 3, \cdots. \tag{122}$$

The equations:

$$\int^x \frac{A \, dx}{x - b} = A \log |x - b| \quad \text{and}$$

$$\int^x \frac{A \, dx}{(x - b)^n} = \frac{-A}{(n - 1)(x - b)^{n-1}}, \quad n = 2, 3, \cdots \quad (123)$$

give the integrals for the terms for real roots.

For the terms arising from complex roots, we note that:

$$\frac{A + Bi}{(x - a - bi)^n} + \frac{A - Bi}{(x - a + bi)^n} = 2\mathbf{R} \frac{A + Bi}{(x - a - bi)^n}, \quad (124)$$

if a, b, A, and B are all real numbers. By equation (108) we have:

$$\int^x 2\mathbf{R} \frac{A + Bi}{(x - a - bi)^n} dx = \frac{-2}{(n - 1)} \mathbf{R} \frac{A + Bi}{(x - a - bi)^{n-1}}, \quad n = 2, 3, \cdots \quad (125)$$

and

$$\int^x 2\mathbf{R} \frac{A + Bi}{x - a - bi} dx = 2\mathbf{R}[(A + Bi) \log (x - a - bi)] \quad (126)$$

where the relations of the derivatives to the integrands follow from section 112.

We may obtain other expressions for the integral (126), since

$2\mathbf{R}[(A + Bi) \log (x - a - bi)]$

$$= 2A \log |x - a - bi| - 2B \arg (x - a - bi)$$

$$= \log |x - a - bi|^{2A} - \arg (x - a - bi)^{2B} \quad (127)$$

$$= A \log [(x - a)^2 + b^2] + 2B \tan^{-1} \frac{b}{x - a}. \quad (128)$$

The form (127) enables us to write the sum of a number of such terms with a single use of the symbols log and arg, thus theoretically enabling us to find the value of any rational integral with only one use of the logarithmic tables and one use of the trigonometric tables, since the terms involving logarithms from real roots may be written $\log |x - b|^A$.

Since

$$\tan^{-1} u = \cot^{-1} \frac{1}{u} = \frac{\pi}{2} - \tan^{-1} \frac{1}{u}, \quad (129)$$

we have

$$2B \tan^{-1} \left[\frac{b}{x - a} \right] = -2B \tan^{-1} \left[\frac{x - a}{b} \right] + B\pi. \quad (130)$$

If we make this substitution and absorb the constant $B\pi$ in the constant of integration, we may deduce from the form (128) that

$$\int^x 2\mathbf{R} \frac{A+Bi}{x-a-bi}\, dx = A \log{[(x-a)^2 + b^2]} - 2B \tan^{-1} \frac{x-a}{b}. \qquad (131)$$

This last form is the most familiar, and usually the one best adapted to computation.

If we expressed the integral as a real function, we should write:

$$\int^x \frac{P+Qx}{x^2+px+q}\, dx = \frac{Q}{2} \log{(x^2+px+q)}$$
$$+ \frac{2P-Qp}{\sqrt{4q-p^2}} \tan^{-1} \frac{2x+p}{\sqrt{4q-p^2}}. \qquad (132)$$

Thus even the real form of the integrated expression has constants more closely related to the form of the integrand (131) than to the form of the integrand (132).

The advantage of using the decomposition of section 115 over using that of section 118 is slight for simple conjugate complex roots, but is much greater when there are multiple complex roots. In that case, for multiple quadratic factors we must develop reduction formulas, which essentially take us back from the real coefficients P_j and Q_j, appearing in numerators $P_j + Q_j x$, to the original conjugate complex numerators, $A_j \pm B_j i$. That the reduction formulas must do this may be seen from equation (125), which shows that, in complex form, each pair of terms of a given degree taken by itself has a simple integral.

Since the coefficients in the decomposition are determined, they may be found either by the method of undetermined coefficients, the method of section 116, or by using the fact that an identity must be true for any values of x, conveniently chosen. The work may sometimes be shortened by subtracting the development up to a certain stage.

For example, if a third degree denominator has one real root and one pair of conjugate complex roots, we may determine the term for the real root by equation (244) of section 116, and subtract the polynomial and the fraction for this root to obtain a term like that in equation (132).

Again, if a denominator has one multiple real root and a number of simple real roots, we may subtract the terms for the simple roots, as well as the terms of the polynomial, and then determine the terms for the multiple root by expanding the resulting numerator in the appropriate Taylor's development.

Another method of determining the integral is to use the reasoning of this section to predict the form of the integral, except for the coefficients, and then directly determine the coefficients of the integral by the method of undetermined coefficients.

138. Rationalizable Integrands. Several other classes of integrals may be reduced to integrals of rational functions. To describe some of these classes, we shall denote a rational function of one variable, u, by $R(u)$, and a rational function of two variables, u and v, by $R(u,v)$, so that this last is the quotient of two functions, each a polynomial in the two variables u and v.

Then the integrand $R\left(x, \left[\dfrac{ax + b}{cx + d}\right]^{1/q}\right)$ is rationalizable when q is an integer. For, if $ad - bc = 0$, the second variable is a constant, and the integrand is already a rational function of x. When $ad - bc \neq 0$, the relation $\left[\dfrac{ax + b}{cx + d}\right]^{1/q} = t$ makes x a rational function of t, $g(t)$. Thus $g'(t)$ is rational, and the new integrand obtained from equation (96), $R[g(t),t]g'(t)$ is a rational function of t.

An important special case is $R(x, \sqrt{ax + b})$.

Again, the integrand $R(e^{ax})$ is reducible by the substitution $ax = \log t$, to the integral of $R(t)/at$, which is a rational function of t.

Any rational function of trigonometric functions of x may be written in the form $R(\sin x, \cos x)$. An integrand of this type may be reduced by the substitution $t = \tan \dfrac{x}{2}$ to the integral of $R\left(\dfrac{2t}{1 + t^2}, \dfrac{1 - t^2}{1 + t^2}\right)\dfrac{2}{1 + t^2}$, which is a rational function of t.

We may always rationalize an integrand of the form

$$R(x, \sqrt{ax^2 + bx + c}).$$

We assume $a \neq 0$, since the integrand with $a = 0$ is of a type already discussed.

If the roots of $ax^2 + bx + c = 0$ are p and q, real and unequal, we may write $ax^2 + bx + c = a(x - p)(x - q)$. If we put $a(x - p) = t^2(x - q)$, $x = g(t)$ is a rational function of t, so that $g'(t)$ is also rational. The transformed integrand is $R\{g(t),t[g(t) - q]\}g'(t)$, which is rational in t.

When the roots are equal, $q = p$, $\sqrt{ax^2 + bx + c} = \sqrt{a}(x - p)$, so that the integrand is rational in x. In this case a must be positive, since the integrand is assumed to be real.

When the roots are conjugate complex numbers, $r \pm is$,

$$ax^2 + bx + c = a(x - r - is)(x - r + is) = a[(x - r)^2 + s^2], \quad (133)$$

and again a must be positive in order to make the radical real. In this case we put $(x - r)^2 + s^2 = [(x - r) + t]^2$, which makes $x = g(t)$ a rational function of t, so that $g'(t)$ is also rational. The transformed integrand is $R[g(t),g(t) - r + t]g'(t)$, which is rational in t.

139. Other Elementary Integrals. Let $I(u)$ be an inverse trigonometric function, an inverse hyperbolic function, or the logarithm (inverse exponential function). Let $B'(x)$ be the derivative of an explicit algebraic function, $B(x)$, and let $A(x)$ also be an explicit algebraic function. Then the integrand $I[A(x)]B'(x)$ may be simplified by an integration by parts:

$$\int^x I[A(x)]B'(x) \, dx = I[A(x)]B(x) - \int^x I'[A(x)]A'(x)B(x) \, dx. \quad (134)$$

The new integrand, $I'[A(x)]A'(x)B(x)$, is an explicit algebraic expression and may be rationalizable if the functions $A(x)$ and $B(x)$ are sufficiently simple.

In particular, if $A(x) = x$ and $B(x)$ is a rational function, the new integrand $I'(x)B(x)$ will either be rational, or of the form $R(x,\sqrt{ax^2 + bx + c})$, which is rationalizable. Thus an inverse function of x times a polynomial may be integrated by this process.

The problem of integrating a real polynomial in any number of variables, each of which is either x, an exponential e^{ax}, or a sine or cosine function $\sin bx$, $\cos cx$, is immediately reducible to the problem of integrating terms of the form $x^n e^{Ax}$, where n is a positive integer, and A is a real or complex number. When A is complex, the indefinite integral is to be understood in the sense of section 135. An integration by parts may be used to reduce the exponent of n by unity,

$$\int^x x^n e^{Ax} \, dx = x^n \frac{e^{Ax}}{A} - \frac{n}{A} \int^x x^{n-1} e^{Ax} \, dx, \quad (135)$$

so that n such integrations will reduce the problem to

$$\int^x e^{Ax} \, dx = \frac{e^{Ax}}{A}. \quad (136)$$

Our purpose in the last three sections is to give the student some general idea of the classes of integrals which either will be found in integral tables or may readily be reduced to integrals given in the tables. The general methods here given are often much longer than special devices adapted to particular cases or to the construction of a table of integrals. Also there are a number of alternative procedures which are sometimes preferable. For example, if the form of the integral is predictable to within a number of constants, these may be found by the method of undetermined coefficients.

Any indefinite integral taken from an integral table may be verified by differentiation, which always provides the simplest proof of such a formula if the answer is known.

140. Non-elementary Integrals. Most integrals not of the types discussed in the last three sections nor immediately transformable into one of these types cannot be evaluated in terms of a finite combination of elementary functions. In a few special cases, the non-elementary character of an integral has been proved, by showing that the function defined by the integral with variable upper limit has some property not enjoyed by any elementary function. The character of the argument is somewhat similar to that given in section 92 to prove that the logarithmic function is not an algebraic function.

A few of the simpler non-elementary integrals are those with integrands, e^x/x, $\sin x/x$, $\cos x/x$, which lead to new functions known as the exponential integral, the sine integral, and the cosine integral. The integrals

$$\int_0^x e^{-x^2}\, dx, \quad \int_0^x \sin x^2\, dx, \text{ and } \int_0^x \cos x^2\, dx \qquad (137)$$

are known as the probability integral, the Fresnel sine integral, and the Fresnel cosine integral. We shall discuss practical methods of constructing tables of these functions in section 331. Such tables are available and enable us to evaluate these integrals and any others easily reducible to them.

The simplest algebraic integrands which in general lead to non-elementary integrals are those given by $R[x, \sqrt{P(x)}]$ where $P(x)$ is a polynomial of the third or higher degree, and R is a rational function of the two variables as in section 138, where we showed that this integral was elementary if $P(x)$ was of the first or second degree.

Since the square root of a polynomial with multiple roots may be written as a polynomial times the square root of a new polynomial with all its roots simple, we may, and shall, assume that all the roots of $P(x)$ are simple. When the polynomial with simple roots is of degree three or four, the integral of $R[x, \sqrt{P(x)}]$ is called an elliptic integral.

141. Elliptic Integrals. The special elliptic integrals

$$F(k,\phi) = \int_0^\phi \frac{d\phi}{\sqrt{1 - k^2 \sin^2 \phi}} = \int_0^{\sin \phi} \frac{dx}{\sqrt{(1 - x^2)(1 - k^2 x^2)}},$$
$$0 < k < 1, \quad (138)$$

the elliptic integrals of the first kind, and

$$E(k,\phi) = \int_0^\phi \sqrt{1 - k^2 \sin^2 \phi} \, d\phi = \int_0^{\sin \phi} \frac{\sqrt{1 - k^2 x^2}}{\sqrt{1 - x^2}} \, dx,$$

$$0 < k < 1, \quad (139)$$

the elliptic integral of the second kind, have been tabulated by Legendre for real values of k between 0 and 1.

The elliptic integral of the third kind,

$$\Pi(k,\alpha,\phi) = \int_0^\phi \frac{d\phi}{(\sin^2 \phi - \alpha) \sqrt{1 - k^2 \sin^2 \phi}}$$

$$= \int_0^{\sin \phi} \frac{dx}{(x^2 - \alpha) \sqrt{(1 - x^2)(1 - k^2 x^2)}} \quad (140)$$

where k is real, $0 < k < 1$, and α may be complex, has been only partially tabulated. For $\alpha = 0$, see problem 47 of Exercises VI, p. 238.

We shall now prove that:

If $P(x)$ is a polynomial of at most the fourth degree with real coefficients and if R is a rational function of two variables with real coefficients, while x is restricted to a range in which $P(x)$ is positive, the indefinite integral

$$\int^x R[x, \sqrt{P(x)}] \, dx$$ *can be expressed as a linear combination of terms,*

each of which is either an elementary function, or an elliptic integral of the first, second, or third kind.

As was indicated in the preceding section, the integral is rationalizable if $P(x)$ is of the first or second degree, or has multiple roots.

When $P(x)$ is of the third degree it has at least one real root, r, and we may write:

$$P(x) = (x - r)(ax^2 + bx + c), \quad a \neq 0. \quad (141)$$

Thus, for a range of x such that $x > r$, we may make the change of variable $x = r + z^2$, $dx = 2z \, dz$. The radical becomes:

$$\sqrt{P(x)} = z \sqrt{az^4 + (2ar + b)z^2 + ar^2 + br + c} = z \sqrt{Q(z)}. \quad (142)$$

Hence the new integrand is of the same type as the old, but the new radicand involves no odd powers. For a range of x such that $x < r$, we put $x = r - z^2$. We note that in either case,

$$\frac{dx}{\sqrt{P(x)}} = \frac{2 \, dz}{\sqrt{Q(z)}}. \quad (143)$$

Finally, let us assume that $P(x)$ is a fourth degree polynomial without multiple roots. It may be factored into two real quadratic factors:

$$P(x) = a(x^2 + px + q)(x^2 + p'x + q'), \quad a \neq 0. \tag{144}$$

We wish to reduce this to a form where p and p' are zero, and attempt to do this with a linear fractional transformation:

$$x = \frac{f + gz}{1 + z}. \tag{145}$$

This will make

$$a(x^2 + px + q)(1 + z)^2 = Az^2 + B,$$
$$(x^2 + p'x + q')(1 + z)^2 = A'z^2 + B', \tag{146}$$

if

$$2fg + p(f + g) + 2q = 0 \quad \text{and} \quad 2fg + p'(f + g) + 2q' = 0. \tag{147}$$

When $p \neq p'$, these relations are equivalent to

$$f + g = 2\frac{q - q'}{p' - p} \quad \text{and} \quad fg = \frac{pq' - qp'}{p' - p}, \tag{148}$$

which may be solved with real values of f and g if

$$0 < \tfrac{1}{4}(f - g)^2(p' - p)^2$$

or

$$(q - q')^2 - (p' - p)(pq' - qp') > 0. \tag{149}$$

Let us now put

$$x^2 + px + q = (x - r)(x - \bar{r})$$

and

$$x^2 + p'x + q' = (x - r')(x - \bar{r}'). \tag{150}$$

Then the expression just written becomes:

$$(r\bar{r} - r'\bar{r}')^2 - (r + \bar{r} - r' - \bar{r}')[r\bar{r}(r' + \bar{r}') - r'\bar{r}'(r + \bar{r})]. \tag{151}$$

But this may be written

$$(r - r')(r - \bar{r}')(\bar{r} - r')(\bar{r} - \bar{r}'), \tag{152}$$

since it vanishes when $r = r'$, and so admits the factor $r - r'$, and the other three factors by symmetry, and finally is a fourth degree polynomial with the term $r^2\bar{r}^2$, so that the multiplicative constant is unity.

If both quadratic factors have complex roots, r and $\bar{r}$ are conjugate complex quantities and so are r' and $\bar{r}'$. Thus the first and fourth, and the second and third factors, are conjugate and so have a positive product. Again, if r and $\bar{r}$ are conjugate, and the other two roots are real, then the first and third factors are conjugate, and so are the second and fourth. Finally, if all four roots are real, we may take the two algebraically greatest roots as r and $\bar{r}$, and all four factors will be positive.   No factor can be zero, since our fourth degree polynomial has distinct roots.

Thus, if $p \neq p'$ we may find real values of f and g such that the rational transformation (145) makes

$$\sqrt{P(x)} = \frac{\sqrt{(Az^2 + B)(A'z^2 + B')}}{(1 + z)^2} = \frac{\sqrt{Q(z)}}{(1 + z)^2}. \tag{153}$$

From the relation (149), $g \neq f$, and we note that

$$\frac{dx}{\sqrt{P(x)}} = (g - f) \frac{dz}{\sqrt{Q(z)}}. \tag{154}$$

When $p = p'$, we put $x = z - \dfrac{p}{2}$, $dx = dz$, which makes

$$
\begin{aligned}
P(x) &= a(x^2 + px + q)(x^2 + px + q') \\
&= a\left(z^2 + q - \frac{p^2}{4}\right)\left(z^2 + q' - \frac{p^2}{4}\right) = Q(z), \tag{155}
\end{aligned}
$$

and

$$\frac{dx}{\sqrt{P(x)}} = \frac{dz}{\sqrt{Q(z)}}. \tag{156}$$

Our discussion shows that the integral of $R[x, P(x)]$ is either rationalizable or reducible by real substitutions to the integral of a similar expression with

$$P(x) = (Ax^2 + B)(A'x^2 + B'), \tag{157}$$

where A, B, A', and B' are all real.

We observe that, if the radicand of equation (142) does not have real factors of this form, it may be factored and transformed by the process used for the $P(x)$ of equation (144).

142. General Reductions.   We assume the radicand has the form given in equation (157), and proceed to certain methods of simplifying our problem.   While it is logically simpler to use this order to avoid unnecessary repetition, practically it is preferable to apply these general reductions before transforming the radicand.   This may greatly simplify the formal work, even if the reductions have to be applied again to some of the terms after the radicand is transformed.

Let us denote $P(x)$ by v^2, so that the integrand is $R(x, v)$.   By using the identities

$$v^{2n} = (v^2)^n = [P(x)]^n, \quad v^{2n+1} = v[P(x)]^n, \tag{158}$$

we may express the integrand in the form

$$\frac{K + Lv}{M + Nv}, \tag{159}$$

where K, L, M, N are polynomials in x. Now rationalize the denominator,

$$\frac{(K + Lv)(M - Nv)}{(M + Nv)(M - Nv)} = \frac{KM - LNv^2 + (LM - KN)v}{M^2 - N^2v^2}, \quad (160)$$

and replace v^2 by $P(x)$. This reduces the integrand to the form $U + Vv$, where U and V are rational functions of x.

Since U is a rational function, we need only consider integrands of the form:

$$Vv = \frac{Vv^2}{v} = \frac{W}{v}, \quad (161)$$

where W is a new rational function of x.

The rational function W can be decomposed into a polynomial and a number of partial fractions, which reduces the integral to a sum of terms of the two forms:

$$\text{(a)} \quad a_n \int^x \frac{x^n}{v} \, dx, \quad \text{and} \quad \text{(b)} \quad b_n \int^x \frac{1}{v(x - r)^n} \, dx. \quad (162)$$

There will be terms of the second form, (b), for each real or complex root, r, of the denominator of W.

In order to reduce these integrals (b), we observe that:

$$\frac{d}{dx}\left[\frac{v}{(x - r)^m}\right] = \frac{vv'(x - r) - mv^2}{(x - r)^{m+1}v} = \frac{\frac{1}{2}P'(x)(x - r) - mP(x)}{(x - r)^{m+1}v}$$
$$= \frac{c_4(x - r)^4 + c_3(x - r)^3 + c_2(x - r)^2 + c_1(x - r) + c_0}{(x - r)^{m+1}v}, \quad (163)$$

since the numerator, a fourth degree polynomial, may be expanded in powers of $(x - r)$. By integration, we find from this that

$$\frac{v}{(x - r)^m}\bigg|_{x_0}^{x} = c_4 \int_{x_0}^{x} \frac{dx}{v(x - r)^{m-3}} + c_3 \int_{x_0}^{x} \frac{dx}{v(x - r)^{m-2}}$$
$$+ c_2 \int_{x_0}^{x} \frac{dx}{v(x - r)^{m-1}} + c_1 \int_{x_0}^{x} \frac{dx}{v(x - r)^{m}} + c_0 \int_{x_0}^{x} \frac{dx}{v(x - r)^{m+1}}. \quad (164)$$

If $c_0 \neq 0$, this relation may be solved for the last integral to give a reduction formula by which an integral of type (b) with $n = m + 1$ may be expressed in terms of an algebraic function and four integrals of type (b) with $n = m - 3, m - 2, m - 1$ and m.

If $c_0 = 0$, and $m \neq 0$, it follows from equation (163) that $P(r) = 0$. Hence $P'(r) \neq 0$, and $c_1 \neq 0$. In this case the relation (164) may be solved for the integral of type (b) with $n = m$ to give a reduction formula by which such an integral may be expressed in terms of an algebraic function and three integrals of type (b) with $n = m - 3$, $m - 2$ and $m - 1$.

In any case, by starting with the integral of type (b) for a given root for which n is largest and, at each stage, combining together all the integrals with the same power of $(x - r)$, we may reduce all the integrals of type (b) for a given root r to the integrals:

$$\int^x \frac{1}{(x-r)v}\,dx, \int^x \frac{1}{v}\,dx, \int^x \frac{x-r}{v}\,dx, \int^x \frac{(x-r)^2}{v}\,dx. \quad (165)$$

The last three integrals may be combined with the integrals of type (a) of (162). The first integral may be written:

$$\int^x \frac{1}{(x-r)v}\,dx = \int^x \frac{x+r}{(x^2-r^2)v}\,dx$$

$$= \int^x \frac{x\,dx}{(x^2-r^2)v} + r \int^x \frac{dx}{(x^2-r^2)v}. \quad (166)$$

If we make the substitution $x^2 = z$, we find:

$$\int^x \frac{x\,dx}{(x^2-r^2)v} = \int^z \frac{dz}{2(z-r^2)\sqrt{(Az+B)(A'z+B')}}, \quad (167)$$

which is a rationalizable integral. This shows that we need only consider, in addition to integrals of type (a) of (162), integrals of the form:

$$\int^x \frac{dx}{(x^2-r^2)v}. \quad (168)$$

We next consider the reductions of integrals of type (a). If we put $r = 0$, $m = -M$, equation (163) may be written:

$$\frac{d}{dx}(x^M v) = \frac{d_4 x^{M+3} + d_2 x^{M+1} + d_0 x^{M-1}}{v}, \quad (169)$$

since $P(x)$ and hence $P'(x)x$ contain no odd powers of x. For $M > 0$, $d_4 \neq 0$, since $d_4 = (2 + M)AA'$. This equation leads to a reduction formula by which an integral of type (a) involving x^{M+3} can be reduced to two other integrals of the same type involving the exponents $M + 1$ and $M - 1$.

We only apply this for odd values of M, when all the exponents in the integrals are even, since for odd exponents the integrals of type (a) are rationalizable. In fact, if $x^2 = z$,

$$\int^x \frac{x^{2n+1}}{v}\,dx = \int^z \frac{z^n\,dz}{2\sqrt{(Az+B)(A'z+B')}}. \quad (170)$$

By repeated reduction of the integrals with even exponents, starting with the term with highest exponent, we may reduce the integrals of type (a) to the two:

$$\int^x \frac{x^2}{v}\, dx \quad \text{and} \quad \int^x \frac{dx}{v}. \tag{171}$$

Thus our problem is now reduced to integrals of three types, the two just written and those of the form (168).

143. Transformations of the Radical. We must now develop real substitutions which will transform the radicand

$$v^2 = P(x) = (Ax^2 + B)(A'x^2 + B') \tag{172}$$

into that of the standard forms,

$$(1 - x^2)(1 - k^2x^2) \quad \text{with} \quad k < 1. \tag{173}$$

Since $P(x)$ is positive, we may so select the signs of the constants that both factors $Ax^2 + B$ and $A'x^2 + B'$ are positive. Since all the roots of $P(x)$ are distinct, a real range for which $P(x)$ is positive can not include a root of $P(x)$. Hence neither of the factors can change sign in the range.

We next consider two special substitutions. The first is:

$$z^2 = Ax^2 + B, \quad z > 0, \tag{174}$$

which makes:

$$\frac{dx}{\sqrt{(Ax^2 + B)(A'x^2 + B')}} = \frac{dz}{\sqrt{(z^2 - B)(A'z^2 + AB' - A'B)}}, \tag{175}$$

the factors on the right being positive if $A > 0$.

The second substitution is:

$$z = -\frac{1}{x}, \tag{176}$$

which makes

$$\frac{dx}{\sqrt{(Ax^2 + B)(A'x^2 + B')}} = \frac{dz}{\sqrt{(Bz^2 + A)(B'z^2 + A')}} \tag{177}$$

If B and B' are both negative, A and A' must both be positive, and the second transformation just made leads to a form in which the new values of B and B' are both positive.

If one, say B, is negative and the other, B', is positive, the first transformation (174) leads to a form in which the new values of B and B' are positive if $(AB' - A'B) > 0$. But, since the factors are positive, for some values of x we have:

$$Ax^2 > -B \quad \text{and} \quad B' > -A'x^2 \tag{178}$$

and hence, since $-B$ and B' are positive,

$$AB'x^2 > -BB' > A'Bx^2, \quad \text{so that} \quad AB' > A'B, \quad (179)$$

and the condition is satisfied.

Thus we obtain a form in which B and B' are both positive, and we may factor them out without changing the signs and so write the radical in the form:

$$\sqrt{(1 + Ax^2)(1 + A'x^2)}. \quad (180)$$

If A is negative, and A' positive, the first transformation (174) reduces the radical to

$$\sqrt{(1 - z^2)([A' - A] - A'z^2)}, \quad (181)$$

where the signs of the factors are the reverse of those in equation (175) since A is now negative. In the new form A and A' are both negative.

If A and A' are both positive, the first transformation (174) reduces the radical to:

$$\sqrt{(z^2 - 1)(A'z^2 + [A - A'])}, \quad (182)$$

and we may choose the notation so that $A' > A$. If we then apply the second transformation, (177), we shall reduce the radical to:

$$\sqrt{(1 - z^2)(A' - [A' - A]z^2)}. \quad (183)$$

Thus, in the reduced form for the radical given by the expression (180), either A and A' are both negative, or we may make them both negative by an appropriate combination of the two transformations. We need therefore only consider radicals of the form:

$$\sqrt{(1 - a^2x^2)(1 - b^2x^2)}, \quad a^2 > b^2, \quad (184)$$

and if we make the transformation

$$ax = z, \quad a > 0, \quad (185)$$

we shall have:

$$\frac{dx}{\sqrt{(1 - a^2x^2)(1 - b^2x^2)}} = \frac{dz}{a\sqrt{(1 - z^2)\left(1 - \dfrac{b^2}{a^2}z^2\right)}}. \quad (186)$$

The discussion shows that by combinations of transformations of the three types (174), (176), and (185) we may take integrals of the type $\displaystyle\int^x \frac{dx}{v}$ into others of the same type, in which v^2 has the standard form (173) times a constant factor.

For a range, or portion of a range, including no positive values, we may put $z = -x$, which leads to a new range including no negative values. Thus we may assume both limits positive or zero, and, since the integral over x_1, x_2 is that over $0, x_2$ minus that over $0, x_1$, we may assume the lower limit 0. The positive upper limit is less than 1, since the factor $(1 - x^2)$ is positive. Hence if we put $x = \sin \phi$, we may take ϕ in the first quadrant and write:

$$\int_0^x \frac{dx}{\sqrt{(1 - x^2)(1 - k^2 x^2)}} = \int_0^\phi \frac{d\phi}{\sqrt{1 - k^2 \sin^2 \phi}}, \qquad (187)$$

the standard form for the elliptic integral of the first kind.

The transformations (174) and (185) do not essentially change integrals of the form (168), merely replacing the radicand by one of the standard form (173), and introducing a constant factor and a new constant in place of r^2. However, the transformation (176) makes:

$$\int^x \frac{dx}{(x^2 - r^2)v} = -\frac{1}{r^2} \int^z \frac{z^2 \, dz}{\left(z^2 - \frac{1}{r^2}\right) v_1}$$

$$= -\frac{1}{r^2} \int^z \frac{dz}{v_1} - \frac{1}{r^4} \int^z \frac{dz}{\left(z^2 - \frac{1}{r^2}\right) v_1}. \qquad (188)$$

This is a combination of the first form, already disposed of, and an integral essentially of the form (168). Thus we need only consider integrals of the form (168) with radicands in the standard form (173). As before, we may assume the lower limit 0 and the upper limit positive and less than 1. Putting $x = \sin \phi$ we find

$$\int^x \frac{dx}{(x^2 - r^2)v} = \int^\phi \frac{d\phi}{(\sin^2 \phi - r^2) \sqrt{1 - k^2 \sin^2 \phi}}, \qquad (189)$$

which is the standard form of the elliptic integral of the third kind.

Finally we must consider integrals of the form $\int^x \frac{x^2 \, dx}{v}$. These are replaced by a constant times an integral of the same type, by the transformation (185), and by a combination of one of the same type and one of the first form by the transformation (174). The transformation (176) leads to an integral of the third kind, (189), with $r = 0$. When we do not use the transformation (176), or use it twice, we obtain a new integral of the form we started with, with the radicand in the standard form (173). We then write:

$$\int^x \frac{x^2}{v} \, dx = -\frac{1}{k^2} \int^x \frac{1 - k^2 x^2}{v} \, dx + \frac{1}{k^2} \int^x \frac{dx}{v}. \qquad (190)$$

The last integral written is of the first form.   For the other integral, we assume the lower limit 0 and the upper limit positive, put $x = \sin \phi$, and write:

$$\int_0^x \frac{1 - k^2 x^2}{v} \, dx = \int_0^x \sqrt{\frac{1 - k^2 x^2}{1 - x^2}} \, dx = \int_0^\phi \sqrt{1 - k^2 \sin^2 \phi} \, d\phi. \quad (191)$$

This is the standard form for the elliptic integral of the second kind.

This completes the proof of the theorem stated in section 141.

144. Elliptic Integrals of the First Kind.   We note that the transformations used may change an integrand of the form x^2/v, where $v^2 = P(x)$ is any polynomial of the fourth degree, into a combination of standard elliptic integrals involving all three kinds.   In particular, this will generally be the case when the linear fractional transformation (145) is used.

However, as we noted, each transformation takes the differential expression dx/v into another expression of this same form.   This proves:

An integral of the form $\int^x dx/\sqrt{P(x)}$, *where $P(x)$ is a real polynomial of the third or fourth degree, with no multiple roots, can always be reduced to an elliptic integral of the first kind.*

In particular, the integral

$$\int_a^x \frac{dx}{\sqrt{4x^3 - g_2 x - g_3}} = \int_a^x \frac{dx}{\sqrt{4(x - e_1)(x - e_2)(x - e_3)}},$$
$$e_1 + e_2 + e_3 = 0 \quad (192)$$

is of this form.   We shall show in section 170 that this integral approaches a limit as $x \to +\infty$.   Thus we may write the integral as $u(x) - u(a)$, with the constant so determined that $u(x) \to 0$ as $x \to +\infty$.   The inverse of this function $u(x)$, the Weierstrass $\wp$ function, plays an important rôle in the theory of elliptic functions.   These are functions related to the functions inverse to those defined by certain elliptic integrals.

In many problems of mechanics, the solution is given in the form $s = \int^t dx/\sqrt{P(x)}$, where $P(x)$ is a cubic.   In this case, if the three roots of $P(x)$ are a_1, a_2, and a_3, and

$$a_1 + a_2 + a_3 = 3b, \quad s = s_0 \text{ when } t = t_0, \quad (193)$$

we may write the relation as

$$t = b + \wp \, (s - c), \quad (194)$$

where c is defined by $\wp (s_0 - c) = t_0 - b$, and $\wp$ is formed with roots

$$e_1 = a_1 - b, \quad e_2 = a_2 - b, \quad e_3 = a_3 - b. \tag{195}$$

While this does not lead to a numerical evaluation, it does express the solution in terms of a function whose properties have been extensively studied.

145. Numerical Integration. We shall develop two formulas for obtaining an approximate value of an integral when the integrand is a specific function whose values can be calculated. These formulas are practically useful when the integral either can not be easily expressed in terms of functions already tabulated, when the procedure for doing this is long, or when it leads to a complicated final expression.

We obtain these approximations by replacing the integrand in the whole or a part of the interval of integration by a simpler expression, and by integrating this latter expression. For example, if we replace any integrand $f(x)$ by a first degree function taking the same values at a and b, or

$$g(x) = f(a) + \frac{x - a}{b - a} [f(b) - f(a)], \tag{196}$$

we find:

$$\int_a^b g(x) \, dx = \frac{b - a}{2} [f(a) + f(b)], \tag{197}$$

as an approximation to

$$\int_a^b f(x) \, dx. \tag{198}$$

If the function $f(x)$ is continuous, it has an indefinite integral $F(x)$, for which

$$f(x) = F'(x), \tag{199}$$

and

$$\int_a^b f(x) \, dx = F(b) - F(a). \tag{200}$$

Thus the error E, or correction term to be added to the approximate value (197) to give the correct result, is:

$$E = F(b) - F(a) - \frac{b - a}{2} [f(a) + f(b)]. \tag{201}$$

If the function $f(x)$ has a second derivative throughout the open interval a,b we may obtain another expression for E. To do this, put

$$b - a = 2u, \ a + b = 2c, \text{ so that } a = c - u \text{ and } b = c + u. \tag{202}$$

From this and equation (199) we have:

$$E = F(c + u) - F(c - u) - u[F'(c + u) + F'(c - u)]. \quad (203)$$

We then proceed as we did in section 91.   We define the constant

$$K = \frac{E}{u^3}, \quad (204)$$

and then consider the function:

$$G(x) = F(c + x) - F(c - x) - x[F'(c + x) + F'(c - x)] - Kx^3. \quad (205)$$

This function is zero for $x = u$, by the two preceding equations.   It evidently is zero for $x = 0$.   Hence by Rolle's theorem its derivative

$$G'(x) = -x[F''(c + x) - F''(c - x)] - 3Kx^2, \quad (206)$$

is zero for some value u' between 0 and u.   From

$$0 = -u'[F''(c + u') - F''(c - u')] - 3Ku'^2, \quad (207)$$

we find:

$$K = -\frac{2}{3}\frac{F''(c + u') - F''(c - u')}{2u'}. \quad (208)$$

The 2 is inserted to make the fraction with denominator $2u'$ have the form of a difference quotient.   By the law of the mean, this equals the derivative of $F''(x)$ at some point x_0 between $c - u'$ and $c + u'$, and therefore between a and b.   Thus

$$K = -\frac{2}{3}F'''(x_0) = -\frac{2}{3}f''(x_0), \quad (209)$$

and

$$E = Ku^3 = -\frac{2}{3}f''(x_0)u^3. \quad (210)$$

If we divide the interval of integration into n equal parts, each of width

$$h = \frac{b - a}{n}, \quad (211)$$

by points x_k, and denote the value of the integrand at x_k by y_k,

$$y_k = f(x_k) = f(a + kh), \quad (212)$$

we may apply the preceding approximation to each part, with

$$u = \frac{h}{2}. \quad (213)$$

The sum of the approximations is:

$$T = h \left(\frac{y_0}{2} + y_1 + y_2 + \cdots + y_{n-1} + \frac{y_n}{2} \right). \tag{214}$$

This is known as the *trapezoidal* rule, since the graph of the function of equation (196) is a straight line, and the integral (197) corresponds to the area under this straight line, or that of a trapezoid. If the exact value of the integral is

$$T + E, \text{ then } E = -\frac{h^3}{12} n f_2 = -\frac{(b-a)^3}{12n^2} f_2. \tag{215}$$

Here, if the second derivative $f''(x)$ is continuous in a,b, then f_2 is the value at some point of the interval, since it is an average and therefore an intermediate value. Also, if $f''(x)$ preserves its sign, the error has

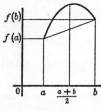

FIG. 15.

the sign opposite to this. In all cases, if M is the least upper bound of $|f''(x)|$ in the interval, f_2 is numerically at most M. Thus the error may be made small by taking n sufficiently large.

A better approximate formula is obtained by using a second degree curve, whose graph is a parabola,

$$g(x) = A + Bx + Cx^2, \tag{216}$$

which has the same values as $f(x)$ at a,b and the point halfway between, $c = \dfrac{a+b}{2}$. These determine the coefficients uniquely. For simplicity, we write in place of equation (216),

$$g(x) = A' + B'(x - c) + C'(x - c)^2, \tag{217}$$

define u as in equation (202), and find that this makes $g(c - u)$, $g(c)$, and $g(c + u)$ agree with $f(a), f(c)$, and $f(b)$ if:

$$g(x) = f(c) + [f(b) - f(a)]\frac{x - c}{2u} + [f(a) + f(b) - 2f(c)]\frac{(x - c)^2}{2u^2}. \tag{218}$$

For the approximation to the integral (200) we have:

$$\int_a^b g(x)\,dx = \int_{c-u}^{c+u} g(x)\,dx = \frac{u}{3}[f(a) + f(b) + 4f(c)]$$

$$= \frac{b-a}{6}[f(a) + 4f(c) + f(b)]. \tag{219}$$

In this case the error E to be added is:

$$E = F(b) - F(a) - \frac{b-a}{6}[f(a) + 4f(c) + f(b)], \qquad (220)$$

or, in view of equation (202):

$$E = F(c+u) - F(c-u) - \frac{u}{3}[F'(c+u) + 4F'(c) + F'(c-u)]. \qquad (221)$$

We now assume that $f(x)$ has a fourth derivative, so that $F(x)$ has a fifth derivative throughout the interval. Define the constant K by

$$K = \frac{E}{u^5}, \qquad (222)$$

and consider the function:

$$G(x) = F(c+x) - F(c-x)$$
$$- \frac{x}{3}[F'(c+x) + 4F'(c) + F'(c-x)] - Kx^5. \qquad (223)$$

We find, successively:

$$G'(x) = \frac{2}{3}[F'(c+x) + F'(c-x) - 2F'(c)]$$
$$- \frac{x}{3}[F''(c+x) - F''(c-x)] - 5Kx^4, \qquad (224)$$

$$G''(x) = \frac{1}{3}[F''(c+x) - F''(c-x)]$$
$$- \frac{x}{3}[F'''(c+x) + F'''(c-x)] - 20Kx^3, \qquad (225)$$

$$G'''(x) = -\frac{x}{3}[F^{IV}(c+x) - F^{IV}(c-x)] - 60Kx^2. \qquad (226)$$

Each of these functions reduces to zero when $x = 0$. But, from equations (221) and (222), $G(u) = 0$. Hence, by Rolle's theorem $G'(x)$ is zero for some value between 0 and u, say u'. It follows that $G''(x)$ is zero for some value between 0 and u', say u''. Similarly $G'''(x)$ is zero for some value u''', and

$$-\frac{u'''}{3}[F^{IV}(c+u''') - F^{IV}(c-u''')] - 60Ku'''^2 = 0. \qquad (227)$$

We deduce from this that:

$$K = -\frac{1}{90}\frac{F^{IV}(c+u''') - F^{IV}(c-u''')}{2u'''}. \qquad (228)$$

By the law of the mean, the fraction in the form of a difference quotient equals the derivative of $F^{IV}(x)$ at some point x_0 between $c - u'''$ and $c + u'''$, and therefore between a and b. Thus

$$K = -\frac{1}{90} F^V(x_0) = -\frac{1}{90} f^{IV}(x_0)u^5. \qquad (229)$$

If we divide the interval of integration into an even number of equal parts, say $2m$, each of width

$$h = \frac{b - a}{2m}, \qquad (230)$$

by points x_k, and define the y_k by equation (212), we may apply the approximation to each consecutive pair of parts x_0, x_2; x_2, x_4; $\cdots$; x_{2m-2}, x_{2m}. The sum of the approximations is:

$$S = \frac{h}{3}(y_0 + 4y_1 + 2y_2 + 4y_3 + 2y_4 + \cdots + 4y_{2m-1} + y_{2m}). \qquad (231)$$

This is known as *Simpson's* rule. If the exact value of the integral is

$$S + E, \quad \text{then} \quad E = -\frac{h^5}{90} mf_4 = -\frac{(b-a)^5}{180(2m)^4} f_4. \qquad (232)$$

Here, if the fourth derivative $f^{IV}(x)$ is continuous in a, b, then f_4 is the value at some point of the interval. Also, if $f^{IV}(x)$ preserves its sign, the error has the sign opposite to this. In all cases, if M is the least upper bound of $|f^{IV}(x)|$ in the interval, f_4 is numerically at most M.

A comparison of equations (215) and (232) shows that, if the bounds for the second and fourth derivative are of the same order of magnitude, the error in using Simpson's rule will be roughly $h^2/15$ times the error in using the trapezoidal rule with $n = 2m$, and hence much less when h is smaller than unity.

Practically, it is not always easy to determine bounds for the derivatives. However, we may use the corresponding finite differences to estimate their size. This results from the discussion in section 93. If the nth difference changes slowly in the intervals under consideration, equation (300) of that section suggests that we may take

$$\frac{\Delta^n f(x)}{h^n} \quad \text{as an approximation to } f^{(n)}(x), \qquad (233)$$

at least as to its order of magnitude. The estimated error when using Simpson's rule will then be $-\dfrac{b - a}{180} \Delta_4$, where Δ_4 is an average value of the fourth difference computed for the increment h. The corresponding estimated error when using the trapezoidal rule is $-\dfrac{b-a}{12}\Delta_2$, with Δ_2 an average value of the second difference.

EXERCISES VI

1. If $f(x) = f(-x)$, $f(x)$ is called an even function. If $f(x)$ is even and integrable, show that $\displaystyle\int_{-a}^{0} f(x)\,dx = \int_{0}^{a} f(x)\,dx = \frac{1}{2}\int_{-a}^{a} f(x)\,dx$, by using the fundamental definition of an integral.

2. If $f(x) = -f(-x)$, $f(x)$ is called an odd function. If $f(x)$ is odd and integrable, show that $\displaystyle\int_{-a}^{0} f(x)\,dx = -\int_{0}^{a} f(x)\,dx$, and that $\displaystyle\int_{-a}^{a} f(x)\,dx = 0$.

3. Prove that any single-valued function of an even function is even, and hence that for any continuous function $F(u)$, the result of problem 1 applies to $F(x^2)$ and $F(\cos x)$.

4. Prove that the product of any number of even functions and an odd number of odd functions is odd, and hence that the result of problem 2 applies to $xF(x^2)$ and $xF(\sin^2 x)$, where $F(u)$ is any continuous function.

5. For the integrals over the intervals $c-a,c$; $c,c+a$; and $c-a,c+a$ of a function such that $f(c+x) = f(c-x)$: state and prove a result analogous to that of problem 1. Similarly, for a function such that $f(c-x) = -f(c+x)$ deduce a result analogous to that of problem 2.

6. A function is said to be periodic of period p if $f(x+p) = f(x)$. If such a function is integrable, show that for n any positive integer,

$$\int_{a}^{a+p} f(x)\,dx = \int_{0}^{p} f(x)\,dx, \text{ and } \int_{a}^{a+np} f(x)\,dx = \int_{0}^{np} f(x)\,dx = n\int_{0}^{p} f(x)\,dx.$$

7. Prove that any single-valued function of a periodic function is periodic. In particular show that if $F(u)$ is any continuous function, $F(\cos x)$ and $F(\sin x)$ may be used in the result of problem 6 with $p = 2\pi$ in all cases, and with $p = \pi$ if $F(u)$ is an even function.

8. If $f(x)$ is a continuous monotonic function, prove that $\displaystyle\int_{a}^{b} f(x)\,dx$ is between $(b-a)f(a)$ and $(b-a)f(b)$. In particular, show that for positive values of p and q, $\displaystyle\int_{0}^{1} \frac{dx}{(x^p+1)^q}$ lies between 2^{-q} and 1.

9. If $f(x)$ is a continuous monotonic function, prove that the integral $\displaystyle\int_{p-a}^{p+a} f(x^2 - 2px + q)\,dx$ is between $2af(q-p^2)$ and $2af(a^2 + q - p^2)$. In particular, show that $\displaystyle\int_{1}^{3} \frac{dx}{(x^2 - 4x + 8)^r}$ lies between $2\cdot 4^{-r}$ and $2\cdot 5^{-r}$.

10. For $\int_0^a x\, dx$, verify that the sum S_n of equation (76), section 128, is $\dfrac{n(n+1)}{2n^2}\, a^2$, and hence $\rightarrow \dfrac{a^2}{2}$ when $n \rightarrow +\infty$.

11. For $\int_0^a e^x\, dx$, verify that the sum S_n is $(e^a - 1)\, \dfrac{ae^{\,a/n}}{n(e^{a/n} - 1)}$, and hence approaches $e^a - 1$ when $n \rightarrow +\infty$.

12. Calculate the sums S_n for the integrals $\int_0^a \sin x\, dx$ and $\int_0^a \cos x\, dx$. *Hint:* If the sums are S_n and C_n, $C_n + iS_n$ is the sum for $\int_0^a e^{ix}\, dx$, which equals $(e^{ia} - 1)\, \dfrac{ae^{ia/n}}{n(e^{ia/n} - 1)}$.

13. Using examples 2 and 3 of Exercises I, verify that for $\int_0^a x^m\, dx$, $S_n = \dfrac{a^{m+1}}{n^{m+1}}\left(\dfrac{n^{m+1}}{m+1} + a_m n^m + \cdots + a_0\right)$ and hence $\rightarrow \dfrac{a^{m+1}}{m+1}$ when $n \rightarrow +\infty$.

14. Calculate the sum S of equation (62), section 127, for points of subdivision $x_k = r^k$, for $\int_1^a x\, dx$. *Answer:* $\dfrac{r(a^2 - 1)}{r+1}$, which $\rightarrow \dfrac{a^2 - 1}{2}$ when $n \rightarrow +\infty$, where $r^n = a$, so that $r \rightarrow 1$.

15. As in problem 14, calculate S for $x_k = r^k$ for $\int_1^a x^m\, dx$. *Answer:* $\dfrac{r^m(a^{m+1} - 1)(r - 1)}{(r^{m+1} - 1)}$ which $\rightarrow \dfrac{a^{m+1} - 1}{m+1}$.

16. Prove that $\lim\limits_{n \rightarrow -1} \dfrac{x^{n+1} - 1}{n+1} = \log x$. This proves that $\lim\limits_{n \rightarrow -1} \int_1^x x^n\, dx = \int_1^x \dfrac{1}{x}\, dx$.

17. Let a,b be divided into n equal parts by $n - 1$ intermediate points $x_k = a + \dfrac{k(b - a)}{n}$. Prove that for any integrable function $f(x)$, the limit of the average of the n values $f(x_k)$, as $n \rightarrow +\infty$, is $\dfrac{1}{b - a} \int_a^b f(x)\, dx$. Illustrate for $f(x) = (b - x)(x - a)$, for which the limit is $\dfrac{(b - a)^2}{6}$.

18. Prove that $\lim\limits_{n \rightarrow +\infty} n \sum\limits_{k=1}^n \dfrac{1}{n^2 + k^2} = \dfrac{\pi}{4}$. *Hint:* Identify with a sum approximating $\int_0^1 \dfrac{dx}{1 + x^2}$.

19. Prove that $\lim\limits_{n \to +\infty} \dfrac{1}{n^2} \sum\limits_{k=1}^{n} \sqrt{n^2 - k^2} = \dfrac{\pi}{4}$. *Hint:* Identify with a sum approximating $\int_0^1 \sqrt{1 - x^2}\, dx$.

20. Prove that the limits in problems 18 and 19 are the same if the sums be taken from $k = p$ to $k = n + q$, instead of from $k = 1$ to $k = n$, where p and q are any fixed integral values.

21. If $A(x)$ and $B(x)$ are polynomials, show that $\int^x \dfrac{A(x)}{B(x)}\, dx$ contains a term $\dfrac{A(b)}{B'(b)} \log |x - b|$ for each simple root b of $B(x)$. These terms give the complete evaluation if $B(x)$ is of higher degree than $A(x)$ and has all its roots real and simple. *Hint:* Use section 116.

22. Using problem 36, Exercises V, evaluate $\int^x \dfrac{dx}{x^n - 1}$. *Answer:* A term $\dfrac{1}{n} \log |x - 1|$, for n even a term $-\dfrac{1}{n} \log |x + 1|$, and·in all cases $\left[\dfrac{n-1}{2}\right]$ other terms of the form $2\mathbf{R}\, \dfrac{b_k}{n} \log\,(x - b_k)$, with $b_k = e^{i\alpha_k}$, $\alpha_k = \dfrac{2\pi k}{n}$, or more explicitly, $\dfrac{\cos \alpha_k}{n} \log |1 - 2x \cos \alpha_k + x^2| - \dfrac{2}{n} \sin \alpha_k \tan^{-1}\left\{\dfrac{x - \cos \alpha_k}{\sin \alpha_k}\right\}$.

23. A curve whose equation is $f(x,y) = 0$ is said to be *unicursal* if the equation can be identically satisfied by putting x and y each equal to a rational function of a parameter t, and these functions give all points (x,y) of the curve. If, for the range considered, $f(x,y) = 0$ defines y in terms of x, and $R(x,y)$ is a rational function of x and y, show that the integral $\int^x R(x,y)\, dx$ is rationalizable.

24. If $f(x,y)$ is a polynomial of the nth degree, and x_0,y_0 is a multiple point of the $(n - 1)$st order, then $f(x,y) = 0$ is the equation of a unicursal curve as defined in problem 23. *Hint:* Any line $y - y_0 = t(x - x_0)$ will cut the curve in at most one point distinct from x_0,y_0, so that if we eliminate y between the two equations, we shall have a first degree equation in x. Thus x and hence y may be expressed rationally in terms of t.

25. If $P_n(x,y)$ is a homogeneous polynomial of the nth degree, and $P_{n-1}(x,y)$ is a homogeneous polynomial of the $(n - 1)$st degree, then $P_n(x,y) + P_{n-1}(x,y) = 0$ is the equation of a unicursal curve. The cubic $x^3 + y^3 = xy$ is an example. *Hint:* Use problem 24, with $(x_0,y_0) = (0,0)$. For the cubic, $y = tx$, $x = \dfrac{t}{1 + t^3}$, $y = \dfrac{t^2}{1 + t^3}$.

26. The curve $f(x,y) = 0$ is unicursal if the equation obtained by eliminating y from $f(x,y) = 0$ and $y = mx + t$ is of the first degree in x. This is analogous to the situation of problem 24 with the multiple point " at infinity in the direction of $y = mx$." In fact, the projective transformation $X = \dfrac{1}{x}$, $Y = \dfrac{y - mx}{x}$ takes $f(x,y) = 0$ into $F(X,Y) = 0$ of the form described in problem 25, since $y = mx + t$ becomes $Y = tX$.

27. Use the procedure of problem 26, with $y = x + t$ to rationalize $y(x - y)^2 = x$, and hence show that when this relation holds, $\displaystyle\int^x \dfrac{dx}{x - 3y} = \frac{1}{2} \log |(x - y)^2 - 1|$.

28. For a conic, $n = 2$, and in place of the multiple point of order $n - 1$ of problem 24, we only need a simple point, so that any point will do. If $y^2 = ax^2 + bx + c$, and $y_0^2 = ax_0^2 + bx_0 + c$, show that $y - y_0 = t(x - x_0)$ leads to a substitution that will rationalize $\displaystyle\int^x R(x, \sqrt{ax^2 + bx + c})\, dx$. In particular, when $c > 0$, one possibility is $x_0 = 0$, $y_0 = \sqrt{c}$ and $y = \sqrt{c} + tx$.

29. In problem 28, if $a > 0$, show that we may apply the method of problem 26 with $m = \sqrt{a}$, and use $y = \sqrt{a}x + t$ to rationalize the integral of $R(x, \sqrt{ax^2 + bx + c})$.

30. Show that if a curve is unicursal, its inverse curve under the transformation of problem 15, Exercises V, is also unicursal. In particular, for the lemniscate $(x^2 + y^2)^2 = (x^2 - y^2)$, express x and y rationally in terms of t by applying problem 29 to the inverse curve $Y^2 = X^2 - 1$, obtaining $x = -\dfrac{t(t^2 + 1)}{t^4 + 1}$ and $y = \dfrac{t(t^2 - 1)}{t^4 + 1}$. Hence show that when x and y are related by the equation of the lemniscate,

$$\int^x \frac{dx}{y(x^2 + y^2 + \frac{1}{2})} = 2 \log \left| \frac{x - y}{x^2 + y^2} \right|.$$

31. Prove that, if $g(x)$ can be integrated $m + 1$ times in explicit terms, the integral of $x^m g(x)$ can be found by $m + 1$ integrations by parts. *Hint:* Write $g(x) = f^{m+1}(x)$, and use induction.

32. If $g(x)$ can be integrated $m + 1$ times in explicit terms, the integral of $g(x)$ times any polynomial in x of degree at most m can be found by integrating by parts. *Hint:* Use problem 31.

33. Assuming that $\displaystyle\int^x g(x)\, dx = f(x)$, a known function, show that the integral of the inverse function $g^{-1}(x)$ can be found explicitly. *Hint:* If $y = g^{-1}(x)$, $\displaystyle\int^x g^{-1}(x)\, dx = \int^y y g'(y)\, dy = \int^y y f''(y)\, dy$. Now use problem 31.

34. Let $y = f^{-1}(x)$ be the inverse of a function $f(y)$ which is a polynomial in any number of variables, each of which is y, e^{ay}, $\sin by$, or $\cos by$. Show that if $P(x,y)$ is any polynomial, then $\displaystyle\int^x P(x,y)\, dx$ can be evaluated in terms of elementary functions. As particular cases we have $y = \log x$, $y = \sin^{-1} x$, $y = \cos^{-1} x$, $y = \sinh^{-1} x$, and $y = \cosh^{-1} x$. *Hint:* If $x = f(y)$, $\int^x P[x, f^{-1}(x)]\, dx = \int^y P[f(y), y]\, f'(y)\, dy$, an integral discussed in section 139.

35. If $R(\cos x, \sin x, y)$ is a rational function of the three variables, and $y^2 = a + b \cos x + c \sin x$, show that the integral of R is in general an elliptic integral. *Hint:* Put $t = \tan \dfrac{x}{2}$ as in section 138.

36. Show that if $c = 0$ and $b = \pm a$, or if $b = 0$ and $c = \pm a$, the integral of problem 35 is rationalizable.

37. Using an argument similar to that of section 142, show that the integral of $R(x, y)$, any rational function, with $y^2 = ax^2 + bx + c$ may be reduced to the calculation of integrals of the form $\displaystyle\int^x \frac{x\, dx}{y}$, $\displaystyle\int^x \frac{dx}{y}$, and $\displaystyle\int^x \frac{dx}{(x - r)y}$. This procedure is often preferable to a direct rationalization of the original function, since these three forms may be treated as in the next four problems.

38. If $a \neq 0$ in problem 37, verify the reduction formula

$$\int^x \frac{x\, dx}{y} = \frac{y}{a} - \frac{b}{2a} \int^x \frac{dx}{y}.$$

39. When $y^2 = ax^2 + bx + c$, show that $\displaystyle\int^x \frac{dx}{y} = \frac{2}{b}\sqrt{bx + c}$ if $a = 0$, $b \neq 0$; $\displaystyle\int^x \frac{dx}{y} = \frac{-1}{\sqrt{-a}} \sin^{-1} \frac{2ax + b}{\sqrt{b^2 - 4ac}}$ if $a < 0$; and that

$$\int^x \frac{dx}{y} = \frac{1}{\sqrt{a}} \log\left[ax + \frac{b}{2} + \sqrt{a(ax^2 + bx + c)} \right] \text{ if } a > 0.$$

40. If $y^2 = ax^2 + bx + c$, and r is real, show that the substitution $x = r - \dfrac{1}{z}$ will reduce the integral $\displaystyle\int^x \frac{dx}{(x - r)y}$ to an integral in z of the type evaluated in problem 39.

41. If $y^2 = ax^2 + bx + c$, $a \neq 0$, and r is not real, the sum of the conjugate terms

$$k \int^x \frac{dx}{(x - r)y} + \bar{k} \int^x \frac{dx}{(x - \bar{r})y}$$

may be written as $\displaystyle\int^x \frac{(sx + t)\, dx}{(x^2 + p'x + q')\sqrt{a(x^2 + px + q)}}$ with all the constants real. Prove that the transformations used in section 141 to reduce the expression in equation (144) will reduce this integral to

$$C \int^z \frac{z\, dz}{(A'z^2 + B')\sqrt{Az^2 + B}} + D \int^z \frac{dz}{(A'z^2 + B')\sqrt{Az^2 + B}}.$$

If $Az^2 + B = t^2$ in the first integral, and $A + \dfrac{B}{z^2} = t^2$ in the second, the new

form is $\displaystyle\int^t \frac{dt}{Et^2 + F}$, which may be evaluated as in section 137.

42. Show that the integrand $R(x, \sqrt{ax + b}, \sqrt{cx + d})$ may be rationalized.
Hint: Put $ax + b = aA\left(t + \dfrac{1}{t}\right)^2$ and $cx + d = cA\left(t - \dfrac{1}{t}\right)^2$ if a and c have the

same sign and if this makes $A = \dfrac{1}{4}\left(\dfrac{b}{a} - \dfrac{d}{c}\right)$ have the same sign as a and c.
Otherwise reverse the sign of A by interchanging a, b and c, d. If a and c
have opposite signs, put $ax + b = aA\left(\dfrac{2t}{1 + t^2}\right)^2$ and $cx + d = -cA\left(\dfrac{1 - t^2}{1 + t^2}\right)^2$,

choosing the notation so that $A = \dfrac{b}{a} - \dfrac{d}{c}$ has the same sign as a and $-c$.

43. Show that the integrand $R\left(x, \sqrt{\dfrac{ax + b}{px + q}}, \sqrt{\dfrac{cx + d}{px + q}}\right)$ may be rationalized.

Hint: Put $y = \dfrac{1}{px + q}$ and then use problem 42.

44. Show that $\displaystyle\int^x (ax + b)^p x^q \, dx$, where p and q are rational, can be rationalized if p, q or $p + q$ is an integer. *Hint:* The first two cases reduce to one treated in section 138. When $p + q$ is an integer, the integral is reduced to this case by putting $t = a + \dfrac{b}{x}$.

45. If n is a positive integer, show that $\displaystyle\int^x x^{-n} e^x \, dx$ may be reduced by

successive partial integration to the exponential integral $\displaystyle\int^x \frac{e^x}{x} \, dx$.

46. If $a_{n-1} = a(x) \neq 0$ in problem 8 of Exercises IV, show that $W = W_0 e^{A(x)}$,
when $A(x) = \displaystyle\int_{x_0}^x a(x) \, dx$ and W_0 is the value of the Wronskian W at x_0. This
proves that if $W \neq 0$ at one point x_0, it is always distinct from zero.

47. Show that an elliptic integral of the third kind with $\alpha = 0$ in (140), or $r = 0$ in (189) may be expressed in terms of elliptic integrals of the first and second kinds. *Hint:* Use (169) with $M = -1$.

CHAPTER VII

INTEGRABLE FUNCTIONS

In the last chapter it was proved that a sufficient condition for a function to be integrable is that it be continuous. We here derive several necessary and sufficient conditions for the integrability of a bounded function.

These conditions enable us to show in particular that a bounded function continuous at all points of an interval with the exception of a finite, or enumerably infinite, number of points is integrable. We also show that monotonic functions are integrable and that a class of functions related to them, the functions of bounded variation, are integrable.

146. Integrable Functions. In section 121 we defined a bounded function $f(x)$ as integrable on the closed interval a,b, if

$$S = \sum_{i=1}^{n} f(\xi_i)\delta_i \tag{1}$$

approached a finite limit for any sequence of subdivisions of the interval a,b such that $\delta_M \to 0$, and if this limit was the same for all sequences.

We recall that the subdivisions were determined by points:

$$a = x_0 < x_1 < x_2 < \cdots < x_n = b, \tag{2}$$

that

$$\delta_i = x_i - x_{i-1} \quad \text{and that} \quad \delta_M = \max(\delta_i), \tag{3}$$

while the ξ_i were any values such that

$$x_{i-1} \leqq \xi_i \leqq x_i. \tag{4}$$

147. Upper and Lower Integrals. Let the function $f(x)$ be bounded on the closed interval a,b. Then, by section 31, it has a greatest lower bound m and a least upper bound M for this interval. Similarly, in each closed subinterval x_{i-1},x_i, $f(x)$ has a greatest lower bound m_i and a least upper bound M_i, with

$$m \leqq m_i \leqq M_i \leqq M. \tag{5}$$

For any subdivision (2), we define the *upper sum* by

$$\bar{S} = \sum_{i=1}^{n} M_i\delta_i. \tag{6}$$

Since all the δ_i are positive,

$$\bar{S} = \sum_{i=1}^{n} M_i \delta_i \geqq \sum_{i=1}^{n} m \delta_i \geqq m(b - a). \tag{7}$$

Thus all the possible values of $\bar{S}$ are bounded from below, and so by section 10 these values have a greatest lower bound $\bar{I}$. We call $\bar{I}$ the *upper integral* of the function $f(x)$ for the interval a,b. We shall prove that for any sequence of subdivisions for which

$$\delta_M \to 0, \quad \text{we have} \quad \bar{S} \to \bar{I} \quad \text{or} \quad \overline{\int_a^b} f(x) \, dx, \tag{8}$$

the last expression being an alternative notation for $\bar{I}$ in which the function and interval are indicated.

We first consider a function for which $m > 0$, and hence $M > 0$.

From the definition of $\bar{I}$ as a greatest lower bound, there is some subdivision whose upper sum $\bar{S}'$ is such that

$$\bar{I} \leqq \bar{S}' \leqq \bar{I} + \epsilon, \tag{9}$$

for any positive ϵ. Suppose that the subdivision which has $\bar{S}'$ as its upper sum has N subintervals, and designate the points of subdivision by x_j' and the length of the jth subinterval by δ_j'.

Now consider any subdivision with $\delta_M = \eta$, and let its upper sum be $\bar{S} = \sum M_i \delta_i$. We separate this sum into two parts, $\bar{S}_1$, the sum over those intervals which do not include any point x_j' as an interior point, and $\bar{S}_2$, the sum over those intervals which do include one or more points x_j' as interior points. Since there are only $N - 1$ interior points x_j', the sum $\bar{S}_2$ contains less than N terms. For each of these terms M_i is at most M, and δ_i is at most η. Hence we have:

$$\bar{S}_2 \leqq N M \eta. \tag{10}$$

Each term of $\bar{S}_1$ corresponds to an interval consisting entirely of points of some one closed subinterval x_{j-1}, x_j. Let the term of $\bar{S}'$ for this subinterval be $M_j' \delta_j$. Now consider all those terms of $\bar{S}_1, M_{ij} \delta_{ij}$ where ij is a notation for those values of i such that

$$x_{j-1}' \leqq x_{i-1} < x_i \leqq x_j', \tag{11}$$

for any one j. Since the intervals x_{ij-1}, x_{ij} for a particular j are subintervals of the jth interval, and have no common interior points, we have:

$$\sum_i \delta_{ij} \leqq \delta_j \quad \text{and} \quad M_{ij} \leqq M_j'. \tag{12}$$

But $\delta_{ij} > 0$,   and $M_{ij} \geqq m > 0$,   and hence:

$$\sum_i M_{ij}\delta_{ij} \leqq M'_j \sum_i \delta_{ij} \leqq M'_j\delta_j. \tag{13}$$

By summing this for all values of j, we find:

$$\bar{S}_1 \leqq \bar{S}'. \tag{14}$$

From the relations (10) and (14) we may deduce that:

$$\bar{S} = \bar{S}_1 + \bar{S}_2 \leqq \bar{S}' + NM\eta. \tag{15}$$

Again, from the definition of $\bar{I}$ as a greatest lower bound,

$$\bar{I} \leqq \bar{S}. \tag{16}$$

From the relations (16), (15), and (9) we have:

$$\bar{I} \leqq \bar{S} \leqq \bar{I} + \epsilon + NM\eta. \tag{17}$$

For any positive ϵ, the subdivision with upper sum $\bar{S}'$ determines the number N.   If we then take any subdivision with

$$\delta_M = \eta < \frac{\epsilon}{NM}, \tag{18}$$

we shall have:

$$\bar{I} \leqq \bar{S} \leqq \bar{I} + 2\epsilon, \quad \text{or} \quad |\bar{S} - \bar{I}| \leqq 2\epsilon. \tag{19}$$

The last two equations show that:

$$\lim \bar{S} = \bar{I}, \tag{20}$$

for any sequence of subdivisions for which $\delta_M \to 0$, as we set out to prove:

If $m \leqq 0$, we replace $f(x)$ by $f(x) + k$, where $m + k > 0$.   Then $\bar{S}$ and $\bar{I}$ are replaced by $\bar{S} + k(b - a)$ and $\bar{I} + k(b - a)$.   The result, $\lim \bar{S} = \bar{I}$ for $f(x)$, then follows from the corresponding result for $f(x) + k$.

We define the lower sum by:

$$\underline{S} = \sum_{i=1}^n m_i\delta_i. \tag{21}$$

By reasoning as before, it may be proved that all the possible values of $\underline{S}$ have a least upper bound, $\underline{I}$, and that, for any sequence of subdivisions for which

$$\delta_M \to 0, \quad \text{we have} \quad \underline{S} \to \underline{I} \text{ or} \int_{\underline{a}}^b f(x)\, dx. \tag{22}$$

We call the last expression, or $\underline{I}$, the *lower integral* of the function $f(x)$ for the interval a,b.   It follows from the relations (5), (6), and (21) that:

$$\bar{S} \geqq \underline{S}. \tag{23}$$

From this and the relations (20) and (22) we have:

$$\bar{I} \geqq \underline{I}. \tag{24}$$

This explains why we designated $\bar{I}$, a *lower* bound, as an *upper* integral.

It also follows from the definitions (1), (6), and (21) that

$$\bar{S} \geqq S \geqq \underline{S}. \tag{25}$$

If $\bar{I} = \underline{I}$, we may apply the last theorem of section 23 to this relation, in view of equations (20) and (22), and so conclude that, when $\delta_M \to 0$, $\lim S = \bar{I} = \underline{I}$. Thus the function is integrable, and the integral I is the common value of $\bar{I}$ and $\underline{I}$.

We may also prove a converse result. We first note that, for any subdivision determined by points (2), we may find points ξ_i such that

$$M_i - \eta < f(\xi_i) \leqq M_i, \tag{26}$$

by the definition of M_i as a least upper bound, where η is any positive number. For such a choice of the points ξ_i, we have

$$\bar{S} - n\eta < S \leqq \bar{S}. \tag{27}$$

Next consider any sequence of subdivisions for which $\delta_M \to 0$. Let ϵ be any positive number, and take $\eta = \epsilon/n$ in the relation (27) for each subdivision. We thus determine a sequence of sums S which satisfy

$$\bar{S} - \epsilon < S \leqq \bar{S}. \tag{28}$$

Now suppose that the function $f(x)$ is integrable on the interval a,b. Then when $\delta_M \to 0$, $S \to I$. But $\bar{S} \to \bar{I}$, so that it follows from the last relation that

$$\bar{I} - \epsilon < I \leqq \bar{I}, \quad \text{or} \quad \bar{I} = I, \tag{29}$$

since ϵ is arbitrary. Similarly we may show that $\underline{I} = I$. Hence, when $f(x)$ is integrable, $\bar{I} = \underline{I}$.

We have thus proved the theorem of Darboux that:

A necessary and sufficient condition that a bounded function be integrable on an interval is that, for this interval, its upper integral has the same value as its lower integral.

In this case, the integral of the function equals the common value of the upper and lower integral.

148. Outer Content. Let P be a set of points on the interval a,b. The function $\phi(x)$, which is equal to 1 if x is in P, and equal to 0 if x is not in P, is called the *characteristic function* of the set P. The upper integral of $\phi(x)$ for the interval a,b is called the *outer content* of the set P. We denote it by $\bar{C}$, or $\bar{C}(P)$ when more than one point set is to be considered. Thus $\bar{C}$ is the greatest lower bound of all sums

$$\bar{S} = \sum M_i \delta_i, \tag{30}$$

formed for the function $\phi(x)$, using some subdivision determined by points (2). But, for any closed subinterval x_{i-1}, x_i the M_i for the function $\phi(x)$ is 1 if this interval contains any points of P, and the M_i is 0 if the subinterval does not contain any point of P. This shows that $\bar{S}$ is the sum of the lengths of those subintervals which include points of P as interior or end points.

We shall now show that the outer content is determined by sums of lengths of intervals of a less restricted character. Consider any finite number of intervals, F. These intervals may contain points not on the closed interval a,b, may be open or closed, and may or may not overlap. By the length of the set of intervals F, we mean the sum of the lengths of the separate intervals belonging to F. We denote it by L. We shall say that any set of intervals F includes the point set P, if each point of P is an interior or end point of at least one interval of F.

For any set of intervals F, which includes the point set P, we may form a subdivision of the closed interval a,b by the following process. Let a_j be the end points of intervals of F. There is a finite number, N, of such points. Select any positive number ϵ less than the minimum distance between any two distinct a_j, and put $\eta = \epsilon/2N$. Now use a, b and all the points $a_j - \eta$ and $a_j + \eta$ which belong to the open interval a,b as points x_j of a subdivision.

For this subdivision, and the function $\phi(x)$ for the set P, we may form the upper sum, $\bar{S}$ of equation (30). We separate this sum into two parts. Let $\bar{S}_1$ denote the part of the sum for those intervals which do not include any point a_j, and $\bar{S}_2$ denote the part of the sum for those intervals which do include at least one of the points a_j. Since there are at most N intervals containing points a_j, it follows from the choice of η and ϵ that:

$$\bar{S}_2 \leqq 2N\eta \leqq \epsilon. \tag{31}$$

Since every point of P is in some interval of F, and the intervals giving terms in $\bar{S}_1$ include no end points of the original intervals of F, or points a_j, every interval of the subdivision whose length appears in the sum $\bar{S}_1$ multiplied by 1 is entirely contained in some interval F. Moreover, if several such intervals are contained in the same interval F, since they do not overlap or abut, the sum of their lengths is less than the sum of this interval F. This shows that:

$$\bar{S}_1 \leqq L. \tag{32}$$

Consequently, we have:

$$\bar{S} = \bar{S}_1 + \bar{S}_2 \leqq L + \epsilon, \quad \text{and} \quad L \geqq \bar{S} - \epsilon. \tag{33}$$

The length L of any set of intervals F including the point set P is positive. Hence the values of L admit zero as a lower bound and hence have a greatest lower bound L'. Since any sum $\bar{S}$ is the length of a set of subintervals which may be regarded as a set of intervals F including the point set P, and $\bar{C}$ is the greatest lower bound of the values of $\bar{S}$, it follows that:

$$L' \leqq \bar{C}. \tag{34}$$

But if we take a set of intervals F for which $L < L' + \epsilon$, and form the sum $\bar{S}$ which satisfies the relation (33), we shall have:

$$L' > L - \epsilon \geqq \bar{S} - 2\epsilon \geqq \bar{C} - 2\epsilon. \tag{35}$$

Since ϵ is arbitrary, it follows from this relation that

$$L' \geqq \bar{C}. \tag{36}$$

The relations (34) and (36) can only hold together if

$$L' = \bar{C}. \tag{37}$$

This leads to an alternative definition of the outer content of the point set P, as *the greatest lower bound of the lengths of all finite sets of intervals including the point set P.*

149. Zero Content. We have used the term outer content because, in treatments of integration more complete than that given here, an inner content is defined. The inner content is shown to be less than, or equal to, the outer content for all sets. The term content is reserved for those sets with the same outer and inner content. When the outer content is zero, the inner content is necessarily zero, and the set has content zero. Thus we shall use the term zero content in place of outer content zero.

Let $f(x)$ and $g(x)$ be two functions defined on the interval a,b. Let them both be bounded, so that for some M,

$$|f(x)| < M \quad \text{and} \quad |g(x)| < M. \tag{38}$$

Suppose further that $f(x) = g(x)$ for all values of x on the interval a,b which do not correspond to a point of a certain point set P. Then if $\phi(x)$ is the characteristic function of the set P, and we denote the function for which a sum is formed by a subscript, we shall have:

$$|\bar{S}_f - \bar{S}_g| \leqq 2M\bar{S}_\phi \quad \text{and} \quad |\underline{S}_f - \underline{S}_g| \leqq 2M\bar{S}_\phi. \tag{39}$$

If both functions are integrable, we have from either equation

$$|I_f - I_g| \leqq 2M\bar{C}(P),\tag{40}$$

by considering a sequence of subdivisions for which $\delta_M \to 0$.

If the set P is of zero content, we may conclude from the equation (39) that

$$\bar{I}_f = \bar{I}_g \quad \text{and} \quad \underline{I}_f = \underline{I}_g.\tag{41}$$

This shows that, if one function is integrable, the other is also, and the integrals are the same.

This leads us to extend the definition of integration to functions defined at all points of an interval a,b except a set of zero content. If such a function has an integral when we use zero as the value of the function at the points where it is not defined, we say that the function is integrable over the interval a,b. By the result just proved, the function will have the same integral if we use any set of values having an upper bound in place of zero for the set of zero content.

150. Oscillation of a Function at a Point. The oscillation of a bounded function in an interval was defined in section 31 as $M - m$, the excess of the least upper bound over the greatest lower bound for the interval.

Consider now a bounded function $f(x)$ for values near x_0. Let

$$\overline{\lim_{x \to x_0}} f(x) = \bar{f} \quad \text{and} \quad \underline{\lim_{x \to x_0}} f(x) = \underline{f}.\tag{42}$$

Then, for any positive ϵ, in any interval including the point x_0 as an interior point and of sufficiently small length, $h < \delta_\epsilon$, for all values of $x \neq x_0$ we shall have:

$$f(x) < \bar{f} + \epsilon, \quad f(x) > \underline{f} - \epsilon.\tag{43}$$

Also, for any positive η, for some value x' in the interval of length h,

$$f(x') > \bar{f} - \eta, \quad \underline{f}(x') < \underline{f} + \eta.\tag{44}$$

Now let M_0 be the larger of $f(x_0)$ and $\bar{f}$, and m_0 the smaller of $f(x_0)$ and $\underline{f}$. Then the oscillation for the small interval including x_0 cannot exceed

$$M_0 - m_0 + 2\epsilon,\tag{45}$$

and is at least as great as

$$M_0 - m_0 - 2\eta \quad \text{or} \quad M_0 - m_0,\tag{46}$$

since η is still arbitrary after ϵ has been fixed. Thus, for any sequence of intervals, including x_0 as an interior point, whose lengths approach zero, the oscillation approaches $M_0 - m_0$. This is called the *oscillation of the function at the point* x_0.

Since any interval including the point x_0 as an interior point includes a point x' for which the relation (44) holds, for this interval we have:

$$M > M_0 - \eta, \quad m < m_0 + \eta, \tag{47}$$

and

$$M - m > M_0 - m_0 - 2\eta \quad \text{or} \quad M - m \geqq M_0 - m_0, \tag{48}$$

since η is arbitrary. This leads to an alternative definition of the oscillation of a function at a point, as the greatest lower bound of the values of the oscillation of the function for all intervals including the point as an interior point.

If the function is continuous, $\bar{f} = \underline{f} = f(x_0)$, so that $M_0 = m_0$, and the oscillation is zero at the point. Conversely, if $M_0 = m_0$, it follows from $M_0 \geqq f(x_0) \geqq m_0$ that $f(x_0) = M_0 = m_0 = \bar{f} = \underline{f}$, and the function is continuous. Thus:

A necessary and sufficient condition that a function be continuous at a point is that the oscillation at the point be zero.

In applying the definition of oscillation to the left end point a of a closed interval, we use right-hand upper and lower limits, or intervals having a as a left-hand end point. Similarly for the right end point b. The theorem then applies to such points, in view of our conventions as to continuity at the end points of a closed interval.

151. A Condition in Terms of Content. We shall now prove the theorem of Jordan:

For a bounded function to be integrable on an interval, it is necessary and sufficient that the outer content of every point set P_ϵ be zero, where P_ϵ is the set of points on the interval at which the oscillation of the function is greater than or equal to ϵ, any positive number.

We first prove the condition sufficient. We select a positive ϵ. Since the outer content of the point set P_ϵ is zero, the point set P_ϵ may be included in a finite set of intervals F, such that the length of the set F, or sum of the lengths of the separate intervals L, is less than ϵ. If the set F contains N closed intervals a_j, b_j, we replace each such interval by the open interval $a_j - \epsilon/2N, b_j + \epsilon/2N$. In this way we obtain a set of open intervals F', such that the length of the intervals F' or L' is less than 2ϵ, and the set of intervals F' covers the set P_ϵ in the sense of section 11.

We next consider the set of points Q, those points of the closed interval a,b which do not belong to P_ϵ. Since the oscillation of the function at any point x_0 of the set Q is less than ϵ, we may include x_0 in an open interval G_0 such that the oscillation of the function in this interval is less than 2ϵ. Let G be the infinite set of all such intervals G_0. Then, since G covers Q, and F' covers P, the set of intervals G together with the intervals of F' cover all the points of the closed interval a,b in the sense of section 11. Therefore, by the Heine-Borel theorem, we may select from these a finite number of intervals G' which cover all points of the closed interval a,b. Let the end points of the intervals G' be a_i'. There is a finite number N' of such points. Let η be a positive number such that $2N'\eta$ is less than ϵ. We now take a,b and the points $a_j' - \eta$ and $a_j' + \eta$ which belong to the open interval a,b as the points x_i of (2) used to form a subdivision. We distinguish three types of subintervals. Let H_1 be those subintervals which include at least one point a_j' as an interior or end point. For any one a_j' the single interval including it, or the two abutting intervals having it as an end point, must form all or part of the interval $a_j' - \eta, a_j' + \eta$, whose length is 2η. Hence the total length of subintervals H_1 is at most $2N'\eta$, which is less than ϵ.

Any subinterval not H_1 may be included in a single interval G', since it contains no end points of intervals G', or points a_j. We denote by H_2 those subintervals not H_1 which may be included in intervals of G' which are also intervals of F'. Since the subintervals do not overlap, the total length of the subintervals H_2 can not exceed the total length of intervals F', or L' which is less than 2ϵ. Finally we denote by H_3 those subintervals not H_1 which are not H_2. These may be included in intervals of G' which are not intervals of F', and hence must be intervals G_0, in which the oscillation of the function does not exceed 2ϵ.

Let us now form upper and lower sums for our subdivision,

$$\bar{S} = \sum M_i \delta_i, \quad \underline{S} = \sum m_i \delta_i. \tag{49}$$

We have, accordingly,

$$\bar{S} - \underline{S} = \sum (M_i - m_i)\delta_i. \tag{50}$$

For the intervals H_3, the oscillation $M_i - m_i < 2\epsilon$, and as the total length of these intervals is less than $b - a$, we have

$$2\epsilon(b - a) \tag{51}$$

as an upper bound for the contribution to the sum (50) from the intervals H_3. For the intervals H_1 and H_2, the oscillation is at most $M - m$, and as already observed, the total length of the intervals H_1 and H_2 together is at most $\epsilon + 2\epsilon$ or 3ϵ. Thus we have:

$$3\epsilon(M - m) \tag{52}$$

as an upper bound for the contribution to the sum (50) from the intervals H_1 and H_2. This shows that:

$$\bar{S} - \underline{S} < 2\epsilon(b - a) + 3\epsilon(M - m). \tag{53}$$

This inequality will still hold if, instead of the subdivision just used, we use any subdivision obtained from it by introducing new points x_i and retaining all the old ones. We may do this in such a way that $\delta_M \to 0$, and so deduce that:

$$\bar{I} - \underline{I} \leqq 2\epsilon(b - a) + 3\epsilon(M - m). \tag{54}$$

Since ϵ is arbitrary, it follows from this relation that $\bar{I} - \underline{I} = 0$, and the function is integrable by the theorem of Darboux in section 147. This proves the condition sufficient.

To prove the condition necessary, let $\bar{C}_\epsilon$ denote the outer content of the point set P_ϵ. Now consider the sums $\bar{S}$ and $\underline{S}$ for any subdivision. From the definition of oscillation at a point as a lower bound, for any subinterval G including a point of P_ϵ as an interior point the oscillation for the interval is at least ϵ, and $M_i - m_i \geqq \epsilon$. But, the only points P_ϵ not included as such interior points are those which are end points of subintervals. As there are only a finite number of subintervals, say N, we may include them all in a finite set of intervals G' of total length η, by taking each end point of a subinterval in an interval G_0' of length $\eta/2N$. If the total length of the intervals G is L, the intervals G together with G' have a total length $L + \eta$ at most. But they include all the points P_ϵ. Hence, from the definition of $\bar{C}_\epsilon$ as a lower bound, we have:

$$L + \eta \geqq \bar{C}_\epsilon, \quad \text{or} \quad L \geqq \bar{C}_\epsilon, \tag{55}$$

since η is arbitrary for any particular subdivision and fixed ϵ. The contribution from any interval to the sum:

$$\bar{S} - \underline{S} = \sum(M_i - m_i)\delta_i, \tag{56}$$

is positive or zero. But the contribution of the intervals G, which have a total length $L \geqq \bar{C}_\epsilon$ and for which $M_i - m_i > \epsilon$, is at least

$$\epsilon\bar{C}_\epsilon, \tag{57}$$

so that:

$$\bar{S} - \underline{S} \geqq \epsilon\bar{C}_\epsilon. \tag{58}$$

Since this is true for all subdivisions, it follows that:

$$\bar{I} - \underline{I} \geqq \epsilon\bar{C}_\epsilon, \tag{59}$$

for every positive number ϵ. Since $\bar{C}_\epsilon$ is necessarily positive or zero, if it were not zero for all values of ϵ, we should have $\bar{I} - \underline{I} > 0$, and the function would not be integrable. This proves the condition necessary, and completes the proof of the theorem.

152. Exterior Measure. The condition of integrability is simpler when stated in terms of exterior measure, which we shall now define. In the definition of outer content as a lower bound, finite sums of intervals were used, and the sum of their lengths was called the length of the set. For exterior measure, use is made of infinite sequences of sets of intervals, each set of which includes all the intervals in the preceding set and some additional intervals. Each set H_n contains a finite number, N, of intervals. However, the number N will increase indefinitely as n increases. If L_N is the length of H_n, then L_N increases with n, so that either

$$\lim L_N = L, \quad \text{or} \quad \lim L_N = +\infty. \qquad (60)$$

We may form an enumerably infinite set of intervals I_k, by starting with the intervals in H_1 arranged in some order, then using the intervals in H_2, but not in H_1, in some order, and so on. If we denote the length of the first k intervals by L_k, this will be consistent with the definition of L_N, since the first N intervals make up H_N. Since, for any k, we may find two numbers N and N' such that $N \leq k \leq N'$, it follows that:

$$L_N \leq L_k \leq L_{N'}, \quad \text{and} \quad \lim L_k = \lim L_N. \qquad (61)$$

Thus the sequence of sets of intervals with H'_n, made up of the first n intervals I_k, is made up of the same intervals as the original sequence of sets H_n, and has the same length. It has the further property that each set includes just one more interval than the preceding set. We refer to the sequence of sets of intervals H'_n as the set of intervals I_k, and call L the length of the set of intervals.

For any set of points P on a finite interval a,b there are finite or enumerably infinite sets of intervals I_k, which include the points of P in the sense that every point of the set P is a point of at least one of the intervals I_k. Some of these sets of intervals have finite length L, since the single interval of length $b - a$ is one such set. Since these finite lengths L are all positive or zero, they have a greatest lower bound, which we call the *exterior measure* of the set of points P. That is:

The exterior measure of a set of points P on a finite interval is *the greatest lower bound of the lengths of all possible finite or enumerably infinite sets of intervals which include all the points of P.*

This only differs from our second definition of outer content in including the possibility of an enumerably infinite set of intervals. Since we are retaining the possibility of using the finite sets considered in determining outer content, it follows that the greatest lower bound from the new definition will be less than or equal to that found before. Thus, if we use $\overline{M}$ or $\overline{M}(P)$ to denote the exterior measure, we have

$$\overline{M} \leq \overline{C}. \qquad (62)$$

153. Zero Measure. For reasons similar to those mentioned in section 149, we refer to a set of exterior measure zero as a set of measure zero. As a preparation for the proof that certain combinations of sets of measure zero are again sets of measure zero, we discuss a property of enumerable sets.

In section 2 we defined a class of objects as enumerable if it could be arranged in a single discrete sequence. Thus a finite set of intervals, or an enumerably infinite set of intervals I_k, is an enumerable set of intervals. Now consider an enumerable number of enumerable sets of intervals, I_{ij}. For each j, $i = 1, 2, 3, \cdots$ gives an enumerable set of intervals. The enumerable set of sets is obtained by taking $j = 1, 2, 3, \cdots$. For each positive integer k, the intervals I_{ij}, with $i + j = k$, form a finite set of intervals F_k. If we arrange these in order of increasing k, and then arrange the intervals of each set F_k in order of increasing i, all the intervals I_{ij} will be enumerated:

$$I_{11}; \quad I_{12}, I_{21}; \quad I_{13}, I_{22}, I_{31}; \quad I_{14}, I_{23}, I_{32}, I_{41}; \quad \cdots. \qquad (63)$$

This shows that *an enumerable number of enumerable sets of intervals may be enumerated.* Compare Exercises I, problems 12 and 13. If for a particular j, the set of intervals I_{ij} is finite and has N_j intervals, we omit from the sequence (63) all I_{ij} for this j with i greater than N_j. Again, if the number of sets is finite, say N', we omit all intervals I_{ij} with j greater than N'. The sequence of intervals (63) will be enumerably infinite unless we have a finite number of finite sets.

Next consider an enumerable number of sets of points, P_j. Let each set P_j be of measure zero. We may form a composite set P, consisting of all points which are in at least one of the sets P_j. We shall now prove that the set P is also of measure zero.

Since the set of points P_j is of measure zero, it may be included in an enumerable set of intervals whose total length L_j is less than $\epsilon/2^j$, where ϵ is any fixed positive number. Call the intervals of this enumerable set I_{ij}. Then the totality of intervals I_{ij} may be enumerated as in (63). We may use this sequence of intervals to form a sequence of sets of intervals H_n, by taking I_{11} as H_1, I_{11} together with the parts of I_{12} not in I_{11} as H_2, and so on. Then for any n, H_n consists of parts of a finite number of intervals I_{ij}. If N is the largest value of j for any of these, the sum of the lengths of all these intervals I_{ij} used in forming H_n will not exceed:

$$L_1 + L_2 + \cdots + L_N = \frac{\epsilon}{2} + \frac{\epsilon}{2^2} + \cdots + \frac{\epsilon}{2^N} = \epsilon\left(1 - \frac{1}{2^N}\right) < \epsilon. \qquad (64)$$

Thus the length of any set H_n will not exceed ϵ, and hence the length of the enumerable sequence of sets H_n will not exceed ϵ. But there is an enumerable sequence of intervals with the same length as the sequence of sets H_n, and which includes each point in any of the H_n. Thus it includes each point in any of the intervals I_{ij}, and hence each point in any of the sets P_j. This shows that the composite set P may be included in an enumerable set of intervals of total length at most ϵ. But ϵ is arbitrary, so that the measure of the set P is zero.

We have thus proved that:

The set consisting of all points in at least one of an enumerable number of sets of points, each of which is of measure zero, is again of measure zero.

Since a single point may be included in an interval of arbitrarily small length, it is of measure zero. Hence a set consisting of an enumerable number of distinct points is of measure zero. In particular, any set containing only a finite number of points is of measure zero.

Again, consider a set made up of those points of the closed interval 0,1 whose coördinates x are rational numbers. These form a set of measure zero, since they may be enumerated by the method used in section 2. This set illustrates the possibility of inequality in the relation (62). For, if we divide the unit interval into subintervals in any way, every subinterval will contain rational points, so that the outer content of this set is unity. Thus for this set $\bar{M} = 0$, but $\bar{C} = 1$.

154. Closed Sets. A closed set of points was defined in section 12 as one which contained all its limit points. We shall now prove that, whenever the set of points P is closed, the exterior measure of the set P is the same as the outer content, so that we have, in place of the relation (62),

$$\bar{M} = \bar{C} \text{ for closed sets.} \tag{65}$$

We first observe that, from the definition of $\bar{M}$ as a greatest lower bound, there is some enumerable set of intervals including all the points of P whose total length L satisfies:

$$\bar{M} \leqq L < \bar{M} + \epsilon, \tag{66}$$

for any positive ϵ. Let us fix ϵ, and determine an enumerated, non-overlapping set of intervals G of this character. Some of the points of P may be end points of intervals G. If we replace the nth interval of G, with end points a'_n, b'_n, by the open interval $a'_n - \epsilon/2^n, b'_n + \epsilon/2^n$, we obtain a new set of intervals G' such that every point of P is an interior point of an interval G', and the intervals G' cover the set P in the sense of section 11. It follows, from the modified Heine-Borel theorem of section 12, that we may find a finite subset F' of intervals G' which covers the set P. Thus the points of P are included in the finite set of intervals F'.

Let us denote by F the finite set of intervals G associated with those intervals of G' which are in F', and let E denote the finite set of intervals added to the ends of the intervals F to form the intervals F'. Each interval of F, as an interval G, may be associated with a positive integer which gives its place in the enumerated sequence. As there are only a finite number of such integers, there is a largest one, say N. If L_n is the total length of the first n intervals G, we have

$$L_n \leqq L_{n+1} \quad \text{and} \quad \lim L_n = L, \tag{67}$$

so that:

$$L_N \leqq L. \tag{68}$$

Also, if L'_n is the total length of the intervals added to the first n intervals G to form the corresponding intervals G', we have by reasoning, as in equation (64):

$$L'_n < 2\epsilon \quad \text{for all } n. \tag{69}$$

Since the intervals of the set F' are all among the first N intervals G', we have for the total length of the intervals F', or $L(F')$:

$$L(F') \leqq L_N + L'_N \leqq L + 2\epsilon. \tag{70}$$

But, from the definition of $\bar{C}$ as a lower bound of finite sets of intervals which include all the points of P, we have:

$$\bar{C} \leqq L(F'), \tag{71}$$

and hence from the relations (70) and (66),

$$\bar{C} \leqq L + 2\epsilon \leqq \bar{M} + 3\epsilon, \quad \text{or} \quad \bar{C} \leqq \bar{M}, \tag{72}$$

since ϵ is arbitrary. This, combined with the relation (62) shows that $\bar{C} = \bar{M}$ for any closed set P, the relation (65) which we set out to prove.

155. Closure. If we take any point set P, and designate by P' the set consisting of all the limit points of P, then the set consisting of all the points which are in either P or P', or in both, is called the *closure* of the set P. We denote it by $P + P'$, and shall prove that it is always closed. For, if Q is any limit point of this set, any open interval which has Q as an interior point will either contain points of P, or points of P'. But any open interval which contains a point of P' contains a limit point of the set P and hence points of P. Thus any point Q is necessarily a limit point of the set P, and therefore a point of the set P'. Hence the set $P + P'$ contains all its limit points, Q, and is a closed set.

Consider next any finite set of closed intervals F which includes all the points of P. We shall show that F must include all the points of P'. For, if x' is any point of P', we may select a sequence of distinct points of the set P, x_n, such that $\lim x'_n = x'$, as $n \to +\infty$. Since there are only a finite number of intervals in the set F, some one must contain an infinite number of points x_n, and hence the point x', since the interval is closed. This proves that F includes all the points of P'. Since F includes all the points of P, it includes all the points of $P + P'$.

Let us now consider $\bar{C}(P)$, the outer content of P, and also $\bar{C}(P + P')$, the outer content of the closure of P. Since the set $P + P'$ includes all the points of P, any finite set of intervals which includes $P + P'$ includes P. Therefore:

$$\bar{C}(P) \leqq \bar{C}(P + P'). \tag{73}$$

But, for any positive ϵ, we may find a finite set of intervals, F' which includes P and with total length L, such that:

$$\bar{C}(P) \leqq L \leqq \bar{C}(P) + \epsilon. \tag{74}$$

By adding the end points of these intervals to them, we obtain a finite set of closed intervals F with the same total length L. Since the set of closed intervals F includes the set P, it includes the set $P + P'$, and:

$$\bar{C}(P + P') \leqq L. \tag{75}$$

Hence, from the relation (74),

$$\bar{C}(P + P') \leqq \bar{C}(P) + \epsilon, \quad \text{or} \quad \bar{C}(P + P') \leqq \bar{C}(P), \tag{76}$$

since ϵ is arbitrary. A comparison of the relations (76) and (73) shows that:

$$\bar{C}(P + P') = \bar{C}(P), \tag{77}$$

and *the outer content of any set is the same as the outer content of its closure.*

The set of rational points on the interval 0,1 provides an illustration of this theorem. Since every point of the closed interval 0,1 is a limit point of rational points, for this set P the set P' contains all the points of the unit interval. Thus the closure of this set, $P + P'$, consists of the points of the unit interval, and $\bar{C}(P + P') = 1$, in agreement with equation (77) and the fact that $\bar{C}(P) = 1$, which we proved at the end of section 153.

156. A Condition in Terms of Measure. Given any function $f(x)$, bounded on the closed interval a,b, and any positive ϵ, let us consider P_ϵ, defined in section 151 as the set of those points on the interval a,b at which the oscillation of the function $f(x)$ is greater than or equal to ϵ. We recall that the oscillation at a point x_0 is the greatest lower bound of the oscillations for all intervals which include the point x_0 as an interior point. If x_0 is a limit point of points belonging to P_ϵ, every interval including x_0 as an interior point will include a point of P_ϵ, and therefore the oscillation of $f(x)$ for this interval will be at least ϵ. It follows that the oscillation of $f(x)$ at the point x_0 will be at least ϵ, and x_0 is a point belonging to P_ϵ.   This proves that the set of points P_ϵ is closed.

Now let D denote the set of points of the closed interval a,b at which $f(x)$ is not continuous.   We shall prove that if the exterior measure of the set D is zero, the function $f(x)$ is integrable on a,b.   We showed in section 150 that if the oscillation of $f(x)$ at a point is zero, $f(x)$ is continuous at the point, and conversely.   Thus at any point D, the oscillation of $f(x)$ is positive.   Conversely, any point at which the oscillation is positive is a point of discontinuity, and all the points of any set P_ϵ are included in the set D.   Thus any enumerable set of intervals which includes the set D, also includes the set P_ϵ and:

$$\overline{M}(P_\epsilon) \leqq \overline{M}(D). \tag{78}$$

But, since the set P_ϵ is closed, by equation (65), we have:

$$\overline{C}(P_\epsilon) = \overline{M}(P_\epsilon). \tag{79}$$

If now the exterior measure of D is zero, it follows from the last two relations that the outer content of P_ϵ is zero.   As this is true for all ϵ, the function $f(x)$ is integrable on the interval a,b by the theorem of section 151.

We may show conversely that if the function $f(x)$ is integrable, the set D has its exterior measure zero.   To do this, we take $\epsilon = 1/n$, where n is any positive integer, and consider the set P_ϵ.   Since $f(x)$ is integrable, the set P_ϵ has its outer content zero.   Hence by equation (79), its exterior measure is zero.

For $n = 1, 2, 3, \cdots$, the sets P with $\epsilon = 1/n$ form an enumerable number of sets of measure zero, to which we may apply the theorem of section 153 to deduce that the set consisting of all points in at least one of these sets is of measure zero.   But this set is the set D.   For we have already seen that every point in any P_ϵ is a point of D, and at any point of D the oscillation of $f(x),p$, is positive.   Since any positive number p exceeds $1/n$ when n exceeds $1/p$, it follows that every point of D is in all the sets P_ϵ with sufficiently small ϵ, or sufficiently large n.

Thus D is of measure zero when $f(x)$ is integrable, as we set out to prove.   This completes the proof of the theorem of Lebesgue:

For a bounded function to be integrable on an interval, it is necessary and sufficient that the function be continuous at all points of the interval, with the exception of a set of points whose exterior measure is zero.

Let $g(x)$ be a function of x determined by an enumerable number of functions $f_i(x)$, $i = 1, 2, \cdots$, in such a way that $g(x)$ is continuous whenever all of the $f_i(x)$ are continuous.   Then if $g(x)$ is bounded, and all the $f_i(x)$ are bounded and integrable on the interval a,b, the function $g(x)$ is integrable on that interval.

For the points where any one of the functions $f_i(x)$ is discontinuous constitute a set D_i of measure zero. By section 153, the set consisting of all points in at least one of these sets is again of measure zero. But $g(x)$ must be continuous except at points belonging to one of the sets D_i, and hence to this set. Thus, since it is bounded and continuous with the exception of a set of points of measure zero, it is integrable.

In particular, the result applies to a finite number of functions $f_i(x)$, and shows that *a continuous function of a finite number of integrable functions is integrable if it is bounded.*

157. A Special Class of Integrable Functions. A set containing no points is considered to be contained in any interval, and hence to be of exterior measure zero. Thus the theorem of section 122 on the integrability of continuous functions is included in the result just proved.

Again, it was shown in section 153 that a set consisting of an enumerable number of distinct points is of measure zero. Hence we have as an important special case of the theorem of the last section:

A bounded function, continuous on an interval, or continuous at all points except a finite number, or an enumerably infinite number of points, is integrable on the interval.

158. Monotonic Functions. Suppose the function $f(x)$ is defined and monotonically increasing throughout the closed interval a,b in the sense of section 27. Then,

$$\text{if } a \leqq x_1 < x_2 \leqq b, \qquad f(x_1) \leqq f(x_2). \tag{80}$$

In particular we have:

$$f(a) \leqq f(x) \leqq f(b), \tag{81}$$

for all points x of the closed interval, so that the function is bounded. From this, and the theorem of section 27, it follows that as we approach x_0, any point of the interval, from the left, a limit is approached, which we denote by $f(x_0-)$:

$$f(x_0-) = \lim_{x \to x_0-} f(x). \tag{82}$$

Similarly, we use $f(x_0+)$ to mean the limit from the right:

$$f(x_0+) = \lim_{x \to x_0+} f(x). \tag{83}$$

For the oscillation of $f(x)$ in any closed interval $x_0 - h, x_0 + h$, we have

$$f(x_0 + h) - f(x_0 - h), \tag{84}$$

as a consequence of equation (80). Hence, for the oscillation of $f(x)$ at x_0, as defined in section 150, we have:

$$f(x_0 +) - f(x_0 -). \tag{85}$$

Now suppose that there are N interior points x_i of the interval a,b at which the oscillation of $f(x)$ is at least ϵ. From the relations

$$f(a) \leqq f(x_1 -); \quad f(x_i +) \leqq f(x_{i+1} -); \quad f(x_N +) \leqq f(b), \tag{86}$$

it follows that:

$$f(b) - f(a) \geqq N\epsilon, \quad \text{and} \quad N \leqq \frac{f(b) - f(a)}{\epsilon}. \tag{87}$$

This shows that for any given ϵ, there are at most a finite number of points in the sets P_ϵ. By starting with the points at which the oscillation is $\geqq 1$, followed by those at which the oscillation is < 1 and $\geqq 1/2$, and so on, we may enumerate all the points at which the oscillation is not zero. The points added at the nth stage are finite in number, since they are included in P_ϵ, with $\epsilon = 1/n$. Since the function is continuous at all points at which the oscillation is zero, this proves that:

A function, monotonic on a closed interval, is either continuous on the interval or continuous at all points except a finite or an enumerably infinite number of points.

While we have stated the argument for monotonically increasing functions, we may either use a similar argument for monotonically decreasing functions, or replace $f(x)$ by $-f(x)$.

This result, combined with that of section 157, proves that:

A bounded function is integrable on any interval on which it is monotonic.

Or, since a monotonic function on a closed interval is necessarily bounded:

A function monotonic on a closed interval is integrable on that interval.

159. Functions of Bounded Variation. The sum of a monotonically increasing function and a monotonically decreasing function will be continuous unless one of the monotonic functions is discontinuous. Thus any such sum will have at most an enumerable number of discontinuities, and so be integrable on any closed interval.

We may characterize such functions in terms of the notion of variation of a function, which we proceed to define. For a function $f(x)$ defined on a closed interval a,b we may form the sum

$$v = \sum_{i=1}^{n} |f(x_i) - f(x_{i-1})| \tag{88}$$

for any points (2) of a subdivision of the interval a,b. If the values of v for all possible subdivisions are bounded, the function $f(x)$ is said to be of *bounded variation* on the interval. In this case, v has a least upper bound, V, which we call the *total variation* of the function on the interval. Let p denote the sum of those differences $f(x_i) - f(x_{i-1})$ which are positive, and let $-q$ denote the sum of those which are negative. Then:

$$v = p + q, \tag{89}$$

and

$$p - q = \sum_{i=1}^{n} [f(x_i) - f(x_{i-1})] = f(x_n) - f(x_0) = f(b) - f(a). \tag{90}$$

It follows that:

$$2p = v + f(b) - f(a) \quad \text{and} \quad 2q = v + f(a) - f(b). \tag{91}$$

Thus, if the sums v have an upper bound, the sums p and q also have an upper bound. We denote their least upper bounds by P and Q. From the equations (91) we see that a subdivision which makes any one of these numbers approximate its least upper bound does the same for the other two, and

$$2P = V + f(b) - f(a), \quad 2Q = V + f(a) - f(b). \tag{92}$$

Now let $v(x)$ be a number corresponding to v when we take the interval a,x in place of a,b. We may use the value x as one of the points of the subdivision used to calculate a value of v. Also all the terms in the sum for v in equation (88) are positive. Thus any subdivision of the interval a,x giving a value $v(x)$ may be used with any subdivision of the interval x,b to give a value of v which is equal to, or greater than, $v(x)$. This shows that if v is bounded, all the sums $v(x)$ are bounded, and the function is of bounded variation on any interval a,x. If $V(x)$ is the least upper bound for the values of $v(x)$, for a given x, we have:

$$V(x) \leqq V. \tag{93}$$

Also, by using the reasoning with any $x' > x$ in place of b, we see that

$$V(x) \leqq V(x') \quad \text{if} \quad x < x'. \tag{94}$$

Thus the function $V(x)$ is a monotonically increasing function of x.

Now denote the numbers corresponding to P and Q for the interval a,x by $P(x)$ and $Q(x)$. Then, as in equation (92), we have:

$$2P(x) = V(x) + f(x) - f(a) \quad \text{and} \quad 2Q(x) = V(x) + f(a) - f(x). \tag{95}$$

The argument used to establish the relation (94) may be applied to the positive sums for $p(x)$ and $q(x)$, the analogues of p and q for a,x, to show that $P(x)$ and $Q(x)$ are each monotonically increasing functions of x. Finally, from equation (95) we have

$$f(x) = [f(a) + P(x)] - Q(x), \qquad (96)$$

which shows that *every function of bounded variation may be regarded as the sum of a monotonically increasing function and a monotonically decreasing function.*

From this and the remark made at the beginning of this section, it follows that:

Every function of bounded variation on a closed interval is integrable on this interval.

Let us next show that on a closed interval every sum of two monotonic functions is of bounded variation. We first note that if $f(x)$ is monotonically increasing, all the differences $f(x_i) - f(x_{i-1})$ are positive or zero, so that $q = 0$. Hence by equation (90), $p = f(b) - f(a)$ and:

$$Q = q = 0, \quad V = v = P = p = f(b) - f(a). \qquad (97)$$

Thus on a closed interval a monotonically increasing function is of bounded variation. Similarly, on a closed interval a monotonically decreasing function is of bounded variation.

But if we write

$$\delta F_i = F(x_i) - F(x_{i-1}), \qquad (98)$$

and interpret δG_i and δH_i similarly, where

$$H(x) = F(x) + G(x), \qquad (99)$$

we have the relations:

$$\delta H_i = \delta F_i + \delta G_i \quad \text{and} \quad |\delta H_i| \leq |\delta F_i| + |\delta G_i|. \qquad (100)$$

By considering these last relations for $i = 1$ to n and summing, we find that for any subdivision the sum v for $H(x)$ cannot exceed that for $F(x)$ plus that for $G(x)$. This shows that *the sum of two functions of bounded variation is again of bounded variation.*

In particular, on a closed interval any sum of a monotonically increasing function and a monotonically decreasing function is of bounded variation, and the class of such functions is identical with the class of functions of bounded variation, in view of the result deduced from equation (96).

We may replace the monotonic functions of the decomposition by increasing and decreasing functions. For example, we may write

$$f(x) = [f(a) + P(x) + x + k] - [Q(x) + x + k] \qquad (101)$$

in place of equation (96).   We may thus consider a function of bounded variation as equivalent to the difference of two increasing functions, each positive if $k > -f(a) - a$ and $k > -a$, since $P(a) = Q(a) = 0$.   The functions of bounded variation are the most restricted class of functions on a closed interval including all positive increasing functions, and functions which are linear combinations of a finite number of such functions.

160. Operations on Functions of Bounded Variation.   We have already remarked that the sum of two functions of bounded variation is of bounded variation.   This result persists if we replace the fundamental operation of addition by subtraction or multiplication.   For, if y and y' are two functions of bounded variation, we may write:

$$y = s - t \quad \text{and} \quad y' = s' - t', \tag{102}$$

where s, t, s', and t' are all monotonically increasing functions.   Consequently we have

$$y - y' = (s + t') - (t + s'), \tag{103}$$

which shows that the difference of the two functions is the difference between two monotonically increasing functions, and hence is of bounded variation.   Similarly we may deduce from

$$yy' = (ss' + tt') - (st' + ts') \tag{104}$$

that the product of the two functions is of bounded variation.

Since $y'/y = (1/y)y'$, the quotient of y' by y will be of bounded variation if y' and the reciprocal of y is of bounded variation.   We shall show that $1/y$ is of bounded variation on any interval on which y is of bounded variation and uniformly bounded away from zero.   That is, if $y = f(x)$, there is some fixed positive number m such that

$$|f(x)| \geqq m, \tag{105}$$

for all x on the interval considered.

If we put

$$f(x_i) = A \quad \text{and} \quad f(x_{i-1}) = B, \tag{106}$$

we have:

$$\left| \frac{1}{A} - \frac{1}{B} \right| = \left| \frac{B - A}{AB} \right| \leqq \frac{1}{m^2} |A - B|. \tag{107}$$

Hence, with the notation of equation (98),

$$\sum \left| \delta \left(\frac{1}{f} \right)_i \right| \leqq \frac{1}{m^2} \sum |\delta f_i|, \tag{108}$$

and the variation of the reciprocal of $f(x)$ admits $1/m^2$ times the variation of $f(x)$ as an upper bound. This proves that with the restrictions stated, $1/y$ is of bounded variation.

We have thus proved that the quotient of two functions of bounded variation is of bounded variation, provided that the function in the denominator is uniformly bounded away from zero.

161. Continuous Functions of Bounded Variation. We may show that the variation function $V(x)$, as well as the functions $P(x)$ and $Q(x)$, are continuous functions of x at any value x_0 where $f(x)$ is continuous. In view of the relations between the three functions given in equation (95), it is sufficient to prove the property for $V(x)$.

Let $f(x)$ be continuous at x_0. Then, for any positive ϵ,

$$|f(x') - f(x_0)| < \epsilon, \quad \text{if} \quad |x' - x_0| < \delta_\epsilon. \tag{109}$$

From the definition of V as an upper bound, there is a subdivision of a,b which makes

$$v > V - \epsilon. \tag{110}$$

Since the sum v may increase but cannot decrease, if we use additional points of subdivision and retain all those already present, we may assume that x_0 is a point of the subdivision, and that if x' is the next following point of subdivision, $|x' - x_0| < \delta_\epsilon$. We shall then have for this subdivision:

$$v(x') = v(x_0) + |f(x') - f(x_0)| \leqq v(x_0) + \epsilon. \tag{111}$$

We must also have:

$$V(x') \leqq v(x') + \epsilon. \tag{112}$$

For, if $V(x')$ exceeded $v(x') + \epsilon$, there would be some subdivision of a,x' with a sum exceeding this. But $v(x')$ is that part of the sum used to form v coming from the interval a,x'. By using the new points for a,x' and the old points for x',b, we should have a sum for a,b exceeding $v + \epsilon$, and hence V, which contradicts the property of V as an upper bound.

By the property of $V(x_0)$ as an upper bound,

$$v(x_0) \leqq V(x_0). \tag{113}$$

We may deduce from the last three relations that

$$V(x') \leqq V(x_0) + 2\epsilon. \tag{114}$$

But $V(x)$ increases monotonically with x, so that

$$0 \leqq V(x') - V(x_0) \leqq 2\epsilon, \tag{115}$$

and this relation holds if x' is replaced by any point between x_0 and x'.

Similarly, we may assume that the subdivision for v contains a point x'', the next point preceding x_0, with $|x'' - x_0| < \delta_\epsilon$, and deduce the relations:

$$v(x_0) = v(x'') + |f(x_0) - f(x'')| \leqq v(x'') + \epsilon, \qquad (116)$$

$$V(x_0) \leqq v(x_0) + \epsilon, \quad \text{and} \quad v(x'') \leqq V(x''), \qquad (117)$$

so that: $\qquad\qquad V(x_0) \leqq V(x'') + 2\epsilon. \qquad\qquad\qquad (118)$

Hence, since $V(x)$ is monotonically increasing,

$$0 \leqq V(x_0) - V(x'') \leqq 2\epsilon, \qquad (119)$$

and x'' may be replaced by any point between x'' and x_0.

The relations (115) and (119) show that

$$|V(x) - V(x_0)| \leqq 2\epsilon, \qquad (120)$$

for any point x in the interval $x'' \leqq x \leqq x'$, and hence for all x, such that

$$|x - x_0| < \min (x - x'', x' - x). \qquad (121)$$

Since ϵ and hence 2ϵ is arbitrary, this shows that the function $V(x)$ is continuous at x_0.

Since the functions $P(x)$ and $Q(x)$ are continuous when $f(x)$ is continuous, we see from equation (101) that:

Any continuous function of bounded variation may be written as the difference of two continuous increasing functions.

EXERCISES VII

1. Let P_r denote the point set consisting of all points with rational coördinates on the closed interval 0,1. If $\phi(x)$ is the characteristic function of this set, as in section 148, show that for the interval 0,1 the upper integral of $\phi(x)$ is 1 and the lower integral of $\phi(x)$ is zero.

2. Let $F(x)$ and $G(x)$ be each integrable functions on the integral 0,1, with $F(x) \leqq G(x)$ on this interval. If the function $f(x)$ equals $G(x)$ when x is a point of P_r of problem 1, and $f(x)$ equals $F(x)$ when x is not a point of P_r, show that:

$$\overline{\int}_0^1 f(x)\, dx = \int_0^1 G(x)\, dx \quad \text{and} \quad \underline{\int}_0^1 f(x)\, dx = \int_0^1 F(x)\, dx.$$

3. Let P_1 be any set of points on the interval 0,1 and P_2 be the set of points on the interval not in P_1. If every point of the interval is a limit point of points of P_1 and also a limit point of points of P_2, show that the results of problems 1 and 2 are unchanged if we replace P_r by P_1.

4. Let the function $f(x)$ be defined on the interval 0,1 by the following conditions: If x is irrational, $f(x) = 0$. At the end points, $f(0) = f(1) = 1$. For a rational value of x, p/q in its lowest terms, $f(p/q) = 1/q$. Prove that the oscillation of $f(x)$ is zero for irrational x, and is $f(x)$ for rational x.

5. Prove that the function $f(x)$ of problem 4 is integrable on the interval, 0,1.

6. Let $g(q)$ be any function of q for which $\lim g(q) = 0$ as $q \to +\infty$. Define $f(x)$ as in problem 4, except at the points p/q, and put $f(p/q) = g(q)$. Prove that the results of problems 4 and 5 still hold.

7. Cantor's ternary set is obtained by removing an enumerable sequence of open intervals from the closed interval 0,1 as follows: First remove the open interval 1/3, 2/3, or middle-third open interval. Then remove the middle-third open interval from each interval that remains, and repeat the process indefinitely. Thus at the second stage two open intervals are removed, 1/9,2/9 and 7/9,8/9. At the nth stage 2^{n-1} intervals each of length $1/3^n$ are removed. Prove that this set is of content zero. *Hint:* After each step the intervals left have a total length 2/3 that of the preceding stage. Hence after n steps the intervals left have a total length $(2/3)^n$. But these contain all points of the set, and as $n \to +\infty$, $(2/3)^n \to 0$.

8. Let q be any number such that $0 < q < 1$. Remove an open interval of length q from the interval 0,1, and then from each interval that remains remove an open interval contained in it q times its length. Repeat the process indefinitely, and let P_q denote the set that is left. The special case where the intervals are centered, and $q = 1/3$, is described in problem 7. Prove that the set P_q is of content zero. *Hint:* By reasoning as in problem 7, show that the intervals left after n steps is $(1 - q)^n$, which $\to 0$.

9. We may form a set by the process of problem 8 using a sequence of numbers $q_1, q_2, q_3, \cdots$ between 0 and 1 instead of a fixed number, using q_n for all intervals at the nth stage. Show that the magnitude of the outer content of the set is $\lim (1 - q_1)(1 - q_2) \cdots (1 - q_n)$ as n becomes infinite. The limit always exists, since the product is positive and decreasing with n.

10. If a sequence of positive numbers decreases with n, it approaches a limit, $a_n \to a$. If $a_1 < 1$, we may define a sequence of numbers q_n successively, by setting $q_1 = 1 - a_1$, and for $n > 1$, $q_n = 1 - a_n/a_{n-1}$. Show that by using these in place of the q_n of problem 9, we obtain a set with outer content a.

11. Prove that the set obtained by removing an enumerable number of non-overlapping open intervals from a closed interval is a closed set. The sets of problems 7, 8, 9, 10 are examples. *Hint:* Since any point not in the set is in an open interval composed of similar points, it is not a limit point of the set. Hence all limit points of the set are in the set, and it is closed.

12. Prove, conversely to problem 11, that any closed set on a finite interval may be obtained by removing a suitable sequence of open intervals from a certain closed interval. *Hint:* the greatest lower bound of the set, a, is in the set. Similarly, for the least upper bound, b. The set is on a,b. If x is any point of a,b not in the set it is in some open interval x',x'' composed of similar points where x' and x'' are in the set, so that the same interval is obtained if we start with any point of it distinct from x. Since such intervals do not overlap and are all on a,b, there are only a finite number whose length exceeds $1/n$, and they may be enumerated.

13. If a function $f(x)$ is continuous on each of the open intervals removed to form the set P_q of problem 8, it is integrable on the interval 0,1.

14. Let P_a denote the point set consisting of all points on the closed interval 0,1 whose coördinates are algebraic numbers, as in Exercises II, problems 26, 30, and 33. Prove that the set P_a is of measure zero, but of outer content 1.

15. By interpreting the meaning of the result of problem 14 that P_a is of measure zero, deduce that there are points on the interval 0,1 not in P_a. This proves again that there are transcendental numbers, a result of problem 34 of Exercises II.

16. Prove that if a set consists of a finite number of points, it is of content zero. Use this and the theorem of section 151 to deduce an alternative proof of the fact that a bounded function is integrable if it is monotonic.

17. If $f(x)$ is monotonic on the open interval a,b and as $x \to a+$, $f(x) \to -\infty$, as $x \to b-$, $f(x) \to +\infty$, $f(x)$ is continuous except on an enumerable set of points. *Hint:* Put $F(x) = \tan^{-1} f(x)$, and show that $f(x)$ is continuous wherever $F(x)$ is. But the argument of section 158 applies to $F(x)$.

18. If $f(x)$ is monotonic on any interval, it is continuous except on an enumerable set of points. The interval may be open or closed, and may be replaced by the ranges $-\infty$, $+\infty$, or $-\infty, b$, or $a, +\infty$. *Hint:* Reduce to a bounded function as in problem 17.

19. Prove that, if $f(x)$ is bounded and integrable, then $|f(x)|$ is integrable.

20. Prove that if $f(x)$ satisfies a Lipschitz condition, equation (77) of section 128, then $f(x)$ is of bounded variation.

21. Prove that if $g(x)$ is bounded and integrable, and $f(x) = \int_a^x g(x)\,dx$, then $f(x)$ is of bounded variation. Also that for $f(x)$, $V(x) = \int_a^x |g(x)|\,dx$, $P(x) = \int_a^x g_1(x)\,dx$ and $Q(x) = \int_a^x g_2(x)\,dx$, where $g_1(x) = 0$ when $g(x) \leqq 0$, and $g_1(x) = g(x)$ when $g(x) > 0$; while $g_2(x) = 0$ when $g(x) \geqq 0$, and $g_2(x) = -g(x)$ when $g(x) < 0$. Compare problems 19 and 20.

CHAPTER VIII

EXTENSIONS AND APPLICATIONS OF INTEGRATION

The process of integration defined in section 121 in certain cases determined the Riemann integral of a bounded function over an interval as the limit of a special type of sum. Here we consider some modifications of this fundamental definition of integration.

We first discuss the Stieltjes integral, which is derived from two functions. We next consider a type of sum involving a function of several variables, each of which is in turn a function of a single variable. We show that, under certain conditions, the limits of sequences of such sums are Riemann integrals. Then we consider the improper integrals of the first kind, which are applicable to certain functions over an infinite range, and the improper integrals of the second kind, which are applicable to certain unbounded functions.

Finally, we consider some geometric and physical interpretations of the various types of integrals.

162. The Stieltjes Integral. Let the two functions $f(x)$ and $g(x)$ be each single-valued in the closed interval a,b. Consider an arbitrary division of the interval a,b into subintervals determined by the points

$$a = x_0 < x_1 < x_2 < \cdots < x_n = b, \tag{1}$$

and choose any points ξ_i such that

$$x_{i-1} \leqq \xi_i \leqq x_i. \tag{2}$$

Then we may form the sum

$$S = \sum_{i=1}^{n} f(\xi_i)[g(x_i) - g(x_{i-1})], \tag{3}$$

analogous to that used in section 121. This sum depends on the number n, the choice of the x_i, and the choice of the ξ_i.

Now consider any infinite discrete sequence of sums S_t of this type for which

$$\lim_{t \to +\infty} \delta_M = 0, \tag{4}$$

and where, as before,

$$\delta_M = \max \delta_i \quad \text{and} \quad \delta_i = x_i - x_{i-1}. \tag{5}$$

264

If, for any such sequence, the values of S_t approach a finite limit, and if this limit has the same value I_S for all such sequences, then I_S is called the *Stieltjes integral* of the function $f(x)$ with respect to the function $g(x)$, over the interval a,b.

We speak of the sum S of equation (3) as a Stieltjes sum. If we define:

$$\delta g_i = g(x_i) - g(x_{i-1}), \tag{6}$$

the Stieltjes sum (3) may be written:

$$S = \sum_{i=1}^{n} f(\xi_i)\,\delta g_i. \tag{7}$$

For reasons similar to those stated in section 127, this suggests the notation for the Stieltjes integral:

$$\lim S_t = I_S = \int_a^b f(x)\,dg \quad \text{or} \int_a^b f(x)\,dg(x). \tag{8}$$

We say that $f(x)\,dg(x)$ has a Stieltjes integral if there is a unique limit I_S.

When we wish to refer to the sums and integrals of section 121, in contradistinction to those of this section, we shall call them Riemann sums and Riemann integrals. The Stieltjes integral, as defined in this section, includes the Riemann integral as the special case for which $g(x) = x$.

163. A Sufficient Condition. We shall now show that, if $f(x)$ is continuous on the closed interval a,b and $g(x)$ is monotonically increasing throughout the same closed interval, then $f(x)\,dg(x)$ has a Stieltjes integral.

Since the function $g(x)$ is monotonically increasing, all the differences:

$$\delta g_i = g(x_i) - g(x_{i-1}) \tag{9}$$

will be positive or zero.

Now select any positive η and determine a δ_0 such that, for any two points x_i and x_2 in the closed interval,

$$|f(x_2) - f(x_1)| < \epsilon, \text{ if } |x_2 - x_1| < \delta_0, \text{ where } \epsilon = \frac{\eta}{g(b) - g(a)}. \tag{10}$$

We consider two sums:

$$S = \sum_{i=1}^{n} f(\xi_i)\,\delta g_i \quad \text{and} \quad S' = \sum_{j=1}^{n} f(\xi_j')\,\delta' g_j, \tag{11}$$

such that

$$\delta_M \leqq \frac{\delta_0}{2} \quad \text{and} \quad \delta_M' \leqq \frac{\delta_0}{2}, \tag{12}$$

where δ_M is defined for the first sum by equation (5) and δ_M' is similarly defined for the second sum. These sums are analogous to the Riemann sums in equation (9) of section 122. By reasoning similar to that used to derive equation (19) in section 122, we may show that, for the Stieltjes sums of equation (11),

$$|S - S'| \leqq \sum_{k=1}^{p} \epsilon \, \delta''g_k, \tag{13}$$

where p and x_k'' are defined by equation (12) of section 122 and

$$\delta''g_k = g(x_k'') - g(x_{k-1}''). \tag{14}$$

Since all the $\delta''g_k$ are positive or zero, and:

$$\sum_{k=1}^{p} \delta''g_k = g(x_p'') - g(x_0'') = g(b) - g(a), \tag{15}$$

it follows from the relation (13) and the last equation of (10) that:

$$|S - S'| \leqq \epsilon[g(b) - g(a)] \leqq \eta. \tag{16}$$

We may now apply to this equation the argument based on equation (20) in section 122 and draw the following conclusions: Any sequence of Stieltjes sums (11) for which $\delta_M \to 0$, approaches a limit. This limit, I_S, is the same for all such sequences. Any Stieltjes sum with $\delta_M < \delta_0/2$ approximates the value of the integral to within η.

By similar reasoning, or by noting that if $h(x)$ is monotonically decreasing, $g(x) = -h(x)$ is monotonically increasing, we may prove that the same results hold for monotonically decreasing functions. Accordingly, we formulate the theorem:

The Stieltjes integral of $f(x)\,dg(x)$ exists in any closed interval in which $f(x)$ is continuous and $g(x)$ is monotonic.

164. Duhamel Sums. Let

$$y_j = f_j(x), \; j = 1, 2, \cdots, k \tag{17}$$

be k continuous functions of the variable x in the closed interval a,b. If A_j is the minimum and B_j the maximum of the function $f_j(x)$, the values of y_j will all lie in the k-dimensional interval:

$$K \; : \; A_j \leqq y_j \leqq B_j. \tag{18}$$

Next let

$$F(y_j) = F(y_1, y_2, \cdots, y_k) \tag{19}$$

be a continuous function of the k variables y_j throughout the closed interval K. Then, by section 35, $F(y_j)$ is uniformly continuous in this closed interval, is bounded, and takes on its maximum and minimum values.

If we consider the equations (19) and (17) as defining F as a function of x,

$$G(x) = F[f_j(x)],\tag{20}$$

this will be a continuous function of x throughout the closed interval a,b by section 36.

For any arbitrary subdivision of the interval a,b by points (1) we select k sets of points satisfying the relation (2). We denote the points of the jth set by ξ_{ij} so that, for $j = 1, 2, 3, \cdots, k$,

$$x_{i-1} \leqq \xi_{ij} \leqq x_i.\tag{21}$$

We now form the sum:

$$S_D = \sum_{i=1}^{n} F[f_j(\xi_{ij})]\delta_i \quad \text{where} \quad j = 1, 2, \cdots, k,\tag{22}$$

and δ_i is defined by equation (5). We shall refer to a sum of this type as a *Duhamel sum*.

We shall show that any sequence of Duhamel sums for which

$$\delta_M \to 0, \quad \text{where} \quad \delta_M = \max \delta_i,\tag{23}$$

approaches as a limit the Riemann integral:

$$I = \int_a^b G(x)\, dx = \int_a^b F[f_j(x)]\, dx.\tag{24}$$

To prove this, first select any positive η, define:

$$\epsilon = \frac{\eta}{b - a},\tag{25}$$

and determine a δ' of uniform continuity such that

$$|F(y_j'') - F(y_j')| < \epsilon, \quad \text{if} \quad |y_j'' - y_j'| < \delta'; \quad j = 1, 2, \cdots, k,\tag{26}$$

and y_j'' and y_j' are in the closed interval K.

Next select a δ'' such that:

$$|f_j(x'') - f_j(x')| < \delta' \text{ for } j = 1, 2, \cdots, k \text{ if } |x'' - x'| < \delta''.\tag{27}$$

Now consider any Duhamel sum (22) with $\delta_M < \delta''$. For any ξ_i satisfying equation (2) we have from equation (21):

$$|\xi_{ij} - \xi_j| \leqq \delta'', \quad \text{for} \quad j = 1, 2, 3, \cdots, k.\tag{28}$$

It follows from this that:

$$|F[f_j(\xi_{ij})] - F[f_j(\xi_i)]| < \epsilon.\tag{29}$$

This enables us to compare the Duhamel sum S_D with the Riemann sum for the same subdivision:

$$S = \sum_{i=1}^{n} G(\xi_i)\delta_i = \sum_{i=1}^{n} F[f_j(\xi_i)]\delta_i. \tag{30}$$

We find:

$$|S_D - S| \leqq \sum_{i=1}^{n} |F[f_j(\xi_{ij})] - F[f_j(\xi_i)]|\delta_i$$

$$\leqq \epsilon \sum_{i=1}^{n} \delta_i \leqq (b - a)\epsilon \leqq \eta, \tag{31}$$

by equation (25).

Since S is a Riemann sum for the integral (24), it follows from section 122 that there is a δ_0 for the η here used such that

$$|I - S| < \eta, \quad \text{if} \quad \delta_M < \frac{\delta_0}{2}. \tag{32}$$

Consequently,

$$|I - S_D| < 2\eta, \quad \text{if} \quad \delta_M < \min\left(\frac{\delta_0}{2}, \delta''\right). \tag{33}$$

This proves the theorem:

Any sequence of Duhamel sums (22) *involving one continuous function of k variables and k continuous functions of a single variable, formed for a sequence of subdivisions for which* $\delta_M \to 0$, *approaches as a limit the Riemann integral* (24).

If $h(x)$ is any bounded function having a Riemann integral on the closed interval a,b, and if $G(x)$ is a continuous function on this interval, the product $h(x)G(x)$ will be bounded on this closed interval and continuous at all points where $h(x)$ is continuous. Thus, by the remarks at the end of section 156, the product will be integrable. Now consider any Riemann sum:

$$S = \sum_{i=1}^{n} h(\xi_i)G(\xi_i)\delta_i, \tag{34}$$

and the Duhamel sum formed for the same subdivision, with the function $G(x)$ defined by equation (20):

$$S_D = \sum_{i=1}^{n} h(\xi_i)F[f_j(\xi_{ij})]\delta_i. \tag{35}$$

If H is an upper bound for $h(x)$ on the interval, we have

$$|S - S_D| \leqq H\eta \quad \text{when} \quad \delta_M < \delta_j'', \tag{36}$$

by reasoning similar to that used for equation (31).

Now consider any sequence of values of S_D, formed for subdivisions with $\delta_M \to 0$.   The sequence of values of S, formed for the same values of δ_i and the same subdivisions, approach a limit:

$$I = \int_a^b h(x)G(x) \, dx. \tag{37}$$

Since, for values sufficiently far out in the sequence, we shall have $\delta_M < \delta''$ and $|I - S| < \eta$, for such values:

$$I - (H + 1)\eta < S_D < I + (H + 1)\eta, \tag{38}$$

which shows that the values of S_D approach the limit I, since η is arbitrary.

165. Properties of Stieltjes Integrals.   If the function $g(x)$ has a derivative throughout the open interval a,b it follows from the law of the mean that, for a suitable value of ξ_i' in the interval x_{i-1},x_i:

$$g(x_i) - g(x_{i-1}) = g'(\xi_i')(x_i - x_{i-1}) = g'(\xi_i')\delta_i. \tag{39}$$

Consequently the Stieltjes sum (7) may be written:

$$S = \sum_{i=1}^n f(\xi_i) \, \delta g_i = \sum_{i=1}^n f(\xi_i)g'(\xi_i')\delta_i. \tag{40}$$

This is a Duhamel sum similar to that of equation (35), with $k = 1$. We may take either $f(x)$ or $g'(x)$ as the function $h(x)$, and the other factor as the function $G(x)$.   Thus, if either of these functions is integrable, and the other continuous, any sequence of values for subdivisions with $\delta_M \to 0$ will approach a limit, and that limit will be the Riemann integral

$$\int_a^b f(x)g'(x) \, dx \tag{41}$$

for all such sequences.   In particular, this proves that:

If $f(x)$ is an integrable function on the closed interval a,b and $g(x)$ has a derivative $g'(x)$, continuous on this closed interval, then $f(x) \, dg(x)$ has a Stieltjes integral, which may be expressed as a Riemann integral of $f(x)g'(x)$:

$$\int_a^b f(x) \, dg(x) = \int_a^b f(x)g'(x) \, dx. \tag{42}$$

Now suppose that $g(x)$ is monotonic on the closed interval a,b and that $f(x)$ has a continuous derivative on this interval.   Then, by section 163, the Stieltjes integral $\int_a^b f(x) \, dg(x)$ exists.   And, by the theorem just proved, the Stieltjes integral $\int_a^b g(x) \, df(x)$ exists.

Now let us consider the identity:

$$f(x'')[g(x'') - g(x')] + g(x')[f(x'') - f(x')] =$$
$$f(x'')g(x'') - f(x')g(x'). \quad (43)$$

We may deduce from this that:

$$\sum_{i=1}^{n} f(x_i)\, \delta g_i + \sum_{i=1}^{n} g(x_{i-1})\, \delta f_i = f(x_n)g(x_n) - f(x_0)g(x_0)$$
$$= f(x)g(x)\Big|_a^b. \quad (44)$$

Since the last expression is independent of the subdivision, and the terms in the left member are particular Stieltjes sums for functions whose Stieltjes integrals exist, we find by taking a sequence of subdivisions with $\delta_M \to 0$ that:

$$\int_a^b f(x)\, dg(x) + \int_a^b g(x)\, df(x) = f(x)\, g(x)\Big|_a^b. \quad (45)$$

This is equivalent to

$$\int_a^b f(x)\, dg(x) = f(x)g(x)\Big|_a^b - \int_a^b g(x)f'(x)\, dx. \quad (46)$$

The last two equations have a formal similarity to the rule of integration by parts, and we have proved that:

If $f(x)$ has a derivative $f'(x)$ which is continuous on the closed interval a,b, and if $g(x)$ is a monotonic function on this interval, the evaluation of the Stieltjes integral of $f(x)\, dg(x)$ may be reduced to the evaluation of a Riemann integral by an integration by parts, according to equation (46).

We note that the Stieltjes integral is linear in $f(x)$ and also linear in $g(x)$. That is, multiplying either $f(x)$ or $g(x)$ by a constant k multiplies the integral by k. Also

$$\int_a^b u\, dg + \int_a^b v\, dg = \int_a^b (u+v)\, dg, \quad (47)$$

and

$$\int_a^b f\, du + \int_a^b f\, dv = \int_a^b f\, d(u+v), \quad (48)$$

if each of these integrals exists. If f is continuous, and u and v are both monotonically increasing, this will necessarily be the case. If one is increasing and the other decreasing, each of the integrals will still exist in the sense of section 162. In this case the expression on the right of equation (48) is sometimes defined as the value of the left member, which is the same for any decomposition of the function of bounded variation $(u + v)$ into the sum of two monotonic functions.

The Stieltjes integral of $f(x)\, dg(x)$ is unchanged by the addition of a constant to the function $g(x)$.

When $g(x)$ is a monotonically increasing function, the δg_i are all positive or zero. Hence most of the discussion of section 124 may be applied to the Stieltjes integral of $f(x)\, dg(x)$. In particular, if m and M are bounds for $f(x)$ in the closed interval a,b and $g(x)$ is monotonically increasing in this interval:

$$m[g(b) - g(a)] \leqq \int_a^b f(x)\, dg \leqq M[g(b) - g(a)]. \qquad (49)$$

166. Improper Integrals of the First Kind. So far we have only considered finite intervals, determined by finite limits of the integrals. Let us now consider a function $f(x)$, integrable over the interval a,x for all values of $x \geqq a$. If, as $x \to +\infty$, the integral approaches a finite limit, we write:

$$\int_a^\infty f(x)\, dx = \lim_{x \to +\infty} \int_a^x f(u)\, du = L. \qquad (50)$$

We say that the integral on the left *converges* when there is a finite limit, or converges to L to indicate the limit approached. When no finite limit is approached as $x \to +\infty$, we say that the integral *diverges*, or fails to converge.

By the Cauchy convergence criterion, the limit will exist if and only if, for each positive ϵ, there is a value X_ϵ, such that:

$$\left| \int_a^{x''} f(u)\, du - \int_a^{x'} f(u)\, du \right| < \epsilon, \quad \text{for any } x'' > x' > X_\epsilon. \qquad (51)$$

Now suppose that $p(x)$ is a function whose values are all greater than or equal to zero for all $x \geqq A \geqq a$, and that

$$|f(x)| \leqq p(x), \quad \text{if} \quad x \geqq A. \qquad (52)$$

Then

$$\left| \int_a^{x''} f(u)\, du - \int_a^{x'} f(u)\, du \right| = \left| \int_{x'}^{x''} f(u)\, du \right| \leqq \int_{x'}^{x''} |f(u)|\, du$$

$$\leqq \int_{x'}^{x''} p(u)\, du. \qquad (53)$$

But, since $p(x) \geqq 0$,

$$\left| \int_A^{x''} p(u)\, du - \int_A^{x'} p(u)\, du \right| = \int_{x'}^{x''} p(u)\, du. \qquad (54)$$

The last two relations show that any X_ϵ for the function $p(x)$ will serve as an X_ϵ for $f(x)$. This enables us to deduce the convergence of the integral

$$\int_a^\infty f(x)\, dx \quad \text{from that of} \quad \int_A^\infty p(x)\, dx. \tag{55}$$

The integral of $p(x)$ from A to x increases monotonically with x. Hence $\int_A^\infty p(x)\, dx$ must converge if there is an upper bound to the values of $\int_A^x p(x)\, dx$ for all $x > A$.

With the same conventions made for the relation (50), we write:

$$\int_{-\infty}^a f(x)\, dx = \lim_{x \to -\infty} \int_x^a f(u)\, du. \tag{56}$$

We also define:

$$\int_{-\infty}^\infty f(x)\, dx = \int_{-\infty}^a f(x)\, dx + \int_a^\infty f(x)\, dx, \tag{57}$$

and extend the definition:

$$\int_b^a f(x)\, dx = -\int_a^b f(x)\, dx, \tag{58}$$

so that it applies when the limits a,b are replaced by a, ∞; by $-\infty, a$; or by $-\infty, \infty$.

All of the integrals of this section, defined in terms of a bounded function on an infinite interval by a process derived from, but not identical with, that of section 121, are known as improper Riemann integrals, or simply *improper integrals* of the first kind.

Improper Stieltjes integrals with infinite limits are defined in a similar manner. We may show that if $f(x)$ and $p(x)$ are two functions for which the relation (52) holds, and $g(x)$ is monotonically increasing, the convergence of

$$\int_A^\infty p(x)\, dg(x) \quad \text{implies that of} \quad \int_a^\infty f(x)\, dg(x). \tag{59}$$

167. Improper Integrals of the Second Kind. If the function $f(x)$ is not bounded in the closed interval a,c the process of integration defined in section 121 is not applicable for this interval. But, if the function is bounded and integrable over the interval a,x for every value of x in the open interval a,c, and if the integral approaches a finite limit as $x \to c-$, we write

$$\int_a^c f(x)\,dx = \lim_{x \to c-} \int_a^x f(u)\,du, \tag{60}$$

and say that the integral on the left converges. We say it diverges if it does not converge.

As in the last section, we may conclude that if

$$p(x) \geqq 0 \quad \text{and} \quad |f(x)| \leqq p(x) \quad \text{for} \quad a \leqq A \leqq x < c, \tag{61}$$

the convergence of

$$\int_A^c p(x)\,dx \text{ implies that of } \int_a^c f(x)\,dx. \tag{62}$$

Moreover, the integral of $p(x)$ over A,c must converge if there is an upper bound to the values of $\displaystyle\int_A^x p(x)\,dx$ for all $A < x < c$.

Similarly, we use

$$\int_c^b f(x)\,dx = \lim_{x \to c+} \int_x^b f(u)\,du, \tag{63}$$

as the definition of the left member, if $f(x)$ is unbounded in the closed interval c,b but is such that the limit on the right exists.

We extend the relation

$$\int_a^b f(x)\,dx = \int_a^c f(x)\,dx + \int_c^b f(x)\,dx, \tag{64}$$

which holds when all the integrals are proper Riemann integrals, to define the integral on the left when one or both of the integrals on the right are defined by equations (60) or (63).

All of the integrals of this section, defined in terms of a function not bounded on a finite interval, but bounded and integrable if we omit all points belonging to any open interval including a point c, are known as *improper integrals* of the second kind.

168. Bounded Functions. We have only used equations (60) and (63) as definitions of the left member when the function $f(x)$ was unbounded in every open interval including the point c. Suppose, now, that $f(x)$ is bounded on the closed interval a,c and integrable over the interval a,x for every value of x in the open interval a,c. Then if we take any finite value as the value of $f(x)$ at c, the resulting function will be integrable on the closed interval a,c as we proceed to show.

This will follow from the theorem of section 156 if we show that the points of discontinuity of $f(x)$ on a,c form a set of measure zero. Select any positive η. Then, since $f(x)$ is integrable on $a,c - \eta$, the points of discontinuity of $f(x)$ on the closed interval $a,c - \eta$ form a set of measure zero and hence may be included in an enumerable set of intervals G of total length $< \eta$. But these intervals, together with the closed interval $c - \eta,c$ include all the points D, and have a total length $< 2\eta$. Since η is arbitrary, this proves our contention that D is of measure zero.

By the convention made in section 149, we may leave $f(x)$ undefined at c, and still consider $f(x)$ integrable on the closed interval a,c. Thus the integral in the left member of equation (60) is already defined. However, in this case $\int_a^x f(u)\, du$ is a continuous function of x in the closed interval, by section 127, so that equation (60) holds.

This proves that we may use equation (60) whenever the limit on the right exists, without verifying that the function is unbounded. Similar remarks apply to equation (63).

169. Improper Integrals. Let the interval a,b be composed of n intervals c_{i-1},c_i where

$$a = c_0 < c_1 < c_2 < \cdots < c_n = b. \tag{65}$$

Then, if the integral of $f(x)$ is defined for each of the intervals c_{i-1},c_i either as a proper integral, or as an improper integral of the second kind by equations similar to (60) or (63), we define:

$$\int_a^b f(x)\, dx = \sum_{i=1}^n \int_{c_{i-1}}^{c_i} f(x)\, dx. \tag{66}$$

We use a similar equation if a,b is replaced by $-\infty,b$; by a,∞ or by $-\infty,\infty$, provided the improper integrals of the first kind so introduced converge and are defined by equations similar to equations (50) or (56).

The equation (66) enables us to reduce the evaluation of any improper integral of the kind here considered to that of a finite number of integrals of elementary type.

Such integrals may sometimes be computed by the methods of section 126. We proved there that if $f(x) = F'(x)$ was an integrable function over the interval a,b then

$$\int_a^b f(x)\, dx = F(b) - F(a). \tag{67}$$

Now consider equation (50). Suppose that $F'(x) = f(x)$ for all $x \geqq a$, where $f(x)$ is integrable over every interval a,x. If we write

$$F(x)\Big|_a^\infty = \lim_{x \to +\infty} F(x) - F(a), \tag{68}$$

when the limit on the right exists, we have:

$$\int_a^\infty f(x)\,dx = F(x)\Big|_a^\infty. \tag{69}$$

We may also conclude that if the limit on the right in the equation (68) does not exist as a finite limit, the integral on the left in equation (69) does not converge.

Consider next equation (60). Suppose that $F'(x) = f(x)$ for all x in the open interval a,c where $f(x)$ is integrable in every interval a,x. If we write

$$F(c-) = \lim_{x \to c-} F(x) \tag{70}$$

when the limit on the right exists, we have:

$$\int_a^c f(x)\,dx = F(x)\Big|_a^{c-} = F(c-) - F(a). \tag{71}$$

We may also conclude that if the limit on the right in equation (70) does not exist as a finite limit, the integral on the left in equation (71) does not converge.

If $F(x)$ is related to $f(x)$ by $F'(x) = f(x)$ for all x in each of the n open intervals c_{i-1},c_i and the integrals of elementary type in equation (66) all exist, we have:

$$\int_a^b f(x)\,dx = \sum_{i=1}^n [F(c_i-) - F(c_{i-1}+)], \tag{72}$$

where $F(c+)$ is defined by an equation similar to (70).

Whenever $F(c_i-) = F(c_i+)$, the terms involving c_i on the right in equation (72) will cancel. In particular, if $F(x)$ is continuous throughout the closed interval a,b the equation (72) may be replaced by:

$$\int_a^b f(x)\,dx = F(b) - F(a). \tag{73}$$

The equation (72) may also be used for proper integrals, provided the interval may be decomposed into a finite number of intervals c_{i-1},c_i for each of which an indefinite integral $F(x)$ may be found.

When we change the variable in an integral by a substitution, either to simplify its evaluation or for some other purpose, we may convert a proper integral into an improper integral, or vice versa. For example, if $x = 1/u$,

$$\int_1^\infty \frac{dx}{x^2} = \int_0^1 du = 1, \tag{74}$$

and
$$\int_0^1 \frac{dx}{\sqrt{x}} = \int_1^\infty u^{-\frac{3}{2}} du = 2. \tag{75}$$

In this case an improper integral of the second kind is converted into one of the first kind.

As examples of equations (69) and (71) we have:

$$\int_0^\infty \frac{dx}{1 + x^2} = \tan^{-1} x \Big|_0^\infty = \frac{\pi}{2}, \tag{76}$$

and

$$\int_0^1 \frac{dx}{\sqrt{1 - x^2}} = \sin^{-1} x \Big|_0^{1-} = \frac{\pi}{2}. \tag{77}$$

The introduction of improper integrals enables us to consider certain special values of the limits in the integrals of sections 137 through 144. For example, in section 141, we may take the upper limit for x as 1. This corresponds to $\phi = \pi/2$, since $x = \sin \phi$. The resulting elliptic integrals are known as the complete elliptic integrals. They are convergent improper integrals of the second kind when x is the variable, but become proper integrals in the variable ϕ.

170. Particular Convergent and Divergent Integrals. Since:

$$\int^x x^{-a} dx = \frac{x^{-a+1}}{1 - a}, \quad a \neq 1 \quad \text{and} \quad \int^x x^{-1} dx = \log x, \tag{78}$$

it follows that

$$\int_1^\infty x^{-a} dx \text{ converges if and only if } a > 1, \tag{79}$$

and

$$\int_0^1 x^{-a} dx \text{ converges if and only if } a < 1. \tag{80}$$

Similarly, for any $b > c$,

$$\int_c^b (x - c)^{-a} dx \text{ converges if and only if } a < 1. \tag{81}$$

We may conclude from this and equations (61) and (62) that, if $F(x)$ is bounded and integrable in the closed interval c,b, the integral

$$\int_c^b (x - c)^{-a} F(x) dx \text{ converges if } a < 1. \tag{82}$$

In particular, this will be true if $F(x)$ is continuous throughout the closed interval c,b, or continuous except at c, with $\lim_{x \to c+} F(x)$ finite.

The same discussion applies if $b < c$, either to the integral as written or from b to c, if $F(x)$ is continuous throughout the closed interval b,c or continuous except at c with $\overline{\lim\limits_{x \to c-}} F(x)$ finite. Equation (77) and the complete elliptic integrals are examples with $c = 1$ as the upper limit, $a = 1/2$ and $F(x)$ continuous. An example with $\overline{\lim} F(x) = 1$ is

$$\int_c^b (x - c)^{-\frac{2}{3}} \sin \frac{1}{x - c}\, dx. \tag{83}$$

Again, assuming that $\overline{\lim\limits_{x \to c+}} F(x)$ is finite,

$$\int_c^b (x - c)^{-a} \log (x - c) F(x)\, dx \text{ converges if } a < 1. \tag{84}$$

For we may write

$$a = a' - p, \quad \text{with} \quad p > 0 \quad \text{and} \quad a' < 1, \tag{85}$$

and then put

$$(x - c)^{-a} \log (x - c) F(x) = (x - c)^{-a'}[(x - c)^p \log (x - c)] F(x). \tag{86}$$

By section 92, $\lim\limits_{x \to c} (x - c)^p \log (x - c) = \lim\limits_{h \to 0} h^p \log h = 0$, so that when $x \to c$, the factor in the brackets approaches zero. Hence the integral in equation (84) converges by equation (82).

Similarly, any factor which as $x \to c$ is an infinity of lower order than any arbitrary positive power of $(x - c)$ will not affect the convergence. Note that a may be zero in equation (84).

Again, if $P(x)$ is positive, has a positive lower bound, and is integrable in the closed interval c,b, the integral

$$\int_c^b (x - c)^{-a} P(x)\, dx \text{ diverges if } a \geqq 1. \tag{87}$$

In fact, if this integral converged, it would imply that the integral of equation (81) converged for a value of $a \geqq 1$.

In particular, if $P(x)$ is continuous except at c, and $\lim\limits_{x \to c+} P(x) > 0$, or $\lim\limits_{x \to c+} P(x) = +\infty$, the conclusion follows. When $b < c$, we consider the $\overline{\lim}$ as $x \to c-$.

An argument similar to that used to prove equation (84) shows that

$$\int_c^b e^{|x-c|^{-p}} P(x)\, dx \text{ diverges, if } p > 0. \tag{88}$$

Also the product of $P(x)$ by any positive factor which, as $x \to c+$, is an infinity of higher order than $(x - c)^{-1}$ used as an integrand leads to **a** divergent integral.

From equation (79) we may conclude that, if $F(x)$ is integrable over all the finite intervals A,x and $\overline{\lim_{x \to +\infty}} F(x)$ is finite, then

$$\int_A^\infty x^{-a} F(x) \, dx \text{ converges if } a > 1, \tag{89}$$

and any factor which, as $x \to +\infty$, is an infinity of lower order than any arbitrary positive power of x will not affect the convergence.

Also, if $P(x)$ is positive and integrable over all the finite intervals A,x and $\varliminf_{x \to +\infty} P(x) > 0$, then

$$\int_A^\infty x^{-a} P(x) \, dx \text{ diverges if } a \leqq 1. \tag{90}$$

This integral will diverge if the integrand is the product of $P(x)$ by any positive function which, as $x \to +\infty$, is an infinity of higher order than x^{-1}.

In section 144 we defined $u(x)$, the inverse of the Weierstrass $\wp$ function by conditions equivalent to the definition

$$\int_{+\infty}^x \frac{dx}{\sqrt{4x^3 - g_2 x - g_3}} = u(x). \tag{91}$$

That this integral converges follows from equation (89) with $a = 3/2$.

171. Arc Length. A continuous sensed arc is any ordered set of points (x,y) in the plane which can be represented by two equations,

$$x = f(t) \quad \text{and} \quad y = g(t), \tag{92}$$

for values of t in some closed interval a,b where these functions are each continuous throughout the closed interval. When the functions are such that if t' and t'' are any two values each in the closed interval

$$a \leqq t \leqq b, \tag{93}$$

the relations

$$f(t') = f(t'') \quad \text{and} \quad g(t') = g(t'') \text{ imply that } t' = t'', \tag{94}$$

the correspondence between the points of the arc and the t interval (93) is one to one. An arc is said to be *simple*, if the parameter t can be so chosen that this is the case.

The order relations of points on the arc is determined by the order of the corresponding values of t. This is the only geometrical significance of the parameter. Two arcs consisting of the same points, in the same order, are considered identical. Thus

$$x = t^2, \ y = 0, \ -1 \le t \le 1 \tag{95}$$

and

$$x = 1 - \cos t, \ y = 0, \ -\frac{\pi}{2} \le t \le \frac{\pi}{2} \tag{96}$$

represent the same arc, but this arc is not simple. The arc

$$x = t, \ y = 0, \ 0 \le t \le 1 \tag{97}$$

is a simple arc, identical with a portion of the arc given by equations (95) or (96).

A polygonal line is an arc consisting of a finite number of straight line segments. We may obtain a polygonal line inscribed in an arc by selecting $n - 1$ intermediate values of t,

$$a = t_0 < t_1 < t_2 < \cdots < t_n = b, \tag{98}$$

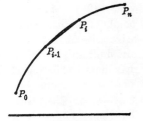

FIG. 16.

which determine $n - 1$ intermediate points of the arc, P_i, and by joining each pair of consecutive points P_{i-1}, P_i by a straight line segment or chord. Any choice of $n - 1$ intermediate points P_i will determine a subdivision of the t interval similar to (98) for any choice of the parameter. Let L_n denote the total length of the inscribed polygonal line. Let us put

$$\delta t_i = t_i - t_{i-1}, \ \delta x_i = f(t_i) - f(t_{i-1}), \ \delta y_i = g(t_i) - g(t_{i-1}). \tag{99}$$

Then

$$L_n = \sum_{i=1}^{n} P_{i-1}P_i \quad \text{and} \quad P_{i-1}P_i = \sqrt{\delta x_i^2 + \delta y_i^2}. \tag{100}$$

But, by reasoning as in section 98 we may show that

$$|\delta x_i| \le P_{i-1}P_i, \ |\delta y_i| \le P_{i-1}P_i \quad \text{and} \quad P_{i-1}P_i \le |\delta x_i| + |\delta y_i|. \tag{101}$$

It follows that

$$\sum_{i=1}^{n} |\delta x_i| \quad \text{or} \quad \sum_{i=1}^{n} |\delta y_i| \le L_n \le \sum_{i=1}^{n} |\delta x_i| + \sum_{i=1}^{n} |\delta y_i|. \tag{102}$$

If t' and t'' are any two values each in the closed interval (93), corresponding to the points P' and P'', the length of $P'P''$ is a continuous function of t' and t'', and so takes on its maximum. This maximum chord is called the diameter of the arc.

If we consider any polygonal line such that d_M, the maximum diameter of any of the arcs $P_{i-1}P_i$, is at most ϵ, then any polygonal line obtained by inserting additional points of subdivision will have all its chords at most ϵ. If every sequence of inscribed polygonal lines for which $d_M \to 0$ leads to a sequence of values of L_n approaching a limit L, the same for all such sequences, we say that the arc has a length L. We must use d_M, instead of maximum chord, since our arcs are not necessarily simple. If, for example, our arc was like a figure 8, a subdivision of one of the loops might be considered to be a subdivision of the entire figure with all the chords small, but would have a polygonal length approximating only one half of the total arc.

The first sum of the relation (102) is similar to the sum v, for the function $f(t)$, used to obtain its variation as in section 159. Suppose the value of the sum is v_0 for any particular subdivision by intermediate values (98). Since v increases or remains unchanged when additional points of subdivision are added, there will be subdivisions with max δt_i arbitrarily small and with $v \geqq v_0$. And, since the functions $f(t)$ and $g(t)$ are uniformly continuous, there will be such subdivisions with the maximum oscillation of $f(t)$ and $g(t)$ in any subarc arbitrarily small. Thus these subdivisions will have d_M arbitrarily small. Since for such sums $L_n \geqq v \geqq v_0$, if the limit L exists it will be at least v_0 and $v_0 \leqq L$. Thus L is an upper bound for v for all subdivisions, and the function $f(t)$ is of bounded variation.

Similar reasoning may be used for $g(t)$, and hence:

If a continuous sensed arc has a finite arc length, the functions expressing the coördinates in terms of any parameter are each of bounded variation.

To prove a converse result, suppose next that $f(t)$ and $g(t)$ are each of bounded variation. Then by equations (100) and (102):

$$L_n = \sum_{i=1}^{n} P_{i-1}P_i \leqq \sum_{i=1}^{n} |\delta x_i| + \sum_{i=1}^{n} |\delta y_i|. \qquad (103)$$

This shows that all the values of L_n are less than the sum of the total variation of $f(t)$ plus that of $g(t)$ for the interval. Hence the values L_n are bounded, and so have a least upper bound which we denote by L.

The distances between any three points satisfy the relation:

$$P_{i-1}P_i \leqq P_{i-1}P_j + P_jP_i, \qquad (104)$$

as we proved analytically in section 98. This shows that if we insert one additional point of subdivision P_j between P_{i-1} and P_i, the new value which replaces L_n will be equal to or greater than L_n. Moreover, since each of the new chords will be at most equal to the diameter of the arc, the increase in value can not exceed twice this diameter, or twice d_M.

Since L is a least upper bound, there is a subdivision with a polygonal line of length exceeding $L - \epsilon$. Let the points of this subdivision be P_j', corresponding to t_j'. Suppose there are $N - 1$ interior points, and denote the polygonal length by L_N' so that:

$$L_N' \geqq L - \epsilon. \tag{105}$$

Now consider any subdivision with $d_M < \dfrac{\epsilon}{2N}$. Let its points of subdivision be P_i, corresponding to t_i of (98), and let its polygonal length be L_n. Then

$$L_n \leqq L. \tag{106}$$

Form a new subdivision by using the points P_i together with the points P_j' distinct from all the P_i. If this has m points, $m < n + N$. Denote the polygonal length by L_m''. Since we have added to the P_i less than N new points, which form at most $2N$ new chords, each at most $\epsilon/2N$, we have:

$$L_m'' \leqq L_n + 2N \cdot \frac{\epsilon}{2N} \leqq L_n + \epsilon. \tag{107}$$

But the subdivision which gave L_m'' could be obtained from that which gave L_N' by adding points of subdivision, so that:

$$L_m'' \geqq L_N'. \tag{108}$$

We may deduce from the last four numbered inequalities that:

$$L - 2\epsilon \leqq L_n \leqq L. \tag{109}$$

This shows that, for any sequence of subdivisions for which $d_M \to 0$, the numbers L_n will differ from L by at most 2ϵ, beyond a certain point in the sequence. Since ϵ is arbitrary, we may conclude that $\lim L_n = L$, and the arc has a length. Thus:

A continuous sensed arc has a finite arc length if the functions expressing the coördinates in terms of any parameter are each of bounded variation.

In this case the arc length will be the least upper bound of the lengths of all inscribed polygonal lines.

As we have defined it, arc length is independent of the choice of parameter, except as this determines order on the sensed arc. Thus arc length is a geometric quantity related to the sensed arc.

172. Simple Arcs. For a simple arc, any sequence of subdivisions such that max $P_{i-1}P_i \to 0$ is also a sequence for which $d_M \to 0$, as we shall now prove. To do this, suppose that there is a sequence of subdivisions with max $P_{i-1}P_i \to 0$, but such that d_M does not approach zero.

Then for some positive ϵ, for each integer n there would be a subdivision with $d_M > \epsilon$, and with max $P_{i-1}P_i < 1/n$, since for some ϵ there would be subdivisions with $d_M > \epsilon$ arbitrarily far out in the sequence. This would enable us to find a pair of points on the curve for which

$$\text{chord } P_n'P_n'' < \frac{1}{n} \quad \text{and} \quad \text{diameter } P_n'P_n'' > \epsilon. \tag{110}$$

But $f(t)$ and $g(t)$ are continuous functions, so that the chord $P'P''$ corresponding to any two values of t, t' and t'', is a continuous function of these two variables on a closed two-dimensional interval. Thus it is uniformly continuous, and there is a δ such that

$$P'P'' < \epsilon, \quad \text{when} \quad |t'' - t'| < \delta. \tag{111}$$

Since the arc $P_n'P_n''$ contains some chord of length $> \epsilon$, it must include a pair of points whose values of t differ by more than δ. Hence the values of t corresponding to P_n' and P_n'', say t_n' and t_n'', must differ by more than δ, so that:

$$|t_n'' - t_n'| \geqq \delta. \tag{112}$$

Now keep ϵ fixed, and let n take in succession the values 1, 2, 3, $\cdots$. Either all of the points t_n' coincide for sufficiently large values of n, or else the infinite set has at least one limit point, by section 9. In either case a subset of values of n can be selected such that the corresponding values of t_n' approach a limit, say t_0'. Similarly, from these values of n a second subset of values of n can be selected, say m, such that the values of t_m'' approach a limit, say t_0''. Then we have:

$$\lim t_m' = t_0' \quad \text{and} \quad \lim t_m'' = t_0' \tag{113}$$

It follows from the relations (110), (112), and (113) that

$$\text{chord } P_0'P_0'' = 0, \quad |t_0'' - t_0'| \geqq \delta. \tag{114}$$

This contradicts the condition that the arc be simple, and hence proves the assumption that d_M does not approach zero was false.

Thus for simple arcs, when max chord $P_{i-1}P_i \to 0$, $d_M \to 0$. But from the definition of diameter, when $d_M \to 0$, max chord $P_{i-1}P_i \to 0$. Hence, *in defining the length of a simple continuous sensed arc, we may consider sequences for which* max chord $P_{i-1}P_i \to 0$, *instead of those for which* $d_M \to 0$.

173. Variation. If $f(t)$ is a continuous function of bounded variation on the closed interval a,b the equations

$$x = f(t) \quad \text{and} \quad y = 0 \tag{115}$$

determine a continuous sensed arc, whose length is the total variation of $f(t)$ for the interval a,b. Since $f(t)$ is uniformly continuous, any sequence of subdivisions for which max $\delta t_i \to 0$ will be such that $d_M \to 0$. This proves:

For a continuous function of bounded variation, the total variation $V = \lim \sum |\delta f_i|$ for any sequence of subdivisions for which max $\delta t_i \to 0$.

174. Properties of Arc Length. From the corresponding properties of polygons, it follows that the arc length of a curve, or continuous sensed arc, as defined in section 171 is such that:

If an arc is divided by a point into two arcs, the total length is the sum of the lengths of the two parts. That is,

$$L_a^b = L_a^c + L_c^b, \tag{116}$$

where we use sub- and superscripts to denote the end points, as we do for integrals. As for the integrals, we may define

$$L_a^b = -L_b^a, \tag{117}$$

and write the preceding relation more symmetrically as

$$L_a^b + L_b^c + L_c^a = 0. \tag{118}$$

From the symmetry of this relation it will hold for any three values of a, b, c regardless of their order.

If we denote the variation of $f(t)$ from a to t by Vf_a^t, and similarly that of $g(t)$ by Vg_a^t, we may deduce from equation (102) and the preceding section that:

$$Vf_a^b \quad \text{or} \quad Vg_a^b \leqq L_a^b \leqq Vf_a^b + Vg_a^b. \tag{119}$$

As this holds for any interval whose end points are in a,b, we may apply it to the interval $t, t + h$ where t is in the open interval and h is sufficiently small. We may then deduce from the last part of the relation and the continuity of the variations which was proved in section 161 that the arc length is a continuous function of the values of t at the end points. Also, from the first part of the relation and the increasing character of the variations, we may deduce that L_a^t increases monotonically with t. It will actually increase with t as t increases from t' to t'', unless $f(t)$ and $g(t)$ each have zero variation for this interval t',t''. In this case, the functions are constant, and, for any t such that

$$t' \leqq t \leqq t'', \ f(t) = f(t') \quad \text{and} \quad g(t) = g(t'). \tag{120}$$

Thus this can not happen in the case of a simple arc. In fact, since broken lines are at least as great as their chords, the same is true of arc lengths, and if P' and P'' are distinct points, and t' and t'' corresponding values of the parameter we shall have:

$$L_a^{t'} \leqq L_a^{t''} \quad \text{if} \quad t' \leqq t''. \tag{121}$$

The only function of the parameter was to order the points. The last relation shows that the points will be correctly ordered if we take the arc length itself,

$$s = L_a^t, \tag{122}$$

as the parameter. In this way we obtain a representation of the arc:

$$x = F(s), \quad y = G(s), \tag{123}$$

with geometric significance. These functions will each be continuous, since we may conclude from equation (101) that:

$$|\delta x_i| \quad \text{or} \quad |\delta y_i| \leqq P_{i-1}P_i \leqq \delta s_i. \tag{124}$$

175. Integral for Arc Length. Now suppose that for some choice of the parameter t, the functions $f(t)$ and $g(t)$ each have derivatives continuous over the closed interval a,b. In this case the functions $f(t)$ and $g(t)$ will necessarily be of bounded variation, as we proceed to show. By the law of the mean,

$$\delta f_i = f(t_i) - f(t_{i-1}) = f'(t_i') \, \delta t_i, \tag{125}$$

for a suitable choice of t_i' in the interval t_{i-1},t_i. Hence

$$\sum_{i=1}^n |\delta f_i| = \sum_{i=1}^n |f'(t_i')| \, \delta t_i. \tag{126}$$

When we let max $\delta t_i \to 0$, the right member approaches a limit by section 122. Hence the sum on the left is bounded, and the function is of bounded variation. In fact, by section 173 we find from the limiting relation:

$$Vf_a^b = \int_a^b |f'(t)| \, dt. \tag{127}$$

A similar argument applies to $g(t)$.

It follows from the last theorem of section 171 that the curve has an arc length. To express this as an integral, we first deduce from equation (125) and the similar equation for $g(t)$ that:

$$\sum_{i=1}^n \sqrt{\delta f_i^2 + \delta g_i^2} = \sum_{i=1}^n \sqrt{[f'(t_i')]^2 + [g'(t_i'')]^2} \, \delta t_i. \tag{128}$$

As this is a Duhamel sum, and the functions are continuous, by the theorem of section 164, for any sequence of subdivisions for which max δt_i or $\delta_M \to 0$, this approaches a Riemann integral. Since any such sequence corresponds to a sequence of subdivisions with $d_M \to 0$, the polygonal lengths will approach L. It follows that:

$$L_a^b = \int_a^b \sqrt{[f'(t)]^2 + [g'(t)]^2}\, dt. \tag{129}$$

If we denote the integral from a to t by s, we have, since the integrand is continuous:

$$\frac{ds}{dt} = \sqrt{[f'(t)]^2 + [g'(t)]^2}. \tag{130}$$

As a consequence of this:

$$ds^2 = dx^2 + dy^2. \tag{131}$$

176. Ratio of Arc to Chord. Let us consider the ratio of an arc joining two points corresponding to t_1 and t_2, to the corresponding chord. For the chord we have as in equation (126)

$$P_1P_2 = \sqrt{[f'(t')]^2 + [g'(t'')]^2}\,\delta t, \tag{132}$$

where t' and t'' are two suitable values between t_1 and t_2. But, since the integrand of equation (129) is continuous, we have by the mean value theorem for integrals

$$\text{arc } P_1P_2 = \int_{t_1}^{t_2} \sqrt{[f'(t)]^2 + [g'(t)]^2}\, dt$$
$$= \sqrt{[f'(t''')]^2 + [g'(t''')]^2}\,\delta t. \tag{133}$$

This shows that

$$\frac{\text{chord } P_1P_2}{\text{arc } P_1P_2} = \frac{\sqrt{[f'(t')]^2 + [g'(t'')]^2}}{\sqrt{[f'(t''')]^2 + [g'(t''')]^2}}. \tag{134}$$

Next suppose P_0 is a point corresponding to t_0, and that $f'(t_0)$ and $g'(t_0)$ are not both zero. Then if P_1 approaches P_0, t_1 approaches t_0. For, suppose that $f'(t_0) \neq 0$. Then if $f'(t_0) = M$, for a suitable h,

$$|f'(t) - f'(t_0)| < \frac{M}{2} \quad \text{and} \quad |f'(t)| > \frac{M}{2} \quad \text{if} \quad |t - t_0| < h. \tag{135}$$

Hence, if $|t_1 - t_0| < h$,

$$P_1P_0 \geqq \frac{M}{2}|t_1 - t_0|, \tag{136}$$

since we may replace P_2 by P_0 in equation (132). This proves that $|t_1 - t_0|$ must approach zero with P_1P_0. Similarly if P_2 approaches P_0, t_2 approaches t_0.

Now let P_1 and P_2 each approach P_0. Then t_1 and t_2 each approach t_0. Hence t', t'' and t''' in equation (134) each approach t_0. Since the numerator and denominator each approach the same non-zero limit, it follows that the right member of equation (134) approaches unity.

If we use the procedure of section 61, and recall equation (131), we may determine an angle ϕ such that:

$$dx = ds \cos \phi, \quad dy = ds \sin \phi. \qquad (137)$$

Since these equations make

$$\frac{dy}{dx} = \tan \phi, \qquad (138)$$

ϕ is the slope angle of the curve.

We may take s as the parameter, as in equation (123). If, when we do this, ϕ is a continuous function of s, we say that the curve has a continuously turning tangent, or is *smooth*. In this case we have from equations (137):

$$F'(s) = \frac{dx}{ds} = \cos \phi, \quad \text{and} \quad G'(s) = \frac{dy}{ds} = \sin \phi. \qquad (139)$$

Thus the derivatives are continuous functions of the parameter s, and are never both zero since $\cos^2 \phi + \sin^2 \phi = 1$. Hence for a smooth curve, we may take any point as the point P_0 of the above discussion.

We note conversely that if, for some choice of the parameter, $f(t)$ and $g(t)$ have continuous derivatives, never both zero, the curve is smooth. For in this case, by equation (130), $ds/dt > 0$, so that the function $s(t)$ determines a continuous inverse function, $t(s)$, and since $\tan \phi = g'(t)/f'(t)$, ϕ is a continuous function of t and hence of s.

We may summarize the principal result of this section in the following statement:

If the two end points which determine an arc and a chord of a smooth curve each approach the same point of the curve, the ratio of the arc to the chord approaches unity.

177. Material Curves. One of the fundamental concepts of theoretical mechanics is the material particle, or mass point. The mass point is a point associated with a positive number. If the point is in a plane, and the mass is m, each triplet m, x, y determines a mass point.

Let us next consider a particular arc of a smooth curve. If we associate with each subarc of this curve a mass proportional to its length,

$$m_a^b = D L_a^b, \qquad (140)$$

we determine a material curve which is homogeneous, or of constant density D. Let s denote the length of arc between one end and a variable point of our fundamental arc, and $m(s)$ the corresponding mass. Then

$$m(s) = Ds \quad \text{and} \quad m_{s'}^{s''} = D(s'' - s'). \tag{141}$$

If we associate a positive continuous function $D(s)$ with a smooth arc, we determine a material curve of variable density. For subarcs the mass is given by:

$$m(s) = \int_0^s D(s) \, ds \quad \text{and} \quad m_{s'}^{s''} = \int_{s'}^{s''} D(s) \, ds. \tag{142}$$

The laws of mechanics for continuous systems are obtained by extending those for a finite number of particles by the following process. We divide the continuous system into n parts, and replace each part by a single particle whose coördinates are those of some point of the part, and whose mass or force component is the total mass or force component of the part. Let Q_n denote any expression with physical significance for the finite system of n particles. If, for any sequence of subdivisions such that the maximum diameter of the parts, $d_M \to 0$, the expression Q_n approaches one and the same limit Q, we assign to Q the same physical significance for the continuous system that Q_n has for the n particles. We also extend any law involving one or more quantities Q_n to the quantities Q.

That the laws obtained in this way will not depend on the choice of coördinates, or of parameters follows from their significance for the finite systems.

Our method of extending the geometric concept of length from polygonal lines to curved arc, while not identical with this process, was in principle similar to it.

It is not always emphasized that the process merely suggests the new laws and definitions.   It does not prove them, since a continuous system is not a large number of particles and additional assumptions are needed to derive laws for such systems.

For systems of particles, the moment about the y-axis is given by:

$$M\bar{x} = \sum_{i=1}^n x_i m_i. \tag{143}$$

For any subdivision of a material curve, this leads to

$$\sum_{i=1}^n x(s_i') D(s_i'') \, \delta s_i, \tag{144}$$

where s_i' is the arc length to an arbitrary point of the ith part, and s_i'' is the value obtained by applying the law of the mean for integrals to

$$\int_{s_{i-1}}^{s_i} D(s)\, ds = D(s_i'')\, \delta s_i, \tag{145}$$

which represents the mass of the nth part by equation (142). Since the functions in the Duhamel sum (144) are continuous, it follows that a limit is approached when $d_M \to 0$, and hence max $\delta s_i \to 0$. We define this limit as the moment of the material arc about the y-axis, and write

$$m(s)\bar{x}(s) = \int_0^s x(s)D(s)\, ds. \tag{146}$$

Since the left member of equation (143) is the product of the x coördinate of the center of gravity by the total mass for the system of n particles, we give a similar significance to the left member of equation (146). The factor $m(s)$ is defined by equation (142), and equation (146) then defines $\bar{x}(s)$, the x coördinate of the center of gravity for the material curve.

The moment about the x-axis, and $\bar{y}(s)$, are similarly defined. Thus we have

$$m(s)\bar{y}(s) = \int_0^s y(s)D(s)\, ds, \tag{147}$$

and the moment about any line in the plane may be found from these as for particles. Similarly, from the products of inertia for the system of particles in a plane we are led to define:

$$I_{xx} = \int_0^s x^2 D\, ds, \quad I_{xy} = \int_0^s xy D\, ds, \quad I_{yy} = \int_0^s y^2 D\, ds. \tag{148}$$

The moment of inertia about any line is obtained from the integrals in the same way it is found from the corresponding sums for particles.

178. Specific Force. We may associate a continuous function $P_x(s)$ with a material curve, the applied specific force in the x direction. The total force in the x direction for any part of the curve is then determined by

$$F_x(s) = \int_0^s P_x(s)\, ds \quad \text{or} \quad F_x\bigg|_{s'}^{s''} = \int_{s'}^{s''} P_x(s)\, ds. \tag{149}$$

The second expression is the force on a subarc with end points s' and s''. Similar definitions apply for the component in the y direction, and for that perpendicular to the plane, or in the z direction.

If all the applied forces are in the same direction, say parallel to the

y-axis, we may define the x coördinate of their resultant by an equation similar to equation (146) for $\bar{x}(s)$. The process of the preceding section also leads us to define the total moment about any line for the forces applied to the system in terms of such integrals as

$$\int_0^s y(s)P_x(s)\,ds, \tag{150}$$

by equations similar to those which hold for sums.

The laws of motion for rigid systems of particles may now be extended to such equations as:

$$\int_0^s D(s)\,ds\,\frac{d^2\bar{x}}{dt^2} = \int_0^s P_x(s)\,ds, \quad \text{or} \quad m(s)\,\frac{d^2\bar{x}}{dt^2} = F_x(s), \tag{151}$$

for the motion of translation of the center of gravity, and

$$\int_0^s (X^2 + Y^2)D(s)\,ds\,\frac{d^2\theta}{dt^2} = \int_0^s (XP_y - YP_x)\,ds, \tag{152}$$

for the rotation about the center of gravity, where

$$X = x - \bar{x} \quad \text{and} \quad Y = y - \bar{y} \tag{153}$$

are the coördinates referred to the center of gravity.

For the attraction of a particle on a unit mass located at the origin, we have for the specific force in the x direction:

$$\frac{\gamma m}{x^2 + y^2}\,\frac{x}{\sqrt{x^2 + y^2}}, \tag{154}$$

and the process of extension leads us to define the attraction of a material curve on a unit particle at the origin as a force whose x component is

$$A_x = \gamma \int_{s'}^{s''} \frac{xD}{(x^2 + y^2)^{\frac{3}{2}}}\,ds. \tag{155}$$

We note that in the theory of electricity the charge density is analogous to D, except that it may be negative as well as positive.

179. Stieltjes Integrals. In our discussion of the last three sections, we assumed the density continuous and the curve smooth. Under these conditions, we may convert the integrals from integrals with respect to s to integrals with respect to other parameters, as x or y for restricted parts of the curve by using the results of section 175.

However, as given our argument applies to any continuous curve which has an arc length, since for such a curve x and y are continuous functions of s.

Again, the function $m(s)$ as defined by equation (142) has a derivative, $dm/ds = D(s)$. We may relax this restriction, by merely requiring $m(s)$ to be any monotonically increasing function of s. In this case, we define the density as $m'(s)$ for those values of s at which the function has a derivative. At other values the density is not defined. We replace $D(s)\, ds$ by dm in equations (146), (147), and (148): these become Stieltjes integrals, which exist since x and y are continuous functions of s and since m is monotonically increasing.

Similar remarks apply to the integrals of section 178, with $P_x(s)\, ds$ replaced by dF_x, where F_x is any function of s of bounded variation.

These extensions enable us to treat the case of a material curve with continuous density, with a certain number of material particles attached to it, by one expression. Also the forces may either result from continuous specific forces or be applied at one point, like the continuous and point loads in the theory of beams. In such equations as (151) and (152) we frequently have a continuous density, but a simple sum on the right. The use of the Stieltjes integral is of more theoretical than practical value here, since in any case where its value can be easily computed, this is done by reducing it to sums and Riemann integrals.

180. Line Integrals. Let $P(x,y)$ be any continuous function of x and y in some two-dimensional region including all the points on an arc of a curve having an arc length. Along the arc, $s' \leqq s \leqq s''$, the coördinates $x(s)$ and $y(s)$ will each be a continuous function of bounded variation.

Let us form any subdivision of the arc by points (x_i, y_i) corresponding to values s_i, and form the sum

$$S = \sum_{i=1}^{n} P(x_i', y_i'')\, \delta x_i, \qquad (156)$$

where x_i' corresponds to s_i', and y_i'' corresponds to s_i'', and s_i' and s_i'' are any two values of s of the closed interval s_{i-1}, s_i.

Since $x(s)$ is continuous and of bounded variation, by section 161 we may write

$$x(s) = f(s) - g(s), \qquad (157)$$

where $f(s)$ and $g(s)$ are each continuous, increasing functions of s throughout the closed interval s', s''. By section 37, if

$$p' = f(s'), \ p'' = f(s'') \quad \text{and} \quad q' = g(s'), \ q'' = g(s''), \quad (158)$$

the equation $p = f(s)$ defines an inverse function $s = f^{-1}(p)$, continuous and increasing throughout the closed interval p', p''. Similarly the equation $q = g(s)$ defines an inverse function, $s = g^{-1}(q)$, continuous and increasing throughout the closed interval q', q''. And, by section 36, we may consider $x = x(s)$ and $y = y(s)$ as continuous functions either of p or of q. Now write

$$S = \sum_{i=1}^{n} P(x'_i, y''_i)\, \delta p_i - \sum_{i=1}^{n} P(x'_i, y''_i)\, \delta q_i. \tag{159}$$

From the increasing relation of s to p, and p to s, if s_i corresponds to p_i, the p_i will determine a subdivision of p', p'', and s'_i and s''_i will correspond to values p'_i and p''_i in the closed interval p_{i-1}, p_i. Thus the first sum is a Duhamel sum when p is the independent variable, and the second sum is a Duhamel sum when q is the independent variable. Moreover, from the fact that p is a uniformly continuous function of s, any sequence of subdivisions for which $d_M \to 0$ and hence $\delta s_i \to 0$, will be such that max $\delta p_i \to 0$. Similarly it will make max $\delta q_i \to 0$. Thus, for any such sequence of subdivisions, by section 164, each of the sums will approach a Riemann integral, and the limit of S will be:

$$\int_{p'}^{p''} P(x,y)\, dp - \int_{q'}^{q''} P(x,y)\, dq. \tag{160}$$

It is natural to abbreviate this expression as

$$\int P(x,y)\, dx, \tag{161}$$

with the supplementary conditions:

$$s' \leqq s \leqq s'', \; x = x(s), \; y = y(s). \tag{162}$$

The expression (161) is called a *line integral*.

We may use any other parameter in place of s, provided that we use only sequences of subdivisions such that $d_M \to 0$. In some cases, analogous to the situation in section 165, some sequences with max $\delta x_i \to 0$ or max $\delta t_i \to 0$, where t_i is the parameter, may not give the correct limit.

When the arc is smooth,

$$\int P(x,y)\, dx = \int P[x(s), y(s)] \frac{dx}{ds}\, ds, \tag{163}$$

since we may replace $\delta p_i - \delta q_i$ by δx_i or $x'(s'''_i)\, \delta s_i$ in equation (159), and regard this as a Duhamel sum for the integral in equation (163). In this case, for any parameter t such that $s(t)$ has a continuous derivative,

$$\int P(x,y)\, dx = \int P[x(t), y(t)] \frac{dx}{dt}\, dt. \tag{164}$$

The entire discussion applies with x and y interchanged to the line integral

$$\int Q(x,y)\, dy. \tag{165}$$

We usually consider the typical line integral in two variables to be of the form:

$$\int P(x,y)\, dx + Q(x,y)\, dy, \tag{166}$$

with supplementary conditions similar to those in equation (162). This is defined to mean the sum of the two line integrals (161) and (165).

181. Work. If a particle is under the influence of a force with components F_x and F_y, each being constant, the total work done by the force during any displacement from the point (x_1,y_1) to (x_2,y_2) is by definition

$$F_x(x_2 - x_1) + F_y(y_2 - y_1). \tag{167}$$

Suppose a particle moves along any curve having an arc length, under the influence of a force with components $F_x(x,y)$ and $F_y(x,y)$. Such a variable force is called a *force field*. We shall assume that the particle remains inside some region in which each of the functions $F_x(x,y)$ and $F_y(x,y)$ is continuous. If we make a subdivision of the arc, $s' \leqq s \leqq s''$ determined by points of subdivision s_i, and replace the variable force components in the subdivision s_{i-1},s_i by the values for x_i',y_i'', we are led to associate the sum

$$\sum_{i=1}^{n} F_x(x_i',y_i'')\, \delta x_i + \sum_{i=1}^{n} F_y(x_i',y_i'')\, \delta y_i \tag{168}$$

with the work done for successive displacements along the subarcs. In accordance with our general procedure, we take

$$x_i' = x(s_i') \quad \text{and} \quad y_i'' = y(s_i''), \tag{169}$$

where s_i' and s_i'' each lie in the closed interval s_{i-1},s_i. The discussion of the preceding section shows that, for any sequence of subdivisions for which $d_M \to 0$, the sum (168) approaches one and the same limit, namely, the line integral

$$\int F_x(x,y)\, dx + F_y(x,y)\, dy, \tag{170}$$

where

$$s' \leqq s \leqq s'' \quad \text{and} \quad x = x(s),\ y = y(s). \tag{171}$$

We accordingly define the work done by the variable force or force field, for the displacement over the arc, as this line integral.

182. Impulse. For the motion of a particle of constant or variable mass m along the x-axis, we have:

$$\frac{d}{dt}(mv) = F, \quad \text{where} \quad v = \frac{dx}{dt}. \tag{172}$$

If we define the momentum by

$$M = mv, \quad \text{then} \quad M - M_0 = \int_{t_0}^{t} F\, dt. \tag{173}$$

If we assume that F is a continuous function of the time, it follows that the momentum M has a continuous time derivative:

$$\frac{dM}{dt} = F. \tag{174}$$

Instead of requiring F to be continuous, we may start with M as a function of t and define the force as dM/dt at points where M has a derivative. At other points F is undefined. We then have:

$$mv - (mv)_0 = \int_{t_0}^{t} dM, \tag{175}$$

where the integral on the right is a Stieltjes integral. On any closed interval where F is continuous, in the integral dM may be replaced by $F\, dt$. And, if an impulse I acts at time t we have:

$$\int_{t-}^{t+} dM = \lim_{\substack{h \to 0+ \\ k \to 0+}} \int_{t-k}^{t+h} dM = I. \tag{176}$$

183. Improper Integrals. Since the arc length is a continuous function of the parameter, in any case where the discussion of section 175 applies to every arc with end points in the open interval a,b, the arc length will be given by the integral from a to b if this exists as a proper or improper integral. These considerations also apply to the other integrals with physical meaning. For the arc length, an example is the quadrant of a circle defined by

$$x = \sqrt{1 - t^2},\ y = t,\ 0 \leqq t \leqq 1, \tag{177}$$

for which

$$L_0^1 = \int_0^1 \frac{dt}{\sqrt{1 - t^2}} = \frac{\pi}{2}. \tag{178}$$

184. Higher Dimensions. With only minor modifications, most of the results on curves in two dimensions obtained in the last few sections apply to curves in three or more dimensions. In particular, such a curve has an arc length when all the coördinates are expressed in terms of a parameter by continuous functions of bounded variation.

When all these functions have continuous derivatives, we have:

$$L_a^b = \int_a^b \sqrt{\sum_{i=1}^n [f_i'(t)]^2}\, dt. \tag{179}$$

Likewise the discussion of material curves and the integrals and laws involving them applies in all essentials to material curves in three-dimensional space.

The concept of line integral is also readily extended to three or more dimensions.

EXERCISES VIII

1. Let p_i be $n + 1$ points on the closed interval a,b such that $a = p_0 < p_1 < p_2 < \cdots < p_n = b$. Suppose that the function $g(x)$ is monotonic in the closed interval a,b and constant in each open interval p_{i-1},p_k. If $F(x)$ is continuous on a,b, show that

$$\int_a^x F(x)\, dg(x) = F(p_0)[g(p_0+) - g(p_0)] + \sum_{i=1}^k F(p_i)[g(p_i+) - g(p_i-)]$$

(a) if $p_k < x < p_{k+1}$; and (b) if $x = p_k$, with $g(p_k)$ in place of $g(p_k+)$.

2. If $G(x) = h(x) + g(x)$, where $h(x)$ has a continuous positive derivative and $g(x)$ is the function of problem 1, show that

$$\int_a^x F(x)\, dG(x) = \int_a^x F(x)h'(x)\, dx + \int_a^x F(x)\, dg(x),$$

the sum of a Riemann integral and the integral found in problem 1.

3. If for each value of n, the numbers p_i and q_i satisfy the relations $i - 1 \leqq p_i \leqq i$ and $i - 1 \leqq q_i \leqq i$, prove that:

$$\lim_{n\to\infty} \sum_{i=1}^n \frac{1}{\sqrt{2n - p_i}\sqrt{2n + q_i}} = \frac{\pi}{6}.$$

Hint: Identify with a Duhamel sum having $\displaystyle\int_0^{\frac{1}{2}} \frac{dx}{\sqrt{1 - x^2}}$ as a limit.

4. If $F(g)$ is a continuous function of g, and $g(x)$ has a derivative which is continuous and positive for the values considered, show that the value of the Riemann integral of $F(g)\, dg$ from $g(x_1)$ to $g(x_2)$ is equal to the value of the Stieltjes integral of $F(g)\, dg$ from x_1 to x_2.

5. If $g(x) = 1$, for $0 \leqq x < 1$, and $g(x) = 4$, for $1 < x \leqq 2$, evaluate the integral $\displaystyle\int_0^2 x\, dg(x)$. *Hint:* Use equation (46), or problem 1. The result is 3.

6. If $P(x)$ is a polynomial of the nth degree with no real root $> a$, and $p > \dfrac{1}{n}$, prove that $\displaystyle\int_a^\infty [P(x)]^{-p}\, dx$ converges.

7. If $P(x)$ is a polynomial with no roots in the closed interval a,b except c, and this is a multiple root of the mth order, prove that $\int_a^b [P(x)]^{-p} dx$ converges if $mp < 1$.

8. If $p > 0$, prove that $\int_a^\infty e^{-x^p} dx$ converges. Also that $\int_a^\infty P(x)e^{-x^p} dx$ converges, where $P(x)$ is any polynomial.

9. Show that $\int_a^\infty \log |P(x)| \, dx$ diverges if $P(x)$ is any polynomial, not identically equal to 1.

10. If $r = r(\theta)$, $x = r \cos \theta$, and $y = r \sin \theta$, determine x and y in terms of the parameter θ, express the differential of arc in terms of θ, and hence show that in polar coördinates

$$ds^2 = dr^2 + r^2 \, d\theta^2.$$

11. If ϕ_0 is the value of the slope angle for a curve at x_0, y_0, the equations of a circle tangent to the curve at x_0, y_0 may be written: $x = x_0 - R \sin \phi_0 + R \sin u$, $y = y_0 + R \cos \phi_0 - R \cos u$, where u is a parameter. For the circle, when $u = \phi_0$, $x = x_0$, $y = y_0$, $dy/dx = \tan \phi_0$ and $d^2y/dx^2 = \sec^3 \phi_0/R$. Verify that, for the curve $d^2y/dx^2 = \sec^3 \phi \, d\phi/ds$ at any point. Hence, if $R = ds/d\phi$ at ϕ_0, the circle will have the same first and second derivative as the curve at x_0, y_0. It is the circle of curvature of the curve at x_0, y_0. The radius of curvature is $\rho = ds/d\phi$, and the center of curvature is $X = x - \rho \sin \phi$ and $Y = y + \rho \cos \phi$.

12. The locus of the center of curvature is the evolute of the curve. By problem 11, if x, y, ϕ and $\rho = ds/d\phi$ are expressed in terms of any parameter, the equations of the evolute are: $X = x - \rho \sin \phi$ and $Y = y + \rho \cos \phi$. Use these to show that the tangent to the evolute is normal to the original curve, and that for any two values of the parameter between which ρ preserves its sign the difference of the values of ρ for the two points equals the arc of the evolute between the corresponding points. *Hint:* $dx = ds \cos \phi = \rho \cos \phi \, d\phi$ and $dy = ds \sin \phi = \rho \sin \phi \, d\phi$. It follows that $dX = -d\rho \sin \phi$ and $dY = d\rho \cos \phi$, so that $dY/dX = -\cot \phi = (Y - y)/(X - x)$ and $dS = |d\rho|$.

13. Using primes to denote differentiation with respect to the parameter, show that $\rho = \dfrac{[x'^2 + y'^2]^{3/2}}{x'y'' - x''y'}$. This takes the familiar form $\dfrac{[1 + y'^2]^{3/2}}{y''}$, when x is the parameter. *Hint:* Differentiate $\tan \phi = y'/x'$ and use $\rho = s'/\phi'$ to eliminate ϕ'.

14. If the parameter is the time, show that the acceleration has a tangential component dv/dt and a normal component v^2/ρ, where $v = ds/dt$. *Hint:* Use problem 46 of Exercises V.

15. If x and y are each elementary functions of a parameter, the equations

$$X = x - \frac{y'(x'^2 + y'^2)}{y''x' - x''y'} \quad \text{and} \quad Y = y + \frac{x'(x'^2 + y'^2)}{y''x' - x''y'}, \quad \text{determine } X \text{ and } Y \text{ as}$$

elementary functions of the parameter. From problems 12 and 13 deduce that the arc length of this curve is expressible as an elementary function of the parameter. Illustrate for $x = a \cos t$ and $y = b \sin t$.

16. If ρ is a given function of ϕ, the coördinates are determined in terms of ϕ to within additive constants, corresponding to the location of the origin. Prove that the coördinates and the arc length will all be elementary functions of ϕ if

$$\int \rho \, d\phi, \int \rho \sin \phi \, d\phi, \text{ and } \int \rho \cos \phi \, d\phi \text{ are elementary functions.}$$

17. By problem 16, if ρ is a rational function of $\sin \phi$ and $\cos \phi$ the coördinates and arc length will be elementary functions. Illustrate in the following special cases: (a) $\rho = \sec^2 \phi$, the catenary $y = \cosh x$; (b) $\rho = \sec^2 \phi \csc \phi$, $y = e^x$; (c) $\rho = \tan^n \phi \sec^2 \phi \csc \phi$, $[(n + 1)y]^n = (nx)^{n+1}$.

18. Show that the functions of problem 16 will be elementary if ρ is a rational function of $\sin (\phi/n)$ and $\cos (\phi/n)$, where n is an integer. An example is $\rho = \sin^{n-2} (\phi/n)$, where in polar coördinates $(n - 1)r = n \sin^{n-1}[\theta/(n - 1)]$ and $n\theta = (n - 1)\phi$.

19. Verify that the following simple algebraic curves have arc lengths expressible in terms of elementary functions. (a) $y^2 = x^2/3 + bx^3$; (b) $y^2 = x^2/8 + bx^4$; (c) $y^n = kx^{n+1}$, where n is a positive or negative integer. Part (c) is essentially the same as the curve in problem 17(c).

20. If ρ is a polynomial in ϕ and terms of the type $\cos a\phi$, $\sin b\phi$, and $e^{c\phi}$; x, y, and s will be elementary functions of ϕ as in problem 16. Here, however, they will be polynomials in ϕ and the sines, cosines, and exponentials. Hence any integral of the form $\int x^n y^m \, ds$, where m and n are positive integers or zero, will be a function of ϕ of the same type. Thus for such a curve, regarded as a homogeneous material curve, its center of gravity and moment of inertia about a coördinate axis will be elementary. Simple examples are: (a) $\rho = 1$, the circle; (b) $\rho = \phi$, the involute of the circle; (c) $\rho = e^{a\phi}$, the equiangular spiral; (d) $\rho = \sin \phi$, the cycloid; (e) $\rho = \sin k\phi$ the epi- and hypo-cycloids.

21. Suppose that for one curve $x = x_1(\phi)$, $y = y_1(\phi)$, and $s = s_1(\phi)$, while for a second curve $x = x_2(\phi)$, $y = y_2(\phi)$, and $s = s_2(\phi)$. Show that the curve with $x = x_1(\phi) + x_2(\phi)$, $y = y_1(\phi) + y_2(\phi)$ has ϕ as its slope angle, and $s = s_1(\phi) + s_2(\phi)$. This enables us to combine curves with simple expressions for their arcs to obtain new ones.

22. If, for an arc of a curve for which ρ preserves its sign, we have $\rho = \dfrac{ds}{d\phi} = f(\phi)$, prove that for the corresponding arc of the evolute we have $\dfrac{dS}{d\phi} = f'(\phi)$, if S is measured in the direction in which ρ increases. Show also that, if the evolute is referred to axes obtained from the original axes by a rotation in the proper direction through $\pi/2$, ϕ is the slope angle for the evolute.

23. Deduce from problem 22 that for the curves in problem 20, (a) is the evolute of (b); (c) and (d) have evolutes of the same size and shape as the original curve; and (e) has an evolute of the same shape as the original curve.

24. For a space curve with x as the parameter, $y = y(x)$, and $z = z(x)$, let primes denote differentiation with respect to x. Prove that, if $2z' = y'^2$, $s = x + z +$ constant. Illustrate for $y = x^2$, $z = 2x^3/3$.

25. As a generalization of problem 24, prove that, if

$$z' = \frac{1 + y'^2 - (a + by')^2}{2a + 2by'},$$

then $s = ax + by + z +$ constant. If y is any function of x for which the expression has an elementary integral, this leads to a space curve with elementary arc length.

26. Let $c(x)$ be continuous, $p(x) \geqq 0$, and $P(x) = \int_a^x p(x) \, dx$, a proper or improper integral for $a \leqq x \leqq b$. Then, for any x on the closed interval a,b the Stieltjes integral $\int_a^x c(x) \, dP(x)$ equals the proper or improper Riemann integral $\int_a^x c(x)p(x) \, dx$. *Hint:* If S is a Stieltjes sum with δ_M such that the oscillation of $c(x)$ in any interval $< \epsilon$, then $\left| \int_{x_{i-1}}^{x_i} c(x)p(x) \, dx - c(\xi_i)\delta P^i \right| \leqq \epsilon \, \delta P_i$, so that $\left| \int_a^b c(x)p(x) \, dx - S \right| \leqq \epsilon P(b)$. For improper integrals, as in section 169, we need only treat the case where $p(x)$ is unbounded near b. By the result for proper integrals, the two are equal on $a,b - h$. Let $h \to 0$. The limit of the Riemann integral exists, since $p(x)$ is integrable. Hence the improper Stieltjes integral exists and equals the other.

27. Let $u = \int_a^x U \, dx$ and $v = \int_a^x V \, dx$, where, if the integrals are improper, $\int_a^b |U| \, dx$ and $\int_a^b |V| \, dx$ exist. Then the rule of integration by parts applies in the form $\int uV \, dx = uv - \int Uv \, dx$. *Hint:* Write $u = u_1 - u_2$, where $u_1 = U$ or 0 according as $U > 0$ or not, $u_2 = -U$ or 0 according as $U < 0$ or not, and similarly $v = v_1 - v_2$. This reduces the problem to the case where U and V are each $\geqq 0$. By problem 26, the integrals may then be replaced by Stieltjes integrals, and the relation is $\int u \, dv = uv - \int v \, du$. This holds for proper Stieltjes integrals by section 165, and for improper ones we may take limits, since u and v are continuous.

CHAPTER IX

INFINITE SERIES AND INFINITE PRODUCTS

The question of whether an infinite series converges or not, from one point of view, is a special case of the problem of determining whether a variable, defined for a discrete infinite sequence of values, approaches a limit. Thus many of the theorems concerning infinite series are immediate corollaries of the results for limits proved in Chapter II. Our reason for not explicitly introducing infinite series earlier is that the discussion of certain tests for convergence is simplified by the use of integrals.

After deducing a number of tests for the convergence of infinite series of real or complex terms, we define infinite products, and prove several theorems concerning such products and their convergence.

185. Infinite Series, Convergence. Let $u_1, u_2, u_3, \ldots$ be any enumerated discrete sequence of real or complex numbers. Then the expression

$$u_1 + u_2 + u_3 + \cdots \quad \text{or} \quad \sum_{n=1}^{\infty} u_n, \tag{1}$$

sometimes abbreviated to $\sum u_n$, is called an *infinite series*. The general term is u_n, and is a function of n defined for positive integral values. The sum to n terms, or the nth partial sum, is

$$s_n = \sum_{k=1}^{n} u_k = u_1 + u_2 + u_3 + \cdots + u_n. \tag{2}$$

We note that in this finite sum k is a dummy index, as defined in section 127.

A *convergent* series is one for which, as n becomes infinite, s_n approaches a finite limit s. That is,

$$s = \lim_{n \to \infty} s_n. \tag{3}$$

We call s the sum or value of the series, say that this series converges to s, and write

$$s = \sum_{n=1}^{\infty} u_n. \tag{4}$$

By a real series we mean one for which the values of all the u_n are real numbers. A series of complex terms, with

$$u_n = a_n + ib_n, \tag{5}$$

298

has as its partial sum

$$s_n = \sum_{k=1}^{n} a_k + i \sum_{k=1}^{n} b_k. \tag{6}$$

Consequently, by section 99, the series will converge if and only if the two real series with terms a_n and b_n converge. Moreover, when the series is convergent,

$$s = \sum_{n=1}^{\infty} a_n + i \sum_{n=1}^{\infty} b_n. \tag{7}$$

Thus the question of convergence of any series of complex terms is equivalent to a similar question for two real series, the real and imaginary component series. Also the sum of the series of complex terms is a simple combination of the sums of the two real series.

186. Divergence. A divergent series is one which does not converge. For such a series, s_n does not approach a finite limit. For a real series, if $\lim s_n = +\infty$, we say that the series diverges to infinity, and if $\lim s_n = -\infty$, that it diverges to minus infinity. In all other cases where s_n is real and the series diverges, the upper and lower limits of s_n as defined in section 23 will be different. If these limits are both infinite, $\overline{\lim} s_n = +\infty$ and $\underline{\lim} s_n = -\infty$, we say that the series oscillates infinitely. If the upper and lower limits are one infinite and one finite, we say that the series oscillates semi-infinitely. If the upper and lower limits are both finite and distinct we say that the series oscillates finitely.

The behavior of a divergent series of complex terms is best described by applying the expressions just defined to its real and imaginary component series, which are both real series. We note that if the series of complex terms is divergent, one but not both of the component series may converge.

187. Elementary Transformations. I. *If a finite number of terms of a series are changed, the new series $\sum u_n'$ will converge or diverge with the old series, $\sum u_n$.*

To prove this, let K be the largest subscript of a term changed. Then, for all $n > K$, we have:

$$s_n - s_K = s_n' - s_K'. \tag{8}$$

This shows that s_n' approaches a limit if and only if s_n does. Also when either and hence both series converge, we have:

$$s' = s + s_K' - s_K. \tag{9}$$

II. *The omission of a finite number of terms from the enumerated sequence of terms or the insertion of a finite number of terms in any positions does not affect the convergence or divergence of a series.*

To establish this, let the largest subscript of any of the p terms omitted be K, and let the sum of the terms omitted be T. Then, if we denote the nth partial sum of the new series by s_n', for all $n > K$, we have:

$$s_n' = s_{n+p} - T. \tag{10}$$

Since $n + p \to \infty$ when $n \to \infty$, s_n' approaches a limit if and only if s_n does. And, when both series converge,

$$s' = s - T. \tag{11}$$

This proves the statement on omission of terms. The insertion of terms is merely the inverse operation.

III. *If C is a constant, distinct from zero, and $u_n' = Cu_n$, the series $\sum u_n'$ converges or diverges with $\sum u_n$.*

For, in this case

$$s_n' = Cs_n, \tag{12}$$

so that s_n' approaches a limit if and only if s_n does. And, when both approach limits,

$$s' = Cs. \tag{13}$$

We note that inserting parentheses in the expression for an infinite series as an unending sum has the effect of omitting certain values of s_n. For example,

$$(u_1 + u_2) + (u_3 + u_4) + \cdots \tag{14}$$

may be regarded as an infinite series with $u_n' = u_{2n-1} + u_{2n}$. Thus $s_n' = s_{2n}$, and the odd partial sums are omitted from consideration. Hence the insertion of parentheses will always change a convergent series into a convergent series with the same sum. The operation will also change a real series diverging to plus infinity, or to minus infinity, into a second real series with similar behavior. However, it may make an oscillating series converge. For example:

$$1 - 1 + 1 - 1 + 1 - 1 + \cdots \text{ oscillates finitely}, \tag{15}$$

$$(1 - 1) + (1 - 1) + (1 - 1) + \cdots \text{ converges to } 0, \tag{16}$$

$$1 + (-1 + 1) + (-1 + 1) + \cdots \text{ converges to } 1. \tag{17}$$

The example shows that the omission of parentheses may change a convergent series to a divergent series.

188. The General Condition.   Let us apply the Cauchy convergence criterion of section 99 to the variable s_n.   We note that

$$s_{k+p} - s_k = u_{k+1} + u_{k+2} + \cdots + u_{k+p}. \tag{18}$$

If p is an arbitrary positive integer, and k any integer exceeding N, then k and $k + p$ will be any two distinct integers exceeding N.   Consequently, from the condition that s_n approaches a finite limit, it follows that:

A necessary and sufficient condition for the convergence of the infinite series $\sum u_n$ is that, for any positive quantity ϵ, there is some positive integer N_ϵ such that for any integer $k > N_\epsilon$, and all positive integers p,

$$|u_{k+1} + u_{k+2} + \cdots + u_{k+p}| < \epsilon. \tag{19}$$

Although this condition is too general to be of much practical use as it stands, the necessary condition may be restricted to give a simple sufficient condition for divergence.   To derive this, suppose that $\sum u_n$ converges.   Then the relation (19) holds for all positive p, and hence in particular for $p = 1$.   Thus

$$|u_{k+1}| < \epsilon, \quad \text{if} \quad k > N_\epsilon. \tag{20}$$

That is, as $k \to \infty$, $\lim u_k = 0$, and the *individual terms of a convergent series must approach zero* as we go out in the enumerated sequence.   This condition is not enough to insure convergence, as we see from the series:

$$1 + \tfrac{1}{2} + \tfrac{1}{2} + \tfrac{1}{4} + \tfrac{1}{4} + \tfrac{1}{4} + \tfrac{1}{4} + \tfrac{1}{8} + \cdots, \tag{21}$$

formed of successive blocks of 2^n terms, each equal to $1/2^n$.   The series diverges, since the sum to $2^k - 1$ terms is k.

However, it follows from the condition that if, as $n \to \infty$, u_n does *not* approach zero, then $\sum u_n$ diverges.

189. Series and Limits.   Every convergent series leads to a variable s_n approaching a finite limit s.   Conversely, every variable a_n assuming a discrete set of values which approaches a finite limit A as $n \to \infty$, may be related to a convergent series.   For, if we put

$$u_1 = a_1, \; u_k = a_k - a_{k-1}, \quad k > 1, \tag{22}$$

we find

$$s_n = a_1 + (a_2 - a_1) + \cdots + (a_n - a_{n-1}) = a_n. \tag{23}$$

This shows that the series $\sum u_n$ has its partial sums $s_n = a_n$, and so converges to the sum A.

Similar relations hold between divergent series and variables a_n assuming a discrete set of values which do not approach a finite limit as $n \to \infty$.

Thus from one point of view the terminology of infinite series merely furnishes a second notation for the behavior of discrete sequences, and results for series are theorems on enumerated sequences expressed in terms of the differences of consecutive elements.

190. Positive Series. We call $\sum u_n$ a positive series if each of the terms u_n is real and positive or zero. We shall indicate this by writing p_n in place of u_n. We treat such series separately because of their simplicity. Furthermore, we often deduce the convergence of other series from that of one or more positive series related to them.

The positive series $\sum p_n$ has

$$s_{n+1} - s_n = p_{n+1} \geqq 0, \quad \text{so that} \quad s_{n+1} \geqq s_n. \tag{24}$$

Thus s_n is a monotonically increasing variable, and it follows from the theorem of section 27 that:

A necessary and sufficient condition for the convergence of a positive series is that for all n there is some number M independent of n, such that:

$$s_n \leqq M. \tag{25}$$

191. Comparison Tests. Let $\sum p_n$ and $\sum p_n'$ be two positive series. We may deduce the convergence of the primed series from that of the unprimed series in the following cases:

I.   If $p_n' \leqq p_n$,

II.   If $p_n' = a_n p_n$ and $a_n \leqq A$,

III.   If $\lim\limits_{n \to \infty} \dfrac{p_n'}{p_n} = L$,   a finite limit.

IV.   If $\dfrac{p_{n+1}'}{p_n'} \leqq \dfrac{p_{n+1}}{p_n}$.

These may be proved as follows. In case I, $s_n' \leqq s_n$, so that $s_n' \leqq M$ if $s_n \leqq M$. Similarly, in case II, $p_n' \leqq A p_n$, and $s_n' \leqq AM$ if $s_n \leqq M$. In case III, we note that if $n \geqq N_\epsilon$, $p_n'/p_n < L + \epsilon$. Thus, if $L + \epsilon = A$, $p_n' \leqq A p_n$ and by the condition II, $\sum\limits_{n=N}^{\infty} p_n'$ converges with $\sum\limits_{n=N}^{\infty} p_n$. But the addition of terms to the first series to obtain $\sum\limits_{n=1}^{\infty} p_n'$, and the omission of terms from $\sum\limits_{n=1}^{\infty} p_n$ to obtain the second series, has no effect on convergence, by the second result of section 187. Thus $\sum p_n'$ converges with $\sum p_n$ in case III.

To prove case IV, we use the identity:

$$\frac{p_n}{p_1} = \frac{p_n}{p_{n-1}} \cdot \frac{p_{n-1}}{p_{n-2}} \cdot \ldots \cdot \frac{p_2}{p_1}, \tag{26}$$

and the corresponding one for the p_k'. It follows from these and the condition IV that

$$\frac{p_n'}{p_1'} \leqq \frac{p_n}{p_1}, \tag{27}$$

so that we may use condition II, with $A = \dfrac{p_1'}{p_1}$.

Since the convergence of p_n implies that of p_n', the divergence of p_n' implies that of p_n, under any of the above conditions. Since we are here starting with p_n', it is more natural to state that we may deduce the divergence of the primed series from that of the unprimed series in the following cases:

I'.   If $p_n' \geqq p_n$,

II'.   If $p_n' = b_n p_n$ and $b_n \geqq B > 0$,

III'.   If $\lim\limits_{n \to \infty} \dfrac{p_n'}{p_n} = L > 0$, or $+\infty$.

IV'.   If $\dfrac{p_{n+1}'}{p_n'} \geqq \dfrac{p_{n+1}}{p_n}$.

From the discussion of section 187 it follows that in cases I, II, and IV or I', II', and IV' the conclusion will follow if the conditions hold for all terms after some particular value N of n.

192. The Integral Test. *If $f(x)$ is a positive, monotonically decreasing function of x, for all x greater than or equal to K, a fixed positive integer, and if the improper integral $\displaystyle\int_K^\infty f(x)\,dx$ converges, then the series with $p_n = f(n)$ converges, and conversely the integral will converge if the series does.*

To prove this, we first observe that

$$f(k) \leqq f(x) \leqq f(k-1) \quad \text{for} \quad K \leqq k-1 \leqq x \leqq k, \tag{28}$$

in consequence of the monotonic character of $f(x)$. As a monotonic function, $f(x)$ is integrable over any of the finite intervals defined in equation (28), and we have:

$$f(k) \leqq \int_{k-1}^k f(x)\,dx \leqq f(k-1). \tag{29}$$

Putting $k = K + 1, K + 2, \cdots, n$ and summing, we find:

$$\sum_{k=K+1}^{n} f(k) \leqq \int_{K}^{n} f(x)\, dx \leqq \sum_{k=K}^{n-1} f(k). \tag{30}$$

As the function $f(x)$ is positive, the integral in this equation is monotonically increasing with n.   Thus, if the integral converges as $n \to \infty$, it is bounded.   Hence, by the first inequality the sum is bounded and the series converges.   Again, if the series converges, the finite sum on the right is bounded, and by the second inequality, the integral is bounded and so converges, since it monotonically increases with the upper limit.

Since the series and the integral converge together, they must diverge together.

When both are convergent, we have:

$$\sum_{k=K+1}^{\infty} f(k) \leqq \int_{K}^{\infty} f(x)\, dx \leqq \sum_{k=K}^{\infty} f(k). \tag{31}$$

This test enables us to treat a number of series whose general terms are obtained from the integrals of section 170.   In particular, we note that in consequence of equation (79) of that section,

$$\sum \frac{1}{n^a} \text{ converges if, and only if, } a > 1. \tag{32}$$

193. Geometric Series.   Since

$$1 + r + r^2 + \cdots + r^n = \frac{1 - r^{n+1}}{1 - r}, \tag{33}$$

and

$$\lim_{n \to \infty} r^{n+1} = 0, \quad \text{if} \quad 0 \leqq r < 1, \tag{34}$$

the positive geometric series with $p_n = r^n$ converges.   This fact leads to the following results for positive series:

I.   *If* $\dfrac{p_{n+1}}{p_n} \leqq r < 1,$ *for all* n, *or all* $n \geqq N$, *then* $\sum p_n$ *converges.*   This test is a consequence of section 191, IV, with $p_n' = r^n$, so that $p_{n+1}'/p_n' = r$.

II.   *If* $\dfrac{p_{n+1}}{p_n} \geqq 1$ *for all* n, *or all* $n \geqq N$, *then* $\sum p_n$ *diverges.*   This is a consequence of section 191, IV', with $p_n' = 1$, so that $p_{n+1}'/p_n' = 1$.

III.   *If* $\lim\limits_{n \to \infty} \dfrac{p_{n+1}}{p_n} = L,$ *the series converges if* L *is less than 1, and diverges if* L *is greater than 1.*

In the first case $L < 1$. Hence, if

$$\epsilon = \frac{1 - L}{2}, \quad \epsilon > 0 \quad \text{and} \quad L + \epsilon = \frac{1 + L}{2} < 1. \tag{35}$$

Let us use this as the ϵ in the definition of a limit, and determine N so that

$$\left| \frac{p_{n+1}}{p_n} - L \right| < \epsilon, \quad \text{if} \quad n > N. \tag{36}$$

This implies that

$$\frac{p_{n+1}}{p_n} < L + \epsilon < 1, \quad \text{if} \quad n > N. \tag{37}$$

Hence we may use $L + \epsilon$ as r and apply test I of this section to establish the convergence of $\sum p_n$.

In the second case $L > 1$. Hence if

$$\epsilon = L - 1, \quad \epsilon > 0 \quad \text{and} \quad L - \epsilon = 1. \tag{38}$$

Let us use this as the ϵ in the definition of a limit, and determine N so that

$$\left| L - \frac{p_{n+1}}{p_n} \right| < \epsilon, \quad \text{if} \quad n > N. \tag{39}$$

This implies that

$$\frac{p_{n+1}}{p_n} > L - \epsilon \geqq 1, \quad \text{if} \quad n > N. \tag{40}$$

The divergence of $\sum p_n$ follows from this and test II of this section.

The results I, II, and III which depend on the ratio p_{n+1}/p_n are separately or collectively known as the *test-ratio test*.

A test which depends on the general term of the series is:

IV. *The series p_n converges if $\sqrt[n]{p_n} \leqq r < 1$ for all n, or all $n \geqq N$, and diverges if $\sqrt[n]{p_n} \geqq 1$ for an infinite number of values of n.*

In the first case,

$$\text{if} \quad n \geqq N, \sqrt[n]{p_n} \leqq r \quad \text{and} \quad p_n \leqq r^n \text{ with } r < 1. \tag{41}$$

Thus the convergence of $\sum p_n$ follows from test I of section 191, with $p_n' = r^n$.

In the second case, since $p_n \geqq 1$ for an infinite number of values, we cannot have $\lim p_n = 0$, and the series is divergent by the condition proved at the end of section 188.

From the meaning of upper limit, and IV, we may deduce:

V. *If* $\overline{\lim} \sqrt[n]{p_n} < 1$, *the series converges, while if* $\overline{\lim} \sqrt[n]{p_n} > 1$, *the series diverges.*

194. Harmonic Series. In equation (32) we proved that the harmonic series

$$\sum \frac{1}{n^a} \text{ converges if } a > 1 \quad \text{and diverges if} \quad a \leqq 1. \tag{42}$$

For this series we have:

$$\frac{p_{n+1}}{p_n} = \frac{n^a}{(n+1)^a} = \left(1 + \frac{1}{n}\right)^{-a} = 1 - \frac{a}{n} + o\left(\frac{1}{n}\right), \tag{43}$$

by equation (196) of section 83.

Now consider any positive series with

$$\frac{p'_{n+1}}{p'_n} = 1 - \frac{b}{n} + o\left(\frac{1}{n}\right). \tag{44}$$

This series converges if $b > 1$. To show this, we first select a value of a such that $b > a > 1$. This determines a convergent series with test-ratio given by equation (43). But we have:

$$\frac{p_{n+1}}{p_n} - \frac{p'_{n+1}}{p'_n} = \frac{b-a}{n} + o\left(\frac{1}{n}\right). \tag{45}$$

Since $b > a$, $(b - a)/n$ is positive. The additional terms are of higher order than this in $1/n$ so that for all sufficiently large values of n, say

$$n > N, \quad \frac{p_{n+1}}{p_n} - \frac{p'_{n+1}}{p'_n} > 0, \quad \text{or} \quad \frac{p'_{n+1}}{p'_n} < \frac{p_{n+1}}{p_n}. \tag{46}$$

We now deduce the convergence of p'_n from test IV of section 191.

If the relation (44) holds with $b < 1$, the series $\sum p'_n$ diverges, as we could deduce from a similar argument based on test IV′ of section 191, with $\sum 1/n$ as the comparison series, and $a = 1$ in equation (45).

For positive series with

$$\frac{p'_{n+1}}{p'_n} = 1 - \frac{b}{n} + o\left(\frac{1}{n \log n}\right), \tag{47}$$

we may obtain a theorem which includes the case $b = 1$. To do this we proceed as follows. For the positive, decreasing function, $\dfrac{1}{x \log x}$, we have:

$$\int_2^x \frac{dx}{x \log x} = \log(\log x) - \log(\log 2). \tag{48}$$

When $x \to +\infty$, $\log x$ and $\log (\log x) \to +\infty$, so that the integral does not converge as $x \to +\infty$. Hence, by section 192, the series with $p_n = \dfrac{1}{n \log n}$, $n \geqq 2$, diverges. For this series we have:

$$\frac{p_n}{p_{n+1}} = \frac{(n+1) \log (n+1)}{n \log n}. \tag{49}$$

By the method of section 83, or problem 33 of Exercises IV,

$$\log \left(1 + \frac{1}{n}\right) = \frac{1}{n} + o\left(\frac{1}{n}\right), \tag{50}$$

so that

$$\frac{\log (n+1)}{\log n} = \frac{\log n + \log \left(1 + \dfrac{1}{n}\right)}{\log n} = 1 + \frac{1}{n \log n} + o\left(\frac{1}{n \log n}\right). \tag{51}$$

Hence,

$$\frac{p_n}{p_{n+1}} = \left(1 + \frac{1}{n}\right) \frac{\log (n+1)}{\log n} = 1 + \frac{1}{n} + \frac{1}{n \log n} + o\left(\frac{1}{n \log n}\right). \tag{52}$$

By the procedure of section 83, we may deduce from this for the reciprocal function:

$$\frac{p_{n+1}}{p_n} = 1 - \frac{1}{n} - \frac{1}{n \log n} + o\left(\frac{1}{n \log n}\right). \tag{53}$$

Now consider a series whose test-ratio is given by equation (47) with $b \leqq 1$. From equations (47) and (53) we have:

$$\frac{p'_{n+1}}{p'_n} - \frac{p_{n+1}}{p_n} = \frac{1-b}{n} + \frac{1}{n \log n} + o\left(\frac{1}{n \log n}\right). \tag{54}$$

Since the first term is positive or zero, the second positive, and the last of higher order than the first or second, it follows that the difference is positive for all sufficiently large values of n. Thus, by test IV' of section 191, the series $\sum p'_n$ diverges.

Since terms $o\left(\dfrac{1}{n \log n}\right)$ are also $o\left(\dfrac{1}{n}\right)$, by the result for series with ratio in the form (44), the series with ratio in the form (47) converges if $b > 1$. Thus we may state as the complete result:

If the test-ratio of a series is expressible in the form (47), the series converges if $b > 1$, and diverges if $b \leqq 1$.

We note that if $q > 0$, terms $o\left(\dfrac{1}{n^{1+q}}\right)$ or even $O\left(\dfrac{1}{n^{1+q}}\right)$ are also

$o\left(\dfrac{1}{n \log n}\right)$, by equation (293) of section 92. Thus, in particular, the series with

$$\frac{p'_{n+1}}{p'_n} = 1 - \frac{b}{n} + O\left(\frac{1}{n^{1+q}}\right), \quad q > 0, \tag{55}$$

converges if $b > 1$ and diverges if $b \leqq 1$.

195. Practical Procedure. If p_n is given explicitly as a function of n, we may express the test-ratio as a function of n. Suppose that there is a function $f(x)$, continuous at $x = 0$, such that for some fixed value c and all sufficiently large n,

$$\frac{p_{n+1}}{p_n} = f\left(\frac{1}{n+c}\right). \tag{56}$$

It is possible so to select the function that $c = 0$, but another choice may make $f(x)$ take a simpler form. Then, if $f(0) < 1$, the series is convergent, and if $f(0) > 1$, the series is divergent by test III of section 193.

If $f(0) = 1$, and the function $f(x)$ has a finite second derivative at $x = 0$, by equations (188) and (189) of section 82 there is a development:

$$f(h) = 1 + hf'(0) + O(h^2). \tag{57}$$

If we replace h by $1/(n + c)$ and observe that

$$\frac{1}{n+c} = \frac{1}{n} + O\left(\frac{1}{n^2}\right), \text{ and terms } O\left(\frac{1}{(n+c)^2}\right) \text{ are } O\left(\frac{1}{n^2}\right), \tag{58}$$

we may deduce that

$$\frac{p_{n+1}}{p_n} = 1 + \frac{f'(0)}{n} + O\left(\frac{1}{n^2}\right). \tag{59}$$

As this has the form of equation (55) with $q = 1$, and $b = -f'(0)$, we conclude that the series under discussion is convergent if $-f'(0) > 1$, and divergent if $-f'(0) \leqq 1$. Otherwise expressed, the series is convergent if $f'(0)$ is negative and numerically greater than unity, $f'(0) < -1$. The series is divergent if $f'(0)$ is positive, or numerically less than or equal to unity, $f'(0) \geqq -1$.

We illustrate this procedure for the binomial series, with

$$u_n = \frac{m(m-1)(m-2)\cdots(m-n+1)}{1 \cdot 2 \cdot 3 \cdot \ \cdots \ \cdot n} x^n, \tag{60}$$

when $x = -1$ and m is not zero or a positive integer. For these values, the terms all have the same sign for $n > m$. Hence, if we neglect the terms with $n \leqq m$, if there are any such, we obtain either a positive series, or one obtained from a positive series by multiplying each term by -1, which does not affect either the convergence or the test-ratio. The test-ratio is

$$\frac{u_{n+1}}{u_n} = \frac{n - m}{n + 1} = 1 - \frac{m + 1}{n + 1}, \tag{61}$$

so that

if $c = 1$, $f(x) = 1 - (m + 1)x$, $f(0) = 1$, $f'(0) = -(m + 1)$. (62)

Thus, when $x = -1$, the binomial series with general term given by equation (60) converges if m is positive, and diverges if m is negative. Although we excepted the cases of m zero or a positive integer from the discussion, we need not except them from the conclusion, since in the excepted cases the terms are all zero from a certain point on, and we have convergence. Thus the series converges for all values of $m \geqq 0$, and diverges for all values of $m < 0$, when $x = -1$.

The procedure of this section applies to most of the useful positive series. It is generally the simplest in practice, particularly when p_{n+1} and p_n have common factors. Occasionally, when p_n is an nth power of a simple expression, the tests of section 193, IV and V, are practically the simplest.

196. Absolute Convergence. For any infinite series of real or complex terms, $\sum u_n$, the series whose general term is $|u_n|$ is a positive series. If this positive series converges, the original series necessarily converges. For, we have:

$$|u_{k+1} + u_{k+2} + \cdots + u_{k+p}| \leqq |u_{k+1}| + |u_{k+2}| + \cdots + |u_{k+p}|, \tag{63}$$

so that the sum on the left will be numerically less than ϵ if that on the right is. But, by the condition of section 188, if the positive series $\sum |u_n|$ converges, the sum on the right will be less than any fixed positive quantity ϵ, for all positive p, and all $k > N_\epsilon$, a suitably chosen number. Thus the sum on the left is numerically less than ϵ, for all such choices of p and k, and by the sufficiency of the condition of section 188, the series $\sum u_n$ converges. This proves:

If $\sum |u_n|$ converges, then $\sum u_n$ converges.

When $\sum |u_n|$ converges, the series $\sum u_n$ is said to *converge absolutely*. Thus absolute convergence implies convergence.

Any sufficient condition for the convergence of a positive series, when applied to $\sum |u_n|$, may be used to prove the absolute convergence of $\sum u_n$.

In particular, we note that if

$$\frac{u_{n+1}}{u_n} = F\left(\frac{1}{n+c}\right), \tag{64}$$

for all sufficiently large integral values of n, where $f(x) = |F(x)|$ is continuous at $x = 0$, we have absolute convergence if $f(0) < 1$. Also if $f(x)$ has a finite second derivative at $x = 0$, and $f(0) = 1, f'(0) < -1$, we have absolute convergence by section 195.

Note that the tests for divergence of positive series, for example those of section 195, when applied to $\sum |u_n|$ may show that $\sum u_n$ does not converge absolutely, but do not necessarily prove that the series itself diverges.

If $\sum u_n$ converges, but $\sum |u_n|$ diverges, we say that $\sum u_n$ *converges conditionally.*

197. The Abel Identity. The principal method of proving the convergence of series not absolutely convergent rests on an identity which we proceed to discuss.

Let a finite sequence of positive decreasing quantities be given:

$$p_1 \geqq p_2 \geqq p_3 \geqq \cdots \geqq p_n \geqq 0, \tag{65}$$

and n real or complex quantities:

$$u_1, u_2, u_3, \cdots, u_n. \tag{66}$$

Form the partial sums:

$$s_1 = u_1, \ s_2 = u_1 + u_2, \ \cdots, \ s_n = u_1 + u_2 + \cdots + u_n, \tag{67}$$

and let M be an upper bound for their numerical values,

$$|s_k| \leqq M, \ k = 1, 2, \cdots, n. \tag{68}$$

We shall prove that

$$\left| \sum_{k=1}^{n} p_k u_k \right| \leqq p_1 M. \tag{69}$$

We have:

$$\sum_{k=1}^{n} p_k u_k = p_1 s_1 + p_2(s_2 - s_1) + \cdots + p_n(s_n - s_{n-1}) \tag{70}$$

$$= s_1(p_1 - p_2) + s_2(p_2 - p_3) + \cdots + s_{n-1}(p_{n-1} - p_n) + s_n p_n. \tag{71}$$

This is the *Abel identity.*

The differences in the parentheses of the expression (71) are all positive or zero, so that

$$\left| \sum_{k=1}^{n} p_k u_k \right| \leqq \sum_{k=1}^{n-1} |s_k| (p_k - p_{k+1}) + |s_n| p_n \qquad (72)$$

$$\leqq M[(p_1 - p_2) + (p_2 - p_3) + \cdots + (p_{n-1} - p_n) + p_n] \quad (73)$$

$$\leqq M p_1. \qquad (74)$$

This is the inequality we were seeking to prove.

Suppose next that the u_k and hence the s_k are real.   Let M' and M'' be bounds for all the s_k, so that:

$$M' \leqq s_k \leqq M''. \qquad (75)$$

In this case we may obtain an upper bound for the right member of equation (71) by replacing each s_k by M'', and reducing the expression to $M'' p_1$, analogous to the deduction of equation (74).   Similarly we obtain the lower bound $M' p_1$, so that

$$M' p_1 \leqq \sum_{k=1}^{n} p_k u_k \leqq M'' p_1. \qquad (76)$$

198. The Bonnet Mean Value Theorem.   As an application of the relation (76), we shall prove Bonnet's form of the second mean value theorem for integrals.   The theorem is:

If $f(x)$ is bounded and integrable for $a \leqq x \leqq b$, and $p(x)$ is positive and monotonically decreasing for $a \leqq x \leqq b$, then

$$\int_a^b f(x)p(x) \, dx = p(a) \int_a^\xi f(x) \, dx, \qquad (77)$$

for a suitably chosen value of ξ in the closed interval a,b.

On the interval a,b the function $p(x)$ is integrable by section 158. Hence $f(x)p(x)$ is integrable by the final result of section 156 so that the integral in the left hand side of equation (77) exists.   Also $|f(x)|$ is integrable.

We shall construct a sum which approximates the integral of $f(x)p(x)$. We first select any positive number ϵ, and determine a positive number η such that

$$\eta \int_a^b |f(x)| \, dx < \epsilon. \qquad (78)$$

We then divide the interval from $p(b)$ to $p(a)$ into n equal parts, taking n so large that each part is less than η.   That is,

$$n > \frac{p(a) - p(b)}{\eta}, \quad \delta = \frac{p(a) - p(b)}{n} < \eta. \qquad (79)$$

We denote the points of subdivision by p_k, so that:

$$p_1 = p(a), \ p_{n+1} = p(b), \ p_k = p_1 - (k-1)\delta. \tag{80}$$

We shall associate with these $n + 1$ values x_k. We take $x_1 = a$, $x_{n+1} = b$. For each intermediate p_k, we define x_k as the least upper bound of points u_k such that

$$p(x) \geqq p_k, \ \text{for} \ a \leqq x \leqq u_k. \tag{81}$$

It follows that for the right and left hand limits,

$$p(x_k-) \geqq p_k \geqq p(x_k+). \tag{82}$$

Since $p(x)$ is monotonically decreasing, and $p_k \geqq p_{k+1}$, it follows that $x_k \leqq x_{k+1}$. We may have equality for some values of k. If the inequality holds, and

$$x_k < x < x_{k+1}, \ p_k \geqq p(x) \geqq p_{k+1}. \tag{83}$$

Let us define

$$P(x) = p_k, \ \text{if} \ x_k < x < x_{k+1}. \tag{84}$$

The function $P(x)$ will be defined on a,b except at the points x_k, finite in number. For all other values of x,

$$0 \leqq P(x) - p(x) \leqq p_k - p_{k+1} \leqq \delta < \eta. \tag{85}$$

Consequently, we have:

$$\left| \int_a^b f(x)p(x) \, dx - \int_a^b f(x)P(x) \, dx \right| = \left| \int_a^b f(x)[p(x) - P(x)] \, dx \right|$$

$$\leqq \int_a^b |f(x)| \, |p(x) - P(x)| \, dx$$

$$\leqq \eta \int_a^b |f(x)| \, dx \leqq \epsilon. \tag{86}$$

But we may write:

$$\int_a^b f(x)P(x) \, dx = \sum_{k=1}^n p_k \int_{x_k}^{x_{k+1}} f(x) \, dx = \sum_{k=1}^n p_k u_k, \tag{87}$$

if

$$u_k = \int_{x_k}^{x_{k+1}} f(x) \, dx, \tag{88}$$

so that $u_k = 0$ if $x_k = x_{k+1}$. From the relations (86) and (87):

$$\sum_{k=1}^n p_k u_k - \epsilon \leqq \int_a^b f(x)p(x) \, dx \leqq \sum_{k=1}^n p_k u_k + \epsilon, \tag{89}$$

so that we have approximated the integral by a sum of the type to which the Abel identity applies.

Next let M' and M'' be the minimum and maximum values of the integral of $f(t)$ from a to x, considered as a function of x. Then:

$$M' \leq \int_a^x f(t)\, dt \leq M'', \quad a \leq x \leq b. \tag{90}$$

Also, since the integral is a continuous function of its upper limit x, the values M' and M'' are actually taken on for certain values of the upper limit, x' and x''.

If we form the sums s_k of equation (67), using the u_k of equation (88),

$$s_k = \int_{x_1}^{x_{k+1}} f(x)\, dx = \int_a^{x_{k+1}} f(t)\, dt. \tag{91}$$

Consequently, from the relation (90),

$$M' \leq s_k \leq M''. \tag{92}$$

As this has the same form as the relation (75), we may apply equation (76) and

$$M'p_1 \leq \sum_{k=1}^n p_k u_k \leq M''p_1. \tag{93}$$

It follows from this and the relation (89) that:

$$M'p_1 - \epsilon \leq \int_a^b f(x)p(x)\, dx \leq M''p_1 + \epsilon. \tag{94}$$

But ϵ is arbitrary, so that this relation remains true if we omit the terms $-\epsilon$ and ϵ. Recalling the definition of M' and M'', we may write:

$$p_1 \int_a^{x'} f(t)\, dt \leq \int_a^b f(x)p(x)\, dx \leq p_1 \int_a^{x''} f(t)\, dt. \tag{95}$$

This shows that

$$\int_a^b f(x)p(x)\, dx \text{ is an intermediate value of } p_1 \int_a^x f(t)\, dt, \tag{96}$$

considered as a function of x. Since it is a continuous function of x, the intermediate value must be taken on at some point ξ, and

$$\int_a^b f(x)p(x)\, dx = p_1 \int_a^\xi f(t)\, dt, \quad \text{or} \quad p(a) \int_a^\xi f(x)\, dx. \tag{97}$$

This is equation (77), the conclusion of the theorem.

199. The Abel Tests.   Let $\sum u_n$ be an infinite series, and

$$p_1 \geqq p_2 \geqq p_3 \geqq \cdots \geqq p_n \geqq \cdots \geqq 0 \qquad (98)$$

be a monotonically decreasing infinite sequence of positive numbers. Consider the series $\sum p_n u_n$. By the general condition of convergence of section 188, the convergence of this series depends on the magnitude of the sums:

$$\sum_{m=1}^{p} p_{k+m} u_{k+m}. \qquad (99)$$

If, for all positive p, we have

$$\left| \sum_{m=1}^{p} u_{k+m} \right| \leqq S_k, \qquad (100)$$

then by the relation (74), with slightly different notation,

$$\left| \sum_{m=1}^{p} p_{k+m} u_{k+m} \right| \leqq p_{k+1} S_k. \qquad (101)$$

If the series $\sum u_n$ converges, the relation (100) may be satisfied by values of S_k such that $S_k \to 0$ as $k \to \infty$. Then, since the p_n are monotonically decreasing, the right, and hence the left, member of equation (101) approaches zero as $k \to \infty$. Thus, by the condition of section 188, the series $\sum p_n u_n$ will converge. That is:

If the series $\sum u_n$ converges, and the p_n form a monotonically decreasing sequence of positive numbers, then the series $\sum p_n u_n$ converges.

A related result is:

If the series $\sum u_n$ is such that for some fixed S and all values of k, $\left| \sum_{n=1}^{k} u_n \right| \leqq S$, and if the p_n form a monotonically decreasing sequence of positive numbers approaching zero as a limit, then the series $\sum p_n u_n$ converges.

For, in this case we have:

$$\left| \sum_{m=1}^{p} u_{k+m} \right| = \left| \sum_{n=1}^{k+m} u_n - \sum_{n=1}^{k} u_n \right| \leqq 2S, \qquad (102)$$

and hence

$$\left| \sum_{m=1}^{p} p_{k+m} u_{k+m} \right| \leqq 2p_{k+1} S, \qquad (103)$$

which approaches zero as $k \to \infty$.

In each of these two cases, if S is a bound for all the partial sums s_n, the sum of the series $\sum p_n u_n$ is numerically at most $p_1 S$, since it follows from the inequality (74) that

$$\left| \sum_{n=1}^{p} p_k u_k \right| \leqq p_1 S. \tag{104}$$

We may establish the additional result:

If the series $\sum u_n$ converges and the p_n form a bounded monotonically increasing sequence of positive numbers, then the series $\sum p_n u_n$ converges.

For, if P is any upper bound for the p_n, it follows from the inequality (74), applied to this sum taken in reverse order, that:

$$\left| \sum_{m=1}^{p} p_{k+m} u_{k+m} \right| \leqq p_{k+m} S_k \leqq P S_k, \tag{105}$$

which approaches 0 when $k \to \infty$, since $\sum u_n$ converges.

200. Alternating Series. The series $1 - 1 + 1 - 1 + \cdots$ has sums alternately 1 and 0. Accordingly all the partial sums are bounded. Hence, if we multiply in any monotonically decreasing positive sequence, p_n, approaching zero as a limit, we obtain a convergent series:

$$p_1 - p_2 + p_3 - p_4 + \cdots. \tag{106}$$

Also, since the partial sums of the original series admit unity as an upper bound,

$$\left| \sum_{m=2}^{p} (-1)^{k+m} p_{k+m} \right| \leqq p_{k+2} \leqq p_{k+1}. \tag{107}$$

It follows that the remainder of the series after k terms,

$$\sum_{m=1}^{\infty} (-1)^{k+m} p_{k+m} = (-1)^{k+1} p_{k+1} + \sum_{m=2}^{\infty} (-1)^{k+m} p_{k+m}, \tag{108}$$

is either zero or has the same sign as its first term, and does not exceed this first term in numerical value.

When the p_n decrease, so that $p_{k+2} < p_{k+1}$, the remainder of the series has the same sign as its first term, and is numerically less than this first term.

As an example of an alternating series, the series

$$1 - \tfrac{1}{2} + \tfrac{1}{3} - \tfrac{1}{4} + \cdots \tag{109}$$

converges. Here the p_n decrease.

The series

$$1 - 1 + \tfrac{1}{2} - \tfrac{1}{2} + \tfrac{1}{3} - \tfrac{1}{3} + \cdots \tag{110}$$

converges to 0. Here the remainders are alternately equal to their first term, and to zero.

201. Conditionally Convergent Series. It is shown in problems 10 and 11 of Exercises IX that the sum of the series (109) is log 2, but that if we rearrange the terms, taking p positive to each q negative terms, then the sum is log $(2p^{1/2}/q^{1/2})$.

This illustrates that the sum of a conditionally convergent series may change when we rearrange the terms. Consider any real conditionally convergent series. Let P_n denote the sum of those terms among the first n which are positive, and $-Q_n$ the sum of those terms among the first n which are negative. Since the series converges, we have $\lim_{n \to \infty} (P_n - Q_n) = s$, the sum of the series. But, as the series does not converge absolutely, we have

$$\lim_{n \to \infty} (P_n + Q_n) = +\infty, \text{ so that } \lim_{n \to \infty} P_n = +\infty$$

and

$$\lim_{n \to \infty} Q_n = +\infty.$$

Hence, after any finite number of terms are removed, we may still obtain from either P or Q a number of terms with an arbitrarily large sum, where P denotes the positive terms of the series taken in order, and Q the negative terms with signs reversed, taken in order. This fact suggests a method of rearrangement of the series which will have any given number L, as a sum. We begin with the smallest number of positive terms from P, taken in order, which have a sum greater than L. Then we add the smallest number of terms from $-Q$ to give a sum less than L. We then take additional terms, in order, from P to make the sum greater than L, additional terms from $-Q$ to make the sum less than L, and continue in this way. The resulting series will have a sum L, since the difference between a partial sum and L will be less than the last term of P or Q used, and the individual terms approach zero since the series converges.

Similarly, by using an increasing set of numbers in place of L at each stage, say n, we may make the new series diverge to plus infinity. Or, using $-n$, we could make the new series diverge to minus infinity.

For series of complex terms, the real or imaginary component series may converge absolutely, but at least one of these series will converge conditionally, if the original series does. Hence there are rearrangements of the terms of the original complex series which will alter the sum.

202. Rearrangement of Absolutely Convergent Series. If a series converges absolutely, its sum is independent of the order in which the terms are summed. For, let Σu_n be an absolutely convergent series, and

$\sum u_n'$ the same terms taken in a different order. Select an N such that for every positive integer p,

$$\sum_{m=1}^{p} |u_{n+m}| < \epsilon, \quad \text{if} \quad n > N. \tag{111}$$

Then, for any $n_1 > N$ and $n_2 > n_1 + p_1$ such that *all* the terms of $\sum_{n=1}^{n_1} u_n$ are included in $\sum_{n=1}^{n_2} u_n'$, we have:

$$\left| \sum_{n=1}^{n_2} u_n' - \sum_{n=1}^{n_1} u_n \right| \leqq \left| \sum_{k=1}^{p_1} u_{jk} \right| \leqq \sum_{k=1}^{p_1} |u_{jk}|, \tag{112}$$

where u_{jk} denotes a term with subscript exceeding n_1. If the largest of these subscripts is $n_1 + p_2$, we have:

$$\sum_{k=1}^{p_1} |u_{jk}| \leqq \sum_{m=1}^{p_2} |u_{n_1+m}| < \epsilon. \tag{113}$$

Since n_2 becomes infinite when n_1 does, this proves that

$$\sum_{n=1}^{\infty} u_n' = \sum_{n=1}^{\infty} u_n. \tag{114}$$

The result may be applied to $\sum|u_n|$ and $\sum|u_n'|$, so that the latter series converges, and the rearranged series $\sum u_n'$ converges absolutely.

In rearranging an absolutely convergent series, we may separate its terms into a finite number, q, of infinite sets, and use each set to form a new infinite series. We may then sum each of these q series and add the q sums. Let the separate series be $\sum u_{1n}', \sum u_{2n}', \cdots, \sum u_{qn}'$.

If

$$\sum_{n=1}^{\infty} |u_n| = S, \tag{115}$$

we have:

$$\sum_{n=1}^{p} |u_{rn}'| \leqq \sum_{n=1}^{p_1} |u_n| \leqq S, \tag{116}$$

so that each of the separate series converges absolutely. Now select an N such that the relation (111) holds, and take any $n_1 > N$, and n_2 so large that all the first n_1 terms of the original series are included in the sums to n_2 terms of the q series. Then we have:

$$\left| \sum_{r=1}^{q} \sum_{n=1}^{n_2} u_{rn}' - \sum_{n=1}^{n_1} u_n \right| \leqq \sum_{k} |u_{jk}|, \tag{117}$$

where u_{jk} denotes a term with subscript greater than n_1. If the largest of these subscripts is $n_1 + p_2$, we have:

$$\sum_{k} |u_{jk}| \leqq \sum_{m=1}^{p_2} |u_{n_1+m}|. \tag{118}$$

Since n_2 becomes infinite when n_1 does, this proves that:

$$\sum_{r=1}^{q} \sum_{n=1}^{\infty} u'_{rn} = \sum_{n=1}^{\infty} u_n. \tag{119}$$

In place of a finite number of sets, we may use an enumerably infinite number of sets. Each set may be arranged in an infinite series, and the sums of these series taken as the terms of a new series. As before, we may show that each separate series converges absolutely. We select N and $n_1 > N$ as before, and then take n_2 sufficiently large and a sufficiently large number of the sets, q, so that all the first n_1 terms of the original series are included in the first n_2 terms of the first q series. We again have the relations (117) and (118). Thus the left member of the relation (117) is at most ϵ for all sufficiently large n_1, and we must have:

$$\left| \sum_{r=1}^{q} \sum_{n=1}^{\infty} u'_{rn} - \sum_{n=1}^{\infty} u_n \right| < \epsilon, \tag{120}$$

for sufficiently large q.

This proves that the infinite series whose terms are the sums of the separate series converges to the same sum as the original series.

Conversely, a multiple series, or series of series, may be rearranged as a single series which has the same sum, if the single series is absolutely convergent.

203. Operations on Series. Two convergent series may be added termwise, since if $w_n = u_n + v_n$, then

$$\sum_{n=1}^{p} w_n = \sum_{n=1}^{p} u_n + \sum_{n=1}^{p} v_n, \tag{121}$$

so that

$$\sum_{n=1}^{\infty} w_n = \sum_{n=1}^{\infty} u_n + \sum_{n=1}^{\infty} v_n. \tag{122}$$

The same is true of any finite number of series.

For the product of two convergent series, we have

$$\left[\sum_{n=1}^{\infty} u_n \right] \left[\sum_{n=1}^{\infty} v_n \right] = \lim_{n \to \infty} \left[\sum_{m=1}^{n} u_m \right] \left[\sum_{m=1}^{n} v_m \right] \tag{123}$$

$$= \sum_{n=1}^{\infty} \left[\sum_{m=1}^{n} u_m \sum_{m=1}^{n} v_m - \sum_{m=1}^{n-1} u_m \sum_{m=1}^{n-1} v_m \right]. \tag{124}$$

For $n = 1$, the sums from 1 to 0 are to be replaced by 0.

Suppose that both series are absolutely convergent. Then if

$$\sum_{n=1}^{\infty} |u_n| = S \quad \text{and} \quad \sum_{n=1}^{\infty} |v_n| = T, \tag{125}$$

$$\sum_{m=1}^{p} |u_m| \sum_{n=1}^{q} |v_n| \leqq ST. \tag{126}$$

Thus any arrangement of the double series with general term $|u_m v_n|$ as a single series will have a bounded sum and hence converge. Hence the corresponding series with absolute value signs omitted will converge absolutely, and all rearrangements of $\sum \sum u_m v_n$ will converge to the same sum. Since one arrangement has a sequence of partial sums equal to $\left[\sum_{m=1}^{n} u_m \right] \left[\sum_{m=1}^{n} v_m \right]$, it follows from the relation (123) that:

$$\left[\sum_{n=1}^{\infty} u_n \right] \left[\sum_{n=1}^{\infty} v_n \right] = \sum_{m=1}^{\infty} \sum_{n=1}^{\infty} u_m v_n, \tag{127}$$

when the two original series converge absolutely. The double series on the right may be rearranged in any way without altering the sum. The most useful arrangement generally is:

$$u_1 v_1 + (u_1 v_2 + u_2 v_1) + (u_1 v_3 + u_2 v_2 + u_3 v_1) + \cdots, \tag{128}$$

where the sum of the subscripts in the nth parenthesis is $n + 1$.

204. Practical Tests. The tests for divergence of positive series which show that u_n cannot approach the limit zero may be applied to u_n. Thus,

if $$\lim \left| \frac{u_{n+1}}{u_n} \right| > 1, \quad \text{or} \quad \overline{\lim} \sqrt[n]{|u_n|} > 1, \tag{129}$$

the series u_n diverges.

Absolute convergence is usually proved either by applying the procedure of section 195 to the series $\sum |u_n|$, or by a comparison with a positive series known to be convergent. In this case we deduce the absolute convergence of $\sum u_n$ from the convergence of $\sum p_n$ and the relation $|u_n| \leqq p_n$.

205. Infinite Products. An infinite product is an expression of the form:

$$(1 + u_1)(1 + u_2) \cdots (1 + u_n) \cdots \tag{130}$$

By a real infinite product we mean one for which all the u_n are real. We shall consider only products with no zero factors, so that

$$u_k \neq -1. \tag{131}$$

Analogous to the partial sums of a series, we may form partial products

$$P_n = \prod_{k=1}^{n} (1 + u_k) = (1 + u_1)(1 + u_2)(1 + u_3) \cdots (1 + u_n). \tag{132}$$

If

$$\lim_{n \to \infty} P_n = P, \tag{133}$$

where P is *finite and different from zero*, we say that the infinite product is convergent, and converges to the value P.   We write in this case

$$\prod_{n=1}^{\infty} (1 + u_n) = P \quad \text{or simply} \quad \prod(1 + u_n) = P. \tag{134}$$

We sometimes use $\prod(1 + u_n)$ as an abbreviation for the expression (130) when the initial value is clear from the context.   When P_n either does not approach a limit or approaches a limit zero, we say that the infinite product diverges.   A real divergent infinite product may either diverge to zero, diverge to infinity, or oscillate.   Compare the remarks on the behavior of real series in section 186.

If a finite number of u_k, all preceding the Nth factor, are allowed to be -1, the terms convergent and divergent may be applied to the original product to mean that $\prod_{n=N}^{\infty} (1 + u_n)$ converges or diverges in the sense just defined.   This extension enables us to multiply in or divide out, or change a finite number of factors, zero or not, at the beginning of a product, without affecting its convergence or divergence.

206. The General Condition. *A necessary and sufficient condition for the convergence of the infinite product* $\prod_{n=1}^{\infty} (1 + u_n)$, $u_n \neq -1$, *is that, for any positive number* ϵ, *there is a number* N_ϵ, *such that, for any* $n > N_\epsilon$ *and all positive integers* p,

$$\left| \prod_{k=1}^{p} (1 + u_{n+k}) - 1 \right| < \epsilon. \tag{135}$$

To prove the necessity of the condition, let us suppose that the infinite product converges.   Since P, the limit of P_n, is not zero, we may select a positive number η, with

$$0 < \eta < \frac{|P|}{2}. \tag{136}$$

We next select a number N such that, for $n > N$,

$$|P_n - P| < \eta, \quad \text{or} \quad P_n = P + \theta\eta, \quad \text{with} \quad |\theta| < 1. \tag{137}$$

We will then have:

$$\left| \prod_{m=1}^{n} (1 + u_m) \right| = |P_n| \geqq |P| - |P_n - P| \geqq \frac{|P|}{2}. \tag{138}$$

Also, if $n > N$; $n + p > N$, and

$$P_{n+p} - P = \theta'\eta, \quad |\theta'| < 1. \tag{139}$$

Then

$$\prod_{k=1}^{p} (1 + u_{n+k}) - 1 = \frac{\prod_{m=1}^{n+p} (1 + u_m)}{\prod_{m=1}^{n} (1 + u_m)} - 1 = \frac{P_{n+p}}{P_n} - 1$$

$$= \frac{P + \theta' \eta}{P + \theta \eta} - 1 = \frac{(\theta' - \theta)\eta}{P + \theta \eta}. \qquad (140)$$

Consequently, we have for the absolute value:

$$\left| \prod_{k=1}^{p} (1 + u_{n+k}) - 1 \right| \leq \frac{2\eta}{\dfrac{|P|}{2}} \leq \frac{4\eta}{|P|}. \qquad (141)$$

Since the only condition imposed on η was the relation (136), we may so choose η that the last expression is less than any given ϵ. In fact,

$$\frac{4\eta}{|P|} < \epsilon \quad \text{if} \quad \eta < \frac{|P|\epsilon}{4}. \qquad (142)$$

This proves that the condition is necessary.

We will next prove the sufficiency of the condition. Accordingly, we assume that the condition is satisfied. Then, for any given positive ϵ, we shall have:

$$\left| \prod_{k=1}^{p} (1 + u_{n+k}) - 1 \right| < \epsilon, \qquad (143)$$

or

$$\prod_{k=1}^{p} (1 + u_{n+k}) = 1 + \theta\epsilon, \quad |\theta| < 1, \quad \text{for} \quad n \geq N_\epsilon. \qquad (144)$$

We let N denote N_ϵ for $\epsilon = 1/2$, and only consider values of $\epsilon \leq 1/2$. We also take $N_\epsilon > N$.

Again, we have:

$$\prod_{m=1}^{n+p} (1 + u_m) - \prod_{m=1}^{n} (1 + u_m) = \prod_{m=1}^{n} (1 + u_m) \left[\prod_{k=1}^{p} (1 + u_{n+k}) - 1 \right] \qquad (145)$$

But, from equation (144) with $\epsilon = 1/2$,

$$\frac{P_{N+p}}{P_N} = \prod_{k=1}^{p} (1 + u_{N+p}) = 1 + \frac{\theta}{2}. \qquad (146)$$

Consequently,

$$\frac{1}{2} < \left| \frac{P_{N+p}}{P_N} \right| < 2, \quad \text{and} \quad \frac{|P_N|}{2} < |P_{N+p}| < 2|P_N|. \qquad (147)$$

Let us put

$$M = |P_N|. \tag{148}$$

Then any $n > N$ may be used as $N + p$, so that:

$$\frac{M}{2} < |P_n| < 2M, \quad \text{if} \quad n > N. \tag{149}$$

For any $n > N_\epsilon$, $n > N_\epsilon > N$, so that the relations (143) and (149) both hold.   From these and the identity (145) we may deduce:

$$|P_{n+p} - P_n| < 2M\epsilon, \quad \text{if} \quad n > N_\epsilon. \tag{150}$$

Since M is fixed, and ϵ arbitrary, it follows from this last relation that for $n \to \infty$, P_n approaches a limit by the Cauchy convergence criterion.

Also, since no single factor is zero, M is not zero, and from the relation (149), the limit has a numerical value at least $M/2$, and so is different from zero.

Thus, if the condition is satisfied, the infinite product converges.

As a consequence of the necessity of the condition, we note that, for $p = 1$,

$$|(1 + u_{n+1}) - 1| < \epsilon, \quad \text{or} \quad |u_{n+1}| < \epsilon, \quad \text{for} \quad n > N_\epsilon. \tag{151}$$

This proves that *a necessary condition for the convergence of an infinite product is that* $\lim\limits_{n \to \infty} u_n = 0$.   This condition is the reason for writing the factors as $1 + u_n$.

207. Absolute Convergence.   The expression

$$\prod_{k=1}^{p} (1 + u_{n+k}) - 1, \tag{152}$$

which occurs in the condition for convergence, when multiplied out and the -1 cancelled becomes a polynomial in the u_{n+k} with positive coefficients.   Consequently,

$$\left| \prod_{k=1}^{p} (1 + u_{n+k}) - 1 \right| \leq \prod_{k=1}^{p} (1 + |u_{n+k}|) - 1. \tag{153}$$

It follows from this, and the condition of the preceding section, that if $\Pi(1 + |u_n|)$ converges, then $\Pi(1 + u_n)$ converges.   Under these conditions, the latter product is said to *converge absolutely*.   The absolute convergence of any infinite product depends on the convergence of a positive product, that is one all of whose factors may be written $1 + p_n$, where the p_n are positive or zero.   Accordingly, we consider such positive products.

We begin by applying the law of the mean to e^x, $x \geqq 0$, and so obtain:

$$\frac{e^x - e^0}{x - 0} = e^{\theta x} \geqq 1, \quad \text{or} \quad e^x \geqq 1 + x, \quad x \geqq 0. \tag{154}$$

It follows from this that:

$$1 \leqq \prod_{k=1}^{n} (1 + p_k) \leqq e^{\sum\limits_{k=1}^{n} p_k}. \tag{155}$$

The product of the first n factors of a positive product is a monotonically increasing function of n, and accordingly approaches a limit if it is bounded. If $\sum\limits_{n=1}^{\infty} p_k = s$, then e^s is an upper bound for all the partial products, and these products approach a limit as $n \to \infty$. Since the products are all at least unity, the limit is at least unity, and hence distinct from zero. Thus the infinite product converges.

Conversely, if the infinite product converges, so does the series $\sum p_k$. For we have:

$$1 + \sum_{k=1}^{n} p_k \leqq \prod_{k=1}^{n} (1 + p_k), \tag{156}$$

since the right member, when multiplied out, includes the terms on the left, as well as other additional terms which are positive or zero. This shows that if the product converges, its limit less unity is greater than or equal to any partial sum of the series $\sum p_k$. Thus these partial sums are bounded, and, since the series is a positive series, it converges.

We have thus proved:

A necessary and sufficient condition for the convergence of a positive infinite product $\prod(1 + p_n)$, *is that the positive infinite series* $\sum p_n$ *converges.*

If we consider the p_n as u_n, we may conclude from this that:

A necessary and sufficient condition for the absolute convergence of the infinite product $\prod(1 + u_n)$ *is the absolute convergence of the infinite series* $\sum u_n$.

208. Rearrangement of the Factors. If an infinite product converges absolutely, and we rearrange the factors in any way that neither omits any, nor adds any factors, the new product will converge absolutely, by the properties of series and the theorem just proved. Let P_n be the partial product to n factors of the original product, with factors $(1 + u_n)$, approaching a limit P. Denote by P'_m the partial product to m factors of the rearranged product, with factors $(1 + u'_n)$, approaching a limit P'. By the general condition of section 206, applied to the positive product with factors $(1 + |u_n|)$, there is an N such that

$$\left| \prod_{k=1}^{p} (1 + |u_{n+k}|) - 1 \right| < \epsilon, \quad \text{for} \quad n > N_\epsilon. \tag{157}$$

Now take $n > N_\epsilon$, form P_n, and then take m so large that all the factors of P_n are included in P'_m. Then we have:

$$\left| \frac{P'_m}{P_n} - 1 \right| = \left| \prod_k (1 + u_{jk}) - 1 \right|, \tag{158}$$

where all the u_{jk} have subscripts exceeding n.

From the relation (153) it follows that:

$$\left| \prod_k (1 + u_{jk}) - 1 \right| \leq \prod_k (1 + |u_{jk}|) - 1. \tag{159}$$

Since each factor $(1 + |u_{jk}|)$ is at least unity, if we add additional factors to the product in the right member, this member will be increased, or at least not diminished. Thus, for a suitable positive integer p,

$$\left| \prod_k (1 + u_{jk}) - 1 \right| \leq \prod_{k=1}^{p} (1 + |u_{n+k}|) - 1, \tag{160}$$

and

$$\left| \frac{P'_m}{P_n} - 1 \right| < \epsilon. \tag{161}$$

Since $m \to \infty$ when $n \to \infty$, and $P \neq 0$, we may conclude from this that

$$\left| \frac{P'}{P} - 1 \right| < \epsilon, \quad \text{or} \quad \frac{P'}{P} - 1 = 0, \tag{162}$$

since ϵ is arbitrary. Thus $P' = P$, and we have proved that:

If the factors of an absolutely convergent infinite product are rearranged to give a new product, the new product is also absolutely convergent, and has the same value as the original product.

209. Products of Fixed Sign. If the u_n are all real and negative, we may write the typical factor as $(1 - p_n)$. If the p_n are all less than unity, we have:

$$(1 - p_n)(1 + p_n) = 1 - p_n^2 < 1, \tag{163}$$

and

$$(1 - p_n) < \frac{1}{(1 + p_n)}. \tag{164}$$

Thus

$$\prod_{k=1}^{n} (1 - p_k) < \frac{1}{\displaystyle\prod_{k=1}^{n} (1 + p_k)}. \tag{165}$$

If the series $\sum p_k$ diverges, it follows from the relation (156) that the product $\prod(1 + p_k)$ diverges to $+\infty$, and from the relation (165) that the product $\prod(1 - p_k)$ diverges to zero. On the other hand, if the series $\sum p_k$ converges, then the product $\prod(1 - p_k)$ converges absolutely. Since the infinite product $\prod(1 + u_n)$ as well as the series $\sum u_n$ can only converge if $\lim_{n \to \infty} u_n = 0$, the condition that p_n is less than unity will always hold from a certain factor on, if we have convergence. Thus we may combine the result just found with that for positive products in the theorem:

If, for all sufficiently large n, the u_n are real and of fixed sign, the infinite product $\prod(1 + u_n)$ will converge if and only if the infinite series $\sum u_n$ converges.

That the condition of fixed sign is essential may be seen from the example:

$$u_1 = -\frac{1}{2^{\frac{1}{2}}}, u_2 = \frac{1}{2^{\frac{1}{2}}} + \frac{1}{2}, u_{2n-3} = -\frac{1}{n^{\frac{1}{2}}}, u_{2n-2} = \frac{1}{n^{\frac{1}{2}}} + \frac{1}{n}. \quad (166)$$

The infinite product $\prod(1 + u_n)$ converges. For the individual factors approach unity, and when grouped in pairs we have:

$$(1 + u_{2n-3})(1 + u_{2n-2}) = 1 - \frac{1}{n^{\frac{3}{2}}}, \quad (167)$$

which is the factor of an absolutely convergent infinite product. However, the series $\sum u_n$ diverges, since its $2n$th partial sum is $\sum_{k=2}^{n+1} 1/k$.

EXERCISES IX

1. If $\sum p_n$ is any convergent positive series, a second such series $\sum p_n'$ can be found with $\lim p_n'/p_n = \infty$. *Hint:* We may put $r_0 = s, r_n = s - s_n$, and $p_n' = \sqrt{r_{n-1}} - \sqrt{r_n}$. Then $s_n' = \sqrt{s} - \sqrt{r_n}$, so that the primed series converges to $\sqrt{s}$. And $\dfrac{p_n}{p_n'} = \dfrac{r_{n-1} - r_n}{\sqrt{r_{n-1}} - \sqrt{r_n}} = \sqrt{r_{n-1}} + \sqrt{r_n} \to 0$.

2. If p_n is any divergent positive series, a second such series can be found with $\lim p_n'/p_n = 0$. *Hint:* We may put $p_n' = \sqrt{s_n} - \sqrt{s_{n-1}}$, $p_1' = \sqrt{p_1}$. Then $s_n' = \sqrt{s_n} \to +\infty$, and $\dfrac{p_n'}{p_n} = \dfrac{\sqrt{s_n} - \sqrt{s_{n-1}}}{s_n - s_{n-1}} = \dfrac{1}{\sqrt{s_n} + \sqrt{s_{n-1}}} \to 0$.

3. If the terms of a positive convergent series monotonically decrease as n increases, then $p_n = o(1/n)$. *Hint:* The sum of the terms from that with index $[n/2]$ to n exceeds $(n/2)p_n$, so that if $|s - s_n| < \epsilon$, when $n > N$, $np_n < 2\epsilon$ when $n > 2N$.

4. The condition of problem 3 cannot be improved, since if $f(m)$ is any positive function such that $f(m) \to 0$ as $m \to \infty$, we may find a positive convergent series whose terms monotonically decrease, with $p_m = f(m)/m$ for an infinite number of values of m. *Hint:* Select a series of values of m, m_k, for which $f(m_k) < 1/2^k$, take $f(m_k)/m_k$ as the (m_k)th term, and all terms after the $(m_k - 1)$st which precede this. Then the series converges, since the sum to m_k terms is less than $\sum_{j=1}^{k} f(m_k) < 1$.

5. *Kummer's Criterion.* Let a_n be any sequence of positive numbers, and p_n the terms of a positive series. Form the expressions $a_n \dfrac{p_n}{p_{n+1}} - a_{n+1} = K_n$. The series p_n converges if $\varliminf K_n > 0$, so that for sufficiently large n the K_n exceed some fixed positive number. *Hint:* With a change in the notation, if necessary, we may assume $K_n > A$, for all n. Then $a_n p_n - a_{n+1} p_{n+1} > A p_n$, and summing $a_1 p_1 - a_{n+1} p_{n+1} > A \sum p_n$, so that $\sum p_n$ is bounded.

6. If the positive numbers a_n of problem 5 are such that $\sum 1/a_n$ diverges, and $\varlimsup K_n < 0$, or even $K_n \leqq 0$ for sufficiently large n, the series $\sum p_n$ diverges. *Hint:* Use the test IV′ of section 191, with $\sum 1/a_n$ as the comparison series.

7. Prove that the positive series $\sum p_n$ converges if $\log n \left[n \left(\dfrac{p_n}{p_{n+1}} - 1 \right) - 1 \right]$ has $\varliminf > 1$, and the series diverges if the expression has $\varlimsup < 1$. *Hint:* Put $a_n = n \log n$, and use problems 5, 6 and equation (52) of the text.

8. Deduce the rule of section 194, equation (55) from the preceding problem.

9. Prove that the expression $F(n) = 1 + \dfrac{1}{2} + \dfrac{1}{3} + \cdots + \dfrac{1}{n} - \log n$ is always positive, and decreases with n, so that it approaches a limit as $n \to \infty$. The limit is known as *Euler's constant*, and is denoted by γ, so that $\lim_{n \to \infty} F(n) = \gamma$. In section 323 we shall show how to compute its value, $0.5772157 \cdots$. *Hint:* With $f(x) = 1/x$, we have from equation (30) $\log n \leqq 1 + \dfrac{1}{2} + \cdots + \dfrac{1}{n-1}$, so that $F(n)$ is positive. And from equation (29), $1/n \leqq \log n - \log (n-1)$, so that $F(n) - F(n-1) \leqq 0$, so that $F(n)$ decreases with n.

10. Prove that $1 - \dfrac{1}{2} + \dfrac{1}{3} - \cdots = \log 2$. *Hint:* If s_n is the sum to n terms of $\sum 1/n$, $s_n = \gamma + \log n + o(1)$, by problem 9. For the series of this problem, the sum of $2n$ terms is $s_{2n} - 2 \left(\dfrac{s_n}{2} \right) = \gamma + \log (2n) - (\gamma + \log n) + o(1) = \log 2 + o(1)$. The odd sums also approach $\log 2$, since the separate terms approach zero.

11. Prove that if we rearrange the terms of the series in problem 10, taking alternately blocks of p positive terms and q negative terms in order, the sum of the series is $\log (2p^{1/2}/q^{1/2})$. *Hint:* As in the preceding problem, the sum of the

first $m(p + q)$ terms may be written as $s_{2mp} - \left(\dfrac{s_{mp}}{2}\right) - \dfrac{s_{mq}}{2} = \gamma + \log 2mp -$
$1/2(\gamma + \log mp) - 1/2(\gamma + \log mq) + o(1) = \log 2 + 1/2 \ \log \ (p/q) + o(1)$.
The other sums approach the same limit, since the sum of any group of $2(p + q)$
or fewer terms from $\sum 1/n$, all beyond the Nth is at most $\dfrac{2(p + q)}{N}$ which $\to 0$
when $N \to \infty$.

12. Prove that the positive series $\sum r^n$ converges if and only if $r < 1$ by using
the integral test of section 192.

13. If we start with $n = 2$, the series with $u_n = \dfrac{1}{n \, (\log n)^a}$ has all its terms
positive. It converges if $a > 1$, and diverges if $a \leq 1$. Prove a similar result
when the denominator is $n \, (\log n)(\log^2 n) \cdots (\log^r n)^a$, where $\log^2 n$ means log
log n, and similarly for $\log^r n$. We must start with a large enough value to
make all the numbers whose logarithms are taken greater than unity, and the
condition for divergence is always $a \leq 1$. *Hint:* Use the integral test, and
observe that

$$\frac{d}{dx} (\log^r x) = \frac{1}{x \, (\log x)(\log^2 x) \cdots (\log^{r-1} x)} \, .$$

14. The series $\sum \dfrac{1}{n \log n}$ diverges by problem 13, or section 194. Show that
for this series $p_n = o(1/n)$. This proves that the condition of problem 3 is only
necessary and not sufficient for convergence.

15. Show that the series $\sum x^n/n^n$ is absolutely convergent for all values of x,
and that the same result holds for $\sum R(n)x^n/n^n$, where $R(n)$ is any rational
function of n.

16. Show that $\sum R(n)x^n/n \, !$ is absolutely convergent for all values of x, where
$R(n)$ is any rational function. An example is the series $1 + x + \dfrac{x^2}{2 \, !} + \cdots$

$+ \dfrac{x^n}{n \, !} + \cdots$, which equals e^x for real values of x, by problem 26 of Exercises IV.

17. Show that $\sum n^n x^n$ diverges for all values of x except $x = 0$, and extend the
result to $\sum R(n)n^n x^n$, where $R(n)$ is any rational function not identically zero.

18. Show that $\sum R(n)n \, ! \, x^n$ diverges for all values of x except $x = 0$, where
$R(n)$ is any rational function not identically zero. *Hint:* Use problem 19 of
Exercises III.

19. If $R(n)$ is any rational function, show that $\sum R(n)x^n$ converges absolutely
if $|x| < 1$. Also that it converges for $|x| = 1$ if the degree of the denominator
exceeds that of the numerator by at least two. It diverges for $|x| > 1$, if $R(n)$
is not identically zero.

20. The series with $u_n = 1/n$ diverges, while that with $u_n' = (-1)^n(1/\sqrt{n})$ con-
verges. But $|u_n| \leq |u_n'|$. This illustrates that no comparison test holds for
non-positive series.

21. The series with $u_1 = 1$, $u_2 = \dfrac{ab}{cd} x$ and

$$u_n = \frac{a(a + 1)(a + 2) \cdots (a + n - 1)b(b + 1)(b + 2) \cdots (b + n - 1)}{c(c + 1)(c + 2) \cdots (c + n - 1)d(d + 1)(d + 2) \cdots (d + n - 1)} x^n$$

is known as the hyper-geometric series. If no factor $(a + n)$, $(b + n)$, $(c + n)$ or $(d + n)$ is zero, prove that it converges absolutely if $|x| < 1$, and diverges if $|x| > 1$.

22. If the test-ratio of a series of complex terms has the form $\dfrac{u_{n+1}}{u_n} = 1 + \dfrac{A}{n}$ $+ O\left(\dfrac{1}{n^2}\right)$, prove that the series is absolutely convergent if $\mathbf{R}(A) < -1$. Apply this to show that the hyper-geometric series of problem 21 is absolutely convergent for $x = 1$, if $\mathbf{R}(a + b - c - d + 1) < 0$.

23. If the p_n are a sequence of positive quantities which monotonically decrease to zero, $\sum p_n \sin n\theta$ converges, and if $\theta \neq 0$, $\sum p_n \cos n\theta$ converges. *Hint:* They are the real and imaginary component series of $\sum p_n e^{in\theta}$, and the sums of the geometric series $\sum (e^{i\theta})^n$ have $|s_n| = |1 - e^{i(n+1)\theta}|/|1 - e^{i\theta}| \leq 2/(1 - \cos \theta)$, and so are bounded.

24. The infinite product $\prod \left[1 - \dfrac{b}{n} + O\left(\dfrac{1}{n^2}\right) \right]$ diverges to 0 if $b > 0$, and diverges to $+\infty$ if $b < 0$. Also, for sufficiently large n, the product of n factors is a monotonic function of n. Deduce that if $u_{n+1}/u_n = \left[1 - \dfrac{b}{n} + O\left(\dfrac{1}{n^2}\right) \right] e^{i\theta}$, $\sum u_n$ diverges if $b < 0$, and converges if $b > 0$ and $\theta \neq 0$. *Hint:* Use section 209, and the preceding problem.

25. The binomial series is

$$1 + mx + \frac{m(m - 1)}{2!} x^2 + \cdots + \frac{m(m - 1)(m - 2) \cdots (m - n + 1)}{n!} x^n + \cdots.$$

It follows from problem 29 of Exercises IV that it represents $(1 + x)^m$ for m real and x real and $-1 < x < 1$. Prove that for m real but x complex, the series converges absolutely if $|x| < 1$, and diverges if $|x| > 1$. Also, that for $|x| = 1$, it diverges if $m \leq -1$ and converges if $m \geq 0$. For $-1 < m < 0$, it converges for $|x| = 1$, if $x \neq -1$, and diverges if $x = -1$. *Hint:* Use the preceding problem and section 195.

26. If $m(x)$ is a monotonic function of x, and $f(x)$ is bounded and integrable for $a \leq x \leq b$, prove that there is a value ξ such that

$$\int_a^b f(x)\, m(x)\, dx = m(a) \int_a^\xi f(x)\, dx + m(b) \int_\xi^b f(x)\, dx.$$

Hint: If $m(x)$ is increasing, interchange a and b. If $m(x)$ is decreasing, put $p(x) = m(x) - m(b)$ and apply the Bonnet mean value theorem.

27. If we put $g_0 = 0$, $g_k = s_k$, $f_0 = 0$, $f_k = p_k$ and $\delta g_k = s_k - s_{k-1} = u_k$, $\delta f_k = p_k - p_{k-1}$, the Abel identity (71) may be written:

$$\sum_{k=1}^{n} f_k \, \delta g_k = f_n g_n - f_0 g_0 - \sum_{k=1}^{n} g_{k-1} \, \delta f_k,$$

which is similar to equation (44) of section 165 and shows the relation of the Abel identity to the formula for integration by parts.

28. Complete the details of the following proof of the Bonnet mean value theorem for the restricted case of $f(x)$ continuous, and $p(x)$ having a continuous derivative $p'(x)$. Here we may assume $p(b) \geqq 0$ and $p'(x) \leqq 0$, instead of $p(x)$ positive and monotonically decreasing. If $F(x) = \int_a^x f(u) \, du$,

$$\int_a^b f(x)p(x) \, dx = \int_a^b F'(x)p(x) \, dx = F(b)p(b) - \int_a^b F(x)p'(x) \, dx$$
$$= F(b)p(b) - F(\xi')[p(b) - p(a)],$$

by equation (52) section 125. If this equals $\overline{F}p(a)$, by problem 1 of Exercises V, $\overline{F}$ divides $F(b)$ and $F(\xi')$ in the ratio of $p(a) - p(b)$ to $p(b)$, which is positive. Hence $\overline{F}$ lies between $F(b)$ and $F(\xi')$, and so is assumed at some point ξ. Thus

$$\int_a^b f(x)p(x) \, dx = \overline{F}p(a) = p(a)F(\xi) = p(a) \int_a^\xi f(x) \, dx.$$

29. Prove that if $p(x)$ is positive and monotonically decreasing for $x \geqq a$, and $p(x) \to 0$ as $x \to +\infty$, while for some fixed number M and all values of $x > a$, $\left| \int_a^x f(u) \, du \right| \leqq M$, then $\int_a^\infty p(x)f(x) \, dx$ converges. An example is $\int_a^\infty \frac{\sin x}{x} \, dx$. *Hint:* Deduce $\left| \int_m^{m'} f(x) \, dx \right| = \left| \int_a^{m'} f(x) \, dx - \int_a^m f(x) \, dx \right| \leqq 2M$, if $m, m' > a$, so that $\left| \int_m^{m'} p(x)f(x) \, dx \right| \leqq \left| p(m) \int_m^{m'} f(x) \, dx \right| \leqq 2Mp(m)$. Then use the Cauchy convergence criterion.

30. If a is any complex number $\neq 0$, show that the infinite product $\Pi(1 + x^n/a^n)$ converges if $|x| < |a|$, and diverges if $|x| > |a|$.

31. Show that, for any real x, each of the infinite products:

$$(1 - x)(1 + x)\left(1 - \frac{x}{2}\right)\left(1 + \frac{x}{2}\right)\left(1 - \frac{x}{3}\right)\left(1 + \frac{x}{3}\right)\cdots,$$

$$[(1 - x)e^x]\,[(1 + x)e^{-x}]\left[\left(1 - \frac{x}{2}\right)e^{\frac{x}{2}}\right]\left[\left(1 + \frac{x}{2}\right)e^{-\frac{x}{2}}\right]\cdots, \quad \text{and} \quad \prod_{n=1}^{\infty}\left(1 - \frac{x^2}{n^2}\right)$$

converges to the same function of x, the first conditionally and the other two absolutely, if we regard $[(1 \mp x/n)e^{\pm x/n}]$ as a single factor of the second. In section 285 we shall show that the common limit is $\dfrac{\sin \pi x}{\pi x}$. *Hint:* For the second, from $e^u = 1 + u + O(u^2)$, deduce that for any fixed real x the typical factor is $1 + O(1/n^2)$.

32. Show that if the factors of the first product of problem 31 are rearranged, in the following manner: $(1 + x)\left(1 + \dfrac{x}{2}\right)(1 - x)\left(1 + \dfrac{x}{3}\right)\left(1 + \dfrac{x}{4}\right)\left(1 - \dfrac{x}{2}\right)\cdots$, the new product will converge, and its limit will be 2^x times that of the original product. *Hint:* Let $L(x)$ be the limit of the first product in problem 31, and hence of the second product of that problem, with the factors taken in any order. Then for the product of this problem to $3n$ factors we may write:

$$e^{x\left(1 + \frac{1}{2} - 1 + \frac{1}{3} + \frac{1}{4} - \frac{1}{2}\cdots + \frac{1}{2n} - \frac{1}{n}\right)} L_n(x),$$

where
$$L_n(x) = [(1 + x)e^{-x}]\left[\left(1 + \frac{x}{2}\right)e^{-\frac{x}{2}}\right][(1 - x)e^x]\cdots$$
$$\left[\left(1 + \frac{x}{2n}\right)e^{-\frac{x}{2n}}\right]\left[\left(1 - \frac{x}{n}\right)e^{\frac{x}{n}}\right].$$

With the notation of problem 10, the sum multiplying x in the exponent is $s_{2n} - s_n$, and so has log 2 as its limit by problem 10. Hence, when the factors are taken by threes, the limit is $e^{x \log 2}L(x) = 2^x L(x)$. The product always converges to this limit, since the product of three or fewer consecutive factors approaches 1 as we go out in the product.

33. Prove that the infinite product $\displaystyle\prod\left[1 - \left(1 - \frac{1}{n}\right)^{qn^2} x^n\right]$, $q > 0$ converges absolutely if $|x| < e^q$, and diverges if $|x| > e^q$.

CHAPTER X

PARTIAL DIFFERENTIATION

The application of the process of differentiation to functions of a single variable obtained from functions of several variables by keeping all except one of these fixed, leads to the notion of a partial derivative. After defining partial derivatives and studying their fundamental properties, we discuss certain results on implicit functions and functional dependence related to the expressions known as Jacobians.

210. Partial Derivative. If $f(x,y)$ is a function of the two real variables x and y, for each particular value of y it defines a function of x to which we may apply the process of differentiation:

$$\lim_{h \to 0} \frac{f(x + h, y) - f(x,y)}{h}. \tag{1}$$

If this limit exists for a particular value of x, it defines the derivative of $f(x,y)$ with respect to x, for the particular values of x and y considered. To emphasize that x is not the only variable, we call the limit the partial derivative of $f(x,y)$ with respect to x, and denote it by

$$\frac{\partial f}{\partial x} \quad \text{or} \quad f_x(x,y). \tag{2}$$

211. Total Differential. When y is kept constant, and x is subjected to an increment Δx, we have a partial differential,

$$d_x f = \frac{\partial f}{\partial x} \Delta x. \tag{3}$$

Similarly, if y is subjected to an increment Δy,

$$d_y f = \frac{\partial f}{\partial y} \Delta y. \tag{4}$$

The sum of these two partial differentials,

$$df = d_x f + d_y f = \frac{\partial f}{\partial x} \Delta x + \frac{\partial f}{\partial y} \Delta y, \tag{5}$$

is the *total differential* of f.

We may write

$$\Delta f = df + \alpha[|\Delta x| + |\Delta y|], \tag{6}$$

where α is determined by this equation. If, when Δx and Δy both approach zero, α approaches zero, the function $f(x,y)$ is said to be *differentiable* in x and y.

We shall now prove that:

If both partial derivatives of $f(x,y)$, $\partial f/\partial x$ and $\partial f/\partial y$, are continuous in the two variables x and y at (x_0,y_0), then the function $f(x,y)$ is differentiable for these values.

We have, for h and k sufficiently small,

$$\Delta f = f(x + h, y + k) - f(x,y)$$

$$= f(x + h, y + k) - f(x, y + k) + f(x, y + k) - f(x,y) \tag{7}$$

$$= hf_x(x + \theta_1 h, y + k) + kf_y(x, y + \theta_2 k), \tag{8}$$

by the law of finite increments for functions of one variable, since the assumption that the partial derivatives are continuous at a point implies that these derivatives exist in some two-dimensional region including the point in its interior.

Moreover, if we write:

$$f_x(x + \theta_1 h, y + k) = f_x(x,y) + \epsilon_1, \tag{9}$$

and

$$f_y(x, y + \theta_2 k) = f_y(x,y) + \epsilon_2, \tag{10}$$

it follows from the assumed continuity that $\epsilon_1 \to 0$ and $\epsilon_2 \to 0$, when $h \to 0$ and $k \to 0$. But, from equation (5) and the last three equations, if $h = \Delta x$ and $k = \Delta y$ we have:

$$\Delta f = \Delta x[f_x(x,y) + \epsilon_1] + \Delta y[f_y(x,y) + \epsilon_2] \tag{11}$$

$$= df + \epsilon_1 \Delta x + \epsilon_2 \Delta y. \tag{12}$$

A comparison of this with equation (6) shows that

$$|\alpha| = \frac{|\epsilon_1 h + \epsilon_2 k|}{|h| + |k|} \leq \frac{|\epsilon_1| \, |h|}{|h| + |k|} + \frac{|\epsilon_2| \, |k|}{|h| + |k|} \leq |\epsilon_1| + |\epsilon_2|. \tag{13}$$

This shows that $\alpha \to 0$ when h and k, or Δx and $\Delta y \to 0$, which proves the theorem.

We might have deduced that

$$f(x, y + k) - f(x,y) = kf_y(x,y) + \epsilon_2, \tag{14}$$

where $\epsilon_2 \to 0$ when $k \to 0$, from the mere existence of the partial derivative $\partial f/\partial y$, or $f_y(x,y)$ at the point. Since this could have been used to transform the last two terms of equation (7) into the terms of equation (11) involving Δy, it was unnecessary to assume the continuity of

$f_y(x,y)$. It follows that it is sufficient for the differentiability of $f(x,y)$ to have both partial derivatives exist at a point, and one of them be continuous there.

We also note that, if the function $f(x,y)$ is differentiable, so that the relation (6) holds with $\alpha \to 0$, the relation (12) may be written with $|\epsilon_1| = |\epsilon_2| = |\alpha|$. Since these values of ϵ_1 and ϵ_2 approach zero with α, they each approach zero with Δx and Δy. Thus relation (12), with ϵ_1 and ϵ_2 each approaching zero when Δx and Δy both approach zero, is a consequence of the condition that $f(x,y)$ be differentiable. Such a relation is an alternative condition for differentiability, since by the relation (13) differentiability may be deduced from it.

212. Composite Functions. If x and y are each functions of a third real variable t, we have:

$$\frac{\Delta f}{\Delta t} = \frac{df}{dt} + \epsilon_1 \frac{\Delta x}{\Delta t} + \epsilon_2 \frac{\Delta y}{\Delta t}, \tag{15}$$

as a consequence of equation (12). If the functions $x(t)$ and $y(t)$ each have finite derivatives with respect to t:

$$\frac{dx}{dt} = \lim_{\Delta t \to 0} \frac{\Delta x}{\Delta t}, \quad \frac{dy}{dt} = \lim_{\Delta t \to 0} \frac{\Delta y}{\Delta t}; \tag{16}$$

and when $\Delta t \to 0$, Δx and Δy will also approach zero. Thus, in equation (12), or (15) ϵ_1 and ϵ_2 will approach zero. It follows that:

$$\frac{df}{dt} = \lim \frac{\Delta f}{\Delta t} = \frac{\partial f}{\partial x} \frac{dx}{dt} + \frac{\partial f}{\partial y} \frac{dy}{dt}. \tag{17}$$

Also, for the differential as defined in section 70,

$$df = \left(\frac{df}{dt}\right) dt = \frac{\partial f}{\partial x}\left(\frac{dx}{dt} dt\right) + \frac{\partial f}{\partial y}\left(\frac{dy}{dt} dt\right)$$

$$= \frac{\partial f}{\partial x} dx + \frac{\partial f}{\partial y} dy. \tag{18}$$

This shows that, if x and y are each differentiable functions of t, and $f(x,y)$ is a differentiable function of x and y, the differential of f, when t is the independent variable, has the same form as the total differential when x and y are the independent variables.

If x and y are each functions of two real variables, s and t, and we keep s constant, the same reasoning shows that

$$\frac{\partial f}{\partial t} = \frac{\partial f}{\partial x} \frac{\partial x}{\partial t} + \frac{\partial f}{\partial y} \frac{\partial y}{\partial t}. \tag{19}$$

In this equation, for the t derivatives, s is constant; for the x derivative, y; and for the y derivative, x is constant. When this may lead to confusion, we indicate the variable held fast by a subscript, and write the last equation as:

$$\left(\frac{\partial f}{\partial t}\right)_s = \left(\frac{\partial f}{\partial x}\right)_y\left(\frac{\partial x}{\partial t}\right)_s + \left(\frac{\partial f}{\partial y}\right)_x\left(\frac{\partial y}{\partial t}\right)_s. \tag{20}$$

213. Higher Derivatives. We may form partial derivatives of partial derivatives, as

$$f_{xx}(x,y) = \frac{\partial^2 f}{\partial x^2} = \frac{\partial}{\partial x}\left(\frac{\partial f}{\partial x}\right), \tag{21}$$

or

$$f_{xy}(x,y) = \frac{\partial^2 f}{\partial y\,\partial x} = \frac{\partial}{\partial y}\left(\frac{\partial f}{\partial x}\right). \tag{22}$$

We shall now prove that, *if the first partial derivatives exist in some two dimensional region including (x_0,y_0) and the derivative $f_{xy}(x,y)$ is continuous at (x_0,y_0), then the derivative $f_{yx}(x_0,y_0)$ exists, and $f_{yx}(x_0,y_0) = f_{xy}(x_0,y_0)$.*

We use Δ as an abbreviation for the mixed second difference, so that:

$$\Delta = f(x + h, y + k) - f(x + h, y) - f(x, y + k) + f(x,y). \tag{23}$$

Then, if we write

$$F(x) = f(x, y + k) - f(x,y), \tag{24}$$

$$\Delta = F(x + h) - F(x). \tag{25}$$

From the law of finite increments, we have:

$$\begin{aligned}
\Delta = F(x + h) - F(x) &= hF'(x + \theta h) \\
&= h[f_x(x + \theta h, y + k) - f_x(x + \theta h, y)] \\
&= hkf_{xy}(x + \theta h, y + \theta'k).
\end{aligned} \tag{26}$$

Hence we have:

$$\begin{aligned}
\frac{\Delta}{k} &= \frac{f(x + h, y + k) - f(x + h, y)}{k} - \frac{f(x, y + k) - f(x,y)}{k} \\
&= hf_{xy}(x + \theta h, y + \theta'k).
\end{aligned} \tag{27}$$

Let x and y be the x_0,y_0 of the theorem, and take the limit as $k \to 0$. Then for a sufficiently small h the first partial derivatives exist and we have:

$$f_y(x + h, y) - f_y(x,y) = h \lim_{k \to 0} f_{xy}(x + \theta h, y + \theta'k). \tag{28}$$

Next divide by h, and take the limit as $h \to 0$. Recalling that $f_{xy}(x,y)$ is continuous at the point considered, we have

$$\lim_{h \to 0} \lim_{k \to 0} f_{xy}(x + \theta h, y + \theta' k) = f_{xy}(x,y). \tag{29}$$

This shows that the limit of the left member of equation (28) divided by h, exists, and

$$f_{yx}(x,y) = \lim_{h \to 0} \frac{f_y(x + h, y) - f_y(x,y)}{h} = f_{xy}(x,y), \tag{30}$$

which is the conclusion of the theorem.

It follows from the theorem that, in any higher derivative, say of the nth order, we need not distinguish between the orders in which the variables are taken, provided that all the derivatives of order equal to or less than n exist and are continuous. Thus, with this continuity assumption,

$$\frac{\partial^3 f}{\partial x \, \partial y^2} = \frac{\partial^3 f}{\partial y \, \partial x \, \partial y} = \frac{\partial^3 f}{\partial y^2 \, \partial x}, \tag{31}$$

since

$$\frac{\partial^2}{\partial x \, \partial y}\left(\frac{\partial f}{\partial y}\right) = \frac{\partial^2}{\partial y \, \partial x}\left(\frac{\partial f}{\partial y}\right) \tag{32}$$

and

$$\frac{\partial}{\partial y}\left(\frac{\partial^2 f}{\partial x \, \partial y}\right) = \frac{\partial}{\partial y}\left(\frac{\partial^2 f}{\partial y \, \partial x}\right). \tag{33}$$

214. Functions of n Variables. If $f(x_1, x_2, \cdots, x_n)$ is a function of n variables, the partial derivative $\partial f/\partial x_i$ is defined as the derivative taken with respect to x_i when the remaining variables are held fast. The total differential is

$$df = \sum_{i=1}^{n} \frac{\partial f}{\partial x_i} \, \Delta x_i = \sum_{i=1}^{n} \frac{\partial f}{\partial x_i} \, dx_i, \tag{34}$$

and as for two variables, we find that

$$\Delta f = df + \sum_{i=1}^{n} \epsilon_i \, \Delta x_i, \tag{35}$$

or

$$\Delta f = df + \alpha \sum_{i=1}^{n} |\Delta x_i|, \tag{36}$$

where the ϵ_i and α approach zero with all the Δx_i, if all the partial derivatives are continuous at the point considered.

From the relation (35) we may deduce that, if the x_i are each differentiable functions of m variables y_j, then

$$\frac{\partial f}{\partial y_j} = \sum_{i=1}^{n} \frac{\partial f}{\partial x_i} \frac{\partial x_i}{\partial y_j}. \tag{37}$$

Also, the relation

$$df = \sum_{i=1}^{n} \frac{\partial f}{\partial x_i} dx_i \tag{38}$$

holds whether the x_i are regarded as independent variables, or dependent on the new set of variables y_j. For, if the x_i are functions of y_j, we have for the total differential expression:

$$df = \sum_{i=1}^{n} \frac{\partial f}{\partial x_i} dx_i = \sum_{i=1}^{n} \frac{\partial f}{\partial x_i} \sum_{j=1}^{m} \frac{\partial x_i}{\partial y_j} dy_j, \tag{39}$$

since

$$dx_i = \sum_{j=1}^{m} \frac{\partial x_i}{\partial y_j} dy_j. \tag{40}$$

A comparison of equation (39) with equation (37) shows that

$$df = \sum_{j=1}^{m} \frac{\partial f}{\partial y_j} dy_j, \tag{41}$$

which has the same form as equation (38), and so is valid when the y_j are the independent variables.

215. The Mean Value Theorem. If we abbreviate the function of m variables $f(x_1, x_2, \cdots, x_m)$ by $f(x_i)$, and write

$$x_i = a_i + th_i, \tag{42}$$

we have:

$$f(x_i) = f(a_i + th_i) = F(t), \tag{43}$$

a function of the single variable t.

Also

$$f(a_i) = F(0) \quad \text{and} \quad f(a_i + h_i) = F(1). \tag{44}$$

By the law of finite increments for functions of one variable,

$$F(1) - F(0) = F'(\theta), \quad 0 < \theta < 1. \tag{45}$$

And, from equation (37), we have:

$$\frac{dF}{dt} = \sum_{j=1}^{m} \frac{\partial f}{\partial x_j} h_j. \tag{46}$$

Hence we may conclude that:

$$f(a_i + h_i) - f(a_i) = \sum_{j=1}^{m} \frac{\partial f}{\partial x_j} \bigg| h_j, \tag{47}$$

where the partial derivatives with strokes are to be evaluated at the point:

$$x_i = a_i + \theta h_i. \tag{48}$$

If we put

$$x_i' = a_i \quad \text{and} \quad x_i'' = a_i + h_i, \tag{49}$$

we may write the relation in the form:

$$f(x_i'') - f(x_i') = \sum_{j=1}^{m} \frac{\partial f}{\partial x_j}\bigg|(x_j'' - x_j'), \tag{50}$$

where the derivatives are to be evaluated at:

$$x_i = x_i' + \theta(x_i'' - x_i'), \tag{51}$$

that is, a suitable point on the straight line segment joining x_i' and x_i''. The equation holds if all the partial derivatives exist and are continuous for all values on this line segment.

We may deduce from the mean value theorem that:

A function of several variables, $f(x_i)$, is constant in a connected region if all the partial derivatives $\partial f/\partial x_i = 0$ throughout the region.

For, if the points can be joined by a straight line segment lying wholly in the region, the condition on the partial derivatives, combined with equation (50), shows that:

$$f(x_i'') - f(x_i') = 0, \quad \text{and} \quad f(x_i'') = f(x_i'). \tag{52}$$

But, by the definition of a connected region, any two points of it can be joined by a broken line lying wholly inside the region. It follows from this that the function has the same value at any two points of the region and is therefore a constant.

216. Taylor's Theorem. With the notation of the last section, we may deduce Taylor's theorem for the function of m variables $f(x_i)$ from that for the function of one variable, $F(t)$. We have for $F(t)$:

$$F(t) = F(0) + F'(0)t + F''(0)\frac{t^2}{2!} + \cdots + F^{(n)}(0)\frac{t^n}{n!} + R(t), \tag{53}$$

where $R(t)$ has any of the forms given for $R(h)$ in section 91.

We find from equation (37) as in equation (46):

$$\frac{dF}{dt} = \sum_{j=1}^{m} \frac{\partial f}{\partial x_j} h_j, \tag{54}$$

and by repeated application of equation (37):

$$\frac{d^k F}{dt^k} = \left(\sum_{j=1}^{m} h_j \frac{\partial}{\partial x_j}\right)^k f, \tag{55}$$

where the power is to be expanded by the multinomial theorem, and the terms finally reduced by such relations as:

$$\left(h_1 \frac{\partial}{\partial x_1}\right)^p \left(h_2 \frac{\partial}{\partial x_2}\right)^q \left(h_3 \frac{\partial}{\partial x_3}\right)^r f = h_1^p h_2^q h_3^r \frac{\partial^{p+q+r} f}{\partial x_1^p \, \partial x_2^q \, \partial x_3^r}. \tag{56}$$

We may combine the equations (43), (53), and (55) to give Taylor's theorem for n variables. The result is:

$$f(a_i + h_i) = f(a_i) + \left(\sum_{j=1}^m h_j \frac{\partial}{\partial x_j}\right) f + \frac{1}{2!}\left(\sum_{j=1}^m h_j \frac{\partial}{\partial x_j}\right)^2 f + \cdots$$
$$+ \frac{1}{n!}\left(\sum_{j=1}^m h_j \frac{\partial}{\partial x_j}\right)^n f + R(1). \tag{57}$$

If we use Lagrange's form of the remainder, we have:

$$R(1) = \frac{1}{(n+1)!}\left(\sum_{j=1}^m h_j \frac{\partial}{\partial x_j}\right)^{n+1} f, \tag{58}$$

where the derivatives are to be evaluated at the point

$$x_i = a_i + \theta h_i, \quad 0 < \theta < 1, \tag{59}$$

where θ is a suitably chosen number between zero and one.

217. Implicit Functions. In section 38 we formulated a theorem on the implicit function defined by the equation

$$f(y, x_1, x_2, \cdots, x_k) = f(y, x_i) = 0. \tag{60}$$

The theorem stated that, if $f(y,x_i)$ is continuous in the $k+1$ variables in some $k+1$ dimensional region including y_0, x_{0i} in its interior, $f(y_0, x_{0i}) = 0$, and the function $f(y,x_i)$ is an increasing (or decreasing) function of y, for x_i fixed and y, x_i in the region, then the equation (60) uniquely defines a continuous function:

$$y = F(x_1, x_2, \cdots x_k) = F(x_i). \tag{61}$$

We may replace the condition that $f(y,x_i)$ is an increasing (or decreasing) function of y by the condition that the partial derivative $\partial f/\partial y$ exists and is continuous and different from zero at the point y_0, x_{0i}. For, if the derivative is positive at the point, from the continuity it will be positive in some $k+1$ dimensional region including the point, and in this region $f(y,x_i)$ will be an increasing function of y, for x_i fixed. Similarly, if the derivative is negative at the point, there is some $k+1$ dimensional region in which $f(y,x_i)$ is a decreasing function of y, for x_i fixed.

If all the partial derivatives of $f(y,x_i)$ exist and are continuous at the point (y_0, x_{0i}), we may apply the mean value theorem, equation (47), to $f(y, x_i)$ and obtain:

$$f(y + \Delta y, x_i + \Delta x_i) - f(y, x_i) = \frac{\partial f}{\partial y}\bigg| \Delta y + \sum_{j=1}^{k} \frac{\partial f}{\partial x_j}\bigg| \Delta x_j, \qquad (62)$$

where the derivatives with strokes are to be evaluated at the point

$$y + \theta \Delta y, \quad x_i + \theta \Delta x_i, \qquad (63)$$

for a suitably chosen value of θ between 0 and 1.

If y is related to the x_i by the functional relation (61), the function $f(y, x_i)$ is identically zero, so that the right member of equation (62) is zero. If we put all of the $\Delta x_i = 0$, when $i \neq 1$, and divide by Δx_1, we find:

$$\frac{\partial f}{\partial y}\bigg| \frac{\Delta y}{\Delta x_1} + \frac{\partial f}{\partial x_1}\bigg| = 0, \quad \text{or} \quad \frac{\Delta y}{\Delta x_1} = -\frac{\dfrac{\partial f}{\partial x_1}\bigg|}{\dfrac{\partial f}{\partial y}\bigg|}. \qquad (64)$$

Since the function $F(x_i)$ is continuous, and we have put all the Δx_i except Δx_1 equal to zero, when $\Delta x_1 \to 0$, $\Delta y \to 0$. Also the point at which the derivatives are to be evaluated, (63), approaches y, x_i. Hence, if $\partial f/\partial y$ is not zero at this point, and the partial derivatives $\partial f/\partial y$ and $\partial f/\partial x_1$ are both continuous at this point, we may deduce from equation (64) that:

$$\frac{\partial y}{\partial x_1} = \lim_{\Delta x_1 \to 0} \frac{\Delta y}{\Delta x_1} = -\frac{\dfrac{\partial f}{\partial x_1}}{\dfrac{\partial f}{\partial y}}. \qquad (65)$$

That is, if $f(y, x_i)$ has continuous first partial derivatives at a point, and $\partial f/\partial y \neq 0$ at the point, the equation

$$f(y, x_i) = 0 \quad \text{defines an implicit function} \quad y = F(x_i), \qquad (66)$$

and this implicit function also has continuous first partial derivatives at the point, given by:

$$\frac{\partial y}{\partial x_i} = -\frac{\dfrac{\partial f}{\partial x_i}}{\dfrac{\partial f}{\partial y}}. \qquad (67)$$

For we may take any value of i in place of 1 in the discussion.

If the function $f(y,x_i)$ has all its partial derivatives of the first n orders continuous, the same is true of the function $F(x_i)$, and the higher derivatives of this function may be calculated by repeated partial differentiation from the equation (67).

It may be practically simpler to apply repeated differentiation to the relation $f(y,x_i) = 0$ on the assumption that y is a function of x_i, possessing continuous partial derivatives, and performing certain eliminations.

218. Sets of Implicit Functions.   Consider a set of n functions, each of $n + k$ variables,

$$f_p(y_i,x_j) \text{ where } p, i = 1, 2, \cdots, n \text{ and } j = 1, 2, \cdots, k. \qquad (68)$$

Under certain conditions, the system of n equations

$$f_p(y_i,x_j) = 0, \qquad (69)$$

implicitly determines a set of n functions,

$$y_i = F_i(x_j). \qquad (70)$$

To help us guess the form of one set of sufficient conditions, let us assume that each of the functions $f_p(y_i,x_j)$ possesses first partial derivatives with respect to any of the $n + k$ variables, and that each first derivative is continuous in the set of $n + k$ variables at a particular point $(y_i,x_j) = (y_{0i},x_{0j})$. This implies that the functions themselves are continuous, and in fact differentiable at this point. We also assume that

$$f_p(y_{0i},x_{0j}) = 0. \qquad (71)$$

Further, let us temporarily assume that the system of equations (69) may be solved by a set of n functions $F_i(x_j)$ such that $y_{0i} = F_i(x_{0j})$, and that these functions have first partial derivatives, with respect to each of the k variables x_j, which are continuous in the set of k variables at the point (x_{0j}).

Then, at the point considered, by equation (37), we have:

$$\frac{\partial \bar{f}_p}{\partial x_j} = \frac{\partial f_p}{\partial x_j} + \sum_{q=1}^{n} \frac{\partial f_p}{\partial y_q} \frac{\partial y_q}{\partial x_j}, \qquad (72)$$

where

$$\bar{f}_p(x_j) = f_p[F_i(x_j),x_j]. \qquad (73)$$

Since the implicit functions $F_i(x_j)$ are solutions of the equations (69), the functions $\bar{f}_p(x_j)$ are identically zero, so that the left member of equation (72) is zero, and hence the right member is also zero. Consequently we have:

$$\sum_{q=1}^{n} \frac{\partial f_p}{\partial y_q} \frac{\partial y_q}{\partial x_j} = -\frac{\partial f_p}{\partial x_j}. \qquad (74)$$

For any fixed j, and $p = 1, 2, \cdots, n$, this system of n linear equations in the n partial derivatives $\partial y_q / \partial x_j$ may be solved for these quantities provided that the determinant of the system,

$$\begin{vmatrix} \dfrac{\partial f_1}{\partial y_1} & \dfrac{\partial f_1}{\partial y_2} & \cdots & \dfrac{\partial f_1}{\partial y_n} \\[2ex] \dfrac{\partial f_2}{\partial y_1} & \dfrac{\partial f_2}{\partial y_2} & \cdots & \dfrac{\partial f_2}{\partial y_n} \\[1ex] \cdot & \cdot & & \cdot \\ \cdot & \cdot & & \cdot \\ \cdot & \cdot & & \cdot \\[1ex] \dfrac{\partial f_n}{\partial y_1} & \dfrac{\partial f_n}{\partial y_2} & \cdots & \dfrac{\partial f_n}{\partial y_n} \end{vmatrix}, \tag{75}$$

is not zero.

The determinant (75) is called the *Jacobian* of the n functions f_p with respect to the n variables y_q. We abbreviate it by

$$J \quad \text{or} \quad \frac{\partial(f_1, f_2, \cdots, f_n)}{\partial(y_1, y_2, \cdots, y_n)}, \tag{76}$$

when we wish to indicate the functions and variables.

When the Jacobian is not zero, the solution of the system of equation (74) for a particular derivative $\partial y_q / \partial x_j$ may be written:

$$\frac{\partial y_q}{\partial x_j} = - \frac{\dfrac{\partial(f_1, f_2, \cdots, f_q, \cdots, f_n)}{\partial(y_1, y_2, \cdots, x_j, \cdots, y_n)}}{\dfrac{\partial(f_1, f_2, \cdots, f_n)}{\partial(y_1, y_2, \cdots, y_n)}}. \tag{77}$$

This calculation suggests the theorem:

Let the n functions $f_p(y_i, x_j)$ each possess first partial derivatives with respect to the n variables y_i and the k variables x_j, each derivative being continuous in all $n + k$ variables for a particular value y_{0i}, x_{0j} such that

$$f_p(y_{0i}, x_{0j}) = 0. \tag{78}$$

Then, if the Jacobian is not zero,

$$\frac{\partial(f_1, f_2, \cdots, f_n)}{\partial(y_1, y_2, \cdots, y_n)} \neq 0, \quad \text{at} \quad y_{0i}, x_{0j}, \tag{79}$$

the n equations,

$$f_p(y_i, x_j) = 0, \tag{80}$$

may be simultaneously satisfied by n functions,

$$y_i = F_i(x_j), \tag{81}$$

such that

$$y_{0i} = F_i(x_{0j}). \tag{82}$$

These functions are uniquely defined and continuous in some k-dimensional region including x_{0j} as an interior point, and in this region possess first partial derivatives with respect to the x_j, continuous in these k variables, determined by equations (74) or (77).

We proceed to prove this theorem, using mathematical induction. We have already proved that the theorem is true for $n = 1$, and all values of k, in section 217. Thus we need merely show that the theorem is true for n and all values of k if it is true for all smaller values, namely $1, 2, \cdots, n - 1$ and all values of k.

Let us use C_{pq} to denote the co-factor of the element of the determinant (75) in the pth row and qth column, or $\partial f_p / \partial y_q$. Then, by expanding the determinant in terms of the elements of the last column, we have:

$$J = \sum_{p=1}^{n} \frac{\partial f_p}{\partial y_n} C_{pn}. \tag{83}$$

Since J is not zero at the point considered, not all of the C_{pn} can be zero. By a change of notation, if necessary, we may arrange that $C_{nn} \neq 0$. We assume this done, and note that

$$C_{nn} = \frac{\partial(f_1, f_2, \cdots, f_{n-1})}{\partial(y_1, y_2, \cdots, y_{n-1})}, \tag{84}$$

the Jacobian of the first $n - 1$ functions with respect to the first $n - 1$ variables.

We also recall the theorem that a determinant with two columns identical is zero, from which it follows that:

$$\sum_{p=1}^{n} \frac{\partial f_p}{\partial y_r} C_{pn} = 0, \quad r = 1, 2, \cdots, n - 1. \tag{85}$$

By the hypothesis of the induction, the theorem holds for $n - 1$ dependent variables and $k + 1$ independent variables. Hence, if we consider only the first $n - 1$ equations

$$f_s(y_i, x_j) = 0, \quad s = 1, 2, \cdots, n - 1, \tag{86}$$

and consider y_r, $r = 1, 2, \cdots, n - 1$ as the dependent variables and y_n, x_j as the $k + 1$ dependent variables, we may deduce the existence of $n - 1$ functions $\bar{F}_r(x_j, y_n)$ such that

$$y_{0r} = \bar{F}_r(x_{0j}, y_{0n}), \tag{87}$$

and furthermore if

$$y_r = \bar{F}_r(x_j, y_n), \tag{88}$$

then $\qquad f_s(y_i, x_j)$ or $f_s[\bar{F}_r(x_j, y_n), y_n, x_j] = 0.$ $\qquad$ (89)

It follows from the last equation that:

$$0 = \frac{\partial f_s}{\partial y_n} + \sum_{r=1}^{n-1} \frac{\partial f_s}{\partial y_r} \frac{\partial \bar{F}_r}{\partial y_n}.$$ (90)

Let us next use the equations (88) to eliminate the y_r from the last function $f_n(y_i, x_j)$, and denote the resulting function by:

$$\tilde{f}_n(y_n, x_j) = f_n[\bar{F}_r(x_j, y_n), y_n, x_j].$$ (91)

Then we have:

$$\frac{\partial \tilde{f}_n}{\partial y_n} = \frac{\partial f_n}{\partial y_n} + \sum_{r=1}^{n-1} \frac{\partial f_n}{\partial y_r} \frac{\partial \bar{F}_r}{\partial y_n}.$$ (92)

Let us now multiply each of the $n - 1$ equations (90) by C_{sn}, with s corresponding to the equation used. Let us also multiply the equation (92) by C_{nn} and add the corresponding members of the n equations just constructed. In view of equations (83) and (85) the result may be written:

$$\dot{C}_{nn} \frac{\partial \tilde{f}_n}{\partial y_n} = J.$$ (93)

Since $J \neq 0$, this shows that $\partial \tilde{f}_n / \partial y_n \neq 0$. Consequently, either by the hypothesis of the induction for one dependent variable, or the theorem of section 217, the equation

$$\tilde{f}_n(y_n, x_j) = 0$$ (94)

uniquely determines a function

$$y_n = F_n(x_j)$$ (95)

such that

$$y_{0n} = F_n(x_{0j}) \quad \text{and} \quad \tilde{f}_n[F_n(x_j), x_j] = 0.$$ (96)

Furthermore, the function $F_n(x_j)$ has continuous first partial derivatives.

Finally we consider the n equations:

$$y_r = F_r(x_j) = \bar{F}_r[x_j, F_n(x_j)], \quad \text{and} \quad y_n = F_n(x_j).$$ (97)

From equations (87) and (96), we have:

$$y_{0q} = F_q(x_{0j}), \quad q = 1, 2, \cdots, n.$$ (98)

And, from equations (89) and (96), we have:

$$f_p(y_q, x_j) = 0, \text{ if } y_q = F_q(x_j), \ p = 1, 2, \cdots, n.$$ (99)

Again, the functions $\bar{F}_r(x_j, y_n)$ and $F_n(x_j)$ all possessed continuous first partial derivatives, so that the functions $F_q(x_j)$ also possess continuous first partial derivatives. And, since $\bar{F}_r(x_j,y_n)$ and $F_n(x_j)$ were uniquely determined, the functions $F_q(x_j)$ are uniquely determined. Finally, the conditions assumed to derive equations (72) and (77) are satisfied, so that these equations follow. This completes the proof of the theorem.

As in the case of one independent variable, if the functions $f_p(x_i,y_j)$ possess continuous partial derivatives of the first n orders, the same is true of the $F_q(x_j)$, since in this case the equation (77) may be differentiated m times, $m \leq n$, with respect to any combination of m of the x_j. The higher derivatives may also be obtained by differentiating the equations (99) suitably to obtain a series of equations, of which equation (74) is the first, and by performing certain eliminations. In each case, the determinant of the system of equations in the derivatives of highest order reduces to the Jacobian which is distinct from zero by hypothesis.

For example, if

$$f_i(y_1, y_2, y_3, x_1, x_2, x_3) = 0, \quad \text{and} \quad i = 1, 2, 3, \tag{100}$$

then, for s fixed as any one of 1, 2, or 3 and $i = 1, 2, 3$, the system of equations

$$\frac{\partial f_i}{\partial x_s} + \sum_{p=1}^{3} \frac{\partial f_i}{\partial y_p} \frac{\partial y_p}{\partial x_s} = 0 \tag{101}$$

determines the first derivatives $\partial y_p/\partial x_s$. Again, for t fixed as any one of 1, 2, or 3, the system of equations

$$\frac{\partial^2 f_i}{\partial x_s \, \partial x_t} + \sum_{q=1}^{3} \sum_{p=1}^{3} \frac{\partial^2 f_i}{\partial y_p \, \partial y_q} \frac{\partial y_p}{\partial x_s} \frac{\partial y_q}{\partial x_t} + \sum_{p=1}^{3} \frac{\partial f_i}{\partial y_p} \frac{\partial^2 y_p}{\partial x_s \, \partial x_t}$$

$$+ \sum_{p=1}^{3} \frac{\partial^2 f_i}{\partial y_p \, \partial x_s} \frac{\partial y_p}{\partial x_t} + \sum_{p=1}^{3} \frac{\partial^2 f_i}{\partial y_p \, \partial x_t} \frac{\partial y_p}{\partial x_s} = 0, \tag{102}$$

determines the second derivatives $\partial^2 y_p/\partial x_s \, \partial x_t$ in terms of those already determined.

219. Jacobians and Functional Dependence. In the last section we defined the Jacobian determinant of n functions f_p with respect to n variables y_q as the expression (75). This definition and the abbreviation (76) apply whether the functions f_p are functions of the y_q only, or of these together with other variables, like the $f_p(y_q,x_j)$ which occurred in the theorem on implicit functions. That theorem involved as one condition the non-vanishing of the Jacobian for a particular value. We shall now discuss certain theorems involving the vanishing of the Jacobian identically for all values of the variables.

We first observe that if one of the functions, say f_1, is a constant, each derivative $\partial f_1/\partial y_q = 0$. Hence each element of the first row of the

Jacobian is zero, and the Jacobian itself is zero.   If the value of the constant is k, the equation

$$f_1 - k = 0 \tag{103}$$

holds, so that the f_i satisfy a functional relation.   This is a trivial case of the more general result:

If the n functions of n variables, $f_p(y_i)$ satisfy a functional relation

$$\phi(f_1, f_2, \cdots, f_n) = 0, \tag{104}$$

and the $f_p(y_i)$ as well as $\phi(f_p)$ have continuous first partial derivatives, then the Jacobian of the functions f_p with respect to the y_i vanishes identically.

It is understood that the functional relation (104) holds identically in the y_i, and that the function $\phi(f_p)$ is not identically zero in the f_p, so that it actually involves at least one of the f_p for all the values considered.

The equation (104) together with the conditions of differentiability have as a consequence the equations:

$$\sum_{p=1}^{n} \frac{\partial \phi}{\partial f_p} \frac{\partial f_p}{\partial y_q} = 0. \tag{105}$$

If the Jacobian were different from zero for any one set of values of the variables under consideration, this system of linear equations in $\partial \phi / \partial f_p$ would have a determinant distinct from zero, and therefore would admit only one solution for these quantities, namely $\partial \phi / \partial f_p = 0$.

Since the Jacobian is a continuous function, if it were different from zero at any one point, it would be different from zero in some k dimensional region including this point in its interior.   Hence in this region we would have $\partial \phi / \partial f_p = 0$, so that by the result at the end of section 215, the function ϕ would be constant in this region.   This contradicts the hypothesis that the function $\phi(f_p)$ actually involves at least one of the functions f_p for all the values considered.

Since the Jacobian can never differ from zero, it must vanish identically for all values of the y_i considered.   This proves the theorem.

As a partial converse theorem, we have:

If the n functions of n variables $f_p(y_i)$ each have continuous partial derivatives, and the Jacobian of these functions with respect to y_i is identically zero, then in any region throughout which some minor of the $(n-1)$st order is distinct from zero, the functions satisfy some relation of functional dependence of the type of (104).

To prove this, we use the notation of the last section given in connection with equation (83).   If necessary, we so change the notation that

C_{nn} is the minor of the $(n-1)$st order distinct from zero. Then, by the theorem of section 218, since the Jacobian of the $n-1$ functions f_s, where $s = 1, 2, \cdots, n-1$, with respect to the $n-1$ variables y_r, where $r = 1, 2, \cdots, n-1$ is C_{nn} and hence $\neq 0$, the equations

$$f_s(y_r, y_n) - x_s = 0 \tag{106}$$

may be solved for the y_r in terms of y_n and the x_s to give:

$$y_r = F_r(x_s, y_n). \tag{107}$$

Also, we may use these equations to eliminate the y_r from $f_n(y_i)$ and so obtain:

$$\bar{f}_n(y_n, x_r) = f_n[F_r(x_s, y_n), \, y_n], \tag{108}$$

analogous to equation (91). We also have, analogous to the relation (93):

$$C_{nn} \frac{\partial \bar{f}_n}{\partial y_n} = J. \tag{109}$$

Since $J = 0$, while $C_{nn} \neq 0$, it follows from this that

$$\frac{\partial \bar{f}_n}{\partial y_n} = 0. \tag{110}$$

Let us now take any particular set of values of y_i, y_{0i}, and compute a particular set of x_p, x_{0p} from the equations:

$$f_p(y_{0i}) - x_{0p} = 0, \quad p = 1, 2, \cdots, n. \tag{111}$$

It follows from this and equations (107) and (108) that:

$$x_{0n} = \bar{f}_n(y_{0n}, x_{0r}). \tag{112}$$

This relation does not explicitly involve the y_{0r}, and the right member does not change when we vary y_n, by equation (110). Hence the x_{0p}, or values of the $f_p(y_i)$ satisfy the relation:

$$f_n - \bar{f}_n(y_{0n}, f_r) = 0, \tag{113}$$

which is the relation of functional dependence whose existence is asserted by the theorem. The left member can not be identically zero in the f_p, since its derivative with respect to f_n is unity.

A similar result holds if there are more variables than functions. Thus, let there be n functions $f_p(y_t)$ of the $n + p$ variables y_t. Suppose that in some region each of the Jacobians of the n functions with respect to a set of n variables consisting of $y_1, y_2, \cdots, y_{n-1}$ and one other y_k, selected from $y_n, y_{n+1}, \cdots, y_{n+p}$, is identically zero. Suppose also that C_{nn}, the Jacobian of the first $n-1$ functions f_s with respect to y_r, the first $n - 1$ variables is distinct from zero.   Then we may proceed as before to obtain the equation:

$$\tilde{f}_n(y_k, x_r) = f_n[F_r(x_s, y_k), y_k], \tag{114}$$

analogous to equation (108) and the equations:

$$\frac{\partial \tilde{f}_n}{\partial y_k} = 0, \quad k = n + 1, n + 2, \cdots, n + p, \tag{115}$$

analogous to equation (110).

We may then take a particular set of values y_{0t} and deduce that if

$$x_{0p} = f_p(y_{0t}), \tag{116}$$

then $$x_{0n} = \tilde{f}_n(y_{0k}, x_r). \tag{117}$$

It then follows from the fact that only the y_{0k} occur explicitly, and the partial derivatives of the right member with respect to all the y_k are zero, by equation (115), that the right member does not change when we vary the y_k, in consequence of the result of section 215.   Hence the x_{0p}, or values of the f_p satisfy the relation:

$$f_n - \tilde{f}_n(y_{0k}, f_r) = 0. \tag{118}$$

The statement of the result for $n + p$ variables, as well as the original theorem for n variables, is incomplete without some condition that insures $C_{nn} \neq 0$.   However, in any case where the Jacobian vanishes identically, we may find restricted regions in which n functions of n variables are functionally dependent.   For, if the Jacobian vanishes identically, and the functions are not all constants, some minor is not identically zero.   If $N - 1$ is the order of some minor of highest order not identically zero, we may find some region in which this minor is never zero.   We may then take the $N - 1$ functions which appear in this minor, and any other function of the set as a set to which the second theorem may be applied.   However, the functional relation need not be the same in two different regions, and some points may not be included in any region in which there is a functional relationship.

220. Integrals Containing a Parameter.   If the function $f(x,u)$ is a continuous function of x and u for $u = u_0$ and $a \leqq x \leqq b$, then

$$F(u) = \int_a^b f(x,u) \, dx \tag{119}$$

is a continuous function of u, for the value u_0.   In fact, for any value of x_0 in the interval, there is a $\delta_{\epsilon 0}$ such that

$$|f(x,u) - f(x_0, u_0)| < \epsilon \quad \text{if} \quad |u - u_0| < \delta_{\epsilon 0}, \ |x - x_0| < \delta_{\epsilon 0}. \tag{120}$$

We make the usual modifications for the end points.

Thus each point considered is the center of a square of side $2\delta_{\epsilon 0}$, which determines an interval of length $2\delta_{\epsilon 0}$ on the x-axis, in the xu plane. By the Heine-Borel theorem, there is a finite subset of such intervals which cover the closed interval a,b. If δ is the least of the finite set of numbers $\delta_{\epsilon 0}$, then

$$|f(x,u) - f(x,u_0)| < \epsilon \quad \text{if} \quad |u - u_0| < \delta, \quad \text{and} \quad a \le x \le b. \quad (121)$$

It follows from this that

$$\left| \int_a^b f(x,u) \, dx - \int_a^b f(x,u_0) \, dx \right| < \epsilon(b - a), \quad (122)$$

and hence

$$|F(u) - F(u_0)| < \epsilon(b - a) \quad \text{if} \quad |u - u_0| < \delta. \quad (123)$$

This proves that the function $F(u)$ is continuous at u_0.

Suppose next that the function $f(x,u)$ admits a partial derivative with respect to u,

$$f_u(x,u) = \frac{\partial f}{\partial u}, \quad (124)$$

which is a continuous function of x and u for $u = u_0$, and $a \le x \le b$. Then, reasoning for this function as we did for $f(x,u)$ before, we find, analogous to equation (121), with $u + h$, u in place of u, u_0:

$$|f_u(x, u + h) - f_u(x,u)| < \epsilon, \quad \text{if} \quad |h| < \delta \quad \text{and} \quad a \le x \le b. \quad (125)$$

Next form the difference:

$$F(u + h) - F(u) = \int_a^b [f(x, u + h) - f(x,u)] \, dx. \quad (126)$$

By the law of the mean,

$$f(x, u + h) - f(x,u) = h f_u(x, u + \theta h), \quad 0 < \theta < 1. \quad (127)$$

Consequently, for θ, the appropriate function of x, u, and h:

$$\frac{F(u + h) - F(u)}{h} = \int_a^b f_u(x, u + \theta h) \, dx. \quad (128)$$

This leads us to suspect that the limit, when h approaches zero, might be

$$\int_a^b f_u(x,u) \, dx. \quad (129)$$

To verify this conjecture, we subtract (129) from the integral on the right in equation (128), and find:

$$\left| \int_a^b f_u(x,\, u + \theta h)\, dx - \int_a^b f_u(x,u)\, dx \right|$$

$$= \left| \int_a^b [f_u(x,\, u + \theta h) - f_u(x,u)]\, dx \right|$$

$$\leqq \int_a^b |f_u(x,\, u + \theta h) - f_u(x,u)|\, dx. \quad (130)$$

Although, for the value of u considered, θ is a function of x and h, $0 < \theta < 1$, so that $|\theta h| < \delta$, if $|h| < \delta$. Consequently we may apply the relation (125) and so deduce that the expression (130) $< \epsilon(b - a)$, if $|h| < \delta$. Hence, from equation (128),

$$\left| \frac{F(u + h) - F(u)}{h} - \int_a^b f_u(x,u)\, dx \right| < \epsilon(b - a), \quad \text{if} \quad |h| < \delta. \quad (131)$$

This proves that the difference on the left approaches zero when $h \to 0$, so that $F(u)$ has a derivative, and

$$\frac{dF}{du} = \int_a^b f_u(x,u)\, dx. \quad (132)$$

This is known as Leibniz's rule.

Finally, if a and b are differentiable functions of u, we have from section 214, with $n = 3$, that

$$\frac{dF}{du} = \frac{\partial F}{\partial u}\bigg|_{a,b} + \frac{\partial F}{\partial a}\frac{da}{du} + \frac{\partial F}{\partial b}\frac{db}{du}. \quad (133)$$

From section 129, $\partial F/\partial b = f(b,u)$. And, since

$$F(u) = -\int_b^a f(x,u)\, dx, \quad \frac{\partial F}{\partial a} = -f(a,u). \quad (134)$$

For the first term, we may use equation (132). Hence:

$$\frac{dF}{du} = \int_a^b f_u(x,u)\, dx + f(b,u)\frac{db}{du} - f(a,u)\frac{da}{du}. \quad (135)$$

This rule for differentiating the function $F(u)$ defined by equation (119), when the limits a and b are functions of the parameter u, is a generalization of Leibniz's rule.

EXERCISES X

1. If w is a function of x, y, z, and t, while x, y, and z are each functions of t, show that:

$$\frac{dw}{dt} = \frac{\partial w}{\partial t} + \frac{\partial w}{\partial x}\frac{dx}{dt} + \frac{\partial w}{\partial y}\frac{dy}{dt} + \frac{\partial w}{\partial z}\frac{dz}{dt}.$$

2. If $w = f(x,y)$ and $y = g(x,z)$, show that

$$\left(\frac{\partial w}{\partial x}\right)_s = \left(\frac{\partial w}{\partial x}\right)_y + \left(\frac{\partial w}{\partial y}\right)_x\left(\frac{\partial y}{\partial x}\right)_s.$$

3. Let $F(x,y) = 0$ be the equation of a plane curve, equivalent to $y = f(x)$ for values of x near x_0. Prove that

$$F_x(x_0,y_0)(x - x_0) + F_y(x_0,y_0)(y - y_0) = 0$$

is the equation of the tangent line at x_0,y_0 as defined in problem 11 of Exercises IV.

4. In n-space, $x_i = f_i(t)$, $i = 1, 2, \cdots, n$ are the parametric equations of a curve. Suppose that $x_{i0} = f_i(t_0)$, and that the $f_i'(t_0)$ are not all zero. Show that if the tangent line is defined to be the limiting position of a secant line, the equations of the tangent line may be written $x_i = x_{i0} + uf_i'(t_0)$, where u is the parameter.

5. The equation of a hyper-surface of $n - 1$ dimensions in n-space is $F(x_1, x_2, \cdots, x_n) = 0$, or $F(x_i) = 0$. This will contain the curve of problem 4 if $F[f_i(t)] = 0$ identically in t. In particular, $F(x_{i0}) = 0$, and x_{i0} is a point of the hyper-surface. The tangent line of problem 4 is called a tangent line to the hyper-surface at x_{i0}. Show that all such tangent lines lie in a hyper-plane whose equation is

$$\sum_{i=1}^n \left(\frac{\partial F}{\partial x_i}\right)_0 (x_i - x_{i0}) = 0.$$

This is called the tangent hyper-plane to the hyper-surface at the point x_{i0}.

6. In 3-space $F(x,y,z) = 0$ is the equation of a surface, and it follows as in problem 5 that the tangent plane to the surface at x_0,y_0,z_0 or plane containing all the tangent lines at the point is:

$$(x - x_0)F_x(x_0,y_0,z_0) + (y - y_0)F_y(x_0,y_0,z_0) + (z - z_0)F_z(x_0,y_0,z_0) = 0.$$

Show that if $z = f(x,y)$, the equation of the tangent plane may be written:

$$z - z_0 = \left(\frac{\partial f}{\partial x}\right)_0 (x - x_0) + \left(\frac{\partial f}{\partial y}\right)_0 (y - y_0).$$

7. In n-space, the numbers a_i determine a direction, that of the segment from the origin O to the point A with coördinates a_i. The directions a_i and b_i, or the segments OA and OB, are defined as perpendicular if and only if $\sum_{i=1}^n a_i b_i = 0$.

If the lengths of the segments are defined by the equations $|OA|^2 = \sum_{i=1}^n a_i^2$,

$|OB|^2 = \sum_{i=1}^{n} b_i^2$, $|AB|^2 = \sum_{i=1}^{n} (b_i - a_i)^2$, show that the definition just given is consistent with the Pythagorean relation, $AB^2 = OA^2 + OB^2$.

8. Using the definitions of problems 5 and 7 show that the direction $\left(\dfrac{\partial F}{\partial x_i}\right)_0$ is perpendicular to the direction $x_i - x_{i0}$ or $uf_i'(t_0)$, that is to any tangent line to the hyper-surface at the point x_{i0}. Since it is perpendicular to any segment in the tangent hyper-plane, it is considered perpendicular to the hyper-plane, or to the hyper-surface at the point x_{i0}. Hence the direction $\left(\dfrac{\partial F}{\partial x_i}\right)_0$ is called the normal direction to the surface $F(x_i) = 0$ at x_{i0}.

9. If a_i and b_i are any two directions in n-space, as in problem 7, the only definition of the angle between them consistent with the law of cosines, $|AB|^2 = |OA|^2 + |OB|^2 - 2|OA||OB| \cos \theta$, makes $\cos \theta = \dfrac{\sum a_i b_i}{\sqrt{\sum a_i^2} \sqrt{\sum b_i^2}}$, with i from 1 to n in all sums. When $|OA| \neq 0$ and $|OB| \neq 0$, this will determine a real angle θ with $0 \leqq \theta \leqq \pi$, if $|\cos \theta| \leqq 1$. Prove that this last relation must hold when a_i and b_i are real. *Hint:* Since $\sum (a_i - x b_i)^2$, as a function of x, cannot change sign, the quadratic equation $(\sum b_i^2)x^2 - 2(\sum a_i b_i)x + \sum a_i^2 = 0$ can not have distinct real roots. Hence $(2\sum a_i b_i)^2 - 4(\sum b_i^2)(\sum a_i^2) \leqq 0$.

10. Let $w = f(x,y)$ be a function of x and y to be considered for values near x_0, y_0. Let $x = g(t)$, $y = h(t)$ define a smooth curve through x_0, y_0 so that $x_0 = g(t_0), y_0 = h(t_0)$. Then, if s denotes the arc length of the curve, measured from some fixed point in the direction of increasing t, along the curve w is a function of s. The derivative of w at x_0, y_0 in the direction of the curve is defined as dw/ds at t_0. Prove that this directional derivative is the same for all curves having the same tangent line. Also show that it is a maximum when the direction has components dx/ds and dy/ds which are proportional to $(\partial f/\partial x)_0$ and $(\partial f/\partial y)_0$ with a positive factor of proportionality, a minimum for the opposite direction, and zero for the perpendicular direction. *Hint:* If constants R and a are determined from the equations $R \cos a = (\partial f/\partial x)_0$ and $R \sin a = (\partial f/\partial y)_0$, and

$$\frac{dx}{ds} = \cos \phi, \quad \frac{dy}{ds} = \sin \phi, \quad \text{then} \quad \frac{dw}{ds} = R \cos (\phi - a).$$

11. Let $w = f(x_i)$ be a function of n variables to be considered for values near x_{i0}. If a_i defines a direction and a length $|OA|$ as in problem 7, the directional derivative of w in the direction of a_i is defined as $\dfrac{dw}{ds} = \sum_{i=1}^{n} \dfrac{a_i}{|OA|}\left(\dfrac{\partial f}{\partial x_i}\right)_0$. Using problem 9 to define the angle C between the directions $\left(\dfrac{\partial f}{\partial x_i}\right)_0$ and a_i, and putting $R^2 = \sum_{i=1}^{n} \left(\dfrac{\partial f}{\partial x_i}\right)_0^2$, show that $dw/ds = R \cos C$. Hence show that it is a maximum R and a minimum $-R$ in opposite directions along the **normal**

to the hyper-surface $f(x_i) = f(x_{i0})$ at x_{i0}, and is zero for any direction in the tangent hyper-plane to this hyper-surface at x_{i0}.

12. A function of n variables x_i, $f(x_i)$, is said to be homogeneous in the x_i of the kth degree if $f(tx_i) = t^k f(x_i)$. Prove the theorem of Euler that for such a function

$$\sum_{i=1}^{n} x_i \frac{\partial f}{\partial x_i} = k f(x_i).$$

Hint: Differentiate the fundamental relation with respect to t, and then put $t = 1$.

13. With the assumptions of problem 12, prove further that

$$\left(\sum_{i=1}^{n} y_i \frac{\partial}{\partial x_i} \right)^m f(x_i) \bigg|_{y_i = x_i} = k(k-1) \cdots (k-m+1) f(x_i).$$

Hint: Differentiate the fundamental relation with respect to t m times, and then put $t = 1$. Note that we must not put $y_i = x_i$ until after the differentiations are completed, and it is incorrect to write the left member with the operator $\left(\sum_{i=1}^{n} x_i \frac{\partial}{\partial x_i} \right)^m$ as is done in many texts. In fact,

$$\left(\sum_{i=1}^{n} x_i \frac{\partial}{\partial x_i} \right)^m f(x_i) = k^m f(x_i),$$

by repeated use of problem 12.

14. By section 78, if a partial derivative exists in an open interval, and approaches a limit as we approach one end point, the one-sided partial derivative exists at this point and equals the limiting value. Use this to prove that

$$f_x(x,y) = \lim_{h \to 0} f_x(x+h, y)$$

and

$$f_{yx}(x,y) = \lim_{h \to 0} f_{yx}(x+h, y) = \lim_{h \to 0} f_{xy}(x+h, y),$$

in case the limits on the right all exist, and for the last term, if the mixed derivative is continuous in the open interval. Similar results hold for more variables and other partial derivatives.

15. If $f(x,y) = (x^2 + y^2) \tan^{-1}(y/x)$, then $f_{xy} = f_{yx} = \dfrac{x^2 - y^2}{x^2 + y^2}$ when x and y are not both zero. From this and problem 14, show that $f_{yx}(0,0) = 1$, $f_{xy}(0,0) = -1$.

16. If $f(x,y) = xy \dfrac{x^2 - y^2}{x^2 + y^2}$, then, when x and y are not both zero, $f_{xy} = f_{yx} = \dfrac{x^2 - y^2}{x^2 + y^2} + A(x,y)$, where $A \to 0$ when $x \to 0$ and $y \to 0$ successively in either order. Use this and problem 14 to show that $f_{yx}(0,0) = 1$, $f_{xy}(0,0) = -1$.

17. If $x = r \cos \theta$ and $y = r \sin \theta$, find the partial derivatives $\partial r/\partial x$, $\partial r/\partial y$, $\partial \theta/\partial x$ and $\partial \theta/\partial y$ by considering these equations as implicitly defining r and θ as functions of x and y. Check by solving the equations, and then differentiating.

18. Let $f(x,y,z) = 0$ and $\phi(x,y) = 0$, with both the functions f and ϕ differentiable. If $\partial\phi/\partial y \neq 0$, the second equation defines y as a function of x, and the first will then define z as a function of x if $\partial f/\partial z \neq 0$. Under these conditions, find dz/dx. *Hint:* Use the relations $f_x\,dx + f_y\,dy + f_z\,dz = 0$, and $\phi_x\,dx + \phi_y\,dy = 0$, and eliminate dy. The result is $dz/dx = (\phi_x f_y - \phi_y f_x)/(\phi_y f_z)$.

19. Prove that $\dfrac{\partial(u,v,w)}{\partial(r,s,t)}\dfrac{\partial(r,s,t)}{\partial(x,y,z)} = \dfrac{\partial(u,v,w)}{\partial(x,y,z)}$. *Hint:* Use the rule for multiplying determinants, $|a_{ij}||b_{ij}| = \left|\sum_p a_{ip}b_{pj}\right|$. A similar result holds for n variables.

20. If $f(x,y,z) = 0$, prove that $\left(\dfrac{\partial z}{\partial x}\right)_y \left(\dfrac{\partial x}{\partial y}\right)_z \left(\dfrac{\partial y}{\partial z}\right)_x = -1$.

21. Similar to problem 20, show that if $f(x_i) = 0$, where there are n variables, the product of the n partial derivatives $\dfrac{\partial x_n}{\partial x_1}\dfrac{\partial x_1}{\partial x_2}\dfrac{\partial x_2}{\partial x_3}\cdots\dfrac{\partial x_{n-1}}{\partial x_n} = (-1)^n$, where each derivative is computed with the $n-2$ variables not involved kept fixed.

22. If $F(x,y;u,v) = 0$ and $G(x,y;u,v) = 0$, define u and v as functions of x and y, then $\left(\dfrac{\partial u}{\partial x}\right)_y = -\dfrac{\partial(F,G)}{\partial(x,v)}\bigg/\dfrac{\partial(F,G)}{\partial(u,v)}$.

23. If $F(x,y,z) = 0$, $G(x,y,z) = 0$, prove that

$$\frac{dx}{\dfrac{\partial(F,G)}{\partial(y,z)}} = \frac{dy}{\dfrac{\partial(F,G)}{\partial(z,x)}} = \frac{dz}{\dfrac{\partial(F,G)}{\partial(x,y)}}.$$

24. If $x = f(u,v)$, $y = g(u,v)$, $z = h(u,v)$, then $\left(\dfrac{\partial z}{\partial x}\right)_y = \dfrac{\partial(z,y)}{\partial(u,v)}\bigg/\dfrac{\partial(x,y)}{\partial(u,v)}$.

25. Prove that a necessary condition for a differentiable function of n variables to have a maximum (or a minimum) at x_{i0} is that each partial derivative $(\partial f/\partial x_i)_0 = 0$. *Hint:* It must be a maximum when each variable x_i varies, the rest being fixed. Sufficient conditions may be obtained in terms of the higher degree terms in the Taylor's expansion. Such conditions are practically useless, and it is generally simpler to investigate the sign of $f(x_{i0}) - f(x_i)$ directly.

26. Show that $z = (y - x^2)(y - 2x^2)$ does not have a maximum or minimum for $x = y = 0$, although it has a minimum for $t = 0$ along every straight line $x = at$, $y = bt$. *Hint:* z is negative for (small) values of x,y for which $x^2 < y < 2x^2$ (Peano).

27. *Lagrange's Multipliers.* Let x_i be $n = p + q$ variables subject to the q relations $F_k(x_i) = 0$, $k = 1, 2, \cdots, q$. For the values considered, let the Jacobian of the functions $F_k(x_i)$ with respect to some set of q x_i, which we take as the first q, be different from zero. Then a necessary condition for the function of the restricted variables $f(x_i)$ to have a maximum (or a minimum) at x_{i0} is that for some set of constants λ_k, the relations $\left(\dfrac{\partial f}{\partial x_i}\right)_0 + \sum_{k=1}^{q} \lambda_k \left(\dfrac{\partial F_k}{\partial x_i}\right) = 0$ are satisfied for $i = 1, 2, \cdots, n$. *Hint:* For any differentials dx_i which satisfy the q equations $\sum_{i=1}^{n} \dfrac{\partial F_k}{\partial x_i} dx_i = 0$, we must have $\sum_{i=1}^{n} \dfrac{\partial f}{\partial x_i} dx_i = 0$, where all the partial derivatives are evaluated at x_{i0}. For an arbitrary choice of the last $p\, dx_i$, the first set of equations may be solved for the first $q\, dx_i$. By section 218, the dx_i so found correspond to possible sets of x_i satisfying $F_k(x_i) = 0$. Next we may find constants λ_k, for $k = 1, 2, \cdots, q$ such that the equations

$$\partial f/\partial x_i + \sum_{k=1}^{q} \lambda_k\, \partial F_k/\partial x_i = 0 \text{ hold for } i = 1, 2, \cdots, q.$$ For the dx_i and λ_k

determined, we have $\sum_{i=1}^{n}\left[\partial f/\partial x_i + \sum_{k=1}^{q} \lambda_k\, \partial F_k/\partial x_i \right] dx_i = 0$. But, from the choice of the λ_k, the coefficients of the dx_i for $i = 1, 2, \cdots, q$ are zero. And, as the last $p\, dx_i$ are arbitrary, we may take all but one zero and that one distinct from zero. Hence the last p coefficients must also be zero. This gives the necessary conditions, which in general have only a finite number of solutions, since there are q given equations $F_k(x_i) = 0$, and n conditions, to determine the $n\ x_i$ and the $q\ \lambda_k$.

28. *Inverse Transformations.* If $u_i(x_1,x_2,x_3)$, $i = 1, 2, 3$ are three functions of x_j, $j = 1, 2, 3$, with the Jacobian $\dfrac{\partial(u_1,u_2,u_3)}{\partial(x_1,x_2,x_3)}$ or $\left|\dfrac{\partial u_i}{\partial x_j}\right| \neq 0$ for some range of the x_j, then for some range of the u_i, the x_j are determined as functions of the u_i, $x_j(u_1,u_2,u_3)$. Show that the Jacobian of the inverse transformation, $\left|\dfrac{\partial x_j}{\partial u_i}\right|$ is the reciprocal of that for the direct transformation. *Hint:* Use problem 19.

29. *Curvilinear Coördinates.* If in problem 28 the x_i are Cartesian coördinates, the element of arc length is $ds^2 = \sum_{j=1}^{3} dx_j^2$. Show that in the curvilinear coördinates u_i, $ds^2 = \sum_{j=1}^{3} \sum_{p=1}^{3} \sum_{q=1}^{3} \dfrac{\partial x_j}{\partial u_p} \dfrac{\partial x_j}{\partial u_q} du_p\, du_q$.

30. *Orthogonal Coördinates.* In the notation of problem 29, the equations $u_i(x_j) = u_{i0}$ represent three surfaces through a point u_{i0}, or x_{j0}. Show that the normals to the surfaces for $i = 1$ and $i = 2$ are perpendicular, according to the definition of problem 8, if $\sum_{j=1}^{3} \left(\dfrac{\partial u_1}{\partial x_j}\right)_0 \left(\dfrac{\partial u_2}{\partial x_j}\right)_0 = 0$. When $\sum_{j=1}^{3} \dfrac{\partial u_p}{\partial x_j} \dfrac{\partial u_q}{\partial x_j} = 0$ for all choices of p and $q \neq p$, and all points considered, the coördinates are said to be orthogonal.

31. For the orthogonal coördinates of problem 30, let us put $\sum_{j=1}^{3} \left(\dfrac{\partial u_p}{\partial x_j}\right)^2 = \dfrac{1}{h_p^2}$. Deduce the relations $h_p^2\, \dfrac{\partial u_p}{\partial x_k} = \dfrac{\partial x_k}{\partial u_p}$ and $ds^2 = \sum_{p=1}^{3} h_p^2\, du_p^2$. *Hint:* $\sum_q \dfrac{\partial x_k}{\partial u_q} \dfrac{\partial u_q}{\partial x_j} = \dfrac{\partial x_k}{\partial x_j}$, or 0 if $j \neq k$ and 1 if $j = k$. Multiply by $\dfrac{\partial u_p}{\partial x_j}$ and sum for j, using the relations of problem 30, to get $\dfrac{1}{h_p^2} \dfrac{\partial x_k}{\partial u_p} = \dfrac{\partial u_p}{\partial x_k}$, since the terms on the left vanish unless $q = p$, and those on the right vanish unless $j = k$. From this

$$\sum_{j=1}^{3} \frac{\partial x_j}{\partial u_p} \frac{\partial x_j}{\partial u_q} = \sum_{j=1}^{3} h_p^2 h_q^2 \frac{\partial u_p}{\partial x_j} \frac{\partial u_q}{\partial x_j} = 0 \text{ if } q \neq p \text{ and } = h_p^2 \text{ if } q = p. \quad \text{Now use}$$

problem 29.

32. *The Laplacian.* The expression $\sum_{j=1}^{3} \dfrac{\partial^2 f}{\partial x_j^2}$ is called the Laplacian of the

function $f(x_j)$. It occurs frequently in geometry and mathematical physics.

Prove that in the orthogonal coördinates with $ds^2 = \sum_{p=1}^{3} h_p^2 \, du_p^2$, discussed in

problems 30 and 31, the Laplacian is:

$$\frac{1}{h_1 h_2 h_3} \left\{ \frac{\partial}{\partial u_1} \left(\frac{h_2 h_3}{h_1} \frac{\partial f}{\partial u_1} \right) + \frac{\partial}{\partial u_2} \left(\frac{h_3 h_1}{h_2} \frac{\partial f}{\partial u_2} \right) + \frac{\partial}{\partial u_3} \left(\frac{h_1 h_2}{h_3} \frac{\partial f}{\partial u_3} \right) \right\}.$$

Hint: By direct differentiation, $\dfrac{\partial f}{\partial x_j} = \sum_p \dfrac{\partial f}{\partial u_p} \dfrac{\partial u_p}{\partial x_j}$ and $\dfrac{\partial^2 f}{\partial x_j^2} = \sum_p \dfrac{\partial f}{\partial u_p} \dfrac{\partial^2 u_p}{\partial x_j^2} +$

$\sum_{p,q} \dfrac{\partial^2 f}{\partial u_p \partial u_q} \dfrac{\partial u_p}{\partial x_j} \dfrac{\partial u_q}{\partial x_j}$. From this, $\sum_{j=1}^{3} \dfrac{\partial^2 f}{\partial x_j^2} = \sum_p \dfrac{\partial f}{\partial u_p} \sum_j \dfrac{\partial^2 u_p}{\partial x_j^2} + \sum_p \dfrac{1}{h_p^2} \dfrac{\partial^2 f}{\partial u_p^2}$. To

transform the coefficient of $\dfrac{\partial f}{\partial u_p}$, rewrite the relation of problem 31, $\dfrac{\partial u_p}{\partial x_k} =$

$\dfrac{1}{h_p^2} \dfrac{\partial x_k}{\partial u_p}$, (A) in the form $h_p^2 \dfrac{\partial u_p}{\partial x_j} = \dfrac{\partial x_j}{\partial u_p}$, and deduce $h_p^2 \dfrac{\partial^2 u_p}{\partial x_j^2} + \dfrac{\partial u_p}{\partial x_j} \dfrac{\partial}{\partial x_j} (h_p^2) =$

$\dfrac{\partial}{\partial x_j} \left(\dfrac{\partial x_j}{\partial u_p} \right) = \sum_q \dfrac{\partial^2 x_j}{\partial u_p \partial u_q} \dfrac{\partial u_q}{\partial x_j}$. By the relation (A), the second term on the left is

$\dfrac{1}{h_p^2} \dfrac{\partial x_j}{\partial u_p} \dfrac{\partial}{\partial x_j} (h_p^2)$, or $\dfrac{1}{h_p^2} \dfrac{\partial}{\partial u_p} (h_p^2)$ when we sum for j. The right member is, by

the relation (A): $\sum_q \dfrac{\partial^2 x_j}{\partial u_p \partial u_q} \dfrac{1}{h_q^2} \dfrac{\partial x_j}{\partial u_q}$, or $\sum_q \dfrac{1}{2 h_q^2} \dfrac{\partial}{\partial u_p} \left(\dfrac{\partial x_j}{\partial u_q} \right)^2$. When summed

for j, this is $\sum_q \dfrac{1}{2 h_q^2} \dfrac{\partial}{\partial u_p} (h_q^2)$. Thus we have: $\sum_j h_p^2 \dfrac{\partial^2 u_p}{\partial x_j^2} = \sum_q \dfrac{\partial \log h_q}{\partial u_p} - \dfrac{\partial \log h_p^2}{\partial u_p}$

$= \dfrac{\partial}{\partial u_p} \log \dfrac{h_1 h_2 h_3}{h_p^2}.$

33. For cylindrical polar coördinates, $x = r \cos \theta$, $y = r \sin \theta$, $z = z$.

Show that $ds^2 = dr^2 + r^2 \, d\theta^2 + dz^2$, and the Laplacian, $\dfrac{\partial^2 f}{\partial x^2} + \dfrac{\partial^2 f}{\partial y^2} + \dfrac{\partial^2 f}{\partial z^2}$, is

transformed to $\dfrac{1}{r} \dfrac{\partial}{\partial r} \left(r \dfrac{\partial f}{\partial r} \right) + \dfrac{1}{r^2} \dfrac{\partial^2 f}{\partial \theta^2} + \dfrac{\partial^2 f}{\partial z^2}$. *Hint:* Use problem 32.

34. For spherical polar coördinates, $x = r \sin \phi \cos \theta$, $y = r \sin \phi \sin \theta$, $z = r \cos \phi$. Show that the arc length is $ds^2 = dr^2 + r^2 \sin^2 \phi \, d\theta^2 + r^2 \, d\phi^2$, and the

Laplacian is $\dfrac{1}{r^2} \dfrac{\partial}{\partial r} \left(r^2 \dfrac{\partial f}{\partial r} \right) + \dfrac{1}{r^2 \sin^2 \phi} \dfrac{\partial^2 f}{\partial \theta^2} + \dfrac{1}{r^2 \sin \phi} \dfrac{\partial}{\partial \phi} \left(\sin \phi \dfrac{\partial f}{\partial \phi} \right).$ *Hint:*

Use problem 32.

CHAPTER XI

MULTIPLE INTEGRATION

The notion of multiple integration arises when we extend the operation of integration so as to apply to functions of several real variables taken over regions of more than one dimension. We shall give a detailed discussion for functions of two variables, and two-dimensional regions. The modifications necessary to extend the argument to functions of more variables in regions of higher dimensionality will then be briefly indicated. We then consider certain geometric quantities, such as surface area and volume which are expressible as multiple integrals. We also give a few theorems on the transformation of multiple integrals of a type much used in physical applications.

221. Definition of a Double Integral. Let $f(x,y)$ be a function of the two real variables x and y, continuous throughout the closed rectangle R:

$$a \leqq x \leqq b, \quad c \leqq y \leqq d. \tag{1}$$

To define the double integral of $f(x,y)$ with respect to x and y over R, we first divide the closed interval a,b into n subintervals by a system of intermediate points:

$$a = x_0 \leqq x_1 \leqq x_2 \leqq \cdots \leqq x_n = b. \tag{2}$$

Similarly we divide the closed interval c,d into m subintervals by a system of intermediate points:

$$c = y_0 \leqq y_1 \leqq y_2 \leqq \cdots \leqq y_m = d. \tag{3}$$

We then divide the rectangle into $N = mn$ smaller rectangles, by lines parallel to the axes, $x = x_i$ and $y = y_j$. Let δx_i and δy_j be the dimensions of the ij rectangle, so that

$$\delta x_i = x_i - x_{i-1} \quad \text{and} \quad \delta y_j = y_j - y_{j-1}. \tag{4}$$

Let δA_p denote the area of the pth, or ij rectangle, so that

$$\delta A_p = \delta x_i \, \delta y_j. \tag{5}$$

Next select a point ξ_p, η_p in each closed pth rectangle, and form the sum

$$S = \sum_{p=1}^{N} f(\xi_p, \eta_p) \, \delta A_p. \tag{6}$$

We shall prove that, for any sequence of sums for which

$$\lim \delta_M = 0, \quad \text{where} \quad \delta_M = \max \delta x_i, \ \delta y_j, \qquad (7)$$

the sum S approaches a limit, and that this limit is the same for all such sequences.

Since $f(x,y)$ is continuous in the closed rectangle R, it is uniformly continuous so that, for any positive quantity ϵ, there is a δ_ϵ such that

$$|f(x_2,y_2) - f(x_1,y_1)| < \epsilon, \qquad (8)$$

if

$$|x_2 - x_1| < \delta_\epsilon, \ |y_2 - y_1| < \delta_\epsilon.$$

Now consider the two sums S, given by equation (6) and S' given by

$$S' = \sum_{q=1}^{N'} f(\xi_q', \eta_q') \ \delta A_q', \qquad (9)$$

where

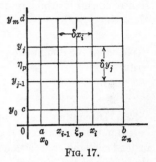

Fig. 17.

$$\delta_M < \delta_{\epsilon/2} \ \text{and} \ \delta_M' < \delta_{\epsilon/2}, \quad \text{with} \quad \delta_M' = \max \delta x_i', \ \delta y_j'. \qquad (10)$$

If we draw all of the parallels to the axes for the first sum, and all those for the second sum not already drawn, we will form a new subdivision of R into small rectangles. If we denote the area of a typical small rectangle of this set by δA_k, we shall have:

$$\sum \delta A_k = (b - a)(d - c). \qquad (11)$$

The difference of the two sums S and S' may be expressed in the form:

$$S - S' = \sum [f(\xi_k, \eta_k) - f(\xi_k', \eta_k')] \ \delta A_k, \qquad (12)$$

where ξ_k, η_k is a point of one of the rectangles used in forming S, and ξ_k', η_k' is a point of one of the rectangles used in forming S'. Moreover these rectangles have points in common. Thus we have:

$$|\xi_k - \xi_k'| < 2\delta_M < \delta_\epsilon \ \text{and} \ |\eta_k - \eta_k'| < 2\delta_M < \delta_\epsilon. \qquad (13)$$

Consequently, from the relation (8), the terms in brackets in equation (12) cannot exceed ϵ in numerical value, so that, from equations (11) and (12) we find:

$$|S - S'| \leqq \epsilon \sum \delta A_k \leqq \epsilon(b - a)(d - c). \qquad (14)$$

As this relation holds for any two sums satisfying the conditions (10), by the Cauchy convergence criterion it follows that any sequence of sums satisfying the condition (7) approaches a limit. That the limit is the same for all sequences follows directly from the relation (14), since we may take S as a sum from one sequence with limit I, and S' from another sequence with limit I', and deduce that:

$$|I - I'| \leqq \epsilon(b - a)(d - c). \tag{15}$$

Hence, since ϵ is arbitrary, it follows that

$$I - I' = 0, \quad \text{or} \quad I' = I. \tag{16}$$

We call I the double integral of $f(x,y)$ taken over the rectangle R and write:

$$I = \int_R f(x,y) \, dA. \tag{17}$$

222. Discontinuities. Most of the discussion of Chapter VII could be extended to double integrals. We shall not do this in detail, but instead shall indicate certain types of discontinuities which do not vitiate the results of the last section.

By the area of a rectangle, we mean the product of the length times the breadth. By the total area of a finite set of rectangles, we mean the sum of the areas of the separate rectangles. We may now define the outer content of P, a set of points in two dimensions, as the greatest lower bound of the areas of all finite sets of rectangles including the point set P.

We assume that the function $f(x,y)$ is bounded, and define its oscillation in any rectangle, or two-dimensional region, as the excess of the least upper bound over its greatest lower bound for the region. The oscillation at a point is the greatest lower bound of the value of the oscillation for all two-dimensional regions including the point as an interior point. Since we may also define the oscillation at a point in terms of

$$f(x_0,y_0), \quad \overline{\lim_{x,y \to x_0,y_0}} f(x,y) \quad \text{and} \quad \underline{\lim_{x,y \to x_0,y_0}} f(x,y) \tag{18}$$

analogous to the definition for functions of one variable given in section 150, the oscillation at a point may be obtained by using rectangles, or even rectangles with sides in given directions, say parallel to the x and y axes. The oscillation of a function is zero at points of continuity.

Now consider a function $f(x,y)$ which may be undefined at certain points U of the rectangle R, but such that the values for all points at which it is defined admit an upper and a lower bound, $|f(x,y)| \leqq K$. We may form a sum S by arbitrarily assigning any values not exceeding K

in numerical value to the points U. If P_ϵ is the set of points of the rectangle R at which the function is either undefined or has an oscillation greater than or equal to ϵ, any positive number, and the outer content of every set P_ϵ is zero, then any sequence of sums S, given by equation (6), which satisfies the condition (7), approaches a limit, and this limit is the same for all sequences.

To prove this, select any positive $\epsilon < 1$. Since the outer content of the set P_ϵ is zero, it may be included in a finite set of rectangles F of total area less than ϵ. Let the sum of the perimeters of the rectangles of F, increased by $4N\epsilon$, where N is the number of the rectangles F, be L. Then, for any subdivision of the rectangle R with $\delta_M < \min(\epsilon, \epsilon/L)$ the total area of all the small rectangles which include points of P_ϵ will not exceed the total area of all the small rectangles which include points of F, and therefore will be at most

$$\epsilon + L\left(\frac{\epsilon}{L}\right) = 2\epsilon. \tag{19}$$

Now consider any two subdivisions for which the sums are S and S', with

$$\delta_M, \ \delta_M' \text{ each } < \max\left(\delta_\epsilon, \ \epsilon, \frac{\epsilon}{L}\right). \tag{20}$$

Then, for the subdivision obtained by combining the two original subdivisions, we shall have a sum which we may consider as made up of two parts, one over rectangles R_1 including points of P_ϵ, and the other over the remaining rectangles R_2.

For the rectangles R_1, we shall have:

$$|f(\xi_k, \eta_k) - f(\xi_k', \eta_k')| \leqq 2K, \tag{21}$$

while the total sum of the rectangles R_1 is at most 2ϵ.

Over the remaining rectangles R_2 the sum may be treated in a manner similar to that used for the right member of the relation (12). Thus, in the present case, we shall have:

$$|S - S'| \leqq \epsilon(b - a)(d - c) + 4\epsilon K. \tag{22}$$

We may apply to this the same argument we previously used in connection with the relation (14). This establishes our contention.

223. Repeated Integrals. Let the function $f(x,y)$ be bounded in the rectangle R, and such that the set of points of R, P_ϵ, where either $f(x,y)$ is undefined, or the oscillation is greater than or equal to ϵ, any positive quantity, is of outer content zero. As in the one-dimensional case, we may use the phrase content zero in place of outer content zero for the reasons given in section 149. We avoid the necessity of considering the points at which the function is not defined by arbitrarily defining the function on these points in any way that does not disturb the bounded character of $f(x,y)$. Thus we might take the function equal to its upper bound on these points, or equal to zero. However it is convenient to be able to vary the choice in different applications.

In particular, the conditions imposed on $f(x,y)$ will be met if the function is continuous in the closed rectangle R.

For each value of y in the closed interval c,d the function $f(x,y)$ is a bounded function of x, and so has an upper integral with respect to x, by section 147,

$$F(y) = \overline{\int_a^b} f(x,y) \, dx. \tag{23}$$

Since the function $f(x,y)$ is bounded,

$$|f(x,y)| \leq K, \tag{24}$$

it follows that for each, and hence for all values of y considered:

$$|F(y)| \leq K(b - a). \tag{25}$$

Thus the function $F(y)$ is bounded, and so has an upper integral,

$$\bar{I}_{xy} = \overline{\int_c^d} F(y) \, dy = \overline{\int_c^d} dy \, \overline{\int_a^b} f(x,y) \, dx. \tag{26}$$

Now consider any subdivision of the rectangle R into $N = mn$ smaller rectangles, as in section 221, defined by the points of subdivision (2) and (3). We may define an integral similar to that given by equation (26) for each pth or ij rectangle, namely,

$$\bar{I}_{ij} \doteq \overline{\int_{y_{j-1}}^{y_j}} dy \, \overline{\int_{x_{i-1}}^{x_i}} f(x,y) \, dx. \tag{27}$$

From the additive property of single upper integrals, we may conclude that:

$$\bar{I}_{xy} = \sum_{i,\,j} \bar{I}_{ij}. \tag{28}$$

Again, if m_{ij} and M_{ij} are respectively the greatest lower bound and least upper bound of $f(x,y)$ in the ij rectangle, we have for each y in this rectangle:

$$m_{ij} \leq f(x,y) \leq M_{ij}, \tag{29}$$

and

$$m_{ij} \, \delta x_i \leq \overline{\int_{x_{i-1}}^{x_i}} f(x,y) \, dx \leq M_{ij} \, \delta x_i, \tag{30}$$

so that:

$$m_{ij} \, \delta x_i \, \delta y_j \leq \bar{I}_{ij} \leq M_{ij} \, \delta x_i \, \delta y_j. \tag{31}$$

Next form a sum S, given by equation (6) and satisfying the condition (20). Separate this sum into two parts as we did at the end of the last section. For those rectangles R_1 containing points of the set P_ϵ, the difference between any term in S and the corresponding term $\bar{I}_{ij}$ will be numerically at most $2K\,\delta x_i\,\delta y_j$. Since the sum of all the rectangles R_1 is less than 2ϵ, the total difference for this part of the sum will not exceed $4K\epsilon$ in numerical value.

For the terms corresponding to rectangles R_2, since the oscillation of $f(x,y)$ is less than ϵ, we shall have:

$$M_{ij} - m_{ij} < \epsilon, \quad \text{and} \quad m_{ij} \leqq f(\xi,\eta) \leqq M_{ij}. \tag{32}$$

Thus the difference for any rectangle ij of S_2 between the term of S and the corresponding term $\bar{I}_{ij}$ will be numerically at most $\epsilon\,\delta x_i\,\delta y_i$. For all these terms, the total difference will not exceed $\epsilon(b - a)(d - c)$ in numerical value.

Thus we have finally:

$$|S - \bar{I}_{xy}| \leqq \epsilon(b - a)(d - c) + 4K\epsilon. \tag{33}$$

Since the limit of S for any sequence for which $\delta_M \to 0$ is I, the double integral, we may deduce from the inequality just written that:

$$|I - \bar{I}_{xy}| \leqq \epsilon(b - a)(d - c) + 4K\epsilon. \tag{34}$$

Since ϵ is arbitrary, this has as a consequence the equation:

$$\bar{I}_{xy} = I. \tag{35}$$

The argument which rested on the inequality (29) would have been equally valid if in equations (26) and (27) we had replaced either or both of the upper integrals by lower integrals. This proves that the function $F(y)$ is integrable. It also shows that the repeated integral is the same as I, the double integral, if we replace the upper integral in equation (23) by the lower integral, or any value intermediate between these two.

We may use the same reasoning with the order of x and y interchanged, and thus find that:

$$\bar{I}_{yx} = I. \tag{36}$$

We may summarize our results as follows:

If the function $f(x,y)$ is bounded throughout the closed rectangle R, and is such that the set of points of R, P_ϵ, where $f(x,y)$ is either undefined, or the oscillation is greater than or equal to ϵ is of outer content zero, then, if we *arbitrarily assign values, bounded as a set, to the points where $f(x,y)$ was originally undefined, we shall have:*

$$\int_R f(x,y)\, dA = \int_a^b dx \overline{\int_c^d} f(x,y)\, dy = \int_c^d dy \overline{\int_a^b} f(x,y)\, dx. \quad (37)$$

In this equation, the upper integrals may be replaced by lower integrals, or any value between the upper and lower integrals.

In particular, if $f(x,y)$ is continuous throughout the closed rectangle R, we shall have:

$$\int_R f(x,y)\, dA = \int_a^b dx \int_c^d f(x,y)\, dy = \int_c^d dy \int_a^b f(x,y)\, dx. \quad (38)$$

If the function $f(x,y)$ is integrable in x for all values of y, we have:

$$\int_R f(x,y)\, dA = \int_a^b dx \int_c^d f(x,y)\, dy. \quad (39)$$

We may also use this equation if $f(x,y)$ is integrable in y for all values of x except a set of one-dimensional content zero, regarding the function to be integrated a second time as undefined on this set. However, our conditions on $f(x,y)$ do not necessarily imply that $f(x,y)$ is integrable in y for all except a set of values of x of content zero. Thus, let $f(x,y) = 0$ for all irrational values of x, as well as $x = 0$ or $x = 1$. For any rational value of x, $0 < x < 1$, p/q in its lowest terms, let $f(p/q,y)$ be zero for y irrational, or $1/q^3 < y < 1$, but let its value be $1/q$ for y rational and $0 < y \leq 1/q^3$.

Consider this function on the rectangle R, $0 \leq x \leq 1$, $0 \leq y \leq 1$. The only points of R where $f(x,y)$ is at least $1/n$ are on the lines $x = p/q$, $q \leq n$. For a particular q, since $0 < p < q$, there are $q - 1$ lines, and the points on each lie upon a segment of length $1/q^3$. Thus, for a given n, the total length of the segments is:

$$\sum_{q=2}^n (q - 1)\, \frac{1}{q^3} < \sum_{q=1}^\infty \frac{1}{q^2} = L, \quad (40)$$

since the series is convergent by section 192. Thus the segments may be enclosed in a finite number of rectangles of arbitrarily small total area by including each segment in a rectangle of width $\epsilon/(L + 1)$, and length so near that of the segment that the sum of the lengths of the rectangles does not exceed $L + 1$.

Since the function $f(x,y)$ is between 0 and $1/n$ on R except for a set of content zero, it follows that each set P_ϵ has a content zero. Thus the function does have a double integral and equation (37) holds. However,

$f(x,y)$ is not integrable for any rational value of x, a set of one-dimensional outer content unity.

224. Other Domains. Let D be any two-dimensional region of the plane, all of whose points are points of some finite rectangle R, and such that each straight line through any interior point of the region cuts the boundary in exactly two points. Let the boundary have two-dimensional content zero. Consider a function $f(x,y)$ defined at all points of D and its boundary, continuous at all interior points of D, and bounded on the closed region D.

We note that if the boundary consists of a continuous curve with an arc length it will necessarily be a set of two-dimensional content zero. For, since the boundary has an arc length, we may write $x = f(t)$ and $y = g(t)$, where $f(t)$ and $g(t)$ are each continuous functions of bounded variation. Let us make a subdivision of the t interval by points t_i, into intervals $t_{i-1} \leq t \leq t_i$. If ϵ_i and ϵ_i' denote the oscillation of the functions $f(t)$ and $g(t)$ in the ith interval, all the points of the ith arc may be included in a rectangle with sides parallel to the axes, and less than $4\epsilon_i\epsilon_i'$ in area. Thus the sum of the areas of all such rectangles will be at most

$$\sum 4\epsilon_i\epsilon_i' \leq 4\epsilon_M \sum \epsilon_i', \qquad (41)$$

where ϵ_M is the maximum of the ϵ_i. Since $f(t)$ is continuous, for any positive quantity ϵ, $\epsilon_M < \epsilon$, when the maximum t subdivision is less than a suitably chosen δ_ϵ. Again, since $g(t)$ is continuous and of bounded variation, by section 173, the sum $\sum \epsilon_i'$ approaches Vg, the variation of $g(t)$. Thus the two-dimensional content of the boundary is less than $4\epsilon Vg$, and thus must be zero since ϵ is arbitrary.

If $f(x,y)$ is any function, continuous at all interior points of D, and bounded on the closed region D, we may define:

$$g(x,y) = f(x,y) \text{ for } x,y \text{ an interior point of } D \qquad (42)$$

and

$$g(x,y) = 0, \text{ for } x,y \text{ a point of } R \text{ not interior to } D. \qquad (43)$$

The double integral of $g(x,y)$ over R exists by section 222. We define the double integral of $f(x,y)$ over D as equal to that of $g(x,y)$ over R:

$$\int_D f(x,y) \, dA = \int_R g(x,y) \, dA. \qquad (44)$$

Suppose that, for values of y between y_1 and y_2, a parallel to the x-axis cuts the boundary in $x_1(y)$ and $x_2(y)$. Then, since $g(x,y)$ is equal to

$f(x,y)$ in the interval $x_1(y)$, $x_2(y)$, and is zero outside this interval, we have:

$$\int_a^b g(x,y)\ dx = \int_{x_1(y)}^{x_2(y)} f(x,y)\ dx. \tag{45}$$

Let us further suppose that all interior points of D have a y for which $y_1 \leqq y \leqq y_2$. Then from this and equation (38) we may conclude that:

$$\int_D f(x,y)\ dA = \int_{y_1}^{y_2} dy \int_{x_1(y)}^{x_2(y)} f(x,y)\ dx. \tag{46}$$

Similarly, if for values between x_1 and x_2 a parallel to the x-axis cuts the boundary in $y_1(x)$ and $y_2(x)$, while all interior points of D have an x for which $x_1 \leqq x \leqq x_2$, then:

$$\int_D f(x,y)\ dA = \int_{x_1}^{x_2} dx \int_{y_1(x)}^{y_2(x)} f(x,y)\ dy. \tag{47}$$

As in the last section, we may allow $f(x,y)$ to be discontinuous at certain points of D, provided that the set of points P_ϵ, at which its oscillation is greater than or equal to ϵ, any positive number, forms a set of zero content. In this case, when making the reduction to a repeated integral, we may have to replace the first integral by an upper or lower integral, or some value between these, as in equation (38).

We may also extend the definition to any domain D' which may be decomposed into a set of points of two-dimensional content zero, together with a finite number of domains D_i of the type previously used, putting:

$$\int_{D'} f(x,y)\ dA = \Sigma \int_{D_i} f(x,y)\ dA. \tag{48}$$

In certain cases, if the integrals over the D_i are written as repeated integrals, some of them may be combined.

Finally we may consider domains D'', generated by removing from a domain of type D' those points which make up some sub-region of type D'. The integral over a region D'' is defined by an expression similar to that in equation (48) with minus signs before the integrals corresponding to domains D_i made up of removed points.

Certain domains D'' may be generated from domains D_i without any additional sets of two-dimensional content zero. We designate by D^* these domains, generated by addition and subtraction from a finite number of regions each of type D.

225. Area. If the domain D is a rectangle R with sides parallel to the axes, the integral of $f(x,y) = 1$ over D or R reduces to the area.

Any domain G whose boundary consists of a finite number of segments parallel to the axes may be decomposed into a finite number of rectangles R, and so for it

$$\text{Area } G = \int_G dA. \tag{49}$$

For any domain D of the type described at the beginning of the last section, we may find two domains of type G, G' and G'', such that all points of G' are interior points of D, and all points of D are interior points of G'', and furthermore:

$$\int_{G''} dA - \int_{G'} dA < \epsilon, \tag{50}$$

where ϵ is any given positive number.

Since we have:

$$\int_{G'} dA \leqq \int_D dA \leqq \int_{G''} dA, \tag{51}$$

we are lead to define:

$$\text{Area } D = \int_D dA. \tag{52}$$

That area, as here defined, is independent of axes follows from the fact that the definition gives the correct value for a triangle or rectangle with sides not parallel to the axes. Or we may note that the area is the outer content of the set of points of D, which was defined in section 222 in a manner independent of axes.

226. The Mean Value Theorem. Suppose that the function $f(x,y)$ is continuous in a closed domain D. Let D be connected, that is, have the property that any two points of D can be joined by a curve consisting entirely of points of D.

Then, since $f(x,y)$ is continuous in a closed region, its values are bounded, and the greatest and least values are taken on, say

$$f(x',y') = m, \quad f(x'',y'') = M, \tag{53}$$

where

$$m \leqq f(x,y) \leqq M. \tag{54}$$

Since the double integral is the limit of a sum of products of values of a function by positive multipliers, if the integrand is increased, the sums and the integral will either remain unchanged or increase. Thus, it follows from the relation (54) that:

$$\int_D m \, dA \leqq \int_D f(x,y) \, dA \leqq \int_D M \, dA. \tag{55}$$

If we write A for the area of D,

$$A = \int_D dA, \tag{56}$$

we have:

$$mA \leqq \int_D f(x,y) \, dA \leqq MA. \tag{57}$$

This shows that the average of the function $f(x,y)$ over D, or

$$\frac{1}{A} \int_D f(x,y) \, dA, \tag{58}$$

lies between m and M, the values at $P' = (x',y')$ and $P'' = (x'',y'')$. Since the domain is connected, we may join these points by an arc, with parameter t varying from t' to t''. Since $f(x,y)$, regarded as a function of t along this arc, is continuous, it takes on every value between m and M. In particular, there is a point of the closed region D, (ξ,η), such that $f(\xi,\eta)$ is equal to the expression (58). Thus:

$$\int_D f(x,y) \, dA = Af(\xi,\eta). \tag{59}$$

This is the mean value theorem for double integrals which holds for integrands continuous on closed, connected domains.

Whenever the integrand $f(x,y)$ admits lower and upper bounds m and M, the inequality (54) holds, and we may deduce from it the relations (55) and (57). Thus, for any bounded function admitting a double integral over D, of area A, we have:

$$mA \leqq \int_D f(x,y) \, dA \leqq MA, \tag{60}$$

where m and M are bounds for the function in D.

227. Other Subdivisions. Instead of using a subdivision of R into rectangles with sides parallel to the axes, we may use any subdivision of R into small domains of type D^* of section 224 to form a sum S. For any function satisfying the condition of section 222, the limit of any sequence of sums of this type for which $d_M \to 0$, where d_M is the largest diameter of any subdivision will be the integral, as we shall now show.

We note first, that our condition that the boundary of a domain D be met by any line containing an interior point of D in exactly two points has, as a consequence, that if we superimpose the subdivision into regions of type D^* on any subdivision into rectangles of type R, the two subdivisions will divide the fundamental rectangle R into only a finite number of domains of type D^*.

As in section 222 these may be divided into two groups, in one of which the oscillation of $f(x,y)$ is less than ϵ at each point, and such that the other group has a total area at most 2ϵ, provided that the rectangular subdivision is sufficiently fine. If, now, we take d_M sufficiently small, so that none of the regions of type D^* includes more than four contiguous rectangles, we may deduce a relation for the difference of the two sums similar in character to the relation (22). It then follows that any sequence of sums with $d_M \to 0$ will have the integral as its limit.

228. n-tuple Integrals. The discussion of the integral of a function $f(x_k)$, where $k = 1, 2, \cdots, n$ may now be carried out in a similar manner to that used for $n = 2$.

We define the volume of an n-dimensional rectangle as the product of its n dimensions, and hence define the outer content of a set of points in the space of the x_k.

For any n-dimensional rectangular interval, we may form a subdivision on each axis, and a sum:

$$S = \sum_{p=1}^{N} f(\xi_{kp}) \, \delta V_p, \tag{61}$$

where

$$\delta V_p = \prod_{k=1}^{n} \delta x_{kp} \tag{62}$$

the n-dimensional volume of the figure with edges δx_{kp}. That is δx_{kp} is the subdivision of the interval on the kth axis, used in forming the pth n-dimensional rectangle.

If any sequence of values of S, corresponding to subdivisions for which the maximum δx_{kp}, or $d_M \to 0$, approaches a limit, the same for all such sequences, we define this as the n-tuple integral of $f(x_k)$. We denote it by

$$\int_{R_n} f(x_k) \, dV_n, \tag{63}$$

where the subscript n on R and V which denotes dimensionality may be omitted if it is clear from the context that these refer to n-dimensional figures.

Whenever the function $f(x_k)$ is such that, for every positive quantity ϵ, the set of points P_ϵ where the oscillation of the function is greater than or equal to ϵ, or the function is undefined, has an n-dimensional outer content zero, the n-tuple integral exists.

Moreover, in this case it may be calculated as a repeated integral, where if any of the intermediate integrals fail to exist, we use the greatest limits of sums, or upper integrals, instead of integrals.

We may replace the rectangular region of integration by other domains, provided these can be decomposed into a finite number of domains of type D. A domain, in n dimensions, is of type D if it is such that each straight line through an interior point cuts the boundary in exactly two points, and if this boundary is a set of n-dimensional outer content zero. The volume of a domain of type D is $\int_D dV_n$, or the outer content of the set of points of D.

If $f(x_k)$ is continuous in a closed connected domain, we have a mean value theorem similar to equation (59), namely:

$$\int_{D_n} f(x_k)\, dV_n = V_n f(\xi_k), \tag{64}$$

for some choice of ξ_k as a point of the domain D_n.

Whenever the integral exists, if m and M are bounds for the integrand, we have:

$$m V_n \leqq \int_{D_n} f(x_k)\, dV_n \leqq M V_n. \tag{65}$$

Finally, we may use subdivisions into domains of type D_n^*, instead of n-dimensional rectangles with sides parallel to the axes, in forming the sums. An n-dimensional domain is of type D_n^* if it may be generated by addition and subtraction from a finite number of regions, each of type D_n.

229. Change of Variable. Consider a set of n equations:

$$x_k = f_k(y_i), \quad k,\ i = 1, 2, \cdots, n, \tag{66}$$

for values of y in some n-dimensional rectangle R_n. Suppose that, in R_n, the functions $f_k(y_i)$ have first partial derivatives, continuous with respect to all n variables, and that the Jacobian:

$$\frac{\partial(f_1, f_2, \cdots, f_n)}{\partial(y_1, y_2, \cdots, y_n)} = \left| \frac{\partial x_p}{\partial y_q} \right| > 0. \tag{67}$$

Then, since the equations may be written:

$$f_k(y_i) - x_k = 0, \tag{68}$$

and the terms x_k have no effect on the derivatives of the left members with respect to the y_i, the Jacobian of this system referred to in section 218 is the same as that written in the relation (67), and by the theorem of section 218, the equations may be solved in the form:

$$y_i = \phi_i(x_k), \tag{69}$$

at least in some region including each point x_k, obtained by equations (66) from a point y_i of R_n. However, if our conditions hold in the closed region R_n, by the Heine-Borel theorem we may select a finite set of regions surrounding points y_i, corresponding to the regions surrounding points x_k, which cover R_n. These separate functions may be pieced together to give solutions of the type (69), defined for a certain range of the x_k, which lead to values of y_i in R_n. While the resulting relation may be selected so as to be continuous for all values considered, and one to one in a suitably chosen region including any point, it is not necessarily one to one for all values considered, since the original equations (66) may give the same value of the set x_k, for two distinct sets of y_k in R_n.

We shall consider only values of y_i in D'_n, a region of type D in R_n, which may of course be R_n itself. We make the further assumption that under the equations (66), the region D'_n is carried into D_n, a region of type D in the x_k space, and also that the region D'_n is transformed into regions of type D in certain other spaces to be introduced presently.

If $g(x_k)$ is any function of the x_k, continuous in D_n, it will determine a function $G(y_i)$, continuous in D'_n in view of equations (66). Under the assumptions made, we may show that:

$$\int_{D_n} g(x_k)\, dV_n = \int_{D'_n} \left| \frac{\partial x_p}{\partial y_q} \right| G(y_i)\, dV'_n, \tag{70}$$

where dV_n is the element of integration as in equation (63), which recalls that the sums involved the elements of volume given by equation (62) for the x_k-space, and dV'_n has a similar meaning for the y_i-space.

We first note that if this rule is valid for a transformation from a set of variables x_k to a set y_i, and also from the set y_i to a new set z_j, the rule will hold for the transformation from the x_k to the z_j, provided that:

$$\frac{\partial(x_1, x_2, \cdots, x_n)}{\partial(y_1, y_2, \cdots, y_n)} \frac{\partial(y_1, y_2, \cdots, y_n)}{\partial(z_1, z_2, \cdots, z_n)} = \frac{\partial(x_1, x_2, \cdots, x_n)}{\partial(z_1, z_2, \cdots, z_n)}. \tag{71}$$

But it follows from section 214 that:

$$\frac{\partial x_k}{\partial z_j} = \sum_{i=1}^{n} \frac{\partial x_k}{\partial y_i} \frac{\partial y_i}{\partial z_j}, \tag{72}$$

and this may be combined with the rule for multiplying determinants to prove the equation (71), as in problem 19 of Exercises X.

Consequently it will be sufficient to prove the equation (70) when we change the variables one at a time, since we may proceed from:

$$x_1, x_2, x_3, \cdots, \text{ to } y_1, x_2, x_3, \cdots, \text{ to } y_1, y_2, x_3, \cdots, \text{ etc.} \tag{73}$$

The Jacobian for each of these intermediate transformations must differ from zero, since their product is that of the original transformation. And, by changing the order of the variables in the intermediate transformations, if necessary, we may make all these Jacobians positive.

We note that, for $n = 1$, the equation (70) holds since it reduces to equation (92) of section 133.

For the first transformation (73) we have:

$$x_1 = F(y_1, x_2, x_3, \cdots, x_n), \ x_2 = x_2, \cdots, x_n = x_n, \tag{74}$$

so that the Jacobian is:

$$\frac{\partial(F, x_2, x_3, \cdots, x_n)}{\partial(y_1, x_2, x_3, \cdots, x_n)} = \frac{\partial F}{\partial y_1}. \tag{75}$$

We now write the n-tuple integral as a repeated integral, using D_{n-1} to denote a domain in the x_k-space with the first axis suppressed.   We have:

$$\int_{D_n} g(x_k) \, dV_n = \int_{D_{n-1}} dV_{n-1} \int_a^b g(x_k) \, dx_1, \tag{76}$$

where a and b are functions of $x_2, x_3, \cdots, x_n$.

By equation (92) of section 133 we may write in place of the inner integral:

$$\int_{a'}^{b'} g(F, x_2, x_3, \cdots, x_n) \frac{\partial F}{\partial y_1} \, dy_1, \tag{77}$$

where a' and b' are functions of $x_2, x_3, \cdots, x_n$ such that:

$$a = F(a', x_2, \cdots, x_n) \quad \text{and} \quad b = F(b', x_2, \cdots, x_n). \tag{78}$$

These equations show that the n-dimensional domain D_n, determined by a,b on the x_1-axis and D_{n-1} in the space of the x_i is that which corresponds to the domain D_n'' determined by a', b' on the y_1-axis and D_{n-1} in the space of $y_1, x_2, \cdots, x_n$.   Thus the integral of the expression (77) over the domain D_{n-1} is equivalent to:

$$\int_{D_n''} g(F, x_2, x_3, \cdots, x_n) \frac{\partial F}{\partial y_1} \, dV_n''. \tag{79}$$

Since this is equivalent to the first integral of equation (76), and the factor in equation (79), $\partial F/\partial y_1$, is the Jacobian of the transformation by equation (75), we have proved that the equation (70) holds when the first variable only is changed.

In a similar way the equation (70) holds for the other transformations (73), and so is valid in general.

The above discussion only applied to domains in which the transformation was one to one, and the Jacobian preserved its sign. However, the formula of transformation may be applied to any domain which is the sum of a finite number of parts, in each of which the transformation is one to one and the Jacobian preserves its sign, together with certain boundary points, provided that the boundary points form a set of zero content in all the spaces considered. This follows by applying the formula of transformation to each part separately, and summing the results.

If we regard the original transformation as a change of coördinates, the volume of the domain D_n is:

$$\int_{D_n} dV_n = \int_{D_n'} \left| \frac{\partial x_p}{\partial y_q} \right| dV_n'. \tag{80}$$

If the x_k are Cartesian coördinates, dV_n is the element of volume as well as the element of integration. For the curvilinear coördinates y_j, dV_n' is the element of integration, but $|\partial x_p / \partial y_q|\, dV_n'$ is the element of volume.

230. Surface Area. Consider a portion of a surface having as its equation

$$z = f(x,y), \tag{81}$$

where the function $f(x,y)$ is single-valued and has continuous partial derivatives throughout some domain D in the x,y plane.

We subdivide the domain D into small areas, and denote by δA either a typical such small area, or its area. Let δS be the part of the surface which projects on the x,y plane into δA. For any point of δS, $P_0 = (x_0, y_0, z_0)$, the tangent plane to the surface will have as its equation:

$$z - z_0 = f_{x0}(x - x_0) + f_{y0}(y - y_0), \tag{82}$$

where
$$f_{x0} = \left(\frac{\partial z}{\partial x} \right)_0 \text{ and } f_{y0} = \left(\frac{\partial z}{\partial y} \right)_0, \tag{83}$$

by problem 6 of Exercises X. Let us recall the definitions of problems 8 and 9 of Exercises X, and denote by γ the angle between the z-axis and the normal direction. Here we take this direction normal to the surface, or to the tangent plane, in the direction of increasing z. Then we have:

$$\cos \gamma = \frac{1}{\sqrt{f_{x0}^2 + f_{y0}^2 + 1}}. \tag{84}$$

Consequently

$$\sec \gamma = \sqrt{f_{x0}^2 + f_{y0}^2 + 1}, \tag{85}$$

and $\sec \gamma$ is a continuous function of x and y in the domain D.

If δT denotes the portion of the tangent plane at P_0 which projects into δA, we shall have

$$\delta A = \cos \gamma \, \delta T, \quad \text{and} \quad \delta T = \sec \gamma \, \delta A. \tag{86}$$

The sum of all the δT is:

$$\sum \delta T = \sum \sec \gamma \, \delta A. \tag{87}$$

When the maximum dimension of the δA, d_M approaches zero, for any sequence of subdivisions, the corresponding sums will approach a limit, the double integral:

$$S = \int \sec \gamma \, dA = \int \sqrt{f_x^2 + f_y^2 + 1} \, dA. \tag{88}$$

We define this to be the area of the surface. From its form, it is

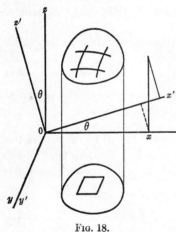

independent of the choice of coördinates in the xy plane. To show that it is independent of the direction of the z-axis, we consider a new set of axes x', y', z' with the same origin. The z'- and z-axes may have arbitrary directions. We use such coördinates that the y- and y'-axes coincide with the line where the planes perpendicular to the z'- and z-axes intersect. Then, if the angle in the $z'x'$ plane from the z'-axis to the z-axis is θ, we have:

$$x' = x \cos \theta + z \sin \theta,$$
$$y' = y, \tag{89}$$

Fig. 18.

so that:

$$\frac{\partial(x',y')}{\partial(x,y)} = \begin{vmatrix} \cos \theta + f_x \sin \theta, & f_y \sin \theta \\ 0, & 1 \end{vmatrix}$$

$$= \cos \theta + f_x \sin \theta. \tag{90}$$

By the definitions of problems 7 and 9 of Exercises X, the direction ratios for the normal at P_0 are

$$-f_x, \; -f_y, \; 1 \tag{91}$$

and those for z' with respect to the first axes are

$$-\sin \theta, \; 0, \; \cos \theta. \tag{92}$$

Hence, if γ' is the angle between the z'-axis and the normal, we have:

$$\cos \gamma' = \frac{f_x \sin \theta + \cos \theta}{\sqrt{f_x^2 + f_y^2 + 1}} = \frac{\partial (x',y')}{\partial (x,y)} \cos \gamma, \qquad (93)$$

by equations (84) and (90). From this and the rule for transforming **a** multiple integral established in the last section:

$$\int_{D'} \sec \gamma' \, dA' = \int_D \sec \gamma' \frac{\partial (x',y')}{\partial (x,y)} \, dA = \int_D \sec \gamma \, dA. \qquad (94)$$

This proves that, as defined, surface area is not dependent on the coördinates used.

231. Intrinsic Definition of Surface Area. An alternative definition of surface area, which from its nature is independent of coördinates, is the following. We first define the approximate area of a surface element as the area of its projection on the tangent plane at any one of its points. We then consider any subdivision of a surface into elements, and define the approximate area for this subdivision as the sum of any approximate areas of each of its elements. Finally we consider a sequence of subdivisions of the surface into elements, such that $d_M \to 0$, where d_M denotes the maximum dimension of all the elements for a particular subdivision. We shall show that for any such sequence, the approximate areas approach a limit, the same for all such sequences. This limit is defined as the surface area.

To prove that the limit exists, and that the present definition is equivalent to that of the last section, let us consider a particular subdivision of the surface into elements. For any one element, let δS be the area as calculated by equation (88), and T_1 be the tangent plane used for the approximate area. Denote the projection of δS on the plane T_1 by δT_1 and use the plane T_1 as the xy plane in applying equation (88). Then

$$\delta S = \int_{\delta T_1} \sec \gamma \, dA = \sec \overline{\gamma} \, \delta T_1, \qquad (95)$$

by the mean value theorem, where $\sec \overline{\gamma}$ is the value of the integrand at $\overline{P}$, a suitably chosen point of δS, and so is the value corresponding to the angle $\overline{\gamma}$ between the z-axis and the normal at P.

Since f_x and f_y are continuous throughout the closed domain D, they are uniformly continuous throughout this region. If we divide the direction ratios for the normal given by equation (91) by the square root of the sum of their squares, we obtain the direction cosines

$$l = \frac{-f_x}{\sqrt{f_x^2 + f_y^2 + 1}}, \ m = \frac{-f_y}{\sqrt{f_x^2 + f_y^2 + 1}}, \ n = \frac{1}{\sqrt{f_x^2 + f_y^2 + 1}}. \qquad (96)$$

These will also be uniformly continuous in D. Hence, when the maximum diameter d_M of the elements δS is less than a suitably chosen δ_ϵ, the oscillation of these direction cosines will not exceed ϵ, an arbitrarily chosen number which we take less than unity. Let l, m, n be the direction cosines of the normal to the plane T_1, and $\bar{l}, \bar{m}, \bar{n}$ those at $\overline{P}$. Then if we write

$$\bar{l} = l + a, \overline{m} = m + b, \overline{n} = n + c, \tag{97}$$

we shall have a, b, c all numerically at most ϵ. Since

$$l^2 + m^2 + n^2 = 1 \quad \text{implies} \quad |l|, |m|, |n| \leq 1, \tag{98}$$

it follows that:

$$\cos \overline{\gamma} = l(l + a) + m(m + b) + n(n + c)$$
$$= 1 + 3\theta\epsilon, \quad \text{where} \quad |\theta| \leq 1. \tag{99}$$

But, from equation (95), $\delta T_1 = \cos \overline{\gamma} \, \delta S$, so that

$$\delta T_1 - \delta S = (\cos \overline{\gamma} - 1) \, \delta S = 3\theta\epsilon \, \delta S. \tag{100}$$

Thus, for the sums approximating the areas under the two definitions, we have

$$\sum \delta T_1 - \sum \delta S = 3\theta'\epsilon \sum \delta S, \quad \text{where} \quad |\theta'| \leq 1. \tag{101}$$

But, for a sufficiently fine subdivision, $d_M < \delta'$, if S is the integral defined by equation (88), the approximating sum $\sum \delta S$ satisfies:

$$|S - \sum \delta S| < \epsilon, \tag{102}$$

so that:

$$|\sum \delta T_1 - S| < \epsilon + 3\epsilon(S + 1) \leq \epsilon(3S + 4). \tag{103}$$

Since this holds for arbitrarily small ϵ, when d_M is sufficiently small, it follows that when $d_M \to 0$, the sum T_1 approaches S as a limit. Thus the definition of this section leads to a unique result, and is equivalent to the definition of the preceding section.

232. Intrinsic Coördinates. Suppose that, in a certain u, v domain, the equations:

$$x = F(u,v), \, y = G(u,v), \, z = H(u,v) \tag{104}$$

are such that each of the three functions has first partial derivatives, continuous in u and v, and that

$$\frac{\partial(x,y)}{\partial(u,v)} > 0. \tag{105}$$

Then, by the theorem of section 218, the first two equations may be solved for u and v in terms of x and y, at least in a restricted range. On substituting these values in the third equation, we obtain an equation of the form (81). Thus, in a suitably restricted u,v domain, the equations (104) represent a portion of a surface. The area of this surface is given by equation (88). But, as in section 218, we find:

$$\frac{\partial z}{\partial x} = - \frac{J_{yz}}{J_{xy}}, \quad \frac{\partial z}{\partial y} = - \frac{J_{zx}}{J_{xy}}, \tag{106}$$

where

$$J_{yz} = \frac{\partial(y,z)}{\partial(u,v)}, \quad J_{zx} = \frac{\partial(z,x)}{\partial(u,v)} \quad \text{and} \quad J_{xy} = \frac{\partial(x,y)}{\partial(u,v)}. \tag{107}$$

Thus, by equation (85),

$$\sec \gamma = \frac{\sqrt{J_{yz}^2 + J_{zx}^2 + J_{xy}^2}}{J_{xy}}. \tag{108}$$

Here J_{xy} is positive by the relation (105).

By applying the rule of transformation (70) to the expression for area of a surface given by equation (88), we find:

$$S = \int \sec \gamma \, dA_{xy} = \int \sec \gamma \, J_{xy} \, dA_{uv}, \tag{109}$$

where the subscripts indicate the space in which the elements of integration are to be formed. We may deduce from equations (108) and (109) that:

$$S = \int \sqrt{J_{yz}^2 + J_{zx}^2 + J_{xy}^2} \, dA_{uv}. \tag{110}$$

This is the expression for surface area in terms of the parameters u and v.

We shall next consider a curve in the surface. Since the equations

$$u = u(t), \quad v = v(t) \tag{111}$$

may be combined with equations (104) to give x, y, and z as functions of t; if suitable restrictions as to differentiability are imposed on the functions $u(t)$ and $v(t)$ they will determine a smooth curve in space, which also lies in the surface. By section 184, for the arc length of such a curve, we have:

$$s = \int \sqrt{\left(\frac{dx}{dt}\right)^2 + \left(\frac{dy}{dt}\right)^2 + \left(\frac{dz}{dt}\right)^2} \, dt. \tag{112}$$

To express this in terms of u and v, we use subscripts to denote partial derivatives, and use the equations:

$$\frac{dx}{dt} = x_u \frac{du}{dt} + x_v \frac{dv}{dt} \quad \text{or} \quad dx = x_u \, du + x_v \, dv, \tag{113}$$

together with

$$dy = y_u \, du + y_v \, dv \quad \text{and} \quad dz = z_u \, du + z_v \, dv. \tag{114}$$

We find from these that

$$dx^2 + dy^2 + dz^2 = E \, du^2 + 2F \, du \, dv + G \, dv^2, \tag{115}$$

where, with sums ranging over x, y and z,

$$E = \sum x_u^2, \ F = \sum x_u x_v \quad \text{and} \quad G = \sum x_v^2. \tag{116}$$

This enables us to replace equation (112) by:

$$s = \int \sqrt{E\left(\frac{du}{dt}\right)^2 + 2F\left(\frac{du}{dt}\right)\left(\frac{dv}{dt}\right) + G\left(\frac{dv}{dt}\right)^2} \, dt. \tag{117}$$

We abbreviate this by writing

$$ds = \sqrt{E \, du^2 + 2F \, du \, dv + G \, dv^2}. \tag{118}$$

By expanding the determinants, and making use of equation (116), we find that:

$$J_{yz}^2 + J_{zx}^2 + J_{xy}^2 = EG - F^2. \tag{119}$$

Thus, we may write in place of the equation (110),

$$S = \int \sqrt{EG - F^2} \, dA_{uv}. \tag{120}$$

We abbreviate this by writing

$$dS = \sqrt{EG - F^2} \, du \, dv. \tag{121}$$

A comparison of this with equation (118) shows that the element of area on a surface is completely determined by the expression for the element of arc in terms of the parameters u and v.

This fact could be used in place of the direct argument of section 230 to show that the definition of surface area there given did not depend on the choice of axes.

233. Signed Elements. So far we have taken the elements of arc or volume in two or more dimensions as positive. This necessitated certain restrictions. For example, in section 229 we took the Jacobian of transformation as positive. This ruled out such a transformation as

$$x' = y, \quad y' = x. \tag{122}$$

For this transformation, which interchanges the rôles of x and y,

$$\frac{\partial(x',y')}{\partial(x,y)} = -1. \tag{123}$$

We seek now to broaden our point of view.

For the integral on an interval, we took the elements as positive at first, and then, if $a < b$, considered the integral from b to a as the negative of that from a to b. We may proceed similarly for the line integrals of section 180. Thus for ordinary or line integrals the sign depends on the limits, or boundary points.

Now consider a two-dimensional domain, bounded by a smooth closed curve. At each point of the curve, P, points near P on the normal to the curve at P are separated by P into an inner segment and an outer segment. If we arbitrarily select a direction along the curve as positive, at any point the angle from the tangent to the curve in the positive direction, and the inner normal to the curve will either be $90°$, or $-90°$, and will preserve its sign for the whole curve. Since the sign of this angle depends on the orientation of the axes, for a particular set of axes we may define a positive direction on the curve as that for which the angle is $90°$, or such that the relation of the positive direction on the curve to the inner normal direction is the same as that of the positive x-axis to the positive y-axis. We regard this direction as bounding the area of the curve taken as positive. Similarly we regard the curve, traversed in the opposite direction, as bounding the area of the curve considered as negative.

Similarly, for a closed surface in three dimensions, which bounds a volume, we may determine at each point a direction of an inner normal, and a direction of an outer normal. In a portion of such a surface, we may have u,v coördinates which are determined by curves such that any u curve cuts each v curve at a non-zero angle. Let us assign positive directions to the u and v curves, for example taking the direction in which v increases as the positive direction along all curves u equals constant. Then, if the orientation of the tangents to the u,v curves and the inner normal is the same as that of the x-, y- and z-axes, we consider the portion of the surface taken as positive for the u,v coördinates to be associated with the volume bounded taken as positive.

If we are working in a two- or three-dimensional space, we consider a particular set of axes for this space as positive. We then regard any set of axes with the same orientation as a positive set, and any set obtained from a positive set by reversing one axis as negative. In calculating a multiple integral, we take dV_n as the positive product, or the negative of this according as the axes are a positive or a negative set. With this convention, we may extend the equations (70) and (80) as well as the formula for the element of volume given in connection with the latter to transformations where the Jacobian is negative throughout.

When we are working at the same time with integrals of different orders, we begin with the definition of a positive orientation for the largest dimension used. We then use this, and the association of the inner normal with the last coördinate, to determine the positive orientation in a figure of dimension one lower, which bounds a surface or volume. Thus, from a set of axes in three dimensions regarded as positive, we can determine when a set of coördinate curves on a surface which bounds a volume is to be taken as positive. From this, we can proceed to determine when a curve on the surface which bounds an area is to be taken as positive.

Our conclusions persist if the bounding curves or surfaces are made up of a finite number of smooth pieces. We call such curves or surfaces piecewise smooth.

234. Green's Theorem in a Plane. This theorem asserts that, if P and Q are any two functions of x and y for which the partial derivatives $\partial P/\partial y$ and $\partial Q/\partial x$ are continuous throughout the area A, of suitably restricted type, then

$$\int_C P\,dx + Q\,dy = \int_A \left(\frac{\partial Q}{\partial x} - \frac{\partial P}{\partial y}\right) dA_{xy}, \tag{124}$$

where the first expression is a line integral as defined in section 180. It is taken about C, a closed piecewise smooth curve bounding the area A. We assume that the area A is of type D^* defined at the end of section 224. Both C and A must be taken with a positive orientation in accordance with the convention of the preceding section.

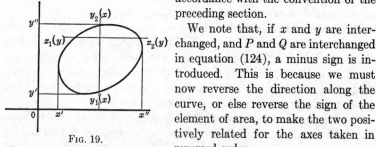

Fig. 19.

We note that, if x and y are interchanged, and P and Q are interchanged in equation (124), a minus sign is introduced. This is because we must now reverse the direction along the curve, or else reverse the sign of the element of area, to make the two positively related for the axes taken in reversed order.

To establish the relation, we first consider the case where the area is such that every straight line through an interior point and parallel to either coördinate axis cuts the boundary in exactly two points. Then if the line with coördinate y cuts the boundary in the points $x_1(y)$ and $x_2(y)$, we have:

$$\int_{x_1(y)}^{x_2(y)} \frac{\partial Q}{\partial x}\,dx = Q(x_2,y) - Q(x_1,y). \tag{125}$$

Since the segment x_1, x_2 consists of inner points of the area, our convention is such that the direction of increasing y is positive for x_2 and negative for x_1. Thus, if y' and y'' are the least and greatest values of y, we shall have:

$$\int_{y'}^{y''} Q(x_2, y)\, dy - \int_{y'}^{y''} Q(x_1, y)\, dy = \int_C Q(x, y)\, dy. \qquad (126)$$

If the curve contains a whole segment with $y = y'$, or y'', this contributes nothing to the line integral on the right.

Similarly, if the line with coördinate x cuts the boundary in $y_1(x)$ and $y_2(x)$, we have:

$$\int_{y_1(x)}^{y_2(x)} \frac{\partial P}{\partial y}\, dy = P(x, y_2) - P(x, y_1). \qquad (127)$$

But, from our convention, the positive direction on the curve is now that of increasing x at y_1 and that of decreasing x at y_2. Thus we have:

$$\int_{x'}^{x''} P(x, y_2)\, dx - \int_{x'}^{x''} P(x, y_1)\, dx = -\int_C P(x, y)\, dx. \qquad (128)$$

We may conclude from the last four equations that

$$\int_C P\, dx + Q\, dy = \int_{y'}^{y''} dy \int_{x_1(y)}^{x_2(y)} \frac{\partial Q}{\partial x}\, dx - \int_{x'}^{x''} dx \int_{y_1(x)}^{y_2(x)} \frac{\partial P}{\partial y}\, dy. \qquad (129)$$

But the repeated integrals may be replaced by double integrals over A, so that the result (124) follows.

The equation may be applied to any area A which is the sum of a finite number of pieces of the kind described, if the right member is taken over the total area, and the left over the entire boundary, which may consist of one or more closed curves. If any of the curves bounding parts of A have arcs in common, these will be oriented oppositely for the two parts, since the inner normal of one part will be the outer normal of the other. Thus these arcs may be neglected, since the integrals for them cancel.

235. Exact Differential Expressions. If P and Q have continuous partial derivatives $\partial P/\partial y$ and $\partial Q/\partial x$, and these are equal in a domain D, then for any area A consisting entirely of points of D the integral in the right member of equation (124) will be zero. Hence the line integral

$$\int P\, dx + Q\, dy \qquad (130)$$

will be zero over every closed path C in D which is the boundary of an area A in D. If M and N are any two points in D, joined by two arcs L_1

and L_2 which together bound an area A in D of simple type, then

$$\int_{L_1} P \, dx + Q \, dy - \int_{L_2} P \, dx + Q \, dy = 0. \tag{131}$$

For the difference is the integral over a closed curve, proceeding from M to N along the first arc and from N to M along the second arc. Thus the integral along L_1 equals the integral along L_2.

If L_1 and L_2 do not bound an area of simple type, for example if they intersect an infinite number of times, we may find a third arc L_3 in D, which bounds a simple area with L_1, and a simple area with L_2. In this case the preceding argument shows that the integral over L_3 equals that over L_1 and also equals that over L_2, so that the latter two are equal, and again the integral over L_1 equals that over L_2.

To describe the hypothesis stated, we say that the differential expression $P \, dx + Q \, dy$ is " exact " in D. If x_0, y_0 is a fixed, and x, y a variable point in D, we may write

$$\int_{x_0, y_0}^{x, y} P \, dx + Q \, dy = F(x, y), \tag{132}$$

at least in a suitably restricted portion of D. For, in such a restricted neighborhood, it will be possible to join x_0, y_0 to x, y by paths related like the L_1 and L_2 mentioned above, and we use paths of this type in calculating the left member of equation (132). Let us take x, y and $x + \Delta x, y$ in the restricted portion of D, and use two paths differing by a straight line segment parallel to the x-axis. If x, y is an interior point of the restricted region, for Δx sufficiently small, the line segment will lie in the restricted region. Then we have:

$$F(x + \Delta x, y) - F(x, y) = \int_{x, y}^{x + \Delta x, y} P \, dx. \tag{133}$$

Since y is constant, this is an ordinary integral, and by the mean value theorem is

$$\Delta x \, P(x', y), \tag{134}$$

where x' is a suitably chosen value between x and $x + \Delta x$. Thus

$$\frac{F(x + \Delta x, y) - F(x, y)}{\Delta x} = P(x', y). \tag{135}$$

From the fact that x' is between x and $x + \Delta x$, and that the function $P(x, y)$ is continuous, we may deduce that:

$$\frac{\partial F}{\partial x} = P. \tag{136}$$

In the same way we may prove that

$$\frac{\partial F}{\partial y} = Q. \tag{137}$$

Thus we have

$$dF = \frac{\partial F}{\partial x}\, dx + \frac{\partial F}{\partial y}\, dy = P\, dx + Q\, dy, \tag{138}$$

so that when $P\, dx + Q\, dy$ is an exact differential expression in the sense of this section, there is a function $F(x,y)$ for which $P\, dx + Q\, dy$ is the total differential as defined in section 211.

We observe that, if $G(x,y)$ is any second function which has $P\, dx + Q\, dy$ as the total differential, we have:

$$d(F - G) = 0 \quad \text{and} \quad \frac{\partial(F - G)}{\partial x} = \frac{\partial(F - G)}{\partial y} = 0. \tag{139}$$

Hence by section 215, the function $F - G$ is a constant in some suitably restricted portion of D. Thus:

$$F - G = k \quad \text{and} \quad F(x,y) = G(x,y) + k, \tag{140}$$

so that

$$F(x,y) = F(x,y) - F(x_0,y_0) = G(x,y) - G(x_0,y_0), \tag{141}$$

and by equation (132)

$$\int_{x_0,y_0}^{x,y} P\, dx + Q\, dy = G(x,y) - G(x_0,y_0). \tag{142}$$

Let us next suppose that we start with the function $F(x,y)$, and form its total differential, which we set equal to $P\, dx + Q\, dy$, as in equation (138). Then, if the partial derivatives of P and Q exist and are continuous, by section 213,

$$\frac{\partial P}{\partial y} = \frac{\partial^2 F}{\partial y\, \partial x} = \frac{\partial^2 F}{\partial x\, \partial y} = \frac{\partial Q}{\partial x}\,. \tag{143}$$

Our discussion shows that, if the derivatives $\partial P/\partial y$ and $\partial Q/\partial x$ both exist and are continuous functions of x and y, the condition

$$\frac{\partial P}{\partial x} = \frac{\partial Q}{\partial y} \tag{144}$$

is both necessary and sufficient for the existence of a function $F(x,y)$ which has $P\, dx + Q\, dy$ as its total differential.

When the condition holds, we call $P\, dx + Q\, dy$ an exact differential expression, and the integral in equation (132) is independent of the path of integration for x,y in a suitably restricted region.

236. Stokes's Theorem. If a portion of a smooth surface in three space is bounded by a piecewise smooth closed curve C, there is a relation analogous to equation (124), namely:

$$\int_C P\,dx + Q\,dy + R\,dz =$$

$$\int_A \left[\left(\frac{\partial R}{\partial y} - \frac{\partial Q}{\partial z} \right) l + \left(\frac{\partial P}{\partial z} - \frac{\partial R}{\partial x} \right) m + \left(\frac{\partial Q}{\partial x} - \frac{\partial P}{\partial y} \right) n \right] dS. \quad (145)$$

In this equation the integral on the left is the line integral taken over the curve C, while that on the right is the surface integral taken over the area A bounded by C. Each of these is to be taken with a positive orientation in accordance with the convention of section 233. The numbers l,m,n are the direction cosines of the normal, or more precisely of that direction on the normal used as the analogue of the z-axis in determining orientation. As in equation (96), they may be obtained by dividing the appropriate direction ratios by the positive square root of the sum of their squares.

For example, if the smooth surface is the x,y plane, the normal to be used is the positive z-axis, so that the direction cosines are $l = m = 0$, $n = 1$ and the equation (145) reduces to equation (124).

The right member of equation (145) is easily recalled if it is written in symbolic determinant form:

$$\int_A \begin{vmatrix} l & m & n \\ \dfrac{\partial}{\partial x} & \dfrac{\partial}{\partial y} & \dfrac{\partial}{\partial z} \\ P & Q & R \end{vmatrix} dS, \quad (146)$$

where the determinant must be expanded in products of elements ordered according to rows, so that the operators of the second row act only on the elements of the third row.

To establish equation (145), it will be sufficient to show that:

$$\int_C P\,dx = \int_A \left(\frac{\partial P}{\partial z}\,m - \frac{\partial P}{\partial y}\,n \right) dS, \quad (147)$$

since the equality of the terms in Q and R will then follow by permuting the letters.

If u and v are parameters in the surface, as in section 232, so chosen as to give a positive system, we may express the integral in the left member of equation (147) in terms of u and v,

$$\int_C P\,dx = \int_C P\,\frac{\partial x}{\partial u}\,du + P\,\frac{\partial x}{\partial v}\,dv. \quad (148)$$

If A' is the area in the u,v plane bounded by the curve in that plane which corresponds to C on the surface, we may apply Green's theorem, equation (124), in the u,v plane and so transform the last expression to:

$$\int_{A'} \left[\frac{\partial}{\partial u}\left(P\frac{\partial x}{\partial v} \right) - \frac{\partial}{\partial v}\left(P\frac{\partial x}{\partial u} \right) \right] dA_{uv}. \qquad (149)$$

The integrand is

$$\frac{\partial P}{\partial u}\frac{\partial x}{\partial v} - \frac{\partial P}{\partial v}\frac{\partial x}{\partial u}, \qquad (150)$$

since the term in the mixed derivative cancels when the surface is such that $\partial^2 x/\partial u\,\partial v$ and $\partial^2 x/\partial v\,\partial u$ exist and are continuous, which we shall assume to be the case.

If we use the relations:

$$\frac{\partial P}{\partial u} = \frac{\partial P}{\partial x}\frac{\partial x}{\partial u} + \frac{\partial P}{\partial y}\frac{\partial y}{\partial u} + \frac{\partial P}{\partial z}\frac{\partial z}{\partial u},$$

$$\frac{\partial P}{\partial v} = \frac{\partial P}{\partial x}\frac{\partial x}{\partial v} + \frac{\partial P}{\partial y}\frac{\partial y}{\partial v} + \frac{\partial P}{\partial z}\frac{\partial z}{\partial v}, \qquad (151)$$

we may reduce the expression for the integrand (150) to

$$-\frac{\partial P}{\partial y} J_{xy} + \frac{\partial P}{\partial z} J_{zx}, \qquad (152)$$

where we use the notation of equation (107).

This shows that

$$\int_C P\,dx = \int_{A'} \frac{\partial P}{\partial z} J_{zx}\,dA_{uv} - \int_{A'} \frac{\partial P}{\partial y} J_{xy}\,dA_{uv}. \qquad (153)$$

If we recall equation (70) for transforming multiple integrals, we may rewrite the right member as

$$\int \frac{\partial P}{\partial z}\,dA_{zx} - \int \frac{\partial P}{\partial y}\,dA_{xy}, \qquad (154)$$

where the integrals are taken over areas in the zx plane and in the xy plane which correspond to A'.

But because of our convention as to orientation we have:

$$dS = \sec \beta\,dA_{zx} = \frac{1}{m}\,dA_{zx} \qquad (155)$$

and

$$dS = \sec \gamma\,dA_{xy} = \frac{1}{n}\,dA_{xy}. \qquad (156)$$

Here equation (155) is obtained from equation (156) by permuting the letters, and equation (156) is obtained from equation (88) and equation (96). We took the positive sign for the radical in equation (88) because the positive area was associated with the standard orientation of the x- and y-axes.

From equations (153) through (156) it follows that:

$$\int_C P \, dx = \int_A \left(\frac{\partial P}{\partial z} m - \frac{\partial P}{\partial y} n \right) dS, \tag{157}$$

which is the equation we were seeking to prove.

By using equations (155), (156) and the third equation obtained from them by permuting the letters, we may write

$$\int \left(\frac{\partial R}{\partial y} - \frac{\partial Q}{\partial z} \right) dA_{yz} + \int \left(\frac{\partial P}{\partial z} - \frac{\partial R}{\partial x} \right) dA_{zx} + \int \left(\frac{\partial Q}{\partial x} - \frac{\partial P}{\partial y} \right) dA_{xy},$$
$$\tag{158}$$

in place of the right member of equation (145). The symbolic form analogous to equation (146) is:

$$\int \begin{vmatrix} dA_{yz} & dA_{zx} & dA_{xy} \\ \dfrac{\partial}{\partial x} & \dfrac{\partial}{\partial y} & \dfrac{\partial}{\partial z} \\ P & Q & R \end{vmatrix}. \tag{159}$$

In the expression (158) the elements of integration must be given proper algebraic signs, determined by the relations:

$$dA_{yz} = l \, dS, \ dA_{zx} = m \, dS, \ dA_{xy} = n \, dS, \tag{160}$$

so that for actual calculation the form (145) is more explicit.

237. Green's Theorem in Three Dimensions. If P, Q and R are three functions of x, y and z which, with the partial derivatives $\partial P/\partial x$, $\partial Q/\partial y$, and $\partial R/\partial z$, are continuous in all three variables in some domain, D, we have:

$$\int_V \left(\frac{\partial P}{\partial x} + \frac{\partial Q}{\partial y} + \frac{\partial R}{\partial z} \right) dV = - \int_S (Pl + Qm + Rn) \, dS, \tag{161}$$

where the triple integral on the left is taken over a volume V, and the double integral on the right over a closed surface S which bounds the volume V. We assume S and V lie in D, and the orientations are so taken that the x-, y-, z-axes have the same orientation as the parametric directions for u and v in S, followed by the direction of the inner normal to the surface, l, m, n. We also assume that V is a domain of type D^*, defined at the end of section 228, and that its boundary, S, is a piecewise smooth surface.

We proceed as in section 234, assuming at first that every straight line through an interior point of V and parallel to one of the coördinate axes cuts S in exactly two points. Then, for x and y fixed, if the points in V form the segment z_1, z_2, we have:

$$\int_{z_1}^{z_2} \frac{\partial R}{\partial z}\, dz = R(x,y,z_2) - R(x,y,z_1). \tag{162}$$

Thus, since the triple integral equals the repeated integral in any order when the integrand is continuous, we have:

$$\int \frac{\partial R}{\partial z}\, dV = \int [R(x,y,z_2) - R(x,y,z_1)]\, dx\, dy$$

$$= \int R(x,y,z_2)\, |dA_{xy}| - \int R(x,y,z_1)\, dA_{xy}. \tag{163}$$

Our conventions make the inner normal at z_1 in the direction of increasing z, while that at z_2 is in the direction of decreasing z. Moreover, parts of S with normals parallel to the xy plane have a projection on the xy plane of zero area. Hence we have:

$$\int_V \frac{\partial R}{\partial z}\, dV = - \int_S R\, dA_{xy} = - \int Rn\, dS, \tag{164}$$

by equation (156).

Similarly, the terms in P and Q in equation (161) may be shown to be equal.

If we use the signed elements given by equation (160), we may write in place of equation (161):

$$\int_V \left(\frac{\partial P}{\partial x} + \frac{\partial Q}{\partial y} + \frac{\partial R}{\partial z} \right) dV = - \left[\int P\, dA_{yz} + \int Q\, dA_{zx} + \int R\, dA_{xy} \right]. \tag{165}$$

The minus sign in equations (161) and (165) disappears if we replace the direction cosines by those for the direction along the outer normal, and modify the signs of the elements to conform with equation (160).

The result applies to any volume V which is the sum of a finite number of pieces of the kind already discussed, as we may show by an argument similar to that used at the end of section 234.

EXERCISES XI

1. Prove that, when $f(x,y)$ is continuous, and $a < b$

$$\int_a^b dy \int_y^b f(x,y)\, dx = \int_a^b dx \int_a^x f(x,y)\, dy.$$

2. Show that, if $f(x,y)$ is continuous, and for all x_0, y_0 in some two-dimensional domain,

$$\int_a^{x_0} dx \int_b^{y_0} f(x,y)\, dy = F(x_0, y_0), \quad \text{then} \quad \frac{\partial^2 F}{\partial x\, \partial y} = f(x,y).$$

Conversely, show that if the second condition holds, then

$$\int_a^{x_0} dx \int_b^{y_0} f(x,y)\, dy = F(x_0, y_0) - F(a, y_0) - F(x_0, b) + F(a, b).$$

3. Show that the area bounded by the lines $x = a$, $x = b$, $y = 0$ and $y = f(x)$, where $f(x) \geqq 0$, is equal to $\int_a^b f(x)\, dx$, or $\int_a^b y\, dx$, if $a < b$.

4. Show that the area of a domain of type D of section 224 equals the line integral $-\int_C y\, dx$, taken over C, the boundary of D, in the positive direction. *Hint:* Take a new x-axis below the points of C, and use problem 3. Check by using Green's theorem.

5. Deduce $\int_C x\, dy$ and $1/2 \int_C (x\, dy - y\, dx)$ as alternative expressions for the area of the domain of problem 4.

6. Using a procedure similar to that of section 225, with comparison areas G' and G'' made up of sectors, and noting that the definitions given of content or area make area $G'' \geqq$ area G if G'' includes all points of G, show that the area of a sector is given by $1/2 \int_a^b r^2\, d\theta$, with $r = f(\theta)$ the equation in polar coördinates of the curve bounding the sector, together with $\theta = a$, $\theta = b$.

7. Identify $1/2 \int (x\, dy - y\, dx)$, taken along the arc bounding the sector, with the integral of problem 6. *Hint:* Either decompose the sector into triangles and areas like that in problem 3, or else note that $x = r \cos\theta$, $y = r \sin\theta$ implies that $x\dfrac{dy}{dt} - y\dfrac{dx}{dt} = r^2\dfrac{d\theta}{dt}$.

8. Deduce from problem 6 that in polar coördinates the repeated integral $\int d\theta \int r\, dr$ represents area. Hence the same is true of the double integral, or repeated integral in reverse order. For the double integral, verify directly by applying the transformation formula of section 229 to $\int dA = \int dx\, dy$.

9. Show that in the transformation to orthogonal curvilinear coördinates of problem 32 of Exercises X, $\left[\dfrac{\partial(x_1,x_2,x_3)}{\partial(u_1,u_2,u_3)}\right]^2 = h_1^2 h_2^2 h_3^2$. Hence show that

$$\int dx_1\, dx_2\, dx_3 = \int h_1 h_2 h_3\, du_1\, du_2\, du_3,$$ taken over corresponding volumes, with proper signs given h_1, h_2, h_3. *Hint:* Use the rule of multiplication of determinants of problem 19, Exercises X and the relations of problem 31 of Exercises X.

10. For the spherical polar coördinates of problem 34 of Exercises X, show that the integral for volume is $\int r^3 \sin\phi\, dr\, d\phi\, d\theta$. *Hint:* Use problem 9.

11. Let $z = f(x,y)$ represent a portion of a surface, and let the projections in the x,y plane of the curves for which γ is constant be found. If the area bounded by one of these curves alone, or with a fixed boundary independent of the curves is $H(\gamma)$, show that the area of the surface may be expressed as $\int H'(\gamma) \sec\gamma\, d\gamma$.

Hint: If ΔH is the area between the curves for γ and $\gamma + \Delta\gamma$, the corresponding part of S, the area of the surface is $\Delta H \sec\overline{\gamma}$, where $\overline{\gamma}$ is a suitable value between γ and $\gamma + \Delta\gamma$.

12. If $r^2 = x^2 + y^2$, $z = f(r)$ is the equation of a surface of revolution. Show that the surface area between two values of r may be written $2\pi \int r\, ds$, where s is arc length. *Hint:* Use problem 11.

13. If one nappe of a cone with vertex at the origin cuts off a surface area Ω from a unit sphere, Ω is called the solid angle for the vertex. If the cone cuts off a simple closed curve on any surface, bounding a surface S, show that the solid angle $\Omega = \displaystyle\int_S \frac{\cos(r,N)}{r^2}\, dS = \int_S \frac{xl + ym + zn}{r^3}\, dS$. Here $r^2 = x^2 + y^2 + z^2$, (r,N) means the angle between the radius drawn from the origin, and the normal N to the surface. The direction cosines of N are l, m, n.

14. Prove Gauss's theorem, that the integral over a simple closed surface, $\displaystyle\int \frac{\cos(r,N)}{r^2}\, dS$, is 4π if S includes the origin as an interior point, 2π if the origin is a boundary point of S at which S has a tangent plane, and 0 if the origin is an exterior point. *Hint:* Use the interpretation of problem 13.

15. If P, Q and R are such functions of x, y and z that $\displaystyle\int_C P\, dx + Q\, dy + R\, dz = f(x,y,z) - f(x_0,y_0,z_0)$ is independent of the path joining $A_0 = (x_0,y_0,z_0)$ and $A = (x,y,z)$, show that $P = \dfrac{\partial f}{\partial x}$, $Q = \dfrac{\partial f}{\partial y}$ and $R = \dfrac{\partial f}{\partial z}$. Also prove the converse.

16. Show that if $r = \sqrt{x^2 + y^2 + z^2}$, then $\displaystyle\int g(r)(x\, dx + y\, dy + z\, dz)$ is independent of the path. In particular evaluate the integral when $g(r) = r^n$.

17. The relation $\dfrac{\partial P}{\partial x} + \dfrac{\partial Q}{\partial y} + \dfrac{\partial R}{\partial z} = 0$ is a necessary and sufficient condition

that $\displaystyle\int (Pl + Qm + Rn)\, dS$ should equal zero when taken over any closed

surface. An example is $P = f(y,z)$, $Q = g(z,x)$, $R = h(x,y)$.

18. If $P = \dfrac{\partial C}{\partial y} - \dfrac{\partial B}{\partial z}$, $Q = \dfrac{\partial A}{\partial z} - \dfrac{\partial C}{\partial x}$, $R = \dfrac{\partial B}{\partial x} - \dfrac{\partial A}{\partial y}$, then

$$\frac{\partial P}{\partial x} + \frac{\partial Q}{\partial y} + \frac{\partial R}{\partial z} = 0.$$

Conversely, if this last condition holds, there are functions A, B, C for which the first three equations hold. *Hint:* If A is any function, and B is determined to within an additive function of y and z by the third relation, then C is determined to within an additive function of z from the differential, exact in x and y

$$dC = \left(\frac{\partial A}{\partial z} - Q\right) dx + \left(P + \frac{\partial B}{\partial z}\right) dy.$$

19. The condition $\dfrac{\partial P}{\partial x} + \dfrac{\partial Q}{\partial y} + \dfrac{\partial R}{\partial z} = 0$ is a necessary and sufficient condition

that $\displaystyle\int (Pl + Qm + Rn)\, dS$ taken over a portion of a surface bounded by a

simple closed curve L should depend only on the boundary, L. *Hint:* For the necessity, note that two surfaces bounded by C together make a closed surface, and use section 237 or problem 17. For the sufficiency, use problem 18 and section 236 to reduce the integral to the line integral $\displaystyle\int_L (A\, dx + B\, dy + C\, dz)$.

20. If V is the volume bounded by a closed surface S, N denotes the outer normal, and otherwise the notation is as in problem 13,

$$V = 1/3 \int_S r \cos\,(r,N)\, dS = 1/3 \int_S (lx + my + nz)\, dS.$$

21. If P, Q, R are homogeneous second degree polynomials in x, y and z, and S is a closed surface bounding a volume whose center of gravity is at the origin, show that $\displaystyle\int (Pl + Qm + Rn)\, dS = 0$.

22. Show that:

$$\int_A u\, \Delta\, v\, dA_{xy} + \int_A \left(\frac{\partial u}{\partial x}\frac{\partial v}{\partial x} + \frac{\partial u}{\partial y}\frac{\partial v}{\partial y}\right) dA_{xy} = \int_C u\,\frac{dv}{dN}\, ds,$$

where C is a closed curve bounding A, $\Delta\, v = \dfrac{\partial^2 v}{\partial x^2} + \dfrac{\partial^2 v}{\partial y^2}$, and $\dfrac{dv}{dN}$ is the directional derivative of v along the outer normal to the curve C. *Hint:* Apply Green's theorem with $P = -u\dfrac{\partial v}{\partial y}$ and $Q = u\dfrac{\partial v}{\partial x}$.

23. With the notation of problem 22, show that:

$$\int_A (u \Delta v - v \Delta u) \, dA_{xy} = \int_C \left(u \frac{dv}{dN} - v \frac{du}{dN} \right) ds.$$

This is often called Green's theorem.

24. With the notation of problem 22, show that:

$$\int_A \Delta u \, dA_{xy} = \int_C \frac{du}{dN} \, ds.$$

25. Show that:

$$\int_V u \Delta v \, dV + \int_V \left(\frac{\partial u}{\partial x} \frac{\partial v}{\partial x} + \frac{\partial u}{\partial y} \frac{\partial v}{\partial y} + \frac{\partial u}{\partial y} \frac{\partial v}{\partial y} \right) dV = \int_S u \frac{dv}{dN} \, dS,$$

where S is a closed surface bounding the volume V, $\Delta v = \dfrac{\partial^2 v}{\partial x^2} + \dfrac{\partial^2 v}{\partial y^2} + \dfrac{\partial^2 v}{\partial z^2}$,

and $\dfrac{dv}{dN}$ is the directional derivative of v along the outer normal to the surface S.

Hint: Apply Green's theorem in three dimensions with $P = u \dfrac{\partial v}{\partial x}$, $Q = u \dfrac{\partial v}{\partial y}$,

$R = u \dfrac{\partial v}{\partial y}$.

26. With the notation of problem 25, show that:

$$\int_V (u \Delta v - v \Delta u) \, dV = \int_S \left(u \frac{dv}{dN} - v \frac{du}{dN} \right) dS.$$

27. With the notation of problem 25, show that:

$$\int_V \Delta u \, dV = \int_S \frac{du}{dN} \, dS.$$

28. We may form multiple Duhamel sums by replacing each y_i in $F(y_i)$ by $f_i(x_1, x_2, \cdots, x_n)$ and otherwise proceeding as in section 164. Show that, when all the functions are continuous, and we use a sequence of subdivisions for which the maximum diameter, $\delta_M \to 0$, the Duhamel sums approach the multiple integral $\int F\,[f_i(x_p)] \, dV_n$, where $dV_n = dx_1 \, dx_2 \cdots dx_n$.

CHAPTER XII

SEQUENCES OF FUNCTIONS

Similar to a sequence of numbers approaching a limit, we may have a sequence of functions approaching a limiting function. When the functions of the sequence are continuous, the condition that the limiting function is continuous reduces to the condition that two operations of taking limits give the same result regardless of the order in which they are applied. An important sufficient condition for this is related to the notion of uniform convergence of a sequence of functions. We accordingly introduce this notion and apply it to other problems involving two limit operations. In connection with the integral of a limiting function we discuss sequences of functions which converge in the mean.

We also investigate certain conditions under which it is possible to select, from an infinite set of functions, a second infinite sequence of functions which approaches a limiting function. The conditions involve a property known as equi-continuity. We discuss this property, and develop certain simple conditions on a sequence which guarantee that it is equi-continuous.

238. Limiting Function. Consider a variable function, $f_t(x)$, defined over some range of the real variable x for an infinite succession of values of t. As in section 17, this succession may be discrete or continuous. As an example of a discrete succession of functions, we have the sum of the first n terms of an infinite series of functions,

$$s_n(x) = \sum_{k=1}^{n} u_k(x), \tag{1}$$

or the product to n factors of an infinite product:

$$p_n(x) = \prod_{k=1}^{n} [1 + u_k(x)]. \tag{2}$$

A continuous succession of functions of the variable x may be obtained from any function of two variables $g(x,y)$, defined for

$$a \leqq x \leqq b, \quad c \leqq y \leqq d, \tag{3}$$

by the following procedure. Select a particular value of y, say y_0, in the open interval c,d and for any continuous sequence of values of t in the interval c,d with $t \to y_0$, define:

$$f_t(x) = g(x,t),$$

(4)

so that each function of the sequence is defined for $a \leqq x \leqq b$.

Let us return to the consideration of a particular sequence of functions, $f_t(x)$. Suppose that there is a function $F(x)$ such that, for a particular value of x, say x_0, we have:

$$\lim f_t(x_0) = F(x_0).$$

(5)

That is, for x_0, corresponding to any positive quantity ϵ, there is a point in the succession of values $T(\epsilon,x_0)$, such that

$$|f_t(x_0) - F(x_0)| < \epsilon, \quad \text{for } t \text{ beyond } T(\epsilon,x_0)$$

(6)

in the succession of values of t.

If the relation (5) holds for all values of x_0 in a given range, say the closed interval a,b, we write:

$$\lim f_t(x) = F(x), \quad a \leqq x \leqq b,$$

(7)

and say that in this range the sequence $f_t(x)$ approaches the limiting function $F(x)$.

239. Uniform Approach. As we have indicated in the notation $T(\epsilon,x_0)$, the values of T for which the condition (6) holds will presumably depend on x_0, as well as on ϵ. In fact, it may be impossible to find any T that will serve for a given ϵ for all values of x in the range. For example, if

$$f_t(x) = \frac{tx}{tx + 1},$$

(8)

where t steadily increases through all positive values from 0 to $+\infty$, and the range for x is $0 \leqq x \leqq 1$, we have

$$F(x) = 1, \text{ if } x \neq 0; \text{ and } F(0) = 0.$$

(9)

For $x_0 > 0$, the condition (6) becomes:

$$|F(x_0) - f_t(x_0)| = \frac{1}{tx_0 + 1} < \epsilon.$$

(10)

For $\epsilon < 1$, this will hold if and only if:

$$t > \frac{\dfrac{1}{\epsilon} - 1}{x_0}.$$

(11)

Thus we may take the right member of the inequality (11) as $T(\epsilon,x_0)$. Any larger value may be used, but no smaller value will serve.

Since $\qquad\qquad F(0) - f_t(0) = 0,$ for all $t,$ $\qquad\qquad$ (12)

we may take $T(\epsilon,0) = 1$ for all values of $\epsilon.$

However, for values of x_0 near 0, the values of

$$\min T(\epsilon,x_0) = \frac{\dfrac{1}{\epsilon} - 1}{x_0} \qquad\qquad (13)$$

are unbounded, since for ϵ fixed and $x_0 \to 0,$ the expression on the right becomes infinite.

Thus in this example for any ϵ with $0 < \epsilon < 1,$ no value will serve as a $T(\epsilon,x_0)$ for all x_0 in the range $0 \leqq x_0 \leqq 1.$

For some sequences $f_t(x),$ for any positive $\epsilon,$ there is a value which will serve as a $T(\epsilon,x_0)$ for this ϵ and all x_0 in the range considered. Thus, if we consider the sequence of functions defined by equation (8) for all values of x in the range $1/2 \leqq x \leqq 1,$ it follows from the relation (11) that $2/\epsilon$ will serve as a $T(\epsilon,x_0)$ for all x_0 in this latter range.

To describe the second situation, we define:

A sequence of functions $f_t(x)$ approaches a limiting function $F(x)$ uniformly in x for a certain range, if, for any given small positive quantity $\epsilon,$ there is a value $t_\epsilon,$ independent of $x,$ such that

$$|F(x) - f_t(x)| < \epsilon, \quad \text{for } t \text{ beyond } t_\epsilon, \qquad\qquad (14)$$

for all x in the range considered.

We use the phrase uniform convergence, to indicate that the limiting function is uniformly approached, and non-uniform convergence to indicate that this is not the case. In particular, we say that an infinite series or product whose terms are functions of x converges uniformly in a certain range, if the partial sums $s_n(x),$ or partial products, $p_n(x)$ approach their limits uniformly for this range.

As the example (8) shows, we may have approach to a limit non-uniform in one range, but uniform in some smaller range.

240. The Cauchy Criterion. If a sequence of functions converges uniformly for a certain range in $x,$ for any given positive quantity $\eta,$ we may take $\epsilon = \eta/2,$ and find a t' equal to a t_ϵ for which the relation (14) holds. If then, u and v are any two values which follow t' in the succession of values, we may put $t = u,$ $\epsilon = \eta/2$ or $t = v,$ $\epsilon = \eta/2$ in the relation (14). From this, as in section 26, we may conclude that:

$$|f_u(x) - f_v(x)| < \eta, \quad \text{for } u,v \text{ beyond } t', \qquad\qquad (15)$$

and all x in the range considered. Thus, when the convergence is uniform, the Cauchy condition holds uniformly throughout the range, in the sense that there is a t' for which equation (15) holds which depends on ϵ but is independent of x.

Conversely, if the Cauchy condition may be satisfied for a sequence of functions $f_t(x)$, for every positive value of ϵ, uniformly throughout a certain range, then the sequence of functions $f_t(x)$ approaches a limiting function $F(x)$ uniformly for this range.

For, by the result of section 26, for any x_0 in the range, the sequence of values $f_t(x_0)$ approaches a limit. We define the function $F(x)$ at x_0 as the value of this limit.

For any positive quantity η, select η' with $0 < \eta' < \eta$. Then there is a t' independent of x, such that the condition (15) holds for η'. Thus, for any x_0 in the range:

$$|f_u(x_0) - f_v(x_0)| < \eta', \quad \text{for } u,v \text{ beyond } t'. \tag{16}$$

Since this relation holds for all v beyond t', we may let v run through the sequence of values of t beyond t'. Then, since under these conditions $f_v(x_0) \to F(x_0)$, we may conclude from the relation (16) that:

$$|f_u(x_0) - F(x_0)| \leq \eta', \quad \text{for } u \text{ beyond } t'. \tag{17}$$

Since $\eta' < \eta$, and the value of t' is independent of x_0, it follows that:

$$|f_t(x) - F(x)| < \eta, \quad \text{for } t \text{ beyond } t', \tag{18}$$

which is the condition for uniform approach to a limit.

Our result may be formulated as a theorem:

A necessary and sufficient condition for a sequence of functions $f_t(x)$ to approach a limiting function $F(x)$ uniformly is that the Cauchy condition (15) can be satisfied for every positive ϵ, uniformly in x for the range considered, that is, by values of t' independent of x.

241. Interchange of Order of Limits. Consider the values of $F(x)$, near $x = a$, where $F(x)$ is the limiting function of a sequence $f_t(x)$. If these values approach a limit, it is

$$\lim_{x \to a} F(x) = \lim_{x \to a} \left[\lim_{t} f_t(x) \right]. \tag{19}$$

Again, if the limits exist, we may take the limits on x and t in reverse order and consider:

$$\lim_{t} \left[\lim_{x \to a} f_t(x) \right]. \tag{20}$$

Even when all the limits exist, the results of (19) and (20) may be different. Thus, for the sequence defined by equation (8), and $a = 0$, we have:

$$\lim_{x \to 0} \left[\lim_{t \to +\infty} \frac{tx}{tx + 1} \right] = 1, \tag{21}$$

while

$$\lim_{t \to +\infty} \left[\lim_{x \to 0} \frac{tx}{tx + 1} \right] = 0. \tag{22}$$

However, for some sequences $f_t(x)$ the two combinations of operations given by the expressions (19) and (20) do have the same value. We give a sufficient condition for this in the theorem:

If $\lim\limits_{t} f_t(x) = F(x)$ *exists, and the approach is uniform for some range in x including the value* $x = a$, *and* $\lim\limits_{x \to a} f_t(x) = G(t)$, *for all t beyond a certain one* t'' *in the sequence, then:*

$$\lim_{x \to a} \left[\lim_{t} f_t(x) \right] \quad and \quad \lim_{t} \left[\lim_{x \to a} f_t(x) \right] \tag{23}$$

both exist and are equal.

From the assumed uniform approach, for any positive quantity ϵ, there is a t_ϵ such that, for all values of x in the range:

$$|f_t(x) - F(x)| < \epsilon, \quad \text{for } t \text{ beyond } t_\epsilon. \tag{24}$$

We take t_ϵ beyond t''. Then, for u and v each values of t beyond t_ϵ, we have:

$$|f_u(x) - f_v(x)| < 2\epsilon, \quad \text{for } u,v \text{ beyond } t_\epsilon. \tag{25}$$

Since this relation holds for all x in the range, we may let $x \to a$ and deduce that

$$|G(u) - G(v)| \leqq 2\epsilon, \quad \text{for } u,v \text{ beyond } t_\epsilon. \tag{26}$$

This is the Cauchy convergence criterion and since it holds for any value of ϵ, with a suitable t_ϵ, we may conclude that, as t runs through its succession, $G(t)$ approaches a limit. Let A denote this limit. Then:

$$A = \lim_{t} G(t) = \lim_{t} \left[\lim_{x \to a} f_t(x) \right]. \tag{27}$$

Let us now select a particular value of t beyond t_ϵ for which $G(t)$ is within ϵ of its limit A. We denote this by w. Then

$$|A - G(w)| < \epsilon. \tag{28}$$

But by the relation (24) which holds for $t = w$,

$$|f_w(x) - F(x)| < \epsilon. \tag{29}$$

Again, since $f_w(x)$ approaches $G(w)$ when $x \to a$, there is a δ such that:

$$|G(w) - f_w(x)| < \epsilon, \quad \text{for} \quad |x - a| < \delta. \tag{30}$$

From the last three relations we may conclude that:

if $\quad |x - a| < \delta, \qquad |A - F(x)| < 3\epsilon. \tag{31}$

This proves that:

$$\lim_{x \to a} F(x) = A, \tag{32}$$

or
$$A = \lim_{x \to a}\left[\lim_t f_t(x) \right]. \tag{33}$$

Equations (27) and (33) together show that the two repeated limits each exist and have equal values. This is the conclusion of the theorem.

242. Two-Dimensional Limits. The theorem of the last section holds when $x \to a$ is replaced by $x \to a+$. In this case it is sufficient if the range of uniformity includes a as a left end point. Similarly we may have $x \to a-$, or $x \to +\infty$, or $-\infty$. With these extensions, x and t play coördinate rôles. Thus we are led to write $g(x,t)$ in place of $f_t(x)$. If we replace t by y, and for definiteness consider the case where $x \to a$ and $y \to b$, the theorem shows that if for all x in some interval including a, $\lim_{y \to b} g(x,y)$ exists and if $\lim_{x \to a} g(x,y)$ exists for all y in some interval including b, and if one of these limits exists uniformly in the variable held fast for all values in its range, then the repeated limits both exist and are equal:

$$\lim_{x \to a}\left[\lim_{y \to b} g(x,y) \right] = \lim_{y \to b}\left[\lim_{x \to a} g(x,y) \right]. \tag{34}$$

A related, but not identical question, is the existence of the double or two-dimensional limit:

$$\lim_{x,y \to a,b} g(x,y) = A. \tag{35}$$

We define this by a method analogous to that used in section 35 to define a continuous function of two variables. That is, we write the relation (35) if, for any positive ϵ, there is a δ such that:

if $\quad |x - a| < \delta, \quad |y - b| < \delta, \quad |A - g(x,y)| < \epsilon. \tag{36}$

As in section 35 we may show that this is equivalent to requiring that for every discrete sequence of points (x_n, y_n) for which $x_n \to a$, $y_n \to b$, we have $\lim g(x_n, y_n) = A$.

We may prove that, *if one of the repeated limits exists and if the inner or first limit exists uniformly with respect to the second variable throughout the range used for it in the repeated limit, then the double limit exists.*

For, if when $y \to b$, $g(x,y)$ approaches $F(x)$ uniformly in y, for $|x - a| < h$, we have for some δ':

$$|F(x) - g(x,y)| < \epsilon \quad \text{for} \quad |y - b| < \delta', \quad |x - a| < h. \quad (37)$$

And, if the repeated limit exists,

$$A = \lim_{x \to a} \left[\lim_{y \to b} g(x,y) \right] = \lim_{x \to a} F(x). \quad (38)$$

Thus, there is a $\delta'' < h$ such that:

$$|A - F(x)| < \epsilon \quad \text{for} \quad |x - a| < \delta''. \quad (39)$$

We may conclude from the relations (37) and (39) that:

$$|A - g(x,y)| < 2\epsilon, \quad \text{if} \quad |x - a| < \delta, \quad |y - b| < \delta, \quad (40)$$

where δ is min (δ', δ''). This is essentially the relation (36) which defines the double limit, so that the double limit exists, and equals the repeated limit under the assumed conditions.

Since the conditions of the theorem of section 241 include the uniformity and imply the existence of the repeated limit, when these conditions hold, the double limit exists and equals the common value of the two repeated limits.

However, the theorem just proved may apply when only one of the repeated limits exists. Thus,

if
$$g(x,y) = y \sin \frac{1}{x}, \; x \neq 0, \; g(0,y) = 0, \quad (41)$$

and if we take 0,0 as the a,b of the discussion we have:

$$\lim_{x \to 0} \left[\lim_{y \to 0} g(x,y) \right] = 0, \quad (42)$$

with the limit for y uniform in x, so that the double limit exists and equals zero. However, when $y \neq 0$ and $x \to 0$, $g(x,y)$ does not approach a limit, so that the repeated limit in the reversed order does not exist.

We also note that the double limit may exist, without either repeated limit existing. An example, with $a,b = 0,0$, is:

$$g(0,y) = g(x,0) = 0,$$

and
$$g(x,y) = (x^2 + y^2) \sin \frac{1}{x} \sin \frac{1}{y} \text{ if } x \neq 0, \quad y \neq 0. \quad (43)$$

243. Continuous Limiting Function. The equations (8) and (9) show that the limiting function may be discontinuous on a range even if all the functions of the sequence approaching it are continuous on the range. However, if all the functions $f_t(x)$ are continuous at the point, and the sequence approaches $F(x)$ uniformly in x for some range including the point a as an interior point, then $F(x)$ is continuous at a. For, by the theorem of section 241, we have:

$$\lim_{x \to a} \left[\lim_t f_t(x) \right] = \lim_t \left[\lim_{x \to a} f_t(x) \right]. \qquad (44)$$

But each function $f_t(x)$ is continuous at a, so that:

$$\lim_{x \to a} f_t(x) = f_t(a). \qquad (45)$$

From this and the fact that:

$$\lim_t f_t(x) = F(x), \qquad (46)$$

we may deduce from equation (44) that:

$$\lim_{x \to a} F(x) = \lim_t f_t(a) = F(a), \qquad (47)$$

which is the condition that $F(x)$ be continuous at a.

The same result holds for a range, and consequently we have the theorem:

The limiting function $F(x)$ of a sequence of functions $f_t(x)$ is continuous in any range in which the separate functions $f_t(x)$ are all continuous, and the sequence approaches $F(x)$ uniformly.

Since elementary operations do not disturb continuity, if the terms of an infinite series are each continuous on a range and the series converges uniformly for this range, then the sum of the series is continuous on this range.

Again, if the factors of an infinite product are each continuous functions on a range and the product converges uniformly for this range, then the function given by the infinite product is continuous on this range.

In all these results the range may be a closed interval, the result holding for the end points by our conventions as to continuity at these points and the fact that our basic theorem holds for $x \to a+$ or $x \to b-$

244. Improper Integrals. Let

$$F(x) = \int_a^\infty g(u,x) \, du \qquad (48)$$

be a convergent improper integral for all values of the parameter x in a certain range. Then, for x in this range

$$F(x) = \lim_{t \to \infty} \int_a^t g(u,x) \, du. \qquad (49)$$

Thus we have a sequence of functions:

$$f_t(x) = \int_a^t g(u,x) \, du, \tag{50}$$

converging to a limiting function. By the Cauchy criterion of section 240, the sequence will converge uniformly if, for each positive ϵ, there is a t_ϵ such that:

$$|f_{t'}(x) - f_{t''}(x)| = \left| \int_{t'}^{t''} g(u,x) \, du \right| < \epsilon, \quad \text{for} \quad t', \ t'' > t_\epsilon. \tag{51}$$

In case $g(u,x)$ is a continuous function of u and x for all values of $u > a$ and all x in the range, the integral in equation (50) is a continuous function of x, by section 220. Hence, if this is the case and if we have uniform convergence for x in the range, by the theorem of section 243, the limiting function or the improper integral in equation (48) will be a continuous function of x.

With slight modification the discussion applies to improper integrals of the second kind.

We may define improper repeated integrals as the limits of proper repeated integrals. If the repeated limits

$$\lim_{x \to \infty} \left[\lim_{y \to \infty} \int_a^x du \int_b^y f(u,v) \, dv \right] \tag{52}$$

and

$$\lim_{y \to \infty} \left[\lim_{x \to \infty} \int_a^x du \int_b^y f(u,v) \, dv \right] \tag{53}$$

both exist, we may not deduce from the fact that:

$$\int_a^x du \int_b^y dv \, f(u,v) = \int_b^y dv \int_a^x f(u,v) \, du \tag{54}$$

that the improper integrals

$$\int_a^\infty du \int_b^\infty dv \, f(u,v), \quad \text{and} \quad \int_b^\infty dv \int_a^\infty f(u,v) \, du \tag{55}$$

exist and have the same value (see problem 27).

If either of the integrals in (55) exist when $f(u,v)$ is replaced by $g(u,v)$ where $|f(u,v)| \leq g(u,v)$, then both the integrals exist and are equal as we see by considering the double series of positive terms

$$\sum\sum a_{mn} \quad \text{where} \quad a_{mn} = \int_n^{n+1} du \int_m^{m+1} g(u,v) \, dv. \tag{56}$$

245. Weierstrass M-test for Uniform Convergence. An important and useful test for uniform convergence of a series is contained in the following theorem:

If $\sum M_k$ is a convergent series of positive terms and if $\sum u_k(x)$ is a series of functions, and if for all k, and all x in a certain range,

$$|u_k(x)| \leqq M_k, \tag{57}$$

then the series $u_k(x)$ converges uniformly in x for the range in question.

Since the series with terms M_k converges, by the theorem of section 188, for each positive quantity ϵ, there is some positive integer N_ϵ, such that, for any integer $k > N_\epsilon$, and all positive integers p

$$|M_{k+1} + M_{k+2} + \cdots + M_{k+p}| < \epsilon. \tag{58}$$

But it follows from the condition (57) that:

$$\left| \sum_{r=1}^{p} u_{k+r}(x) \right| \leqq \sum_{r=1}^{p} |u_{k+r}(x)| \leqq \sum_{r=1}^{p} M_{k+r}. \tag{59}$$

Since the M_k are all positive, the last sum is the same as the sum in the left member of the relation (58), and:

$$\left| \sum_{r=1}^{p} u_{k+r}(x) \right| < \epsilon, \quad \text{if} \quad k > N_\epsilon \quad \text{and} \quad p > 0. \tag{60}$$

That is, the partial sums of the series with terms $u_k(x)$ satisfy the Cauchy convergence criterion uniformly in x for the range considered, and therefore by section 240 the series converges uniformly in x for this range. This proves the theorem.

The condition of the theorem is sufficient but is not necessary. In fact, for some uniformly convergent series there may not be any series of constants M_k for which the condition (57) holds with M_k the terms of a convergent series.

For example, let the range be $0 \leqq x \leqq 1$, and let

$$u_k(x) = 0, \text{ if } x \neq \frac{1}{k}, \quad \text{and} \quad u_k\left(\frac{1}{k}\right) = \frac{1}{k}. \tag{61}$$

The remainder after N terms of the series will be less than ϵ, if $N > 1/\epsilon$, so that the series converges uniformly. However, any M_k satisfying the condition (57) for the entire range will have $M_k \geqq 1/k$, so that the series $\sum M_k$ will diverge.

In place of using a convergent series of positive constants, we could use a series of positive functions of x, $m_k(x)$, uniformly convergent in x for the range in question and such that, for this range:

$$|u_k(x)| \leqq m_k(x). \tag{62}$$

In this case, we deduce from section 240 that for some N_ϵ,

$$\left| \sum_{r=1}^{p} m_k(x) \right| < \epsilon, \text{ if } k > N_\epsilon \text{ and } p > 0. \tag{63}$$

We may use this in place of the relation (58), and complete the argument exactly as before.

We describe the relation (62) by saying that the function $m_k(x)$ dominates the function $u_k(x)$. To indicate that this holds for all k, we say that the series $\sum m_k(x)$ dominates the series $\sum u_k(x)$. Thus the result just proved may be stated as follows:

An infinite series of functions converges uniformly in x for a range if it is dominated by an infinite series of positive functions which converges uniformly in x for the range.

In this and the preceding theorem, since the argument applies equally well to the series $\sum |u_k(x)|$, it follows that the series converges absolutely for any x in the range.

We may extend the considerations to improper integrals and prove that:

The improper integral

$$\int_a^\infty g(u,x) \, du = \lim_{t \to \infty} \int_a^t g(u,x) \, du \tag{64}$$

converges uniformly in x for a range if, for all $u \geqq a$, and all x in the range,

$$|g(u,x)| \leqq M(u), \tag{65}$$

where $M(u)$ is a function, necessarily positive or zero, for which

$$\int_a^\infty M(u) \, du \tag{66}$$

converges.

The proof depends on the fact that the relation (65) implies that:

$$\left| \int_{t'}^{t''} g(u,x) \, du \right| \leqq \int_{t'}^{t''} |g(u,x)| \, du \leqq \int_{t'}^{t''} M(u) \, du. \tag{67}$$

This enables us to proceed from the Cauchy criterion for the sequence of integrals approaching the integral (66) to the Cauchy criterion for the sequence of integrals approaching the integral (64), as expressed in equation (51). Since the latter then holds uniformly in x, the uniform convergence of the improper integral follows. A similar result holds for an improper integral of the second kind.

We have stated the result for a function $M(u)$ independent of x, because this is the most important case in practice. A more **general** result is:

*The improper integral of $g(u,x)$ with respect to u converges uniformly in **x** for a range X, if, for all values of u in U, the range of integration, and all x in the range X, the function $g(u,x)$ is dominated by a function $m(u,x)$, necessarily positive or zero, for which the integral with respect to u over the range U converges uniformly in x for x in X. For any x in X, the improper integral of $g(u,x)$ converges absolutely.*

This is proved by similar reasoning, using the relation:

$$|g(u,x)| \leqq m(u,x), \quad u \text{ in } U, \quad x \text{ in } X, \tag{68}$$

to prove that:

$$\left| \int_{t'}^{t''} g(u,x)\, du \right| \leqq \int_{t'}^{t''} |g(u,x)|\, du \leqq \int_{t'}^{t''} m(u,x)\, du. \tag{69}$$

The range U of u may be a, ∞ as in equation (64), or a,c for **an** improper integral of the second kind.

The Weierstrass M-test depends on the application of the comparison test for convergence. Any other test for the convergence of an infinite series, improper integral, or infinite product may be used to establish convergence uniform with respect to x if the test determines a place in the sequence, independent of x, beyond which the difference between the approximation and the limit is small.

246. Integration of Series. For a sequence of functions, the limit of the sequence of integrals, as well as the integral of the limiting function of the sequence, may both exist without being equal. An example is:

$$f_t(x) = e^{-tx^2}\, 2tx. \tag{70}$$

Here we have:

$$\int_0^1 e^{-tx^2}\, 2tx\, dx = \left. -e^{-tx^2} \right|_0^1 = 1 - e^{-t}, \tag{71}$$

so that:

$$\lim_{t \to +\infty} \int_0^1 e^{-tx^2}\, 2tx\, dx = 1. \tag{72}$$

But:

$$\lim_{t \to +\infty} e^{-tx^2}\, 2tx = 0, \tag{73}$$

so that:

$$\int_0^1 \lim_{t \to +\infty} (e^{-tx^2}\, 2tx)\, dx = 0. \tag{74}$$

However, we may prove a result of somewhat similar character to that of section 241, namely:

If each of the functions $f_t(x)$ is continuous in x for the range $a \leqq x \leqq b$, and if $f_t(x)$ approaches a limiting function $F(x)$ uniformly in x for this range, then:

$$\lim_t \int_a^b f_t(x) \, dx \quad and \quad \int_a^b \lim_t f_t(x) \, dx \tag{75}$$

each exist and the two have the same value.

By the theorem of section 243, the limiting function $F(x)$ is continuous, so that it has an integral. Thus:

$$\int_a^b \lim_t f_t(x) \, dx = \int_a^b F(x) \, dx, \tag{76}$$

exists.

From the assumed uniform convergence, for any positive ϵ, there is a t_ϵ, such that:

$$|F(x) - f_t(x)| < \epsilon, \quad \text{for} \quad t \text{ beyond } t_\epsilon, \quad a \leqq x \leqq b. \tag{77}$$

It follows from this that:

$$\left| \int_a^b F(x) \, dx - \int_a^b f_t(x) \, dx \right| = \left| \int_a^b [F(x) - f_t(x)] \, dx \right|$$

$$\leqq \int_a^b |F(x) - f_t(x)| \, dx$$

$$\leqq |b - a|\epsilon. \tag{78}$$

This shows that:

$$\lim_t \int_a^b f_t(x) \, dx = \int_a^b F(x) \, dx, \tag{79}$$

so that the limit on the left exists. A comparison of equations (76) and (79) shows that the two limits are equal, as stated in the theorem.

Corresponding to a series of integrable functions $\sum u_k(x)$, we may form a series $\sum \int_a^x u_k(x) \, dx$, which we refer to as the integrated series or the series obtained by termwise integration. For a finite sum, we have:

$$\sum_{k=1}^n \int_a^x u_k(x) \, dx = \int_a^x \sum_{k=1}^n u_k(x) \, dx. \tag{80}$$

If the $u_k(x)$ are all continuous functions, the partial sum of the series to n terms,

$$s_n(x) = \sum_{k=1}^n u_k(x) \tag{81}$$

will be a continuous function. If the series converges to $s(x)$ uniformly in a range $a \leqq x \leqq b$, we may apply the theorem just proved to $s_n(x)$, and deduce for any x in this range:

$$\lim_{n \to \infty} \int_a^x s_n(x) \, dx = \int_a^x s(x) \, dx. \tag{82}$$

As the integral on the left is the series obtained by termwise integration, it follows that under the conditions stated the series converges to the integral of the sum function of the original series.

Furthermore, for

$$a \leqq b \leqq B, \quad (b - a)\epsilon \leqq (B - a)\epsilon. \tag{83}$$

Thus the inequality (78) holds with right member $(B - a)\epsilon$, for all b satisfying the relation (83). This proves that the convergence of the first integral of (75) is uniform in b.

These results are expressed in the following theorem:

An infinite series of continuous functions which converges uniformly in x for $a \leqq x \leqq B$ to a sum function $s(x)$ may be integrated termwise over the range a,x to give a new series which converges to the integral of $s(x)$ from a to x. The convergence of the integrated series is uniform in x, for $a \leqq x \leqq B$.

We may also apply the first theorem of this section to improper integrals. If the improper integral

$$\int_r^\infty g(u,x) \, du = \lim_{t \to \infty} \int_r^t g(u,x) \, du \tag{84}$$

converges uniformly in x, for x in the range $a \leqq x \leqq b$, we have:

$$\int_a^b dx \int_r^\infty g(u,x) \, du = \lim_{t \to \infty} \int_a^b dx \int_r^t g(u,x) \, du. \tag{85}$$

But, for the proper integral of a continuous function of two variables:

$$\int_a^b dx \int_r^t g(u,x) \, du = \int_r^t du \int_a^b g(u,x) \, dx, \tag{86}$$

so that under the assumed conditions:

$$\int_a^b dx \int_r^\infty g(u,x) \, du = \int_r^\infty du \int_a^b g(u,x) \, dx. \tag{87}$$

A similar result holds for

$$\int_a^b dx \int_r^c g(u,x) \, du = \int_r^c du \int_a^b g(u,x) \, dx, \tag{88}$$

where the integrand $g(u,x)$ is continuous in the two variables for $a \leqq x \leqq b$ and $r \leqq u < c$, and the integral $\displaystyle\int_r^c g(u,x)\,du$ is an improper integral of the second kind, which converges uniformly with respect to x for $a \leqq x \leqq b$.

247. Dominated Sequences. If, for all t sufficiently far out in the sequence,

$$|f_t(x)| \leqq g(x), \tag{89}$$

we say that the function $g(x)$, necessarily positive or zero, dominates the sequence $f_t(x)$.

We may prove the result of the theorem given in equation (75) with the conditions relaxed near a finite number of points, provided that in some interval including each of these points, the sequence is dominated by a function $g(x)$ integrable over this interval. It will be sufficient to consider one such point, taken as the right-hand end point, and then formulate the theorem in detail for this case as follows:

If each of the functions $f_t(x)$ is continuous in x for the range $a \leqq x < c$, $f_t(x)$ approaches a limiting function $F(x)$ in this range and the convergence is uniform in x for each range $a \leqq x \leqq b$, where b is any number such that $a < b < c$, then if the sequence is dominated in some open interval c',c by a function $g(x)$, integrable in this interval,

$$\lim_t \int_a^c f_t(x)\,dx \quad and \quad \int_a^c \lim_t f_t(x)\,dx \tag{90}$$

each exist and the two have the same value.

To prove this, we select a small positive quantity ϵ, and a number c'', such that $c' < c'' < c$ and

$$\int_{c''}^c g(x)\,dx < \epsilon. \tag{91}$$

We may do this since $g(x)$ is integrable in c', c. And, since $g(x) \geqq 0$, we may take $c'' > a$.

Since each function $f_t(x)$ is continuous in the range $a \leqq x < c$ and dominated by an integrable function in c',c, the integral $\displaystyle\int_a^c f_t(x)\,dx$ exists. Also,

$$\int_a^c f_t(x)\,dx = \int_a^{c-h} f_t(x)\,dx + \theta\epsilon, \tag{92}$$

where

$$|\theta| \leqq 1 \quad \text{if} \quad c'' < c - h < c. \tag{93}$$

Again, by the first theorem of section 246, we may deduce the existence and equality of

$$\lim_t \int_a^{c-h} f_t(x)\, dx = \int_a^{c-h} \lim_t f_t(x)\, dx. \tag{94}$$

But, since the integrand on the right is dominated by $g(x)$ in c',c it follows that the integral exists with upper limit c and that:

$$\int_a^c \lim_t f_t(x)\, dx = \int_a^{c-h} \lim_t f_t(x)\, dx + \theta' \epsilon, \tag{95}$$

where $|\theta'| \leqq 1$.

If we take t' such that for t beyond t' in the sequence the integral in the left member of equation (94) is within ϵ of its limit and take account of equations (92) and (95), we find:

$$\left| \int_a^c \lim_t f_t(x)\, dx - \int_a^c f_t(x)\, dx \right| \leqq 3\epsilon, \ t \text{ beyond } t'. \tag{96}$$

Since ϵ is arbitrary, this proves that:

$$\lim_t \int_a^c f_t(x)\, dx = \int_a^c \lim_t f_t(x)\, dx, \tag{97}$$

and the conclusion of the theorem follows.

In particular, this theorem holds if the functions $f_t(x)$ are all uniformly bounded, since in this case we may take $g(x)$ as a constant.

The theorem may be applied to series, as in the last section, if the partial sums are uniformly bounded or are dominated by an integrable function.

We may also apply it to improper integrals. It sometimes enables us to reverse the order in a repeated integral where both integrals are improper, if for one inner integral the convergence is uniform for the modified outer range and otherwise dominated by an integrable function. For example, if in addition to the conditions used to justify equation (87) we have:

$$\int_r^t \left| g(u,x)\, du \right| \leqq G(x), \quad c' < x, \tag{98}$$

with $G(x)$ integrable from c' to ∞, we may conclude that

$$\int_a^\infty dx \int_r^\infty g(u,x)\, du = \int_r^\infty du \int_a^\infty g(u,x)\, dx. \tag{99}$$

248. Differentiation of Series. Suppose that the sequence of functions $f_t(x)$ is such that

$$\lim_t f_t(a) = F(a), \tag{100}$$

and that the sequence of continuous functions $g_t(x)$, where

$$g_t(x) = \frac{\partial}{\partial x} f_t(x) \tag{101}$$

converges to a function $G(x)$, uniformly in x in the range $a \leqq x \leqq b$. Then we may conclude that there is a function $F(x)$ to which the first sequence $f_t(x)$ converges, and

$$F'(x) = G(x). \tag{102}$$

For, if we apply the theorem of section 246 to the sequence $g_t(x)$, we find:

$$\lim_t \int_a^x g_t(x) \, dx = \int_a^x G(x) \, dx. \tag{103}$$

We also have:

$$\int_a^x g_t(x) \, dx = \int_a^x \frac{\partial}{\partial x} f_t(x) \, dx = f_t(x) - f_t(a), \tag{104}$$

so that:

$$f_t(x) = f_t(a) + \int_a^x g_t(x) \, dx. \tag{105}$$

From this and equations (100) and (103),

$$\lim_t f_t(x) = F(a) + \int_a^x G(x) \, dx. \tag{106}$$

Thus the limit on the left exists and equals $F(a)$ for $x = a$. We call this limit $F(x)$. Then:

$$F(x) = F(a) + \int_a^x G(x) \, dx. \tag{107}$$

It follows from this that the function $F(x)$ has a derivative and $F'(x) = G(x)$, so that the derivative of the limit exists and equals the limit of the derivative, under the conditions stated.

We note that the condition (100) is necessary, as the example

$$f_t(x) = t + \frac{x^2}{t}, \quad \text{where} \quad t \to \infty, \tag{108}$$

shows. Here

$$g_t(x) = \frac{\partial}{\partial x} f_t(x) = \frac{2x}{t}, \tag{109}$$

so that in any bounded range for x, e.g., $0 \leqq x \leqq 1$, $g_t(x)$ is continuous and converges uniformly to the limit 0. However, there is no limit function $F(x)$ of which this is the derivative, since for every value of x, the sequence $f_t(x)$ fails to converge as $t \to \infty$.

Corresponding to a series of functions $\sum u_k(x)$, each of which is differentiable, we may form a series $\sum \partial/\partial x \, u_k(x)$, or $\sum u_k'(x)$, which we refer to as the differentiated series, or series obtained by termwise differentiation. We may apply the preceding considerations to an infinite series and obtain the theorem:

An infinite series of functions, each having a continuous derivative, may be differentiated termwise to give a new series which converges to the derivative of the sum function of the original series, provided that the original series converges at some particular point of the interval $a \leqq x \leqq b$ and provided that the differentiated series converges uniformly in x for this interval.

These last conditions insure that the original series converges, so that there is a sum function and that this sum function has a derivative.

We may apply similar considerations to an improper integral of either kind. For the first kind, the theorem is:

If the improper integral

$$\int_r^\infty g(u,x) \, du \tag{110}$$

converges at some particular point of the interval $a \leqq x \leqq b$ and the derivative $\partial/\partial x \, g(u,x)$ is continuous in the two variables for $a \leqq x \leqq b$ and $u > r$, and such that the improper integral

$$\int_r^\infty \frac{\partial}{\partial x} g(u,x) \, du \tag{111}$$

converges uniformly in x for $a \leqq x \leqq b$, then the integral (110) converges for all values of x in the interval and for x in this interval has a derivative with respect to x given by the integral (111).

The interchange of the operation of differentiation and some limit process may sometimes be justified by establishing the corresponding result for integration by the theorems of section 247, or that given later in sections 251 and 253.

249. Convergence in the Mean. A sequence of functions $f_t(x)$, is said to *converge in the mean* to a function $F(x)$ over the interval a,b if the integral of the square of the error:

$$E_t = \int_a^b |F(x) - f_t(x)|^2 \, dx \tag{112}$$

approaches zero as $t \to \infty$. Since the integrand is always positive or zero, if $|F(x) - f_t(x)| > M$ over one or more subintervals of total length L, or a set of content L,

$$E_t > M^2 L. \tag{113}$$

Thus E_t can not be $< \epsilon$ if $|F(x) - f_t(x)| > k$ on a set of content exceeding ϵ/k^2. This shows that a restriction on E_t implies a restriction on the size of $|F(x) - f_t(x)|$ in the sense of some average, or mean.

If $|F(x) - f_t(x)| < \epsilon$ throughout the interval, we have

$$E_t < \epsilon^2|b - a|, \tag{114}$$

and it follows from this that if the sequence of functions $f_t(x)$ converges to $F(x)$ uniformly, then it also converges in the mean over any finite interval a,b. However the sequence may converge in the mean without converging at any point. To form an example, let us arrange the closed intervals

$$0,\tfrac{1}{2};\tfrac{1}{2},1;0,\tfrac{1}{4};\tfrac{1}{4},\tfrac{1}{2};\tfrac{1}{2},\tfrac{3}{4};\tfrac{3}{4},1;0,\tfrac{1}{8}; \cdots \tag{115}$$

in order and designate the nth interval by I_n. Then define a discrete sequence of functions $f_n(x)$ by

$$f_n(x) = 1 \text{ for } x \text{ in } I_n, \quad f_n(x) = 0 \text{ for } x \text{ not in } I_n. \tag{116}$$

For this sequence of functions, we find:

$$\int_0^1 |0 - f_n(x)|^2 \, dx = \text{length } I_n. \tag{117}$$

As this approaches zero when $n \to \infty$, the sequence converges in the mean to $F(x) = 0$ on the interval $0,1$. However, the sequence does not converge for any value of x in this interval, since for any given x, say x_0, there are functions $f_n(x)$ with n arbitrarily large for which $f_n(x_0) = 0$, and also other values of n arbitrarily large for which $f_n(x_0) = 1$.

The importance of the notion of convergence in the mean is due to the fact that certain processes of integration, when applied to sequences convergent in the mean, lead to sequences which actually converge to a limit in the fundamental sense. To develop this, we shall need an inequality, to which we proceed.

250. The Schwarz Inequality. Let $f(x)$ and $g(x)$ be real functions whose product and squares are integrable on the interval a,b. Then for the repeated integral

$$I = \int_a^b dx \int_a^b \begin{vmatrix} f(x) & f(y) \\ g(x) & g(y) \end{vmatrix}^2 dy, \tag{118}$$

we find by expanding the square, reducing the terms to products of single integrals, and changing the dummy variable y to x,

$$I = 2 \int_a^b [f(x)]^2 \, dx \int_a^b [g(x)]^2 \, dx - 2\left[\int_a^b f(x)g(x) \, dx \right]^2. \tag{119}$$

Since the integrand in the first form of I, (118) is a square, the value of I is positive or zero. Thus we find from the second form of I, (119), that:

$$\left[\int_a^b f(x)g(x)\ dx \right]^2 \leqq \int_a^b [f(x)]^2\ dx \int_a^b [g(x)]^2\ dx, \qquad (120)$$

which is the Schwarz inequality. It states that the square of the integral of the product of two functions does not exceed the product of the integrals of their squares.

251. Integration and Convergence in the Mean. We shall make use of the Schwarz inequality in proving that, if the sequence $f_t(x)$ converges in the mean to $F(x)$, if $g_t(x)$ converges in the mean to $G(x)$ over the interval a,b, and if certain integrals exist, then

$$\lim_t \int_a^b f_t(x)g_t(x)\ dx = \int_a^b F(x)G(x)\ dx. \qquad (121)$$

We begin by applying the Schwarz inequality, (120), to the functions $[F(x) - f_t(x)]$ and $G(x)$. We have:

$$\left[\int_a^b [F(x) - f_t(x)]G(x)\ dx \right]^2 \leqq \int_a^b [F(x) - f_t(x)]^2\ dx \int_a^b [G(x)]^2\ dx, \qquad (122)$$

if these integrals exist. The existence of the first integral on the right is implied by the convergence in the mean of $f_t(x)$ to $F(x)$. The second exists if we make the further assumption that the integrals converge in the mean to functions $F(x)$ and $G(x)$ each having integrable squares. If the integral on the left exists as a proper integral when a finite number of intervals, each of which may be taken arbitrarily small, are removed from the range, as we shall assume, the integral of the left then exists as an improper integral because of the domination given by the inequality (122) for the modified range.

We now note that in the right member of the relation (122), the second factor does not change with t, while the first factor approaches zero as t runs through its sequence. It follows that the same is true of the left member, since this is necessarily positive or zero. This shows that, if the integral on the right exists:

$$\lim_t \int_a^b f_t(x)G(x)\ dx = \int_a^b F(x)G(x)\ dx. \qquad (123)$$

This is the important special case of equation (121) in which all the $g_t(x)$ are identically equal to $G(x)$. We may reverse the rôles of $F(x)$

and $G(x)$ and so write:

$$\lim_t \int_a^b g_t(x)F(x)\,dx = \int_a^b F(x)G(x)\,dx. \tag{124}$$

Now apply the inequality (120) to the functions $[F(x) - f_t(x)]$ and $[G(x) - g_t(x)]$. We have:

$$I_t^2 \leqq \int_a^b [F(x) - f_t(x)]^2\,dx \int_a^b [G(x) - g_t(x)]^2\,dx, \tag{125}$$

where

$$I_t = \int_a^b [F(x) - f_t(x)][G(x) - g_t(x)]\,dx$$

$$= \int_a^b F(x)G(x)\,dx - \int_a^b F(x)g_t(x)\,dx - \int_a^b G(x)f_t(x)\,dx$$

$$+ \int_a^b f_t(x)g_t(x)\,dx. \tag{126}$$

From the assumed convergence in the mean, we see that, when t runs through its sequence, the right member of the relation (125) approaches zero. Hence the same is true of the left member, since $I_t^2 \geqq 0$ and we may conclude that $\lim_t I_t = 0$. But the second and third terms in the right member of equation (126) approach limits given by equations (123) and (124), while the first term is independent of t. Consequently, the last term must approach a limit, and this limit is given by the following:

$$\lim_t \int_a^b f_t(x)g_t(x)\,dx = \int_a^b F(x)G(x)\,dx. \tag{127}$$

This is the result we set out to prove. We have already noticed the special case given in equation (123). A further specialization is obtained by putting $g_t(x) = G(x) = 1$, which gives:

$$\lim_t \int_a^b f_t(x)\,dx = \int_a^b F(x)\,dx. \tag{128}$$

This shows that, if a sequence of functions converges in the mean to a limiting function, the sequence of integrals converges to the integral of the limiting function.

From the positive character of the integrand in equation (112), it follows that, if a sequence of functions is convergent in the mean to $F(x)$ over a,b then it is convergent in the mean over any subinterval. Thus we may replace the limits a and b by any two values in the closed interval a,b in such equations as (123), (127), and (128). In particular we may take the integrals from b to x, where x is any point of the interval, and the convergence will be uniform. Most of the results also hold over infinite ranges, as a, ∞ or $-\infty, \infty$. However, for such ranges uniform convergence does not imply convergence in the mean, and we may no longer deduce equation (128), since a constant greater than zero is not integrable over an infinite range.

252. Approximation in the Mean. If

$$E(f,g) = \int_a^b |g(x) - f(x)|^2 \, dx \tag{129}$$

does not exceed ϵ, we say that the function $f(x)$ approximates $g(x)$ to within ϵ in the mean, for the interval a,b. If we have three functions, $f(x)$ approximating $g(x)$ and $g(x)$ approximating $h(x)$, the following inequality exists between the measures of the approximations:

$$[E(f,h)]^{\frac{1}{2}} \leqq [E(f,g)]^{\frac{1}{2}} + [E(g,h)]^{\frac{1}{2}}, \tag{130}$$

where all the square roots are positive.

To prove this, put:

$$A(x) = |h(x) - g(x)|, \quad B(x) = |g(x) - f(x)|. \tag{131}$$

Then,

$$|h(x) - f(x)| \leqq A(x) + B(x). \tag{132}$$

Thus the inequality (130) will follow if we show that

$$\left\{ \int_a^b [A(x) + B(x)]^2 \, dx \right\}^{\frac{1}{2}} \leqq \left\{ \int_a^b [A(x)]^2 dx \right\}^{\frac{1}{2}} + \left\{ \int_a^b [B(x)]^2 \, dx \right\}^{\frac{1}{2}}, \tag{133}$$

for any two functions $A(x)$ and $B(x)$. Since both members are positive, this will follow from the inequality obtained by squaring both sides. When we do this and cancel corresponding terms, our problem is reduced to proving:

$$2 \int_a^b A(x)B(x) \, dx \leqq 2 \left\{ \int_a^b [A(x)]^2 \, dx \right\}^{\frac{1}{2}} \left\{ \int_a^b [B(x)]^2 \, dx \right\}^{\frac{1}{2}}. \tag{134}$$

But this follows directly from the Schwarz inequality, so that the relation (130) is established.

The result shows that, if $g(x)$ approximates $h(x)$ in the mean to within ϵ and if $f(x)$ approximates $g(x)$ in the mean to within ϵ, then $f(x)$ approximates $h(x)$ in the mean to within 4ϵ.

253. Infinite Series and Mean Convergence. We say that an infinite series converges to a sum function in the mean if the sequence of partial sums $s_n(x)$ converges to a function $s(x)$ in the mean. It follows from equation (128) that, if a series converges in the mean to $s(x)$, the series obtained by termwise integration converges to the integral of $s(x)$, provided the assumptions as to integrability are satisfied. Also from equation (123), we see that the series obtained by multiplying each term by a function $G(x)$ with integrable square and by integrating termwise converges to the integral of $s(x)G(x)$.

254. Equi-continuity. Consider a sequence of functions, $f_t(x)$. Any one of these functions is continuous at a point x_0 if for any positive ϵ, there is a δ such that:

$$|f_t(x) - f_t(x_0)| < \epsilon, \quad \text{if} \quad |x - x_0| < \delta. \tag{135}$$

The possible values of δ will presumably depend on the value of ϵ, the value of x, x_0 and the particular value of t which determines the function considered. We have already shown that a function continuous at all points of a closed interval, say $a \leq x \leq b$, is uniformly continuous on this interval. Thus, if we assume each of the functions is continuous on the closed interval a,b for each ϵ and t, we may select a δ independent of x.

If it is possible to find a δ, for each positive ϵ, which will serve for all values of t, that is for all functions of the sequence, we say that the sequence of functions is *equi-continuous*. The property of equi-continuity is thus continuity not only uniform in the variable x, but also uniform for the different functions considered. For one, or a finite number of functions each continuous on the closed interval a,b the property is automatically satisfied. However, for an infinite number of continuous functions it imposes a restriction. We may apply it to any infinite set of functions, not necessarily ordered, like those of a sequence, and define:

A set of functions is equi-continuous for the closed interval a,b if, for any positive ϵ, there is a value of δ_ϵ, such that for every function $f(x)$ of the set:

$$|f(x) - f(x_0)| < \epsilon, \quad \text{if} \quad |x - x_0| < \delta_\epsilon, \tag{136}$$

where x and x_0 are any two points of the closed interval.

An important consequence of equi-continuity is given by the following theorem, due to Ascoli:

From any infinite set of equi-continuous functions, bounded as a set, a sub-sequence of functions may be selected which converges to a limiting function uniformly on any interval of equi-continuity of the original set.

To prove this theorem, we consider any enumerable set of points everywhere dense on the interval $a \leq x \leq b$, that is a set of points which may be ordered $r_1, r_2, r_3, \cdots$, and such that every point of the interval $a \leqq x \leqq b$ is a limit point of this set. The points on the interval with rational coördinates form one such set.

Now consider the totality of values of functions of the set at the point r_1. If there is only a finite number of distinct values, we may select an infinite subset of functions

$$f_{11}(x), f_{12}(x), f_{13}(x), \cdots \tag{137}$$

which all have the same value at r_1, $F(r_1)$. Otherwise there is an infinity of distinct values, in which case there is a greatest limit point, since they are all bounded. Accordingly, we may select an infinite subset of functions (137) whose values at r_1 approach a limit, $F(r_1)$.

In either case, we have a subset of functions, $f_{1k}(x)$, such that:

$$\lim_{k \to \infty} f_{1k}(r_1) = F(r_1). \tag{138}$$

We next consider the totality of values of the functions $f_{1k}(x)$ at the point r_2. By reasoning as we did before, we may select a subset of these functions, which we relabel as

$$f_{21}(x), f_{22}(x), f_{23}(x), \cdots \tag{139}$$

such that:

$$\lim_{k \to \infty} f_{2k}(r_2) = F(r_2). \tag{140}$$

We continue in this way, obtaining an enumerable number of sequences $f_{nk}(x)$, such that:

$$\lim_{k \to \infty} f_{nk}(r_n) = F(r_n), \tag{141}$$

and each sequence $f_{nk}(x)$ is a subset of the preceding sequence $f_{n-1,k}(x)$.

Finally we consider the diagonal sequence,

$$f_{11}(x), f_{22}(x), f_{33}(x) \cdots \tag{142}$$

For any particular value of n, all the terms of this last sequence after the nth form a subset of the functions $f_{nk}(x)$. Therefore it follows from equation (141) that

$$\lim_{k \to \infty} f_{kk}(r_n) = F(r_n). \tag{143}$$

As this is true for all n, it follows that the sequence of functions (142) approaches a limit at all the points of the everywhere dense set of numbers r_n. For simplicity, we drop one subscript and write $f_k(x)$ for $f_{kk}(x)$ in the sequel.

Now select any positive number ϵ, and a δ_ϵ for which the condition (136) is satisfied for all x in the interval. We may do this since the set of functions is equi-continuous. Next divide the interval a,b into intervals each less than $\delta_\epsilon/2$. Since the points r_n are everywhere dense, we may select one such point in each of these intervals. Let P be the largest subscript for any of these points. Then the finite set of points r_p, with $p \leqq P$ is such that every interval of length δ_ϵ anywhere on our interval will include at least one point r_p.

Since the sequence $f_{kk}(x)$, or $f_k(x)$ is such that:

$$\lim_{k \to \infty} f_k(r_p) = F(r_p), \quad p = 1, 2, \cdots P, \tag{144}$$

we may select an N such that:

$$|f_n(r_p) - F(r_p)| < \epsilon, \quad \text{for} \quad n > N, \ p \leqq P. \tag{145}$$

For, we may do this for each sequence and need merely take the largest of the P values so obtained.

Now consider any value of x on the closed interval a,b. It may or may not be in the set r_n. For some value of p, $p \leqq P$, we have:

$$|r_p - x| < \delta_\epsilon. \tag{146}$$

Consequently, from the condition of equi-continuity:

$$|f_k(r_p) - f_k(x)| < \epsilon \quad \text{for all } k. \tag{147}$$

In particular, for any two values n, n' each greater than N, we have from the last relation:

$$|f_n(r_p) - f_n(x)| < \epsilon, \tag{148}$$

and

$$|f_{n'}(r_p) - f_{n'}(x)| < \epsilon. \tag{149}$$

But, from the relation (145),

$$|f_n(r_p) - f_{n'}(r_p)| < 2\epsilon. \tag{150}$$

From the last three relations, we may conclude that

$$|f_n(x) - f_{n'}(x)| < 4\epsilon, \quad \text{for } n, n' > N. \tag{151}$$

This relation shows that, for any x in the interval, the sequence of functions $f_k(x)$ approaches a limit for $k \to \infty$. We call this limit $F(x)$. Thus:

$$\lim_{k \to \infty} f_k(x) = F(x). \tag{152}$$

Also, since the N of the relation (151) or (145) is independent of x, it follows that the convergence is uniform.

Finally, since the individual functions are continuous, the limit function $F(x)$ is continuous, by section 243. This proves the theorem.

In place of the condition that the set of functions be bounded, it is sufficient to require that the values of the functions at one point be bounded. For, if we select a δ corresponding to ϵ in the condition of equi-continuity, and then select a positive integer n so large that $|b - a| < n\delta$, we may divide the interval a,b into n equal parts by points x_i. Then, from

$$|f(x) - f(x_{i-1})| < \epsilon, \quad \text{if} \quad x_{i-1} \leqq x \leqq x_i, \tag{153}$$

we may deduce that:

$$|f(x) - f(x_0)| < n\epsilon, \tag{154}$$

where x is any point of the interval and x_0 is the point at which the values of the functions are bounded. Thus:

$$|f(x_0)| < M. \tag{155}$$

But from the last two relations:

$$|f(x)| < M + n\epsilon, \tag{156}$$

so that the functions are bounded at all points.

Or, we may merely require that the values of the functions at one point contain a convergent sequence, since this leads to a subset of functions, infinite in number, with values bounded at one point.

That some condition of this kind in addition to the equi-continuity is necessary may be seen from the discrete set of functions $f_n(x) = n$. This set is equi-continuous and in fact any positive number will serve as a δ of equi-continuity for all positive values of ϵ. However, no convergent infinite subset can be found.

255. Tests for Equi-continuity. In section 128 we showed that, if a function had a derivative $f'(x)$ at each point of a closed interval, uniformly bounded so that:

$$|f'(x)| \leqq M, \tag{157}$$

then, for any two points of the interval,

$$|f(x_2) - f(x_1)| < M|x_2 - x_1|. \tag{158}$$

We called the last relation a Lipschitz condition. Such a condition implies continuity, and we may take:

$$\frac{\epsilon}{M} \quad \text{as a possible value of } \delta_\epsilon, \tag{159}$$

in the definition of continuity.

It follows from this that, if each of a set of functions satisfies a Lipschitz condition with the constant the same for all the functions, the set of functions is equi-continuous.

Also, a set of functions each of which has a derivative, the derivatives all admitting the same bound, is necessarily a set of equi-continuous functions.

Under certain restrictions, the set of functions

$$f(x) = \int_a^b K(x,y)g(y) \, dy \qquad (160)$$

give rise to a set of equi-continuous functions. In fact, if the function $K(x,y)$ is a fixed function continuous in the two variables x and y for y in the closed interval a,b and x in the interval under consideration, and if the functions $g(y)$ are uniformly bounded, or at least satisfy the condition

$$\int_a^b |g(y)|^2 \, dy < M \qquad (161)$$

with the same M for all the functions, then the equation (160) defines a set of equi-continuous functions.

To see this, we write:

$$f(x) - f(x_0) = \int_a^b [K(x,y) - K(x_0,y)] \, g(y) \, dy. \qquad (162)$$

We now apply the Schwarz inequality which gives:

$$[f(x) - f(x_0)]^2 \leqq \int_a^b [K(x,y) - K(x_0,y)]^2 \, dy \int_a^b [g(y)]^2 \, dy. \qquad (163)$$

From the assumed continuity of $K(x,y)$, it follows that

$$|K(x,y) - K(x_0,y)| < \epsilon, \quad \text{if} \quad |x - x_0| < \delta_\epsilon, \quad a \leqq y \leqq b, \qquad (164)$$

so that we may conclude from this and equation (161) that

$$[f(x) - f(x_0)]^2 \leqq |b - a|\epsilon^2 M, \quad \text{if} \quad |x - x_0| < \delta_\epsilon. \qquad (165)$$

Since ϵ is arbitrary, this proves that the functions $f(x)$ are members of an equi-continuous set.

256. Several Variables, Complex Variables. The notion of uniform convergence may be extended to functions of more than one variable. Thus, a function of several real variables approaches a limit uniformly in these variables, on a certain range, if beyond a certain point in the sequence, t_ϵ independent of the values of these variables, the difference between the limit and the approximation is numerically less than ϵ. A sequence of continuous functions of several variables, convergent uniformly in these variables, has a limiting function continuous in these variables.

The theorems just mentioned also hold for functions of one or more complex variables.

Similarly the notion of equi-continuity and convergence in the mean may be extended to functions of more than one real variable, or to the complex case.   In extending the idea of convergence in the mean to complex values of the function we must replace the squares of the differences by squares of the absolute value of the differences to preserve the positive nature of the integrand.

EXERCISES XII

1. Let $f_t(x) = \dfrac{1 + tx^2}{1 + tx}$, and $F(x) = \lim\limits_{t \to \infty} f_t(x)$. Show that the convergence is not uniform in any interval including the origin and that $F(x)$ is not continuous at the origin.

2. Let the nth term of an infinite series be

$$u_n(x) = \frac{x}{(1 + nx)(1 + [n + 1]x)} .$$

Show that the sum function $s(x) = \lim\limits_{n \to \infty} s_n(x)$, where $s_n(x) = \sum\limits_{k=1}^{n} u_k(x)$, is discontinuous at $x = 0$.   Deduce that the convergence is not uniform, and verify by studying directly the values of $s(x) - s_n(x)$.   *Hint:* First show that

$$s_n(x) = \frac{1}{1 + x} - \frac{1}{1 + (n + 1)x} .$$

3. Draw conclusions similar to those of problem 2 if $u_n(x) = \dfrac{x}{(1 + x)^n} .$

Hint: Here $s_n(x) = 1 - \dfrac{1}{(1 + x)^n} .$

4. If $u_n(x) = \dfrac{x^m}{1 - x^{2m}}$, where $m = 2^n$, show that the sum function is $\dfrac{x^2}{1 - x^2}$ if $|x| < 1$ and $\dfrac{1}{1 - x^2}$ if $|x| > 1$, and show directly that the convergence is non-uniform near $x = 1$.   *Hint:* Show that $s_n(x) = \dfrac{1}{1 - x^2} - \dfrac{1}{1 - x^{2m}} .$

5. If $f_t(x) = \dfrac{tx}{1 + t^2 x^4}$, $F(x) = \lim\limits_{t \to +\infty} f_t(x) = 0$, and $\displaystyle\int_0^1 F(x)\, dx = 0$. Show that $\lim\limits_{t \to +\infty} \displaystyle\int_0^1 f_t(x)\, dx = \pi/4$, and investigate directly the non-uniformity near 0.

6. If $f_t(x) = \pi t \sin \pi t x$, $0 \leqq x \leqq 1/t$, and $f_t(x) = 0$, for $0 < t$, $1/t < x \leqq 1$, show that $\displaystyle\int_0^1 F(x)\, dx = 0$, where $F(x) = \lim\limits_{t \to +\infty} f_t(x)$, but that

$$\lim\limits_{t \to +\infty} \int_0^1 f_t(x)\, dx = 2.$$

7. Let $u_n(x) = 1$ for all x such that $n = [1/|x|]$, the greatest integer contained in $1/|x|$, and otherwise zero. Show that the series $\sum u_n(x)$ converges to 1 if $0 < |x| \leqq 1$, and otherwise to zero. Also show that the convergence is non-uniform near zero.

8. Show that, as $t \to +\infty$, $f_t(x) = |x|^{1/t}$ converges non-uniformly for x near zero.

9. If $f_t(x) = t^2 x e^{-t^2 x^2}$, and $F(x) = \lim_{t \to \infty} f_t(x)$, show that $\int_0^\infty F(x)\, dx = 0$, but that $\lim_{t \to \infty} \int_0^\infty f_t(x)\, dx = 1/2$. Also show that the values remain 0 and $1/2$ if we replace the upper limit ∞ by p, any positive number.

10. Show that as $t \to \infty$, $f_t(x) = x/(1 + tx)$ converges to 0 uniformly on the interval $0 \leqq x \leqq 1$, but that $g_t(x) = 1/(1 + tx)$ converges to zero, but non-uniformly for values near zero. This shows that multiplying in an unbounded factor, here $1/x$, may disturb uniformity.

11. Show that in problem 10, $g_t(x)$ converges in the mean to its limit, and verify directly that over 0,1 the integral of the limit equals the limit of the integral. Also deduce this result from section 247, with zero as the exceptional point near which $g_t(x)$ is bounded.

12. For x and t positive, show that $f_t(x) = tx(1 - x)^t$ has a single maximum for $x = 1/(t + 1)$ equal to $(1 + 1/t)^{-t-1}$, so that as $t \to \infty$, the maximum approaches $1/e$. Deduce that the convergence is non-uniform near zero, but that the function is bounded. Hence use section 247 to prove that the integral of the limit of $f_t(x)$ equals the limit of the integral over the interval 0 to p, any positive number not exceeding unity. Also show this by direct calculation.

13. The behavior of $g_t(x) = t^2 x(1 - x)^t$ may be deduced from problem 12, since it is $tf_t(x)$. Show that for this function $\int_0^1 \lim_{t \to \infty} g_t(x)\, dx = 0$, but $\lim_{t \to \infty} \int_0^1 g_t(x)\, dx = 1$.

14. Let $g_n(x)$ be a discrete sequence approaching $G(x)$ as n increases through integral values and let the $g_n(x)$ be uniformly bounded, $|g_n(x)| < K$. Then if $f_n(x) = \sum_{p=1}^{n} \frac{1}{p!} g_n(p!\, x)$, $F(x) = \lim_{n \to \infty} f_n(x)$ exists. Show that the convergence will be uniform if $g_n(x) \to G(x)$ uniformly for all values of x.

15. Let $h_n(x)$ be continuous functions with $0 < h_n(x) < K$, converging to $H(x)$ for $-1 \leqq x \leqq 1$. Let $H(0) = 1$, and $H(x) = 0$ for $0 < |x| \leqq 1$. Show that if we put $g_n(x) = h_n(\sin \pi x)$ the sequence $f_n(x)$ defined in problem 14 will converge non-uniformly near every rational value and hence in every interval. A simple example is $h_n(x) = (1 - x^2)^n$, $f_n(x) = \sum_{p=1}^{n} \frac{1}{p!} \cos^{2n}(p!\, \pi x)$.

16. The series with $u_n(x) = (-1)^n/n$ converges uniformly, since the terms are independent of x. Show that it is not dominated by any convergent series of positive terms and so the uniformity can not be proved by the Weierstrass M-test.

17. Draw conclusions similar to those of problem 16 for the uniformly convergent series with $u_n(x) = 1/x$ if $1/(n+1) \leqq 1/x \leqq 1/n$, and $u_n(x) = 0$ for other values of x.

18. Let $u_n(x)$ be the general term of a series proved to be uniformly convergent by the Weierstrass M-test. Show that if $v_n(x)$ form a set of uniformly bounded functions, $|v_n(x)| < K$, then the series $v_n(x)u_n(x)$ converges absolutely and uniformly. An example is $u_n(x) = 1/(n^2 + x^2)$, $v_n(x) = \sin nx$.

19. Show that we may replace the condition on $v_n(x)$ in problem 18 by the condition that $v_n(x)$ approaches a finite limit, uniformly in x, as n increases through integral values. An example is $u_n(x) = 1/(n^2 + x^2)$, $v_n(x) = x^{2n}/(1 - x^{2n})$, for the range $x \geqq 1 + p$, or the range $|x| < 1 - p$, where p is any positive number less than one.

20. If for each fixed x, $v_n(x)$ decreases as n increases and approaches zero uniformly in x, while for all values of n and x under consideration the sums $\sum_{k=1}^{n} u_k(x)$ are numerically less than some fixed number K, the series with general term $v_n(x)u_n(x)$ converges uniformly. An example is $v_n(x) = \dfrac{1}{n + x^2}$, $u_n(x) = \sin nx$. *Hint:* Use section 199.

21. Show that the series with $u_n(x) = \dfrac{(-1)^n}{n} \dfrac{x^{2n}}{1 - x^{2n}}$ converges uniformly in any closed interval not including 1 or -1. *Hint:* Use problem 20.

22. In problem 29 of Exercises IV, the expansion of $(1 + x)^m$ in a power series $\sum_{n=0}^{m} C_n x^n$ was obtained, for $|x| < 1$. In section 195 we showed that this expansion converged for $x = -1$, if $m > 0$, and had all the terms of the same sign after a certain point. Show that the series converges uniformly for $|x| \leqq 1$, and, since it represents a continuous function in this closed interval, must equal $(1 + x)^m$ for $x = 1$, or -1.

23. Prove that $|x| = \sum_{n=0}^{1/2} C_n a^{1-2n} (x^2 - a^2)^n$ for $-a \leqq x \leqq a$, the series of polynomials being uniformly convergent in this interval. *Hint:* Put $|x| = a \left[1 - \left(1 - \dfrac{x^2}{a^2} \right) \right]^{1/2}$ and use problem 22.

24. A continuous function made up of a finite number of linear segments, or a polygonal line, may be expressed as the sum of a linear function and a number of functions of the form $A|x - x_0|$, one for each vertex. Also on a finite closed interval any continuous function may be uniformly approximated by a polygonal function. From these facts, and problem 23, deduce that the continuous function may be uniformly approximated to within any preassigned degree by a polynomial. The theorem is due to Weierstrass, the method of proof here suggested is due to Lebesgue.

25. Let the sequence $f_i(x)$ converge to $G(x)$ uniformly in a closed interval and converge in the mean to $F(x)$, on the same interval. Prove that if $F(x)$ and $G(x)$ are continuous, $F(x) = G(x)$.

26. Let the sequence of functions $f_t(x)$ converge in the mean to $F(x)$ on a closed interval on which $F(x)$ is continuous. Prove that if the functions $f_t(x)$ form an equi-continuous set and any subset is selected which converges at all points of the interval, the limit of this subset will be $F(x)$. *Hint:* Use problem 25.

27. In the open rectangle $a < x < b,\, c < y < d$, let $G(x,y)$ be continuous and $G(x,y) = \partial^2 F / \partial x\, \partial y$. Show that, if the repeated limits exist,

$$\int_c^d dy \int_a^b G(x,y)\, dx = \lim_{\substack{y_1 \to c \\ y_2 \to d}} \left[\lim_{\substack{x_1 \to a \\ x_2 \to b}} H(x_1,y_1,x_2,y_2) \right],$$

where $H(x_1,y_1,x_2,y_2) = F(x_2,y_2) - F(x_2,y_1) - F(x_1,y_2) + F(x_1,y_1)$. This enables us to construct improper repeated integrals whose value depends on the order of integration. Examples are: $F(x,y) = (x - y)/(x + y)$, $G(x,y) = 2(x - y)/(x + y)^3$ or $F(x,y) = \tan^{-1}(y/x)$, $G(x,y) = (y^2 - x^2)/(x^2 y^2)^2$ with b and d positive and a and c either both zero, or both ∞.

28. If for each fixed x, $p(u,x)$ decreases as u increases to ∞ and approaches zero uniformly in x, for $a \le x \le b$, while $\left| \int_0^q f(u,x)\, du \right| < M$ for all positive values of q, then the improper integral $\int_0^\infty p(u,x) f(u,x)\, du$ converges uniformly in x for $a \le x \le b$. *Hint:* See problem 29 of Exercises IX.

29. If $a > 0, b > 0$, and $g'(x)$ is continuous and integrable from 0 to ∞ so that $\int_0^\infty g'(x)\, dx = g(+\infty) - g(0)$, prove that:

$$\int_0^\infty \frac{g(bx) - g(ax)}{x}\, dx = [g(+\infty) - g(0)] \log \frac{b}{a}. \qquad \text{(Elliott.)}$$

Hint: Show that $\int_0^\infty g'(ux)\, dx$ converges uniformly for $a \le u \le b$, and invert the order in $\int_a^b du \int_0^\infty g'(ux)\, dx$. As examples,

$$\int_0^\infty \frac{\tan^{-1} bx - \tan^{-1} ax}{x}\, dx = \frac{\pi}{2} \log \frac{b}{a}\,; \quad \int_0^\infty \frac{e^{-bx} - e^{-ax}}{x}\, dx = \log \frac{a}{b}.$$

30. If $a > 0,\, b > 0$ show that the order may be inverted in $\int_0^\infty dx \int_0^a e^{-ux+ibx}\, du$, and deduce that:

$$\int_0^\infty \frac{(1 - e^{-ax}) \cos bx}{x}\, dx = \frac{1}{2} \log \frac{a^2 + b^2}{b^2},$$

and

$$\int_0^\infty \frac{(1 - e^{-ax}) \sin bx}{x}\, dx = \frac{\pi}{2} - \tan^{-1} \frac{b}{a},$$

31. Show that $\int_0^\infty \frac{\sin bx}{x}\, dx = \frac{\pi}{2}$ if $b > 0$, 0 if $b = 0$, and $-\frac{\pi}{2}$ if $b < 0$.

Hint: For the first case, take the limit as $a \to +\infty$ of the last integral of problem 30, noting that the term in the integral involving e^{-ax} is dominated by

$$\int_0^\infty e^{-ax}\,dx = \frac{1}{a}.$$ For the last case, put $x = -u$.

32. Prove that $\displaystyle\int_0^{\pi/2} d\theta \int_0^\infty e^{-r^2} r\,dr = \int_0^\infty dx \int_0^\infty e^{-x^2-y^2}\,dy$, and deduce that

$\displaystyle\int_0^\infty e^{-x^2}\,dx = \frac{\sqrt{\pi}}{2}$. *Hint:* If we call the first integral with upper limit ∞
replaced by R, I_R, a direct calculation shows that I_R increases with R and approaches $\pi/4$. If the second double integral, with both upper limits ∞ replaced by a is J_a, the positive nature of the integrand shows that J_a increases with a, and $I_a < J_a < I_{2a}$, so that the second double integral converges and to the same value as the first.

33. Show that $\displaystyle\int_0^\infty e^{-x^2-\frac{a^2}{x^2}}\,dx = \frac{e^{-2a}\sqrt{\pi}}{2}$. *Hint:* Either show that if $I(a)$
is the integral, $I'(a) = -2I(a)$; or replace the integral from 0 to ∞ by that from
0 to $a^{\frac{1}{2}}$ plus that from $a^{\frac{1}{2}}$ to ∞. Then put $x = a/u$ in one integral, and take
$x - a/x$ as a new variable. In either procedure the result of problem 32 must
be used.

34. Show that $\displaystyle\int_0^\infty \frac{\sin^2 ax}{x^2}\,dx = |a|\frac{\pi}{2}$. *Hint:* Either integrate by parts, or
differentiate the integral with respect to a, and use problem 31.

35. If $a > 0$, $b > 0$, $\displaystyle\int_1^\infty \frac{f(u)}{u}\,du$ converges and $f(u)$ is continuous for $u > 0$
and has a derivative at $u = 0$, then $\displaystyle\int_0^\infty \frac{f(bx) - f(ax)}{x}\,dx = f(0)\,\log\frac{a}{b}$.
(Frullani.) *Hint:* Deduce

$$\int_0^{aq} \frac{f(u) - f(0)}{u}\,du = \int_0^q \frac{f(ax) - f(0)}{x}\,dx$$

and hence

$$\int_0^q \frac{f(bx) - f(ax)}{x}\,dx = \int_{aq}^{bq} \frac{f(u)}{u}\,du - f(0)\int_{aq}^{bq}\frac{du}{u}.$$

36. Illustrate problem 35 for $f(u) = e^{-u}$, $\sin u$, $\cos u$, and compare the results
with those of problems 29, 31, and 30.

37. Assuming that $g(u) - g(\infty) = f(u)$ satisfies the conditions imposed on
$f(u)$ in problem 35, deduce the equation of problem 29. Show that $\tan^{-1} u$
satisfies these alternative conditions.

38. Deduce the Schwarz inequality from the fact that the quadratic expression in u, $\displaystyle\int_a^b [f(x) - u\,g(x)]^2\,dx$, cannot change sign. Compare the proof of
the inequality for sums in the hint to problem 9, Exercises X.

CHAPTER XIII

FUNCTIONS OF COMPLEX VARIABLES

So far we have only applied the processes of differentiation and integration to functions of a complex variable built up from elementary functions. We now wish to consider the more general functions of a complex variable to which these operations can be applied. Such functions are connected with transformations of the plane which preserve angles and are also coextensive with the class of functions which have power series developments. We call them analytic functions and develop several of their characteristic properties. We illustrate their use in evaluating certain real, definite integrals.

A number of processes are described which, when applied to analytic functions, lead to new analytic functions. Finally we briefly indicate how some of the theorems may be extended to analytic functions of several complex variables.

257. Functions. We have already applied the notion of functional dependence to complex values of the variable in section 101. Let us again consider two complex variables, or variable complex numbers, $z = x + iy$ and $w = u + iv$, with w a function of z. We shall usually take as the range of values of z some two-dimensional region of the plane, for example a circle or a rectangle, in which the function is single-valued.

Thus, each value of z, or (x,y) in the region R will determine a single value of w, or (u,v),

$$w = f(z) = u(x,y) + iv(x,y). \tag{1}$$

Each such function leads to two real, single-valued functions of two real variables, $u(x,y)$ and $v(x,y)$. Conversely each ordered pair of real functions of this type may be used to define a single-valued function of one complex variable.

The function $f(z)$ is continuous for the value z_0, if

$$\lim_{z \to z_0} f(z) = f(z_0), \tag{2}$$

where as in section 102 the limit must exist as a two-dimensional limit of the kind discussed in section 242. Thus, in particular, the limit must equal $f(z_0)$ for every discrete or continuous sequence of values $z_t \to z_0$.

As pointed out in section 102, an equivalent condition for continuity at z_0 is that there is a number δ_ϵ for each positive number ϵ such that:

$$|f(z) - f(z_0)| < \epsilon, \quad \text{if} \quad |z - z_0| < \delta_\epsilon. \tag{3}$$

Also, the function $f(z)$ is continuous at $z_0 = x_0 + iy_0$ if, and only if, the two real functions $u(x,y)$ and $v(x,y)$ are each continuous at (x_0,y_0).

258. Derivatives. We recall the definition of the derivative of $f(z)$ given in section 110, namely,

$$f'(z) = \frac{dw}{dz} = \lim_{\Delta z \to 0} \frac{\Delta w}{\Delta z}, \tag{4}$$

provided the limit exists as a two-dimensional limit.

Let us investigate the conditions that this imposes on u and v. We have:

$$\frac{\Delta w}{\Delta z} = \frac{\Delta u + i\,\Delta v}{\Delta x + i\,\Delta y}. \tag{5}$$

If the limit exists as a two-dimensional limit, it will exist for any sequence of values of $\Delta z \to 0$. In particular, we may take $\Delta y = 0$, and $\Delta x \to 0$ and conclude from equations (4) and (5) that:

$$\frac{dw}{dz} = \frac{\partial u}{\partial x} + i\frac{\partial v}{\partial x}, \tag{6}$$

where the existence of the limits on the right follows from the existence of that on the left by section 99.

Similarly, we may take $\Delta x = 0$, and $\Delta y \to 0$, and deduce that:

$$\frac{dw}{dz} = -i\frac{\partial u}{\partial y} + \frac{\partial v}{\partial y}. \tag{7}$$

As u and v and hence their partial derivatives are real, the last two equations imply that:

$$\frac{\partial u}{\partial x} = \frac{\partial v}{\partial y} \quad \text{and} \quad \frac{\partial u}{\partial y} = -\frac{\partial v}{\partial x}. \tag{8}$$

These are known as the *Cauchy-Riemann* differential equations. It follows from our discussion that:

A necessary condition for $w = u + iv = f(z)$ to have a derivative at $z_0 = x_0 + iy_0$ is that the functions $u(x,y)$ and $v(x,y)$ have first partial derivatives for (x_0,y_0) which satisfy the Cauchy-Riemann differential equations (8).

There are no further conditions of this kind imposed on the values of the partial derivatives of u and v at the point in question.   In fact, we shall prove that:

If $u(x,y)$ and $v(x,y)$ have partial derivatives which are continuous at (x_0,y_0) and satisfy the Cauchy-Riemann differential equations, (8) for (x_0,y_0), then the function $f(z) = u + iv$ has a derivative $f'(z)$ at $z_0 = x_0 + iy_0$.

By section 211, the conditions on u and v make them differentiable in x and y at x_0,y_0, so that:

$$\Delta u = \frac{\partial u}{\partial x} \Delta x + \frac{\partial u}{\partial y} \Delta y + \epsilon_1 \Delta x + \epsilon_2 \Delta y, \tag{9}$$

and

$$\Delta v = \frac{\partial v}{\partial x} \Delta x + \frac{\partial v}{\partial y} \Delta y + \epsilon_3 \Delta x + \epsilon_4 \Delta y, \tag{10}$$

where all the ϵ approach zero with Δx and Δy, or with Δz.

It follows from the equations (8), (9), and (10) that:

$$\Delta u + i \Delta v = \left(\frac{\partial u}{\partial x} + i \frac{\partial v}{\partial x}\right)(\Delta x + i \Delta y) + \epsilon' \Delta x + \epsilon'' \Delta y, \tag{11}$$

where

$$\epsilon' = \epsilon_1 + i\epsilon_3, \quad \text{and} \quad \epsilon'' = \epsilon_2 + i\epsilon_4. \tag{12}$$

Consequently,

$$\frac{\Delta w}{\Delta z} = \frac{\partial u}{\partial x} + i \frac{\partial v}{\partial x} + \epsilon' \frac{\Delta x}{\Delta z} + \epsilon'' \frac{\Delta y}{\Delta z}. \tag{13}$$

Since $|\Delta x| \leqq |\Delta z|$ and $|\Delta y| \leqq |\Delta z|$,

$$\left|\frac{\Delta x}{\Delta z}\right| \leqq 1 \quad \text{and} \quad \left|\frac{\Delta y}{\Delta z}\right| \leqq 1. \tag{14}$$

From this and the expression for the ϵ in equation (12), the last two terms in equation (13) are seen to approach zero with Δz, so that

$$\lim_{z \to 0} \frac{\Delta w}{\Delta z} = \frac{\partial u}{\partial x} + i \frac{\partial v}{\partial x}, \tag{15}$$

and the function $w = f(z)$ has a derivative at z_0.

The added condition of continuity, or some condition to insure that u and v are differentiable is necessary, as the following example shows:

$$u(x,y) = |x|^{\frac{1}{2}} |y|^{\frac{1}{2}}, v(x,y) = 0. \tag{16}$$

For $(x,y) = (0,0)$ each of these functions has both partial derivatives equal to zero, so that equations (8) are satisfied. However, the first function is not differentiable. The function $f(z) = u + iv$ has no derivative at the origin. For,

if $\Delta z = \Delta x + im^2 \Delta x$, $\qquad \lim \dfrac{\Delta w}{\Delta z} = \dfrac{m}{1 + im^2}$, $\qquad$ (17)

which varies with m, so that the two-dimensional limit does not exist.

259. Conformal Transformations. If we represent the values of z in one plane with x and y coördinate axes and the corresponding values of w in a second plane with u and v coördinate axes, we may interpret the relation $w = f(z)$ as a transformation of the points in some region R of the first plane into certain other points of the w plane. Let us assume that the functions $u(x,y)$ and $v(x,y)$ have partial derivatives, continuous at some particular point x_0,y_0 under consideration. Let us also assume that the Jacobian

$$\frac{\partial(u,v)}{\partial(x,y)} = \begin{vmatrix} \dfrac{\partial u}{\partial x} & \dfrac{\partial u}{\partial y} \\[2mm] \dfrac{\partial v}{\partial x} & \dfrac{\partial v}{\partial y} \end{vmatrix} \neq 0, \qquad (18)$$

at this point x_0,y_0. Then, if u_0,v_0 is the point into which x_0,y_0 is transformed, by section 218 there is some two-dimensional neighborhood of u_0,v_0 in which the equations

$$u = u(x,y), \quad v = v(x,y) \qquad (19)$$

have a solution of the form

$$x = x(u,v), \quad y = y(u,v). \qquad (20)$$

These functions will have partial derivatives continuous at u_0,v_0, and by problem 19 of Exercises X, such that:

$$\frac{\partial(x,y)}{\partial(u,v)} = \frac{1}{\dfrac{\partial(u,v)}{\partial(x,y)}} \neq 0. \qquad (21)$$

Any curve in the xy plane passing through the point x_0,y_0 and having a tangent at that point with direction components

$$x' = \frac{dx}{dt} \quad \text{and} \quad y' = \frac{dy}{dt} \qquad (22)$$

will be transformed, at least for some arc including x_0,y_0, into a curve in the uv plane, passing through the point u_0,v_0 and having a tangent at that point with direction components

$$u' = \frac{du}{dt} = u_x x' + u_y y', \tag{23}$$

$$v' = \frac{dv}{dt} = v_x x' + v_y y',$$

by the equations (19). Conversely, any curve in the second plane, with a tangent at u_0,v_0 in the direction given by equations (23) will have some arc transformed by the inverse transformation (20) into an arc through x_0,y_0 with the direction given by equations (22).

As in section 175, we have for the arc length in the uv plane

$$\begin{aligned} s'^2 &= u'^2 + v'^2 \\ &= (u_x^2 + v_x^2)x'^2 + 2(u_x u_y + v_x v_y)x'y' + (u_y^2 + v_y^2)y'^2. \end{aligned} \tag{24}$$

The equations (23) suggest the transformation:

$$U = u_x X + u_y Y, \quad V = v_x X + v_y Y, \tag{25}$$

from an XY plane to a UV plane, where the coefficients are constants, equal to the value of the partial derivatives at x_0,y_0 for the functions of equation (19). If

$$X = x - x_0 \quad \text{and} \quad Y = y - y_0, \tag{26}$$

it follows from the differentiability of the functions that

$$u - u_0 = U + \epsilon_1 X + \epsilon_2 Y \quad \text{and} \quad v - v_0 = V + \epsilon_3 X + \epsilon_4 Y, \tag{27}$$

where, as in equations (9) and (10), all the ϵ approach zero with X and Y. Hence, for points near x_0,y_0 the transformation given by equations (19) may be approximated by putting

$$u - u_0 = U \quad \text{and} \quad v - v_0 = V, \tag{28}$$

and combining equations (25), (26) and (28) to obtain the relation between x,y and u,v. Since the last two of these equations merely change the origin to the points under consideration, the character of the approximating transformation is given by equations (25). These represent an affine transformation, which takes parallel straight lines into parallel straight lines. Equally spaced points on any one line in one plane go into equally spaced points on some line in the second plane. However, while the scale factor is the same for any two parallel lines, it will usually differ for different directions. In fact, a circle in either plane will go into an ellipse in the other plane, and the transformation may be generated by a combination of a rotation and two changes of scale, usually different, along a certain pair of perpendicular axes — the axes which are transformed into the principal axes of the ellipse.

When the two changes of scale are equal, the transformation reduces to a similarity transformation, which may be generated by a combination of a rotation about the origin and an expansion out from the origin or by the same change of scale in all directions. In this case all lengths are changed in the same ratio, and all angles are preserved. The imposing of either of these properties on the affine transformation makes it a similarity transformation. In fact, if we merely require all pairs of perpendicular lines in one plane to go into perpendicular lines, the ellipse which is the image of a circle must have all its pairs of conjugate axes perpendicular and therefore must reduce to a circle, so that the transformation reduces to a similarity transformation.

When the approximate transformation given by equation (25) is a similarity transformation, the transformation given by equation (19) is said to be conformal, or to preserve angles, at the point in question. Since the equations for directions obtained from equations (25) are identical with equations (23), it follows that in this case, two curves in the uv plane intersecting at $u_0 v_0$ cut at the same angle as the curves in the xy plane of which they are the images.

To find the condition for a transformation to be conformal, we note that the circle

$$U^2 + V^2 = 1 \qquad (29)$$

is transformed by the equations (25) into

$$(u_x^2 + v_x^2)X^2 + 2(u_x u_y + v_x v_y)XY + (u_y^2 + v_y^2)Y^2 = 1. \qquad (30)$$

This will reduce to the equation of a circle if, and only if,

$$u_x u_y + v_x v_y = 0, \qquad (31)$$

and

$$u_x^2 + v_x^2 = u_y^2 + v_y^2. \qquad (32)$$

Since we have assumed that the Jacobian of equation (18) is not zero, v_x and v_y cannot both be zero. Suppose $v_y \neq 0$, and put

$$u_x = k v_y. \qquad (33)$$

Then, from equation (31), we find:

$$v_x = -k u_y. \qquad (34)$$

It follows from the last two equations that:

$$u_x^2 + v_x^2 = k^2(u_y^2 + v_y^2). \qquad (35)$$

A comparison of this equation and equation (32) shows that $k^2 = 1$. Thus, either

$$u_x = v_y, \quad u_y = -v_x,$$ (36)

or $$u_x = -v_y, \quad u_y = v_x.$$ (37)

Either of these pairs of equations imply equations (31) and (32).

If a transformation satisfies equations (36) its Jacobian

$$u_x v_y - u_y v_x = u_x^2 + u_y^2 > 0.$$ (38)

But for a transformation satisfying equations (37) its Jacobian

$$u_x v_y - u_y v_x = -u_x^2 - u_y^2 < 0.$$ (39)

The discussion of section 233 shows that in the first case orientation is preserved, while in the second case orientation is reversed. In fact, if we interchange u and v, which reverses sense, the equations (37) reduce to (36).

As the equations (36) are the Cauchy-Riemann differential equations (8), we may summarize our results as follows:

A transformation given by two functions $u = u(x,y)$ and $v = v(x,y)$ with partial derivatives continuous at a point and Jacobian different from zero at the point preserves angles as to magnitude and sense at the point if, and only if, the Cauchy-Riemann differential equations (36) are satisfied.

By the preceding section, under these conditions the function $w(z) = u + iv$ has a derivative given by equation (15),

or $$\frac{dw}{dz} = u_x + iv_x.$$ (40)

From this and equations (36),

$$\left|\frac{dw}{dz}\right|^2 = u_x^2 + v_x^2 = u_x v_y - v_x u_y = \frac{\partial(u,v)}{\partial(x,y)}.$$ (41)

This shows that the derivative is not zero. In fact, from equations (24), (36) and (41) we find:

$$u'^2 + v'^2 = \left|\frac{dw}{dz}\right|^2 (x'^2 + y'^2).$$ (42)

This shows that the numerical value of the derivative is the factor by which the differential of length is multiplied by the transformation. This was to be anticipated from equation (41), which shows that its square is the Jacobian or factor by which the differential of area is multiplied, together with the fact that for differentials the transformation has the character of a similarity transformation.

Some of these facts could be derived otherwise by noting that, when there is a derivative:

$$\lim \frac{|\Delta w|}{|\Delta z|} = \left|\frac{dw}{dz}\right|. \tag{43}$$

Also, if the derivative is not zero its argument is determined to within a multiple of 2π, by section 96, and for a suitable branch

$$\lim \arg \frac{\Delta w}{\Delta z} = \arg \frac{dw}{dz}. \tag{44}$$

That all differential lengths are multiplied by the same factor follows from equation (43), while equation (44) shows that the angle between any direction and its transformed direction is the same, so that angles are preserved as to magnitude and sense.   Hence:

At any point where the function $w(z)$ has a derivative dw/dz distinct from zero, the corresponding transformation preserves angles as to magnitude and sense and has a positive Jacobian.

260. Power Series.   We have seen in section 112 that for a suitably restricted range of the complex variable z, any elementary function has a derivative.   We wish to show now that a more general class of functions of a complex variable which have derivatives, is the class of functions expressible by power series.   For this reason we shall consider power series expansions in some detail.

A *power series* in z is an infinite series whose terms are products of integral powers of z by complex constants:

$$\sum_{n=0}^{\infty} a_n z^n. \tag{45}$$

We may also consider power series in $z - c$, of the form

$$\sum_{n=0}^{\infty} a_n (z - c)^n. \tag{46}$$

As these may be reduced to the first form by putting

$$Z = z - c, \tag{47}$$

most of their properties follow at once from the simpler form, and we shall chiefly confine our attention to this first form (45).

Power series form a natural generalization of polynomials, which are finite sums of similar terms.   A power series may converge for all values of z, as

$$\sum \frac{z^n}{n!}. \tag{48}$$

Or a power series may diverge for all values of z except $z = 0$, as

$$\sum n\,!\,z^n. \tag{49}$$

Also a power series may converge for some values and diverge for others, as

$$\sum z^n. \tag{50}$$

These properties of the examples follow from the test-ratio, which is z/n, nz, z, respectively. Thus we have convergence, when these approach a limit numerically less than one, or for all z in the first case, and for $|z| < 1$ in the third. Similarly we have divergence, when these approach a limit numerically exceeding one, or for all z distinct from zero in the second case and for $|z| > 1$ in the third.

261. Circle of Convergence. We generally omit from consideration, series which converge only for $z = 0$, as being without interest. For series not of this type, considerable information about the points for which they converge is given by the following theorem:

If a power series in z converges for some value of z, say $z_1 \neq 0$, then it converges absolutely for all values of z with $|z| < |z_1|$, and in fact uniformly in any range $|z| \leq r$, where $0 < r < |z_1|$.

From the assumed convergence of the series, $|a_n z_1^n| \to 0$, and so is less than unity for all terms after a certain one, say the Nth. Hence if M is the maximum of the finite set of numbers 1, $|a_p z_1^p|$ for $p = 0, 1, 2, \cdots$, N, we shall have for all n,

$$|a_n z_1^n| \leq M. \tag{51}$$

For any $|z| < |z_1|$, we may find a positive number r such that:

$$|z| < r < |z_1|. \tag{52}$$

If we then put:

$$c = \frac{r}{|z_1|}, \quad c < 1. \tag{53}$$

Hence, for the value of z under consideration,

$$|a_n z^n| = |a_n z_1^n| \left|\frac{z}{z_1}\right|^n \leq Mc^n. \tag{54}$$

But since c is less than unity, Mc^n is the nth term of a convergent geometric series. Thus, by the Weierstrass M-test of sections 245 and 256, the uniform convergence of $\sum a_n z^n$ in the range $|z| \leq r$ follows. The absolute convergence of the series for the z considered, also follows.

The range $|z| \leq r$ is the interior and boundary of a circle, with center at the origin. We shall refer to such a circle as *a circle of uniform con-*

vergence. The theorem just proved shows that, if a series converges for any value not zero, there are such circles.

Recalling sections 243 and 256, and the continuity of the powers of z, we see that the sum of a power series $f(z)$ is a continuous function of z at all points inside or on any circle of uniform convergence.

Suppose that a power series converges for z_1, where $|z_1| = r_1$, and diverges for z_2, where $|z_2| = r_2$. Then, by the theorem just proved, it will converge for all z with $|z| < r_1$. Similarly, it will diverge for all z with $|z| > r_2$, since the convergence for any such value would imply that for z_2, contrary to our assumption. This leads to a separation of values of r into two classes, one containing values of r_1 such that the series converges for all z with $|z| = r_1$ and the other class containing values of r_2 such that the series diverges for some z with $|z| = r_2$. All the conditions of section 6 are satisfied and there is a number R such that the series converges for all z with $|z| < R$, and diverges for all z with $|z| > R$. For $|z| = R$ itself the series may converge or diverge. The circle $|z| = R$ is called the *circle of convergence* of the series. The number R is called the *radius of convergence* of the series. It follows that unless the series converges for no values except $z = 0$, when we put $R = 0$, or converges for all values of z, when we put $R = \infty$, there is a finite radius of convergence. By V of section 193 and section 204,

$$\frac{1}{R} = \overline{\lim} |a_n|^{\frac{1}{n}} \quad \text{or} \quad R = \underline{\lim} |a_n|^{-\frac{1}{n}}. \tag{55}$$

For each of the series

$$\sum_{n=1}^{\infty} z^n, \quad \sum_{n=1}^{\infty} \frac{z^n}{n^2}, \quad \sum_{n=1}^{\infty} \frac{z^n}{n}, \tag{56}$$

we have $R = 1$. For the first, we have divergence at all points of the circle of convergence. For the second we have convergence at all points of the circle of convergence. For the third we have divergence for $z = 1$ and convergence at all other points, by the Abel test of section 199.

262. Differentiation of Power Series. We shall now prove that:

For all values of z inside the circle of convergence of a power series, the function represented by the series has a derivative, whose value is given by the series obtained by termwise differentiation.

To prove this, consider a point z inside the circle of convergence, so that if $|z| = r$, $r < R$. Select a positive number p such that $r + p < r_1 < R$. Then the circle with radius r_1 will be a circle of uniform convergence. Hence, in particular,

$$\sum a_n r^n \quad \text{and} \quad \sum a_n (r + p)^n \tag{57}$$

each converge, so that the series obtained by termwise subtraction likewise converges. Its general term, divided by p, is:

$$a_n \frac{(r + p)^n - r^n}{p} = a_n \left(nr^{n-1} + \frac{n(n - 1)}{2\,!} r^{n-2}p + \cdots \right). \quad (58)$$

The second form shows that it is positive and decreases if p is replaced by any smaller number.

Now let h be any complex number with $|h| < p$, and form the series for the difference quotient,

$$\frac{f(z + h) - f(z)}{h}. \quad (59)$$

The general term is:

$$a_n \frac{(z + h)^n - z^n}{h} = a_n \left(nz^{n-1} + \frac{n(n - 1)}{2\,!} z^{n-2}h + \cdots \right). \quad (60)$$

The numerical value of this is less than the term on the right of equation (58), which was the term of a convergent series of positive terms independent of h. Hence, by the Weierstrass M-test the series with this as its general term converges uniformly in the complex variable h, for $|h| < p$. The terms are continuous functions of z for these values of h, so that the limiting function is continuous, and

$$\lim_{h \to 0} \frac{f(z + h) - f(z)}{h} = \sum_{n=1}^{\infty} na_n z^{n-1}, \quad (61)$$

the value of the series for $h = 0$.

Thus $f(z)$ has a derivative, and

$$f'(z) = \sum_{n=1}^{\infty} na_n z^{n-1}, \quad (62)$$

the series obtained by termwise differentiation.

By equation (55), the radius of convergence of the derived series, R_D, is given by:

$$\frac{1}{R_D} = \overline{\lim_{n \to \infty}} \; |na_n|^{\frac{1}{n}}. \quad (63)$$

But $\lim n^{1/n} = 1$, so that the upper limit is unchanged if we omit this factor and $R_D = R$. Thus the derived series has the same radius of convergence as the original series.

Hence we may repeat the process any number of times and

$$f^{(k)}(z) = \sum_{n=k}^{\infty} n(n - 1) \cdots (n - k + 1)a_n z^{n-k}. \quad (64)$$

263. Integrals. If we wish to define the integral of a continuous function of a complex variable $f(z)$ from z' to z'', we first specify a path, or curve, C in the z plane joining the points representing z' and z''. We must take this path in the region of definition of $f(z)$ and shall usually take it as given by two equations

$$x = x(t), \quad y = y(t), \tag{65}$$

where each of these functions is continuous and of bounded variation. Thus the curve will have a finite arc length.

We then form a sequence of points on the path, corresponding to a subdivision of the t interval which corresponds to the arc:

$$t' = t_0 < t_1 < t_2 < \cdots < t_n = t'', \tag{66}$$

namely,

$$z_k = x(t_k) + iy(t_k), \quad z' = z_0, \quad z'' = z_n. \tag{67}$$

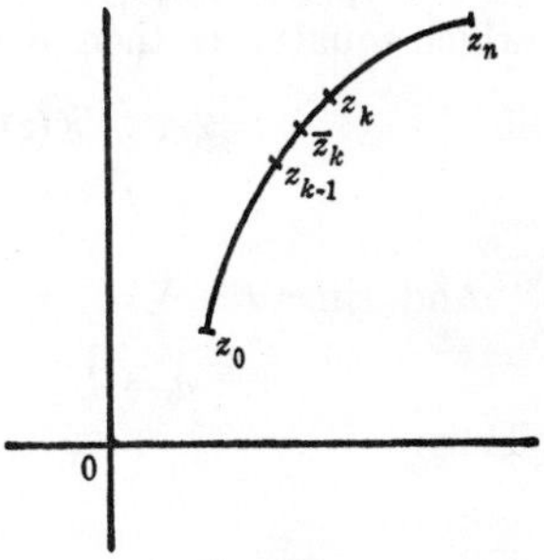

We next select a value in each interval,

$$\bar{t}_k, \quad t_{k-1} \leqq \bar{t}_k \leqq t_k, \tag{68}$$

and put

$$\bar{z}_k = x(\bar{t}_k) + iy(\bar{t}_k). \tag{69}$$

Finally, we form the sum:

Fig. 20.

$$\sum_{k=1}^{n} f(\bar{z}_k) \, \Delta z_k, \quad \text{where} \quad \Delta z_k = z_k - z_{k-1}. \tag{70}$$

We may decompose this into a combination of sums of real terms by writing:

$$z = x + iy, \quad \Delta z = \Delta x + i \, \Delta y, \quad f(z) = u + iv, \tag{71}$$

so that:

$$\begin{aligned} f(z) \, \Delta z &= (u + iv)(\Delta x + i \, \Delta y) \\ &= (u \, \Delta x - v \, \Delta y) + i(u \, \Delta y + v \, \Delta x). \end{aligned} \tag{72}$$

Thus the sum (70) may be reduced to

$$\sum_{k=1}^{n} [u(\bar{x}_k, \bar{y}_k) \, \Delta x_k - v(\bar{x}_k, \bar{y}_k) \, \Delta y_k] \\ + i \sum_{k=1}^{n} [u(\bar{x}_k, \bar{y}_k) \, \Delta y_k + v(\bar{x}_k, \bar{y}_k) \, \Delta x_k]. \tag{73}$$

Each of the terms in brackets is the typical term of the sum for a line integral, as defined in section 180. Consequently, when

$$\delta_M = \max |\Delta z_k| = \max \sqrt{\Delta x_k^2 + \Delta y_k^2} \to 0, \tag{74}$$

these sums each approach line integrals along the path C, and we have

$$\lim_{\delta_M \to 0} \sum_{k=1}^{n} f(\bar{z}_k)\, \Delta z_k = \int_C u\, dx - v\, dy + i \int_C u\, dy + v\, dx. \tag{75}$$

We call this limit the integral of $f(z)$ along the path C and write

$$\int_C f(z)\, dz = \int_C u\, dx - v\, dy + i \int_C u\, dy + v\, dx. \tag{76}$$

The form on the right is easily recalled by formally separating

$$f(z)\, dz = (u + iv)(dx + i\, dy). \tag{77}$$

264. Integral of a Derivative. If there is a function $F(z)$, which in some region including the curve C, has a continuous derivative $F'(z)$ which equals $f(z)$, then by equations (6) and (7) of section 258,

if
$$F(z) = U(x,y) + iV(x,y), \tag{78}$$

$$F'(z) = U_x + iV_x = V_y - iU_y. \tag{79}$$

And, since $F'(z) = f(z) = u + iv$, we have:

$$u = U_x = V_y \quad \text{and} \quad v = V_x = -U_y. \tag{80}$$

Thus:

$$u\, dx - v\, dy = U_x\, dx + U_y\, dy = dU \tag{81}$$

and

$$u\, dy + v\, dx = V_x\, dx + V_y\, dy = dV. \tag{82}$$

Thus both of the line integrals of equation (76) have exact expressions for integrands in this case. Hence, by section 235, we may express the integrals in terms of the end points and

$$\int_{z'}^{z''} f(z)\, dz = \int_C dU + i \int_C dV = \left[U(x,y) + iV(x,y) \right] \Big|_{x',y'}^{x'',y''}$$
$$= F(z'') - F(z'). \tag{83}$$

This shows that the rule for expressing the integral of a continuous function known to be the derivative of another function has the same form for complex variables as that for reals.

Since the form of the derivatives of elementary functions are the same for complex values as for real values, at least in suitably restricted regions, it follows that the methods of integrating functions in terms of elementary functions given in sections 137, 138, and 139 continue to apply when the variables are complex, provided the path of integration lies in a region in which the elementary function which expresses the integral is continuous and single-valued.

Incidentally, the equation (83) shows that if $F(z)$ is single-valued in a region R, and $F'(z) = f(z)$ in R, then the integral of $f(z)$ from z' to z'' is the same for any two paths in R joining z' and z''.

265. An Inequality for Integrals. We may obtain an upper bound for the numerical value of an integral of a continuous function of a complex variable along a path, in terms of a bound for the numerical value of the function and the length of the path. We have:

$$\int_C f(z)\,dz = \lim \sum_{k=1}^{n} f(\bar{z}_k)\,\Delta z_k. \tag{84}$$

Let L be the length of the path C. Then, by section 174, each portion of arc length is at least as great as the corresponding chord, so that:

$$L = \sum \Delta s_k \geq |\Delta z_k|. \tag{85}$$

From our continuity assumptions, $|f(z)|$ has a bound on C, say:

$$|f(z)| \leq M, \text{ on } C. \tag{86}$$

Consequently,

$$|\Sigma f(z_k)\,\Delta z_k| \leq \Sigma |f(z_k)||\Delta z_k| \leq M\Sigma|\Delta z_k| \leq ML. \tag{87}$$

It follows from this and equation (84) that:

$$\left| \int_C f(z)\,dz \right| \leq ML, \tag{88}$$

which is the inequality we were seeking.

This important inequality enables us to extend the results of section 246 to functions of a complex variable. For, let $f_t(z)$ be a sequence of functions approaching $f(z)$ uniformly in z along a path C. Then we have:

$$\left| \int_C f(z)\,dz - \int_C f_t(z)\,dz \right| = \left| \int_C [f(z) - f_t(z)]\,dz \right|$$
$$\leq \int_C |f(z) - f_t(z)|\,dz, \tag{89}$$

since it follows from equation (84) and section 98 that the absolute value of an integral cannot exceed the integral of the absolute value. The right member of the relation (89) will not exceed ϵL,

if

$$|f(z) - f_t(z)| < \epsilon, \text{ on } C. \tag{90}$$

But, in view of the uniform convergence, this will hold for all t beyond some t' in the sequence, for any positive number ϵ. Hence, since L is fixed, it follows that:

$$\lim_t \int_C f_t(z)\, dz = \int_C f(z)\, dz. \tag{91}$$

In particular, a power series may be integrated termwise along any path inside its circle of convergence, since such a path will lie inside some circle of uniform convergence. This result also follows from the theorem on differentiation of power series, combined with equation (83). For cases where the process is valid when one end point is on the circle of convergence, see problem 16 of Exercises XIII, and compare problems 17, 18, and 19.

266. The Cauchy-Goursat Integral Theorem for a Triangle. We have seen that power series represent functions which in certain regions, namely, any circle of uniform convergence, can be differentiated. We shall later prove, conversely, that a function which has a derivative at all points of a two-dimensional region, may be represented by a power series in any circle lying entirely in the region. As a first step toward this, we shall now show that, along any triangle all of whose interior and boundary points belong to the region in which the function has a deriva-

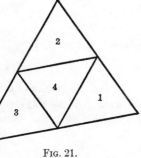

FIG. 21.

tive, the integral of the function is zero.

Consider then any function $f(z)$ which has a derivative at all the interior and boundary points of a triangle and is therefore continuous at all these points. Let us divide the triangle into four triangles of the same shape and dimensions, half as large, by lines through the midpoints of the sides. Then, if T denote the perimeter of the original triangle, traversed in the positive direction as determined by the convention of section 233, and T_j, $j = 1, 2, 3, 4$ denote the perimeters of the four smaller triangles, each traversed in the positive direction, we find that:

$$\int_T f(z)\, dz = \sum_{j=1}^{4} \int_{T_j} f(z)\, dz, \tag{92}$$

since each T_j has two sides a part of T and a third side which is a side of T_4, taken negatively, for $j = 1, 2, 3$.

It follows from this equation that:

$$\left| \int_T f(z)\, dz \right| \le \sum_{j=1}^{4} \left| \int_{T_j} f(z)\, dz \right|. \tag{93}$$

If we denote by C_1 that one, or the one with smallest subscript if there is more than one, T_j for which

$$\left| \int_{C_1} f(z)\, dz \right| \geqq \left| \int_{T_j} f(z)\, dz \right|, \tag{94}$$

we have:

$$\left| \int_{T} f(z)\, dz \right| \leqq 4 \left| \int_{C_1} f(z)\, dz \right|. \tag{95}$$

We now treat the triangle C_1 in the same way we treated the original triangle and so obtain a triangle C_2, such that:

$$\left| \int_{C_1} f(z)\, dz \right| \leqq 4 \left| \int_{C_2} f(z)\, dz \right|. \tag{96}$$

Continuing in this way, we find a sequence of triangles, C_n, such that the length of C_{n+1} is $1/2$ the length of C_n, and

$$\left| \int_{C_n} f(z)\, dz \right| \leqq 4 \left| \int_{C_{n+1}} f(z)\, dz \right|. \tag{97}$$

Hence the length of C_n is $1/2^n$ times the length of T, and

$$\left| \int_{T} f(z)\, dz \right| \leqq 4^n \left| \int_{C_n} f(z)\, dz \right|. \tag{98}$$

As $n \to \infty$, the triangles C_n close down on a point z_0. For, if we take a point in each triangle, we obtain a sequence of points z_n which approach a limit by the Cauchy convergence criterion, say z_0. Since each triangle includes all those which follow, any triangle C_n includes all the z_n with sufficiently large subscripts and therefore their limit point z_0. Again, since the maximum dimension of the triangle C_n approaches zero, there is only one limit point z_0.

Since the point z_0 belongs to the interior or boundary of the first triangle, T, $f(z)$ has a derivative at z_0, and

$$\lim_{z \to z_0} \frac{f(z) - f(z_0)}{z - z_0} = f'(z_0). \tag{99}$$

Hence, for any positive ϵ, there is a δ such that, if $|z - z_0| < \delta$,

$$\frac{f(z) - f(z_0)}{z - z_0} - f'(z_0) = \theta\epsilon, \quad \text{where} \quad |\theta| \leqq 1. \tag{100}$$

When n is large enough, all the points of the triangle with perimeter C_n will lie within δ of z_0. Thus we may use the equation (100) in calculating the integral of $f(z)$ over C_n, and find:

$$\int_{C_n} f(z)\, dz = \int_{C_n} [f(z_0) + (z - z_0)f'(z_0) + (z - z_0)\theta\epsilon]\, dz. \tag{101}$$

The first two terms give zero, since they are the derivative of

$$F(z) = f(z_0)z + \frac{(z - z_0)^2}{2} f'(z_0), \tag{102}$$

which is single-valued for all values of z and the path of integration is closed, and so has the same end points, $z' = z''$ in equation (83). For the third term, we have:

$$\left| \int_{C_n} (z - z_0)\theta(z)\epsilon \, dz \right| \leq \epsilon \text{ (length } C_n)^2. \tag{103}$$

Consequently,

$$\left| \int_{C_n} f(z) \, dz \right| \leq \epsilon \text{ (length } C_n)^2 \leq \epsilon \left(\frac{\text{length } T}{2^n} \right)^2. \tag{104}$$

From this and the relation (98) we find:

$$\left| \int_T f(z) \, dz \right| \leq \epsilon \text{ (length } T)^2. \tag{105}$$

Since the length of T is fixed and ϵ is arbitrary, this proves that:

$$\left| \int_T f(z) \, dz \right| = 0, \quad \text{and hence} \quad \int_T f(z) \, dz = 0, \tag{106}$$

as we set out to prove.

267. The Cauchy-Goursat Integral Theorem. A connected plane region is said to be *simply connected* if every simple closed polygon consisting entirely of points of the region, has all its interior points interior to the region. We shall now prove that:

If a function $f(z)$ has a derivative at each interior point of a simply connected region R, then the integral of $f(z)$ is zero about any closed path consisting entirely of interior points of R.

We first observe that every simple polygon may be decomposed into triangles, by line segments contained in the closed region made up of the polygon and its interior points. The integral of $f(z)$ around the polygon will be the sum of the integrals taken around the component triangles. It will therefore be zero, if the points of the polygon are interior points of R. This result holds for a polygon which intersects itself, since the integral may be decomposed into a finite number of integrals over simple polygons.

Consider next any closed path of integration, C, which is a continuous curve with an arc length and has all its points interior to R. Then each point of C is the center of a circle lying in R and since the points of C form a closed set, we may select a finite number of such circles which include all the points of C. These circles K together form a closed region in R, including C. As $f(z)$ is continuous at all points of this closed region, it is uniformly continuous and we may select a δ for any given positive quantity, ϵ, such that for any two points in this region, whose distance is less than δ, the function $f(z)$ differs by at most ϵ in numerical value.

Next inscribe a polygon P in the curve C, such that each chord is less than δ and also such that,

$$\left| \int_C f(z)\, dz - \sum f(z_k)\, \Delta z_k \right| < \epsilon, \tag{107}$$

where Δz_k correspond to the sides of the polygon. We may do this using, among other points of subdivision, the points where the circumferences of the circles K intersect C. This will insure that the points of the polygon P are all in the closed region consisting of the circles K and therefore interior to R.

For the polygon P, we may form a sum approximating the integral of $f(z)$ over the polygon to within ϵ, using points of subdivision z_j' which include the vertices of the polygon. Then:

$$\left| \int_P f(z)\, dz - \sum f(z_j')\, \Delta z_j' \right| < \epsilon. \tag{108}$$

Then, from the choice of δ, if z_{jk}' is any point of the side of the polygon Δz_k, we have:

$$|f(z_k) - f(z_{jk}')| < \epsilon. \tag{109}$$

Also, since Δz_k equals the sum of certain $\Delta z_j'$, we have:

$$\left| \sum f(z_k)\, \Delta z_k - \sum f(z_j')\, \Delta z_j' \right| \leqq \left| \sum \epsilon\, \Delta z_j' \right| \leqq \epsilon \sum |\Delta z_k| \leqq \epsilon L, \tag{110}$$

where L is the length of the curve C.

From the inequalities (107), (108), and (110), we may conclude that:

$$\left| \int_P f(z)\, dz - \int_C f(z)\, dz \right| \leqq \epsilon(L + 2). \tag{111}$$

Since L is fixed and ϵ is arbitrary,

$$\int_C f(z)\, dz = \int_P f(z)\, dz = 0. \tag{112}$$

268. Multiply Connected Regions. A connected region, not simply connected, is said to be multiply connected. An example is the region consisting of the points inside a large circle and outside a number of small circles having no points in common and all lying inside the large circle.

For a function which has a derivative at all the interior points of a multiply connected region, M, the integral around a closed path in the region is not necessarily zero. However, if all the interior points of the region bounded by the path belong to M, the path is in some simply connected region to which the theorem of the preceding section applies and the integral is zero.

More generally, if we have a number of closed paths C_j', which together form C' the boundary of a multiply connected region M', where C' and M' are interior to M, then the sum of the integrals of $f(z)$ about the

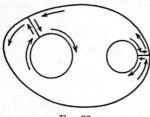

curves C', taken in consistent directions, is zero. Here the consistent directions for smooth curves are determined by a convention similar to that of section 233, that the tangent in the positive direction and the inner normal bear the same relation as that of the positive x-axis to the positive y-axis. For paths C' without tangents at certain points, we may use

FIG. 22.

approximating curves lying in M' which have tangents to determine the directions.

In either case, the multiply connected region may be separated into a finite number of simply connected pieces by curves, or cross-cuts, lying in M'. The integral of $f(z)$ about the boundary of each simply connected piece, taken in the positive direction, is zero. In the sum of these integrals, the integration along each cross-cut is taken twice, in opposite directions and thus cancels, while the remaining boundary of the simply connected pieces makes up the curves C', consistently oriented. This proves the more general result.

269. The Cauchy Integral Formula. Suppose $f(z)$ has a derivative at all points of a simply connected region R. Then, if a is any point of R, the function $f(z)/(z-a)$ has a derivative at all points of R except a. Thus we may apply the theorem of the last section to any multiply connected region bounded by a curve C in R including a as an interior point and a small circle γ with center at a and entirely interior to C. The direction for C may be taken as positively related to the inner direction. Then, since the radius of γ must be extended to give

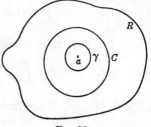

FIG. 23.

the interior of the region, we must take the integral over γ in the direction negatively related to the inner direction. Or, we may form a sum which is zero by taking the integral along γ in the direction positively related to the inner direction and prefixing a minus sign. Thus we find:

$$\int_C \frac{f(z)\,dz}{z-a} - \int_\gamma \frac{f(z)\,dz}{z-a} = 0. \tag{113}$$

But, as $f(z)$ is continuous at a,

$$f(z) = f(a) + \lambda\epsilon, \quad \text{where} \quad |\lambda| < 1, \tag{114}$$

on the circle γ, if the radius ρ is taken sufficiently small. It follows that:

$$\int_\gamma \frac{f(z)\,dz}{z-a} = \int_\gamma \frac{f(a)\,dz}{z-a} + \int_\gamma \frac{\epsilon\lambda(z)\,dz}{z-a}. \tag{115}$$

For the first integral in the right member, we have on putting

$$z - a = \rho e^{i\theta}, \quad dz = \rho i e^{i\theta}\,d\theta, \tag{116}$$

$$\int_\gamma \frac{f(a)\,dz}{z-a} = \int_0^{2\pi} f(a)i\,d\theta = 2\pi i f(a). \tag{117}$$

Here θ plays the rôle of t in section 263. For the last integral in equation (115):

$$\left| \int_\gamma \frac{\epsilon\lambda(z)\,dz}{z-a} \right| \leqq \frac{\epsilon}{\rho} 2\pi\rho \leqq 2\pi\epsilon. \tag{118}$$

Our equations may be combined to give:

$$\left| \int_C \frac{f(z)\,dz}{z-a} - 2\pi i f(a) \right| \leqq 2\pi\epsilon. \tag{119}$$

Hence, since ϵ is arbitrary, the left member is zero and

$$f(a) = \frac{1}{2\pi i} \int_C \frac{f(z)\,dz}{z-a}. \tag{120}$$

This is *Cauchy's integral formula*. It expresses the value of $f(z)$ at any point a interior to a region R in which $f(z)$ has a derivative in terms of the integral taken about any closed path C in R, bounding a simply connected region including the point a. The discussion of section 268 shows that the formula still holds if we use as the path of integration C', the complete boundary of a multiply connected region including a in its interior and lying in R.

270. Taylor's Series. Let the function $f(z)$ have a derivative at all points of a region R. Let a be a point in R, and draw a circle with center a, lying entirely inside R. Let t be a point on this circle and z

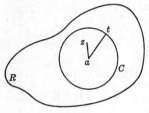

any point inside this circle. Using the circle as the curve C of Cauchy's integral formula for the point z, with t as the variable of integration, we have:

$$f(z) = \frac{1}{2\pi i} \int_C \frac{f(t)\,dt}{t - z}. \qquad (121)$$

Fig. 24.

But we may write:

$$\frac{1}{t - z} = \frac{1}{(t - a) - (z - a)} = \frac{1}{t - a}\left[1 + \frac{z - a}{t - a} + \frac{(z - a)^2}{(t - a)^2} + \cdots\right.$$
$$\left. + \frac{(z - a)^{n-1}}{(t - a)^{n-1}}\right] + \frac{(z - a)^n}{(t - a)^n(t - z)}. \qquad (122)$$

If r is the radius of the circle C,

$$\left|\frac{z - a}{t - a}\right| = \frac{|z - a|}{r} < 1, \qquad (123)$$

so that for z fixed and all values of t on the circle C, the infinite series

$$\frac{1}{t - a} + \frac{z - a}{(t - a)^2} + \frac{(z - a)^2}{(t - a)^3} + \cdots + \frac{(z - a)^{n-1}}{(t - a)^n} + \cdots \qquad (124)$$

converges to $1/(t - z)$. Moreover the convergence is uniform, since the remainder after n terms has a numerical value

$$\left|\frac{(z - a)^n}{(t - a)^n(t - z)}\right| \leqq \left[\frac{|z - a|}{r}\right]^n \frac{1}{|t_1 - z|}, \qquad (125)$$

where t_1 is the point of the circle C nearest to z.

Since $f(z)$ is continuous on C, it is bounded on C, so that termwise multiplication of the series (124) by $f(t)/2\pi i$ will not disturb the uniform convergence. Thus we may integrate the new series termwise and find from equation (121) that

$$f(z) = A_0 + A_1(z - a) + A_2(z - a)^2 + \cdots$$
$$+ A_n(z - a)^n + \cdots, \qquad (126)$$

where

$$A_n = \frac{1}{2\pi i} \int_C \frac{f(t)\,dt}{(t - a)^{n+1}}. \qquad (127)$$

Since the series (126) is a power series convergent for all z with $|z - a| < r$, its radius of convergence is not less than r and it may be differentiated termwise any number of times.   Thus

$$f^{(k)}(z) = \sum_{n=k}^{\infty} n(n-1)(n-2)\cdots(n-k+1)A_n(z-a)^{n-k}. \quad (128)$$

In particular, we may put $z = a$, which gives:

$$f^{(k)}(a) = k! A_k, \quad \text{or} \quad A_k = \frac{f^{(k)}(a)}{k!}. \quad (129)$$

Thus, under the conditions stated, the function $f(z)$ has derivatives of all orders at the point a and the coefficients of its power series expansion about the point a have the same form as those of the Taylor's development of section 89.

271. The Morera Theorem.   As a converse to the Cauchy-Goursat theorem of section 267, we have the theorem of Morera:

If a single-valued continuous function $f(z)$ has its integral zero about every closed path consisting entirely of interior points of a region R, then the function has a derivative at each interior point of R.

To prove this, select any fixed point of the region R, z_0, and consider the integral of $f(z)$ from z_0 to z, a second point of R, along any path lying in R.   If C_1 and C_2 are any two such paths, C_1 and C_2 taken with reversed sense, form a closed path.   Hence, by our hypothesis, the integral over C_1 minus the integral over C_2 is zero.   Thus the integral from z_0 to z is the same for all paths in R, and so may be used to define a single-valued function in R,

$$F(z) = \int_{z_0} f(t)\, dt, \text{ over any path in } R. \quad (130)$$

Let us form the difference quotient of $F(z)$,

$$\frac{\Delta F}{\Delta z} = \frac{F(z+h) - F(z)}{h} = \frac{1}{h}\int_{z}^{z+h} f(t)\, dt. \quad (131)$$

Since $f(z)$ is continuous at z, for any positive ϵ, there is a δ, such that:

$$|f(t) - f(z)| < \epsilon, \quad \text{if} \quad |t - z| < \delta. \quad (132)$$

Thus, if we take $|h| < \delta$ and use a straight line path joining z and $z + h$, which will be in R for h sufficiently small, we may put

$$f(t) = f(z) + \theta\epsilon, \quad \text{with} \quad |\theta| < 1, \quad (133)$$

for the integrand in equation (131). That is:

$$\int_z^{z+h} f(t)\,dt = \int_z^{z+h} [f(z) + \theta\epsilon]\,dt = hf(z) + \int_z^{z+h} \theta\epsilon\,dt. \quad (134)$$

For the last integral

$$\left| \int_z^{z+h} \epsilon\theta(t)\,dt \right| \leqq \epsilon\,|h|. \quad (135)$$

Hence we may conclude from equations (131), and the last two, that:

$$\left| \frac{\Delta F}{\Delta z} - f(z) \right| \leqq \epsilon, \quad (136)$$

for $|h| = |\Delta z|$ sufficiently small. It follows from this that

$$\lim \frac{\Delta F}{\Delta z} = f(z). \quad (137)$$

Thus $F(z)$ has a derivative at z, any point of R. Hence, by the reasoning of the last section, all the derivatives of $F(z)$ exist and in particular the second derivative,

$$F''(z) = f'(z), \quad \text{since} \quad F'(z) = f(z). \quad (138)$$

That is, $f(z)$ has a derivative at any interior point of R, as we set out to prove.

272. Analytic Functions. A single-valued function $f(z)$ is said to be *analytic at a point z*, if it has a derivative at z and at all values in some two-dimensional region including z as an interior point. We say that a function is analytic in a region R, if it is analytic at all points of R. Throughout this section, R will always denote an open two-dimensional region.

By the preceding section, $f(z)$ is analytic in R if it is single-valued and continuous and may be integrated in R in the sense that its integral around every closed path is zero, or between any two points is independent of the path.

Similarly, any function which is analytic in a simply connected region R, satisfies this condition by the Cauchy-Goursat theorem.

By section 262, a function represented by a power series is analytic at all points inside its circle of convergence. Also, by section 270, a function analytic at a point may be represented by a power series expansion about this point.

The last fact shows that an analytic function has derivatives of all orders and hence these are all continuous. Thus, by section 258, if

$f(z) = u + iv$, u and v will each have first partial derivatives which are continuous and satisfy the Cauchy-Riemann differential equations.

We thus have necessary and sufficient conditions for analyticity, or alternative definitions, in terms of derivatives, integrals, power series, or the Cauchy-Riemann differential equations. Each of these is a convenient method of proving analyticity under certain conditions.

A function, proved to be analytic by any of these tests, has all the properties just mentioned. It also possesses derivatives of all orders, each of which, like itself, is continuous and in fact analytic. Also, by the reasoning of section 271, it follows that the integral of an analytic function is an analytic function of its upper limit.

273. Uniformly Convergent Sequences of Analytic Functions. In section 265 we proved that if $f_t(z)$ is a sequence of continuous functions approaching $f(z)$ uniformly for z on a path C, then

$$\lim_t \int_C f_t(z) \, dz = \int_C f(z) \, dz. \tag{139}$$

We may deduce from this that if the sequence of functions $f_t(z)$ approaches $f(z)$ uniformly in an open two-dimensional region R and all the $f_t(z)$ are analytic in R, then $f(z)$ is analytic in R.

For, from the first condition the $f_t(z)$ are continuous functions and each has an integral around every closed path C in R equal to zero. Hence, by equation (139), $f(z)$ has its integral about every closed path C in R equal to zero, so that $f(z)$ is analytic in R.

In particular, the sum function of a series uniformly convergent for z in some open two-dimensional region R is analytic in R if the terms of the series are each analytic in R.

If $f_t(z)$ approaches $f(z)$ uniformly in R, then the function

$$\frac{1}{2\pi i} \frac{f_t(u)}{(u-z)^2} \quad \text{approaches} \quad \frac{1}{2\pi i} \frac{f(u)}{(u-z)^2}, \tag{140}$$

uniformly for u on any circle C with center z lying in R. Hence the integral of the first expression taken over this circle C approaches that of the second over C. If each function $f_t(z)$ is analytic in R, $f(z)$ is analytic in R by the theorem just proved and we may apply equations (127) and (129) to conclude that:

$$f_t'(z) \quad \text{approaches} \quad f'(z). \tag{141}$$

In particular, the sum function of a series of analytic functions may be differentiated termwise at any point z if the separate terms are each analytic and the series converges uniformly, in some two-dimensional region including z as an interior point. Similar reasoning applies to the higher derivatives, so that we may differentiate termwise any number of times.

We may use this to prove the following theorem: *Let*

$$w_k(z) = \sum_{n=1}^{\infty} c_{kn} z^n, \tag{142}$$

and

$$\sum_{k=1}^{\infty} a_k w_k(z) = w(z), \tag{143}$$

with all these infinite series uniformly convergent in some two-dimensional region R including the origin as an interior point. Then, in any circle about the origin lying in R,

$$w(z) = \sum_{n=1}^{\infty} \left(\sum_{k=1}^{\infty} a_k c_{kn} \right) z^n, \tag{144}$$

and the series on the right is the Taylor's series for $w(z)$.

By our hypothesis, each function $w_k(z)$ is analytic in R. Hence from the uniform convergence of the series (143), the function $w(z)$ is analytic in R. Hence $w(z)$ is analytic at $z = 0$ and has a Taylor's series expansion about this point, or in powers of z. The coefficients are given by equation (129), so that:

$$w(z) = \sum_{n=1}^{\infty} \frac{1}{n!} w^{(n)}(0) z^n. \tag{145}$$

But, since the series (142) converges uniformly, it may be differentiated termwise to give:

$$w_k^{(n)}(0) = n! \, c_{kn}. \tag{146}$$

Similarly, by termwise differentiation of the series (143),

$$w^{(n)}(0) = \sum_{k=1}^{\infty} a_k w_k^{(n)}(0). \tag{147}$$

The last two equations prove that:

$$\frac{1}{n!} w^{(n)}(0) = \sum_{k=1}^{\infty} a_k c_{kn}, \tag{148}$$

so that the expansion (144) is the same as the Taylor's expansion (145). Since the function $w(z)$ is analytic in R, the series equals $w(z)$ inside any circle about the origin lying in R.

274. Operations on Power Series. Any operation on one or more analytic functions which leads to an analytic function corresponds to a method of deriving a new power series from one or more given power series. We shall illustrate our remarks for power series about the origin, since for other points we have merely to replace z by $z - a$.

Let
$$f(z) = \sum a_n z^n, \quad \text{for} \quad |z| < R_1 \tag{149}$$
and
$$g(z) = \sum b_n z^n, \quad \text{for} \quad |z| < R_2. \tag{150}$$
Then
$$f(z) + g(z) = \sum (a_n + b_n) z^n, \quad \text{for} \quad |z| < \min (R_1, R_2), \tag{151}$$

since for any z satisfying the inequality each of the series converges absolutely.

Similarly, by section 203, the series may be multiplied to give

$$f(z)g(z) = \sum_{n=0}^{\infty} \left(\sum_{m=0}^{n} a_m b_{n-m} \right) z^n, \quad \text{for} \quad |z| < \min (R_1, R_2). \tag{152}$$

By a repetition of the last process, we may find the series for the successive powers of a given series. For example, in the case of a series with first term zero,

$$h(z) = c_1 z + c_2 z^2 + c_3 z^3 + \cdots, \tag{153}$$

we find for the powers
$$[h(z)]^2 = c_1^2 z^2 + 2c_1 c_2 z^3 + \cdots,$$
$$[h(z)]^3 = c_1^3 z^3 + \cdots,$$
$$\cdot \quad \cdot \quad \cdot \tag{154}$$

Each of these converges inside any circle of uniform convergence for the first series.

Hence, as in section 83, we may find the power series for a function of a function of this type. Thus, from

$$f(h) = \sum a_n h^n, \tag{155}$$

we may find the formal expansion:

$$a_0 + a_1 c_1 z + (a_1 c_2 + a_2 c_1^2) z^2 + (a_1 c_3 + 2a_2 c_1 c_2 + a_3 c_1^3) z^3 + \cdots. \tag{156}$$

That this is the Taylor's series for the function $f[h(z)]$ and hence converges in any circle inside the region in which this function is analytic follows from the result at the end of the last section, provided that the series

$$\sum a_n [h(z)]^n \tag{157}$$

converges uniformly for z in some region including the origin as an interior point. But, since $h(z)$ is continuous at $z = 0$ and is zero for

$z = 0$, there is some region R in the z plane, including the origin in its interior in which:

$$|h(z)| < r, \tag{158}$$

a radius of uniform convergence for the series (155). Then for z in this region, R,

$$|a_n[h(z)]^n| \leqq |a_n|r^n. \tag{159}$$

But the series $|a_n|r^n$ converges, since $a_n r^n$ converges absolutely. Hence, by the Weierstrass M-test, the uniform convergence of the series (157) in R is established.

275. Functions with Parameters. Let $f(z,w)$ be a continuous function of the two complex variables z and w, that is of four real variables, the real and imaginary components of z and w. Then, if for each value of w considered, the function $f(z,w)$ is analytic in some two-dimensional simply connected region R of the z plane, the function

$$F(z) = \int_{C_1} f(z,w)\, dw \tag{160}$$

is analytic in R. For, if C is any closed path in R, we have

$$\int_C dz \int_{C_1} f(z,w)\, dw = \int_{C_1} dw \int_C f(z,w)\, dz = 0. \tag{161}$$

The double integral reduces to a number of double real integrals of continuous functions, for each of which the order may be inverted. Also the second integral is zero, since the integral of $f(z,w)$ with respect to z is zero over C by the Cauchy-Goursat theorem. But the first integral of (161) is the integral of $F(z)$ about any closed curve C in R. Hence the function $F(z)$ is analytic in R by the Morera theorem.

If we replace the path C_1 by a path extending to infinity, or ending at a point at which $f(z,w)$ is not continuous, the integral (160) will still define a function analytic in z, provided that the improper integrals converge uniformly for z in R. For in this case it will be the uniform limit of proper integrals, each of which is analytic in z by the first result. For the same reason, the result persists if, on C, $f(z,w)$ is not necessarily itself continuous in all four real variables, but its integral on C is the uniform limit of integrals of functions each of which is continuous in the two complex variables z and w.

If $f(z,w)$ has a derivative $\partial f/\partial z$ which is a continuous function of the two complex variables z and w,

and if

$$F(z) = \int_C f(z,w)\, dw, \tag{162}$$

then

$$F'(z) = \int_C \frac{\partial f}{\partial z}\, dw. \tag{163}$$

To prove this, we note that since $f(z,w)$ has a derivative with respect to z, it is analytic in z. Hence, by the previous result, the function $F(z)$ is analytic in z. Also, by section 270, we have:

$$F'(z) = \frac{1}{2\pi i}\int_{C'} \frac{F(t)\, dt}{(t-z)^2} \tag{164}$$

where C' is a small circle about z, so that

$$F'(z) = \frac{1}{2\pi i}\int_{C'} dt \int_C \frac{f(t,w)\, dw}{(t-z)^2}. \tag{165}$$

Since the function $f(z,w)$ is continuous in the two complex variables and $t - z \neq 0$ for t on C', we may invert the order of integration. For this is equivalent to the inversion of order in a number of real double integrals, each with a continuous integrand. Furthermore, we have by section 270,

$$\frac{1}{2\pi i}\int_{C'} \frac{f(t,w)\, dt}{(t-z)^2} = \frac{\partial f}{\partial z}. \tag{166}$$

Thus we find:

$$\begin{aligned}
F'(z) &= \int_C dw \frac{1}{2\pi i}\int_{C'} \frac{f(t,w)\, dt}{(t-z)^2} \\
&= \int_C \frac{\partial f}{\partial z}\, dw, \tag{167}
\end{aligned}$$

which is the relation to be established.

276. Laurent's Series. If $f(z)$ is a single-valued analytic function of the complex variable z for all points in a region R including a in its interior, the Taylor's series in powers of $(z - a)$ will represent the function in any circle C of radius r, with a as its center, lying entirely inside the region R.

Now suppose that the function is not necessarily analytic at the point a itself, but is analytic at all other points of R. Then it is possible to represent the function, at all points distinct from a and in any circle of type C, by a series involving both positive and negative powers of $(z - a)$, the Laurent series for the function about a.

To prove this, let us first consider a ring shaped region bounded by two circles, C_1 of radius r_1 and C_2 with radius r_2, $r_1 < r_2$, each with center at a and lying entirely inside R. Then, we may apply the Cauchy integral formula to any point z in this region to obtain:

$$f(z) = \frac{1}{2\pi i} \int_{C'} \frac{f(t)\,dt}{t - z}$$

$$= \frac{1}{2\pi i} \int_{C_2} \frac{f(t)\,dt}{t - z} - \frac{1}{2\pi i} \int_{C_1} \frac{f(t)\,dt}{t - z}. \tag{168}$$

Here the circles C_1 and C_2 are each traversed in the positive direction and the minus sign is due to the fact that C_1 the smaller circle must be traversed negatively when considered a part of C', the boundary of the ring.

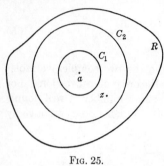

Since $f(t)$ is analytic in R, which includes C_1 and C_2, and z is not on either curve, the first integrand is continuous in z and t and analytic in z, for t on and z inside the outer circle C_2. Therefore the first integral represents an analytic function in this region and so may be expanded in a Taylor's series in positive powers of $(z - a)$ which represents the integral inside C_2, and hence in the ring.

Fig. 25.

The second integrand is continuous in z and t, and analytic in z for t on and z outside the inner circle C_1. Since it is analytic for $|z - a| > r_1$, if we put:

$$Z = \frac{1}{z - a}, \quad \frac{1}{t - z} = \frac{Z}{Z(t - a) - 1} \tag{169}$$

and is analytic for $Z < 1/r_1$. Thus the second integral of (168) is an analytic function of Z for these values and so may be expanded in a series of powers of Z. Since the last fraction of (169) is zero for $Z = 0$, the same is true of the integral and the expansion will contain no constant term. This gives a series of positive powers of Z, or of negative powers of $(z - a)$ which represents the second integral for $Z < 1/r_1$, or $|z - a| > r_1$. That is, outside the circle C_1 and hence in the ring.

On combining the two expansions, we have a series:

$$f(z) = \sum_{n=-\infty}^{\infty} A_n(z - a)^n. \tag{170}$$

If C_3 is any circle with center at a and radius r, with

$$r_1 < r < r_2, \tag{171}$$

the series (170) will converge uniformly for z on the circle C_3. The uniform convergence will not be affected by multiplying by $(z - a)^{-k-1}$ whose numerical value is r^{-k-1} on C_3. And, after multiplication by this factor, we may integrate the series termwise. All the terms give zero except the term $A_k(z - a)^{-1}$ and we find:

$$\int_{C_3} \frac{f(z)\ dz}{(z - a)^{k+1}} = 2\pi i A_k. \tag{172}$$

This determines the coefficients. It follows from the Cauchy integral theorem that the integral will be unchanged if we replace C_3 by any closed curve in R bounding a region including a in its interior. Hence the coefficients are independent of the choice of C_1 and C_2. By taking the radius r_1 sufficiently small, we may make the ring include any point inside C_2 distinct from a. Hence we have:

If the function $f(z)$ is single-valued and analytic in a region R, with the possible exception of the point a and C is any circle with center a lying in R, then the Laurent expansion

$$f(z) = \sum_{n=-\infty}^{\infty} A_n(z - a)^n \tag{173}$$

is valid for all points inside the circle C, distinct from a.

The coefficients are given by

$$A_n = \frac{1}{2\pi i} \int_{C'} \frac{f(z)\ dz}{(z - a)^{n+1}}, \tag{174}$$

where C' is any closed curve in R bounding a region including the point a in its interior.

277. Singular Points. If a function $f(z)$ is not analytic at a, but is single-valued and analytic at all other points of some two-dimensional region including a as an interior point, then a is called an *isolated singular point*. By the preceding section, at any isolated singular point, there is a Laurent expansion of the type (173). If the expansion contains no negative powers, the expansion represents a function analytic at a, so that if we redefine our function at a as A_0, the value of the series, the function will become analytic at a. In this case the point a is called a *removable singularity*. In this case the function only fails to be analytic because it is undefined, or differently defined from A_0, at one point. Since defining $f(a)$ as A_0 makes the function continuous at a, it follows that if $f(z)$ is continuous at a and has at most a removable singularity at a, then $f(z)$ is analytic at a.

If the expansion (173) contains only a finite number of negative powers, so that it can be written:

$$f(z) = \sum_{n=-m}^{\infty} A_n(z - a)^n, \tag{175}$$

then the function is said to have a *pole* at the point, of order m, where m is the highest power of $(z - a)^{-1}$ in the expansion. We note that in this case $f(z)(z - a)^m$ is a power series and so is an analytic function of z at a. Also m is the smallest integer for which this is the case. Since

$$\lim_{z \to a} (z - a)^m f(z) = A_{-m} \neq 0, \tag{176}$$

it follows that, at a pole,

$$\lim |f(z)| = \infty. \tag{177}$$

Since $(z - a)^m f(z)$ is analytic at a and different from zero there, its reciprocal

$$F(z) = \frac{1}{f(z)(z - a)^m} \tag{178}$$

is analytic at a and different from zero there.

When a function is analytic and the first non-zero coefficient of its Taylor's expansion is A_m, so that

$$g(z) = \sum_{n=m}^{\infty} A_n(z - a)^n, \quad A_m \neq 0, \ m > 0, \tag{179}$$

it is said to have a zero of the mth order. A comparison of this with the preceding equation shows that, if $f(z)$ has a pole of the mth order, $1/f(z)$ has a zero of the mth order and conversely if a function has a zero of the mth order its reciprocal has a pole of the mth order.

An isolated singularity which is not removable and not a pole is an *essential singularity*.

If the values of $f(z)$ admit an upper bound in R, so that

$$|f(z)| \leq M, \tag{180}$$

the formula for the coefficients of the negative powers, with the integrals taken over a circle C about a of radius r, shows that:

$$|A_{-m}| = \left| \frac{1}{2\pi i} \int_C \frac{f(z)\, dz}{(z - a)^{-m+1}} \right| \leq Mr^m. \tag{181}$$

Since this cannot change with r and approaches zero when r approaches zero, it follows that all the negative coefficients are zero and the function is either analytic or has a removable singularity at a. (Riemann's theorem.)

If the values of $f(z)$ do not admit an upper bound, for some region including a, there must be a sequence of values, z_n, with

$$\lim_n z_n = a, \quad \lim_n |f(z_n)| = \infty. \tag{182}$$

At a pole,

$$\lim_{z \to a} |f(z)| = \infty, \tag{183}$$

so that this is true for all sequences of values. Conversely, if this is satisfied, the function has a pole at a. For, in this case

$$\lim_{z \to a} \frac{1}{f(z)} = 0, \tag{184}$$

so that the values of $1/f(z)$ admit a bound M in some region including a. Thus, this function has at most a removable singularity at a and becomes analytic if we take 0 as its value at a. If this zero is of the mth order, then $f(z)$ itself has a pole of the mth order.

This shows that, if a function has an essential singularity at a, the function can neither become infinite for all sequences $z_n \to a$, nor approach the same finite value for all sequences $z_n \to a$. It follows that, for suitable sequences of values $z_n \to a$, the function can be made to become infinite, or approach any finite value whatever, as we shall now prove. For there must be a sequence satisfying the relation (182), or the function would admit an upper bound. Again, if $f(z)$ has an essential singularity at a, then $1/[f(z) - b]$ must also have an essential singularity at a, since if it approached the same finite value or became infinite for all sequences $z_n \to a$, the behavior of $f(z)$ would be correspondingly restricted. Thus this function admits a sequence z_n such that:

$$\lim_n z_n = a \quad \text{and} \quad \lim \left| \frac{1}{f(z_n) - b} \right| = \infty. \tag{185}$$

But this implies that:

$$\lim f(z_n) = b, \tag{186}$$

and b is any complex number, so that we have proved our contention. This result is known as Weierstrass's theorem.

278. Residues. The residue of a function $f(z)$ at a is the coefficient of $(z - a)^{-1}$ in its Laurent expansion, or

$$R(a) = A_{-1} = \frac{1}{2\pi i} \int_{C'} f(z) \, dz, \tag{187}$$

where C' is any curve bounding a region including a, such that C' and the region it bounds are interior to R, a region in which $f(z)$ is analytic.

It follows that, for any curve of this type,

$$\int_{C'} f(z)\, dz = 2\pi i R(a). \tag{188}$$

By the Cauchy-Goursat integral theorem, the integral is zero if $f(z)$ is analytic at a. This also follows from the fact that in this case the Laurent expansion reduces to the Taylor's expansion, with no negative powers, so that the residue at a is zero.

Next consider a function analytic throughout a region R, with the exception of a finite number of isolated singularities a_k. Let C be any curve or set of curves forming the complete boundary of a portion of R, along which the function is analytic. Then, if the portion of R bounded includes n of the points a_k, we may surround each of them by a small closed curve C_k so that the curves C_k all taken negatively, together with the curve C taken positively bound a region in which $f(z)$ is analytic. Hence, by the integral theorem, the integral about all of these will be zero and the integral about C will equal the sum of the integrals about C_k, taken positively. But, since each of these integrals is $2\pi i R(a_k)$, it follows that:

$$\int_C f(z)\, dz = 2\pi i \sum_{k=1}^{n} R(a_k). \tag{189}$$

This is known as Cauchy's *residue theorem*.

It may sometimes be applied to the evaluation of real integrals as we shall show in sections 280 and 281.

We note that, at a simple pole,

$$f(z) = A_{-1}(z-a)^{-1} + A_0 + A_1(z-a) + A_2(z-a)^2 + \cdots \tag{190}$$

and hence

$$A_{-1} = \lim_{z \to a} (z-a)f(z). \tag{191}$$

At a pole of higher order than the first, the product $(z-a)f(z)$ becomes infinite. However, the residue is finite. Nevertheless, it is worth while to calculate the limit on the right of equation (191). For, if this is not zero, it shows that the singularity is a pole of the first order and the limit gives the residue. If the product becomes infinite, we have a pole of higher order. In other cases the product approaches different limits for different sequences and we have an essential singularity. In either case further investigation is necessary to determine the residue. For poles of higher order, say the mth, we may use problem 30 of Exercises XIII. Or the coefficient A_{-1} may be obtained by dividing two Taylor's series, or by dividing a Taylor's series by $(z-a)^m$. The division of two Taylor's series is reducible to $(z - a)^{-m}$ times the division of a series by one with non-zero constant term, or multiplication by its reciprocal. This may be accomplished by the procedure of section 83, which is justified for complex values by the theorems of section 274.

In calculating the residue at a simple pole, any analytic factor distinct from zero at a may be replaced by its limiting value. For a multiple pole, or an essential singularity, this procedure is not applicable since equation (191) does not hold. Thus the function $(z - 1)^{-2}$ has a residue zero at $a = 1$, and $(z - 2)^{-1}$ approaches a finite limit at 1, but

$$
\begin{aligned}
(z - 2)^{-1}(z - 1)^{-2} &= (z - 1)^{-2}(-1)\,\frac{1}{1 - (z - 1)} \\
&= -(z - 1)^{-2}[1 + (z - 1) + (z - 1)^2 + \cdots] \\
&= -(z - 1)^{-2} - (z - 1)^{-1} - 1 - \cdots, \quad (192)
\end{aligned}
$$

so that the product $(z - 2)^{-1}(z - 1)^{-2}$ has a residue -1 at $a = 1$.

The methods just mentioned enable us to find the residue of any rational function, or of the product of a rational function times an elementary function, or any analytic function whose Taylor's series at a is known. It is frequently convenient to begin by decomposing the rational function into partial fractions, as in section 115.

279. Change of Variable in an Integral. If we make a change of variable from z to Z by means of an analytic function $z(Z)$ which maps a smooth curve C' in the Z plane into a curve C in the z plane, the integral

$$
\int_C f(z)\, dz \qquad (193)
$$

is transformed into

$$
\int_{C'} f[z(Z)]z'(Z)\, dZ. \qquad (194)
$$

To show this, we introduce a real parameter t along the curve, and reduce each of the above integrals to real line integrals, by expanding:

$$
(u + iv)(dx + i\, dy) = (u + iv)\left(\frac{dx}{dt} + i\,\frac{dy}{dt}\right) dt \qquad (195)
$$

and

$$
(u + iv)\left(\frac{\partial x}{\partial X} + i\,\frac{\partial y}{\partial X}\right)\left(\frac{dX}{dt} + i\,\frac{dY}{dt}\right) dt. \qquad (196)
$$

The second factor represents dz/dZ by equation (6).

But, by the Cauchy-Riemann differential equations:

$$
\frac{\partial x}{\partial X} = \frac{\partial y}{\partial Y} \quad \text{and} \quad \frac{\partial x}{\partial Y} = -\,\frac{\partial y}{\partial X}. \qquad (197)
$$

By using these we find:

$$\left(\frac{\partial x}{\partial X} + i\frac{\partial y}{\partial X}\right)\left(\frac{dX}{dt} + i\frac{dY}{dt}\right) = \left(\frac{\partial x}{\partial X}\frac{dX}{dt} + \frac{\partial x}{\partial Y}\frac{dY}{dt}\right)$$
$$+ i\left(\frac{\partial y}{\partial X}\frac{dX}{dt} + \frac{\partial y}{\partial Y}\frac{dY}{dt}\right). \quad (198)$$

Finally, by the rule for forming total derivatives, this is:

$$\frac{dx}{dt} + i\frac{dy}{dt}. \quad (199)$$

This reduction shows that the expression (196) is the same as the expression (195). Hence, when expressed in terms of the parameter t, both the integrals (193) and (194) assume the same form. Consequently these integrals are equal, as we stated.

280. Real Integrals. Let us consider any rational function of $\sin t$, $\cos t$, which is never infinite for real values of t. Its integral between the limits 0 and 2π may be evaluated by putting

$$z = e^{it}, \ \sin t = \frac{z^2 - 1}{2iz}, \ \cos t = \frac{z^2 + 1}{2z}, \ dt = \frac{dz}{iz}. \quad (200)$$

This reduces the integral to that of a rational function about a circle of radius unity about the origin, with no poles on the circle, so that it may be evaluated in terms of the residues of this function.

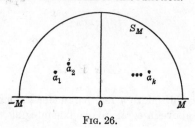

FIG. 26.

If the integral $\displaystyle\int_{-\infty}^{\infty} F(x)\,dx$ converges, it will be the limit of $\displaystyle\int_{-M}^{M} F(z)\,dz$, as $M \to \infty$. Suppose, further, that along some contours S_M, frequently taken as semi-circles, each including the preceding and joining M to $-M$ in the upper half plane, we have:

$$\lim_{M\to\infty} \int_{S_M} F(z)\,dz = 0. \quad (201)$$

Then, if the contour S_M together with the part of the real axis between $-M$ and M includes the n singular points of $F(z)$, a_k and $F(z)$ is analytic at all points in the upper half plane except the points a_k,

$$\int_{-M}^{M} F(z)\, dz + \int_{S_M} F(z)\, dz = 2\pi i \sum_{k=1}^{n} R(a_k). \qquad (202)$$

On taking the limit as M becomes infinite, since n increases it will either approach a finite limit, p, or become infinite. The second integral on the left approaches zero, so that:

$$\int_{-\infty}^{\infty} F(x)\, dx = 2\pi i \sum_{k=1}^{p \text{ or } \infty} R(a_k). \qquad (203)$$

Let the function $Q(z)$ be a rational function whose denominator is of degree $n + s$, $s \geqq 2$, while the numerator is of degree n. Let $Q(z)$ have no poles on the real axis. Then the preceding reasoning applies, with $F(x) = Q(x)$. For, we have:

$$\lim_{z \to \infty} |z^s Q(z)| = k' < k. \qquad (204)$$

Thus, for M sufficiently large, on S_M, a semicircle of radius M,

$$|Q(z)| < kM^{-2}, \qquad (205)$$

so that

$$\left| \int_{S_M} Q(z)\, dz \right| < \pi M k M^{-2}, \qquad (206)$$

which approaches zero when M becomes infinite.

This proves that, if the denominator of a rational function $Q(z)$ is of degree at least two higher than the numerator, has no real roots and has roots $a_1, a_2, \cdots, a_p$ in the upper half plane, then:

$$\int_{-\infty}^{\infty} Q(x)\, dx = 2\pi i \sum_{k=1}^{p} R(a_k). \qquad (207)$$

281. Certain Trigonometric Integrals. If the function $G(z)$ is less than K in absolute value on a semicircle S_M, of radius M, we have on that semicircle:

$$z = Me^{i\theta} = M \cos \theta + iM \sin \theta, \quad dz = iMe^{i\theta}\, d\theta, \qquad (208)$$

and

$$|e^{imz} G(z)| \leqq K e^{-mM \sin \theta}. \qquad (209)$$

But, by problem 46 of Exercises IV,

$$\frac{\sin \theta}{\theta} \geqq \frac{2}{\pi} \quad \text{for} \quad 0 < \theta \leqq \frac{\pi}{2}, \qquad (210)$$

and hence if $m > 0$, as we shall assume,

$$\int_0^\pi e^{-mM\sin\theta}\,d\theta = 2\int_0^{\frac{\pi}{2}} e^{-mM\sin\theta}\,d\theta$$

$$\leq 2\int_0^{\frac{\pi}{2}} e^{-2mM\theta/\pi}\,d\theta \leq \frac{-\pi}{mM}\, e^{-2mM\theta/\pi}\,\Big|_0^{\frac{\pi}{2}} \leq \frac{\pi}{mM}. \qquad (211)$$

It follows from these results that:

$$\left|\int_{S_M} e^{imz}G(z)\,dz\right| \leq \int_{S_M} \left|e^{imz}G(z)iMe^{i\theta}\right|\,d\theta \leq \frac{\pi K}{m}. \qquad (212)$$

If $\lim\limits_{z\to\infty} G(z) = 0$, we may choose a series of values of $K \to 0$ and a corresponding set of semicircles S_M. Thus, for these contours

$$\lim_{M\to\infty} \int_{S_M} e^{imz}G(z)\,dz = 0. \qquad (213)$$

It follows from this by reasoning as in the preceding section that if $G(z)$ is analytic on the real axis and in the upper half plane except at the points a_k,

$$\lim_{M\to\infty} \int_{-M}^{M} e^{imz}G(z)\,dz = 2\pi i \sum_{k=1}^{p} R(a_k), \qquad (214)$$

where the residues on the right are those of $e^{imz}G(z)$.

In particular, if $Q(z)$ is a rational function whose denominator is of degree at least one higher than that of the numerator, then all our conditions will be met if there are no poles on the real axis and we may put $G(z) = Q(z)$. We then have:

$$\int_{-M}^{M} e^{imz}Q(z)\,dz = \int_0^{M} e^{imz}Q(z)\,dz + \int_0^{M} e^{-imz}Q(-z)\,dz, \qquad (215)$$

where we have replaced z by $-z$ in the second integral.

Hence, if $Q(z)$ is an even function, $Q(-z) = Q(z)$, and

$$\lim \int_{-M}^{M} e^{imz}Q(z)\,dz = 2\int_0^{\infty} Q(z)\cos mz\,dz. \qquad (216)$$

Again, if $Q(z)$ is an odd function, $Q(-z) = -Q(z)$, and

$$\lim \int_{-M}^{M} e^{imz}Q(z)\,dz = 2i\int_0^{\infty} Q(z)\sin mz\,dz. \qquad (217)$$

Thus we have, for $Q(z)$ an even rational function of the type described:

$$\int_0^\infty Q(x) \cos mx \, dx = \pi i \sum R(a_k). \tag{218}$$

And for an odd function,

$$\int_0^\infty Q(x) \sin mx \, dx = \pi \sum R(a_k). \tag{219}$$

In both these equations, the residues are those of $e^{imz}Q(z)$.

In the latter case, the integral on the left will converge if $Q(z)$ has a simple pole at the origin, since $\sin mz$ has a zero there. In this case, we may apply the reasoning to the contour consisting of two semicircles, of radii M and M', and the parts of the axes between them. We here let $M \to \infty$ as before and M' approach zero. Then, on the small circle we may write:

$$e^{imz}Q(z) = \frac{R_0}{z} + A(z), \tag{220}$$

where R_0 is the residue of $Q(z)$ at the origin, and $A(z)$ is analytic at the origin. Since $A(z)$ remains bounded, while the length of the path shrinks to zero, the contribution of the second term approaches zero when $M' \to 0$. But that of the first term is $-\pi i R_0$, in the left member, or when transposed $\pi i R_0$. Thus in the case considered the term $R_0/2$ must be added to $R(a_k)$ in equation (219).

An example is $Q(x) = 1/x$, with residue 1 at the origin, so that $R_0/2 = 1/2$, and as there are no other poles:

$$\int_0^\infty \frac{\sin x}{x} \, dx = \frac{\pi}{2}. \tag{221}$$

282. Analytic Continuation. Suppose that a function $f(z)$ is single-valued and analytic throughout some simply connected two-dimensional region R. Then its value at any point interior to R is determined by its Taylor's series development at any point z_0 inside R. For, if z is any other point of R, we may join z_0 and z by a curve lying in R. Since this curve is composed of interior points and with its end points forms a closed set, there is a distance d such that a circle of radius d, with center at any point of the curve, lies in R. Now take a sequence of points on the curve, $z_0, z_1, z_2, \cdots, z_n = z$, such that the distance between any two points is less than d. Then the Taylor's development at z_0 is valid at z_1. Hence it determines all the derivatives of $f(z)$ and so the Taylor's development there. Similarly each development at z_i determines the development at z_{i+1} and so finally the value of the function at z.

The argument shows that any conditions which determine the values of the function and all its derivatives at z_0, for example the values on any arc through z_0, determine the value of the function in R. In particular, if the function is zero along any arc and analytic in R, it must be zero throughout R. This establishes the "principle of the permanence of form," which states that, if $f(z) = g(z)$ along any arc, inside a simply connected region R in which both functions are analytic, the equation holds for all values in R. For, under the assumption, $f(z) - g(z) = 0$ on the arc and therefore throughout R. This explains why the definitions which led to functions e^z and $\sin z$ analytic for all values of z, preserved all the familiar relations involving these functions originally established for real values.

283. Branch Points. If we start with a Taylor's development at a point and a curve through the point, it may be possible to obtain a series of elements or Taylor's expansions which collectively lead to a function single-valued and analytic at all points of the curve, by the process of analytic continuation described in the last section. Now consider a region R consisting of those points inside some circle with center at A, where $z = a$ and not lying on a particular radius AB. Suppose that, starting with an element at some point of R, the process of analytic continuation leads to a function single-valued in R, but to two different elements for each inner point of the radius AB, depending on the side of approach, if we attempt to extend the continuation across AB. Then the element in R determines one branch of a multiple-valued function and a is called a branch point for this branch.

For example, any determination of $\sqrt[n]{z}$, n an integer, $\log z$, or z^c with c not an integer (positive, negative or zero) and any line through the origin determines a single branch of the function, having a branch point at the origin. Again $\log (1 - \sqrt{1 - z})$, with R a circle about the origin, of radius $1/2$, with any radius omitted, leads to a branch with a branch point at the origin for any determination which makes $\sqrt{1 - z} = 1$ at the origin and to a branch which may be continued to a function single-valued and analytic at all points of the circle and in particular at the origin, if the determination makes $\sqrt{1 - z} = -1$ at the origin. This shows that, for a multiple-valued function, a point may be a branch point for some branches and not for others.

In place of a radius AB, we may use another curve joining A to B, on the circle, which prevents us from drawing a closed curve surrounding A in R to define a branch. We modify the definition of branch point accordingly. Such curves AB are known as branch cuts.

If a branch of a function $f(z)$, defined in a region R' consisting of all points outside a circle about the origin, with some curve extending from a point of this circle to infinity removed, is such that when we put $z = 1/Z$, transforming R' into R in the Z plane, the branch $f(1/Z)$ in R has a branch point at the origin, we say that $f(z)$ has a branch point at infinity. Thus z^c, c non-integral, and $\log z$ have branch points at infinity for every branch.

If, in a region either finite or extending to infinity, we locate all possible branch points and draw a curve joining each to infinity, we may obtain a region in which the function considered has a single-valued branch by omitting from the first region all points belonging to the curves drawn. For any pair of branch points, we may replace the lines to infinity by a single line joining the points, if infinity is not a branch point. For example each of the functions

$$\sqrt{(z - a)(z - b)} \quad \text{and} \quad \log (z - a) - \log (z - b)$$

has single-valued branches in the region obtained from the plane by omitting the line segment joining a and b. If infinity is a branch point, we must leave at least one curve joining infinity to a finite point. Thus for $\log (z - a) + \log (z - b)$ we may use a line joining a with b, together with a line joining a with infinity. For $\log (z - a) + \log (z - b) + \log (z - c)$, we may use a line joining a and b, together with a line joining c and infinity.

In any region in which a multiple-valued function has a single-valued branch, we may apply all the theorems on single-valued analytic functions, such as the integral and residue theorems, to this branch.

284. An Expansion in Rational Fractions.   Let $f(z)$ be analytic at all finite points of the plane, except the points $a_1, a_2, a_3, \cdots$, where

$$0 < |a_1| \leq |a_2| \leq |a_3| \leq \cdots \tag{222}$$

and let these be simple poles with residues $b_1, b_2, b_3, \cdots$. Then consider any contour C_n, with no poles on the contour, bounding a region including the first p_n poles. Then, for any value of z distinct from all the a_k, we have:

$$\int_{C_n} f(w) \left[\frac{1}{w - z} - \frac{1}{w} \right] dw$$
$$= 2\pi i \left\{ f(z) - f(0) + \sum_{k=1}^{p_n} b_n \left[\frac{1}{a_n - z} - \frac{1}{a_n} \right] \right\}, \tag{223}$$

by the residue theorem.

If a series of contours can be found, such that as $n \to \infty$, the limit of the integral on the left is zero and $p_n \to \infty$, it follows that:

$$f(z) = f(0) + \lim_{p_n \to \infty} \sum_{n=1}^{p_n} b_n \left[\frac{1}{z - a_n} + \frac{1}{a_n} \right]. \tag{224}$$

In particular, if the contours are similar figures, their lengths, maximum and minimum distances from the origin will all be fixed constants times some dimension M_n. Thus, if

$$|f(w)| \leqq K_n|w|, \quad \text{on} \quad C_n, \tag{225}$$

we shall have:

$$\left| \int_{C_n} f(w) \left[\frac{1}{w - z} - \frac{1}{w} \right] dw \right| = \left| \int_{C_n} \frac{f(w)z \, dw}{w(w - z)} \right| \leqq K_n|z|q, \tag{226}$$

where q is a constant depending on the shape of the contours, providing that the minimum distance from the origin exceeds $2|z|$, or $|w - z| > |w|/2$. Thus the integral will approach zero if we can select constants K_n approaching zero as $n \to \infty$. In particular, in any region inside some large circle and outside a number of small circles about the poles a_k contained in the large circle, the convergence will be uniform.

It follows that, under these conditions, the limit in equation (224) will be approached uniformly for z in such a region.

In particular, if $f(w)$ is uniformly bounded on all the contours, we may take $K_n = q'/M_n$. For this makes $K_n \to 0$ as n and hence $M_n \to \infty$.

As an example, consider the function defined by

$$f(z) = \csc z - \frac{1}{z}, \text{ for } z \neq 0, \text{ and } f(0) = 0, \tag{227}$$

so that $f(0)$ is the limit of $f(z)$ at the removable singularity at the origin. Then, for $z = x + iy$,

$$|\csc z| = \frac{2}{|e^{ix-y} - e^{-ix+y}|} \leqq \frac{2}{|e^y - e^{-y}|}$$

$$\leqq \frac{2}{e - e^{-1}} \quad \text{if} \quad |y| \geqq 1. \tag{228}$$

If we take as the contours, squares with center at the origin, sides parallel to the axes and passing through the points $(n + \frac{1}{2})\pi$, the relation just written gives an upper bound for the part of the contour with $|y| \geqq 1$. But, for the part with $|y| \leqq 1$, since $|\csc z|$ has the period π, we have merely to take an upper bound for $\csc[(\pi/2) + iy]$ for y in this range. Unity is such a bound, since the reciprocal is

$$\sin\left(\frac{\pi}{2} + iy\right) = \cos iy = \cosh y \geqq 1. \tag{229}$$

Thus the expansion is valid for the function defined in (227). Since the poles are at the points n and at these

$$\lim_{z \to n} (z - n\pi) \csc n\pi = (-1)^n \lim_{h \to 0} \frac{h}{\sin h} = (-1)^n, \qquad (230)$$

by equation (191) the residue at n is $(-1)^n$. Since each contour brings in two additional poles, we have:

$$\csc z - \frac{1}{z} = \lim_{p \to \infty} \sum_{n=-p}^{p}{}' (-1)^n \left[\frac{1}{z - n\pi} + \frac{1}{n\pi} \right]. \qquad (231)$$

The prime means that the term for $n = 0$ is to be omitted. For the individual terms of the sum,

$$\left| \frac{1}{z - n\pi} + \frac{1}{n\pi} \right| = \left| \frac{z}{n\pi(z - n\pi)} \right| \leqq \frac{2|z|}{n^2\pi^2}, \quad \text{if } |n\pi| \geqq 2|z|. \quad (232)$$

Consequently, in any finite region not including any of the poles as interior or boundary points, the corresponding infinite series converges absolutely, so that

$$\csc z = \frac{1}{z} + \sum_{n=-\infty}^{\infty}{}' (-1)^n \left[\frac{1}{z - n\pi} + \frac{1}{n\pi} \right] \qquad (233)$$

$$= \frac{1}{z} + \sum_{n=1}^{\infty} (-1)^n \frac{2z}{z^2 - n^2\pi^2}. \qquad (234)$$

The second expression (234) follows directly from (231). The first expression (233), with the terms taken in any order that includes each one at some stage, equals the second because of the absolute convergence.

By similar reasoning, we find that

$$\cot z = \frac{1}{z} + \sum_{n=1}^{\infty} \frac{2z}{z^2 - n^2\pi^2} \qquad (235)$$

$$= \frac{1}{z} + \sum_{n=-\infty}^{\infty}{}' \left[\frac{1}{z - n\pi} + \frac{1}{n\pi} \right]. \qquad (236)$$

In any finite region not including any of the poles as interior or boundary points, the separate terms are analytic and the series (236) converges uniformly. Hence the series may be differentiated termwise to give:

$$\csc^2 z = \sum_{n=-\infty}^{\infty} \frac{1}{(z - n\pi)^2}. \qquad (237)$$

285. The Infinite Product for the Sine. The function $\cot z - 1/z$ has a removable singularity at the origin. And, if we transpose the $1/z$ in equation (236), the origin may be included in the region of uniform convergence.   Hence, on any path in this region joining 0 and z, we may integrate termwise and obtain:

$$\int_0^z \left[\cot z - \frac{1}{z} \right] dz = \sum_{n=-\infty}^{\infty} {}' \int_0^z \left[\frac{1}{z - n\pi} + \frac{1}{n\pi} \right] dz, \qquad (238)$$

or
$$\log \frac{\sin z}{z} = \sum_{n=-\infty}^{\infty} {}' \left[\log \left(1 - \frac{z}{n\pi} \right) + \frac{z}{n\pi} \right], \qquad (239)$$

where the value of each logarithm is determined by continuation along the path from the value 0 for each logarithmic term at $z = 0$.   For example, one determination is fixed if we require that the path never crosses the real axis and for real z is taken in the upper half plane.

For any determination, when we take exponentials, we find:

$$\sin z = z \prod_{n=-\infty}^{\infty} {}' \left[1 - \frac{z}{n\pi} \right] e^{\frac{z}{n}}, \qquad (240)$$

$$= z \prod_{n=1}^{\infty} \left[1 - \frac{z^2}{n^2\pi^2} \right]. \qquad (241)$$

286. Analytic Functions of Several Complex Variables.   We shall define a function of k complex variables as analytic in these variables if it has partial derivatives with respect to each of the k variables and if the function is continuous* in a certain region in the k-dimensional complex, or $2k$-dimensional real space.   We illustrate some of the extensions of the theory by treating the case of two complex variables.

If $f(z_1,z_2)$ is analytic in the two variables, it is analytic in each of them taken separately.   If C_1 and C_2 are circles about z_1 and z_2 in their respective planes and the function is analytic in a region including that obtained by letting the variables range in their circles independently, we have by the Cauchy integral formula for functions of one variable:

$$f(z_1,z_2) = \frac{1}{2\pi i} \int_{C_1} \frac{f(t_1,z_2)}{t_1 - z_1} \, dt_1,$$

and
$$f(t_1,z_2) = \frac{1}{2\pi i} \int_{C_2} \frac{f(t_1,t_2)}{t_2 - z_2} \, dt_2.$$

By combining these two equations we find:

$$f(z_1,z_2) = \frac{1}{(2\pi i)^2} \int_{C_1} dt_1 \int_{C_2} \frac{f(t_1,t_2)}{(t_1 - z_1)(t_2 - z_2)} \, dt_2. \qquad (242)$$

---

* For the Hartogs-Osgood proof that the continuity assumption is superfluous, see vol. II, pp. 180–198 of Osgood's *Funktionentheorie*, — reference 19 of the bibliography.

Since the integrand may be developed in a double power series, which converges uniformly, we may show that an analytic function of two variables always has a power series development. Furthermore, the function possesses continuous derivatives of all orders and the coefficients of the power series are related to the derivatives by formulas similar to those for a Taylor's series, for a function of two real variables.

If we write $f(z_1,z_2) = u + iv$, where u and v are each functions of the four real variables x_1, y_1, x_2, y_2, we find

$$\frac{\partial u}{\partial x_1} = \frac{\partial v}{\partial y_1} \quad \text{and} \quad \frac{\partial u}{\partial y_1} = -\frac{\partial v}{\partial x_1}, \tag{243}$$

with similar formulas for the subscripts 2, in consequence of the Cauchy-Riemann differential equations and the fact that $f(z_1,z_2)$ is analytic in $z_1 = x_1 + iy_1$.

This enables us to show that, if t_1 and t_2 are each analytic functions of z_1 and z_2, while w is an analytic function of t_1 and t_2, then w is analytic in z_1 and z_2. We wish to show that, under the conditions stated, w has a derivative with respect to z_1 given by:

$$\frac{\partial w}{\partial z_1} = \frac{\partial w}{\partial t_1}\frac{\partial t_1}{\partial z_1} + \frac{\partial w}{\partial t_2}\frac{\partial t_2}{\partial z_1}. \tag{244}$$

If we put $t_1 = r_1 + is_1$ and $t_2 = r_2 + is_2$, we have:

$$\frac{\partial w}{\partial t_1}\frac{\partial t_1}{\partial z_1} = \left(\frac{\partial u}{\partial r_1} + i\frac{\partial v}{\partial r_1}\right)\left(\frac{\partial r_1}{\partial x_1} + i\frac{\partial s_1}{\partial x_1}\right). \tag{245}$$

We may use the Cauchy-Riemann differential equations to transform the expansion of this into

$$\frac{\partial u}{\partial r_1}\frac{\partial r_1}{\partial x_1} + \frac{\partial u}{\partial s_1}\frac{\partial s_1}{\partial x_1} + i\left(\frac{\partial v}{\partial r_1}\frac{\partial r_1}{\partial x_1} + \frac{\partial v}{\partial s_1}\frac{\partial s_1}{\partial x_1}\right). \tag{246}$$

We may proceed similarly with the last term of equation (244). As the derivatives are continuous, u and v are differentiable, and by the method of totally differentiating functions of four real variables, we find that:

$$\frac{\partial u}{\partial x_1} = \frac{\partial u}{\partial r_1}\frac{\partial r_1}{\partial x_1} + \frac{\partial u}{\partial s_1}\frac{\partial s_1}{\partial x_1} + \frac{\partial u}{\partial r_2}\frac{\partial r_2}{\partial x_1} + \frac{\partial u}{\partial s_2}\frac{\partial s_2}{\partial x_1}, \tag{247}$$

with a similar equation for $\partial v/\partial x_1$. From these two equations and the transform of the terms in equation (244) given, for the first term, by the expression (246), we find that:

$$\frac{\partial w}{\partial t_1}\frac{\partial t_1}{\partial z_1} + \frac{\partial w}{\partial t_2}\frac{\partial t_2}{\partial z_1} = \frac{\partial u}{\partial x_1} + i\frac{\partial v}{\partial x_1}. \tag{248}$$

But, by the Cauchy-Riemann differential equations, the expression (246) is equal to

$$\frac{\partial v}{\partial s_1}\frac{\partial s_1}{\partial y_1} + \frac{\partial v}{\partial r_1}\frac{\partial r_1}{\partial y_1} - i\left(\frac{\partial u}{\partial s_1}\frac{\partial s_1}{\partial y_1} + \frac{\partial u}{\partial r_1}\frac{\partial r_1}{\partial y_1}\right). \tag{249}$$

Using this as the transform of the first term and the expression with r_1, s_1 changed to r_2, s_2 for the second term and the expansions corresponding to (247) with x replaced by y and then u, x replaced by v, y, we find:

$$\frac{\partial w}{\partial t_1}\frac{\partial t_1}{\partial z_1} + \frac{\partial w}{\partial t_2}\frac{\partial t_2}{\partial z_1} = \frac{\partial v}{\partial y_1} - i\frac{\partial u}{\partial y_1}. \tag{250}$$

A comparison of equations (249) and (250) shows that

$$\frac{\partial u}{\partial x_1} = \frac{\partial v}{\partial y_1} \quad \text{and} \quad \frac{\partial u}{\partial y_1} = -\frac{\partial v}{\partial x_1}. \tag{251}$$

Since the partial derivatives are continuous and these are the Cauchy-Riemann equations, it follows that w is analytic in z_1, and that $\partial w/\partial z_1$ equals the right member of equation (248), so that equation (244) holds, as we stated.

A similar argument holds for z_2 and since the function w is continuous in z_1 and z_2, as a continuous function of continuous functions, it follows that w, involving z_1 and z_2 through the functions t_1 and t_2, is analytic in z_1 and z_2.

These facts all extend to analytic functions of k complex variables. Such functions have derivatives of all orders and Taylor's expansions. Also, any analytic function of analytic functions is again analytic and its derivatives may be computed by the same rule as that for the total differentiation of composite functions of real variables.

One important difference between functions of one and of several complex variables is that the region of convergence of a power series in several variables may be much more complicated than that for one variable.

EXERCISES XIII

1. If $u + iv$ is an analytic function of $z = x + iy$, prove that u and v are each solutions of Laplace's equation:

$$\frac{\partial^2 f}{\partial x^2} + \frac{\partial^2 f}{\partial y^2} = 0.$$

2. In some simply connected region R, let u be a single-valued function which satisfies the equation of problem 1. Show that, with the line integral taken over any path in R from the fixed point a,b to the variable point x,y,

$$v = \int_{a,b}^{x,y} -\frac{\partial u}{\partial y}\, dx + \frac{\partial u}{\partial x}\, dy,$$

is a single-valued function of (x,y), independent of the path. Also show that $u + iv$ is an analytic function of $x + iy$ in R. Assume that u_{yy} is continuous.

3. Illustrate problem 2 for $u = \log(x^2 + y^2)$, with R the region obtained by removing one radius from a circle with center at the origin. This shows the necessity of the condition that R be simply connected, since u satisfies all the other conditions in the circle, with only the center removed.

4. Formulate and prove a theorem on the analytic nature of $u + iv$, analogous to that of problem 2, when v is a solution of Laplace's equation, and

$$u = \int_{a,b}^{x,y} \frac{\partial v}{\partial y}\, dx - \frac{\partial v}{\partial x}\, dy.$$

5. If $z = re^{i\theta}$ and $f(z)$ has a derivative, show that

$$f'(z) = \left(\frac{\partial u}{\partial r} + i\frac{\partial v}{\partial r}\right)e^{-i\theta} = \frac{1}{r}\left(\frac{\partial u}{\partial \theta} + i\frac{\partial v}{\partial \theta}\right)(-ie^{-i\theta}),$$

by taking first $\Delta\theta = 0$, and then $\Delta r = 0$. Hence show that

$$\frac{\partial u}{\partial r} = \frac{1}{r}\frac{\partial v}{\partial \theta} \quad \text{and} \quad \frac{\partial v}{\partial r} = -\frac{1}{r}\frac{\partial u}{\partial \theta}.$$

6. Let q_1 and q_2 be orthogonal curvilinear coördinates (compare problem 31 of Exercises X) in the z plane, so numbered that $\dfrac{\partial(q_1,q_2)}{\partial(x,y)}$ is positive. Show that, if $ds^2 = h_1^2\, dq_1^2 + h_2^2\, dq_2^2$, and $u + iv$ is an analytic function of $z = x + iy$, then

$$\frac{1}{h_1}\frac{\partial u}{\partial q_1} = \frac{1}{h_2}\frac{\partial v}{\partial q_2} \quad \text{and} \quad \frac{1}{h_2}\frac{\partial u}{\partial q_2} = -\frac{1}{h_1}\frac{\partial v}{\partial q_1}.$$

Hint: For new x- and y-axes, tangent to the curves of increasing q_1 and q_2 at the point, $\dfrac{\partial q_2}{\partial x} = 0$, $\dfrac{\partial q_2}{\partial y} = \dfrac{1}{h_2}$, $\dfrac{\partial q_1}{\partial x} = \dfrac{1}{h_1}$, $\dfrac{\partial q_1}{\partial y} = 0$. Now transform the Cauchy-Riemann equations for the new axes.

7. Deduce the last equations of problem 5 from problem 6.

8. Prove that if a power series $\sum a_n z^n$ has for all a_n, $|a_n| \leq n$ and for an infinite number $|a_n| \geq 1/n$, the radius of convergence is 1.

9. Obtain the Taylor's series:

$$(1 + z)^m = 1 + mz + \frac{m(m - 1)}{2!}\, z^2 + \frac{m(m - 1)(m - 2)}{3!}\, z^3 + \cdots$$

where m may be real or complex, and for $|z| < 1$, the series represents the single-valued branch of $(1 + z)^m$ which is 1 for $z = 0$.

10. Prove that the Bessel's function of integral order,

$$J_n(z) = \sum_{k=0}^{\infty} \frac{(-1)^k z^{n+2k}}{2^{n+2k} k \,! \, (n+k) \,!},$$

n zero or a positive integer, is a solution of the differential equation

$$\frac{d^2w}{dz^2} + \frac{1}{z} \frac{dw}{dz} + \left(1 - \frac{n^2}{z^2}\right) w = 0,$$

analytic for all finite values of z.

11. Prove that Legendre's polynomial of order n,

$$P_n(z) = \sum_{k=0}^{[n/2]} (-1)^k \frac{(2n-2k) \,!}{2^n k \,! \, (n-k) \,! \, (n-2k) \,!} z^{n-2k},$$

where $0 \,! = 1$ and $2k \leqq n$ in the sum, is a solution of the differential equation

$$(1 - z^2) \frac{d^2w}{dz^2} - 2z \frac{dw}{dz} + n(n+1)w = 0.$$

12. Prove that the hypergeometric function

$$F(a,b;c;z) = 1 + \frac{ab}{1c} z + \frac{a(a+1)b(b+1)}{1 \cdot 2c(c+1)} z^2 + \cdots$$

is a solution of the differential equation

$$z(1-z) \frac{d^2w}{dz^2} + [c - (a+b+1)z] \frac{dw}{dz} - abw = 0.$$

The series converges by problem 21 of Exercises IX if $|z| < 1$ and by section 282 any analytic continuation from it will be a solution of the differential equation.

13. Let $|c_2 - c_1| < r_1$, the radius of convergence of a power series for $f(z)$ in powers of $z - c_1 = Z_1$. If $Z_2 = z - c_2$, then $Z_1 = Z_2 + c_2 - c_1$. By using this to express the powers of Z_1 as polynomials in Z_2 and collecting terms, we may formally obtain a series in powers of $z - c_2$, or Z_2. Show that the infinite series giving the coefficients will converge, the new series will have a radius of convergence at least equal to $r_1 - |c_2 - c_1|$, and will represent $f(z)$ at any point inside a circle of convergence for both series.

14. Show that the coefficient of Z_2^n in the series described in problem 13 is $f^{(n)}(c_2)/n \,!$ and that the series represents an analytic continuation of $f(z)$, if it converges in any region outside the circle of convergence of the first series.

15. Prove *Abel's theorem:* If a power series converges at any point on the circle of convergence, it converges uniformly on the radius drawn to that point and represents a continuous function on the radius. *Hint:* By putting

$$(z - c)/(z_1 - c) = r,$$

the problem is reduced to discussing $\sum u_n r^n$ for $0 \leqq r \leqq 1$, with $\sum u_n$ convergent. Then the powers r^n may be taken as the p_n of section 199, and the relation (101) of that section shows that the remainder for $\sum u_n r^n$ is dominated by that for $\sum u_n$, so that the convergence is uniform, and the continuity follows.

16. Prove that a power series may be integrated termwise along a radius out to z_1, on the circle of convergence, provided that the integrated series converges at z_1. *Hint:* Use Abel's theorem of problem 15 and section 168.

17. The equation $\int_{z'}^{z''} f(z)\,dz = F(z'') - F(z')$ holds if $F(z)$ is continuous on C and $f(z) = F'(z)$ except at z'', provided that $f(z)$ is dominated by an integrable function on some arc of C which includes z''. A similar result holds for a path to infinity, with $F(z'')$ replaced by $\lim F(z)$, as z approaches z'' on the path. *Hint:* Reason as in section 247.

18. (Hardy) If $\sum a_n z^n$ converges for all finite values of z, for any $p > 0$, the series $\sum e^{-px} a_n x^n$ may be integrated termwise from 0 to ∞ to give $\sum a_n n!\,p^{-n-1}$, provided that the latter series converges. *Hint:* By the uniformity, termwise integration from 0 to M is permissible and the corresponding improper integral will converge to the series as stated if

$$\sum_{n=0}^{\infty}\left[a_n n!\,p^{-n-1} - \int_0^M a_n e^{-px} x^n\,dx \right] \to 0, \quad\text{or}\quad \sum_{n=0}^{\infty}\int_M^{\infty} a_n e^{-px} x^n\,dx \to 0.$$

By repeated integrations by parts, $\int_M^{\infty} a_n e^{-px} x^n\,dx = v_n S_n$, where

$$v_n = a_n n!\,p^{-n-1} \quad\text{and}\quad S_n = \left(1 + \frac{Mp}{1!} + \frac{(Mp)^2}{2!} + \cdots + \frac{(Mp)^n}{n!}\right) e^{-pM}.$$

Since the S_n *increase* (toward unity) with n, we may deduce

$$\left|\sum_{n=m}^{m+k} v_n S_n\right| \leqq R_m S_{m+k} < R_m,$$

by writing the sum backwards and using the Abel inequality of section **197**, where R_m is a bound for the remainder after m terms in $\sum v_n$. But we may make R_m small by a choice of m, since $\sum v_n$ converges and then with fixed m, make the first m terms $v_n S_n$ small by taking M large, since for fixed n, as $M \to \infty$, $S_n \to 0$. Thus the result follows.

19. Prove that $\log 2 = \int_0^1 \frac{dz}{1+z} = 1 - \frac{1}{2} + \frac{1}{3} - \cdots$, by using problem **16**. Compare Exercises IX, problem 10.

20. If $f(z)$ is analytic in and on a circle C about a with radius R and $|f(z)| \leqq M$ on C, then $|f^{(k)}(a)| \leqq k!\,M/R^k$. *Hint:* Use sections 270 and 265.

21. If $c(t)$ is a function continuous on a curve C, the integral $\int_C \frac{c(t)}{t-z}\,dt$, in any simply connected region R containing no points of C, defines an analytic function of z. Note that C need not be closed, $c(t)$ need not be analytic, the values need not approach a limit as we approach a point of C. For regions separated by C, distinct functions may be defined, as in problem 22.

22. Let $f(z)$ be analytic on C, a closed curve and in the region bounded by C. Show that $\int_C \frac{f(t)}{t-z}\,dt$ equals $2\pi i f(z)$ if z is inside C and equals 0 when z is outside C.

23. Let $f(z)$ be analytic inside and on a closed curve C_1 and $g(z)$ be analytic inside and on a closed curve C_2, bounding a region outside of C_1. Show that

$$\frac{1}{2\pi i}\left[\int_{C_1}\frac{f(t)}{t-z}\,dt + \int_{C_2}\frac{g(t)}{t-z}\,dt\right]$$

equals $f(z)$ for z inside C_1 and $g(z)$ for z inside C_2.

24. If $f(z)$ and $g(1/z)$ are each analytic for $|z| \leqq 1$ and C is the circle $z = 1$, then $\dfrac{1}{2\pi i}\displaystyle\int_C\left[\frac{f(t)}{t-z} + \frac{zg(t)}{zt-t^2}\right]dt$ equals $f(z)$ for $|z| < 1$ and equals $g(z)$ for $|z| > 1$. This and problems 22 and 23 illustrate that a single simple " expression " may define distinct analytic functions, that is, not obtainable from one another by continuation, in separated regions.

25. Prove that the series

$$\frac{1+z}{1\cdot 2} + \frac{1+z+z^2}{2\cdot 3} + \frac{1+z+z^2+z^3}{3\cdot 4} + \cdots$$

defines an analytic function for $|z| < 1$.

26. Show that the series of problem 25 equals $1 - \log(1-z)$ for $|z| < 1$. *Hint:* Use the identity

$$\frac{1}{k(k+1)} = \frac{1}{k} - \frac{1}{k+1}$$

to transform the series to $1 + z + \dfrac{z^2}{2} + \dfrac{z^3}{3} + \cdots$.

27. If $f(z)$ is single-valued and analytic for $r_1 \leqq |z-a| \leqq r_2$ and C' is the circle $|z-a| = r_1$ (or r_2), in equation (174), the expansion of equation (173) represents $f(z)$ for $r_1 \leqq |z-a| \leqq r_2$.

28. If $f(z) = 1/(z-b)$, the expansion of problem 27 is:

$$-\frac{1}{b-a} - \frac{z-a}{(b-a)^2} - \frac{(z-a)^2}{(b-a)^3} - \frac{(z-a)^3}{(b-a)^4} - \cdots, \quad \text{if } |z-a| < |b-a|,$$

and $\quad \dfrac{1}{z-a} + \dfrac{b-a}{(z-a)^2} + \dfrac{(b-a)^2}{(z-a)^3} + \dfrac{(b-a)^3}{(z-a)^4} + \cdots, \quad \text{if } |z-a| > |b-a|.$

29. By differentiation termwise, deduce expansions for $1/(z-b)^k$ from those for the first power in problem 28. These may be used to find the expansion for any rational function in a ring $r_1 < |z-a| < r_2$ including none of the poles.

30. If $f(z)$ has a pole of the mth order at a, the residue at a is

$$\frac{1}{(m-1)!}\frac{d^{m-1}}{dz^{m-1}}[(z-a)^m f(z)],$$

evaluated at a. Compare section 116.

31. The series $z + \frac{1}{2}z^2 + \frac{1}{3}z^3 + \cdots$ and

$$-\log 2 + \frac{z+1}{2} + \frac{(z+1)^2}{2\cdot 2^2} + \frac{(z+1)^3}{3\cdot 2^3} + \cdots$$

represent the same function in their common region of convergence, while the series $\pi i - (z - 2) + \dfrac{(z - 2)^2}{2} - \dfrac{(z - 2)^3}{3} + \cdots$ has no region in common with the first series, but may be obtained from it by analytic continuation along a suitable path.

32. If $w = f(z)$ is single-valued, while $z = f^{-1}(w)$ is many-valued, its branch points must be among the points where $f'(z)$ is not finite and distinct from zero. *Hint:* By section 259, when $f'(z) \neq 0$, $dw/dz = 1/f'(z)$, and the inverse function is analytic.

33. Use problem 32 to find possible branch points of $\tan^{-1} z$ and $\sin^{-1} z$, by finding where the expression for the derivative ceases to be finite and distinct from zero and determine which are branch points.

$\qquad$ *Ans.* $\tan^{-1} z$ at i and $-i$; $\sin^{-1} z$ at 1, -1 and ∞.

34. At a the function $w = 2z + (z - a)^{4/3}$ has a branch point, although the expression for the derivative approaches 2. There is no single-valued inverse function, so that the test of problems 32 and 33 does not apply.

35. If $f(z)$ has a zero or a pole at a, then $f'(z)/f(z)$ has a simple pole and its residue is the order of the zero, or minus the order of the pole. *Hint:* Differentiate $\log f(z) = m \log (z - a) + F(z)$, with $F(z)$ analytic at a.

36. If, except for poles inside C, $f(z)$ is analytic inside and on C, and $\neq 0$ on C, $\dfrac{1}{2\pi i} \displaystyle\int_C \dfrac{f'(z)}{f(z)} \, dz$ is always integral and equals the excess of zeros over poles inside C, counting an mth order pole or zero m times. *Hint:* Use problem 35.

37. If C is a circle about the origin of radius M and $P(z)$ is a polynomial of the nth degree, prove that $\displaystyle\lim_{M \to \infty} \int_C \left[\dfrac{P'(z)}{P(z)} - \dfrac{n}{z} \right] dz = 0$. It follows from problem 36 that $P(z)$ has n roots inside C, for M sufficiently large, which gives an alternative proof of the fundamental theorem of algebra. *Hint:* Reason as in section 280, noting that the integrand is rational, with denominator of higher degree than the numerator by at least two.

38. Show that $\displaystyle\int_0^\infty \dfrac{\sin mx}{x(a^2 + x^2)} \, dx = \dfrac{\pi}{2a^2} (1 - e^{-am})$, $m \geqq 0$, $a > 0$.

39. $\displaystyle\int_0^\infty \dfrac{\cos mx}{a^2 + x^2} \, dx = \dfrac{\pi e^{-am}}{2a}$, $\displaystyle\int_0^\infty \dfrac{x \sin mx}{a^2 + x^2} \, dx = \dfrac{\pi e^{-am}}{2}$, $m > 0$, $a > 0$.

Hint: Use problem 38, and differentiate with respect to m. This illustrates that a combination of the method of residues with the devices illustrated in problems 29 through 37 of Exercises XII is often advantageous.

40. Prove that $\displaystyle\int_0^\infty \dfrac{x^{-p}}{1 + x} \, dx = \dfrac{\pi}{\sin p\pi}$, $0 < p < 1$.

Hint: Integrate $z^{-p}/(1 + z)$ around a contour consisting of the positive real axis from h to M, a large circle of radius M about the origin, the real axis from M to h and a small circle of radius h about the origin. As $M \to \infty$, $M^{-p} \to 0$, while as $h \to 0$, $h^{1-p} \to 0$, so that the integrals on the two circles each $\to 0$. If I denotes the integral from h to M, using the positive real determination of x^p, the integral from M to h for the second line segment is $-e^{-2p\pi i}I$, since the sense is reversed and going around the circle changes $\log z$ by $2\pi i$ and so multiplies z^p by $e^{2p\pi i}$. In the cut ring the only pole is at -1, and the residue is $(-1)^p = e^{-p\pi i}$. Hence, in the limit: $(1 - e^{-2p\pi i})I_0 = 2\pi i e^{-p\pi i}$

and
$$I_0 = \frac{2\pi i}{e^{p\pi i} - e^{-p\pi i}} = \frac{\pi}{\sin \pi p},$$

where I_0 is the limit of I as $M \to \infty$, $h \to 0$, or the given integral.

41. Show that, for m and n integral,

$$\int_0^\infty \frac{x^{2m}}{x^{2n} + 1} \, dx = \frac{\pi}{2n \sin \left[\dfrac{2m+1}{2n} \pi \right]}, \, 0 \leqq m < n.$$

For m,n integral this is an example of section 280, but the result is more easily proved and for all real m,n with $0 < 2m + 1 < 2n$ by transforming the integral of problem 40 by $x = u^{2n}$.

42. Show that

$$\int_{-\infty}^\infty \frac{e^{qx}}{1 + e^x} \, dx = \frac{\pi}{\sin q\pi}, \, 0 < q < 1.$$

Hint: Either put $x = e^u$ in the result of problem 40, or integrate around the rectangle $y = 0$, $y = 2\pi$, $x = -R$, $x = R$ with $R \to \infty$. This is essentially the image under $w = \log z$ of the contour used in problem 40.

43. Show that

$$\int_0^\infty \frac{x^{-p} - x^{-q}}{1 - x} \, dx = \pi[\cot q\pi - \cot p\pi], 0 < p < 1, 0 < q < 1.$$

Hint: Integrate $z^{-p}/(1 - z)$ around the contour of problem 40, with the segments from $1 - h$ to $1 + h$, and from $1 + h$ to $1 - h$ replaced by the upper and lower halves of a circle of radius h about $z = 1$. Deduce that:

$$(1 - e^{-2p\pi i})\left[\int_h^{1-h} + \int_{1+h}^M \right] \frac{x^{-p}}{1 - x} \, dx + \pi i(1 + e^{-2p\pi i}) + T = 0,$$

where T denotes terms which $\to 0$ when $h \to 0$ and $M \to \infty$. Then divide by $(1 - e^{-2p\pi i})$, subtract the corresponding equation with q in place of p and take the limit as $h \to 0$ and $M \to \infty$.

44. $\displaystyle\int_{-\infty}^\infty \frac{e^{rx} - e^{sx}}{1 - e^x} \, dx = \pi(\cot r\pi - \cot s\pi), \quad 0 < r < 1, \quad 0 < s < 1.$

Hint: Put $x = e^u$ in the result of problem 43.

45. Show that $\displaystyle\int_0^\pi \log (1 - 2p \cos x + p^2) \, dx = 0$, if $-1 \leqq p \leqq 1$, and $= 2\pi \log |p|$ if $p \leqq -1$, or $p \geqq 1$. *Hint:* The integral is $1/2$ that from 0 to 2π, and hence by equation (200), section 280, is

$$\frac{1}{2i} \int_C \frac{\log (p - z) + \log (pz - 1) - \log z}{z} \, dz,$$

with C a circle of radius unity about $z = 0$. For $0 < p < 1$, exclude a line joining 0 and p and for the logarithms, take arg $(p - z)$ from -2π to 0, arg $(pz - 1)$ and arg z from 0 to 2π. Then the numerator is real on C and single-valued in the slit circle. Hence the integral equals that around C', made up of a line from h to $p - h$, with values approached from below, a small circle C_p of radius h around p, a line from $p - h$ to h, with values approached from above and a small circle C_0 of radius h around O. Along C_p the integral $\to 0$ like $h \log h$, as $h \to 0$, but $\log (p - z)$ is increased by $2\pi i$. The other terms cancel for the h to $p - h$, and the $p - h$ to h parts, but the increase gives

$$\frac{1}{2i} \int_{p-h}^{h} \frac{2\pi i}{z} \, dz = \pi[\log h - \log (p - h)].$$

Along C_0 we get $\pi \log p$ from the term $\log (p - z)$ and $\pi^2 i$ from $\log (pz - 1)$, by using residues. For $\dfrac{1}{2i} \displaystyle\int_{C_0} \dfrac{-\log z}{z} \, dz$, we use the indefinite integral $\dfrac{i}{4} (\log z)^2$ with $\log z$ varying from $\log h$ to $\log h + 2\pi i$, so that this term gives

$$-\pi \log h - \pi^2 i.$$

The sum of the terms $\to 0$ when $h \to 0$. For $p > 1$, put $p = 1/q$,

$$\log (1 - 2p \cos x + p^2) = 2 \log p + \log (1 - 2q \cos x + q^2)$$

and use the first result for the term in q. For p negative, put $p = -q$. For $p = 1$, deduce the continuity of the integral from the fact that the original integrand is dominated by an integrable function near $x = 0$ and converges uniformly in any range from h to π.

46. From $\displaystyle\int_0^\infty e^{-x^2} \, dx = \frac{\sqrt{\pi}}{2}$, problem 32 of Exercises XII, deduce that $\displaystyle\int_0^\infty e^{-x^2} \cos 2bx \, dx = \frac{\sqrt{\pi}}{2} e^{-b^2}$. *Hint:* Integrate e^{-z^2} around a rectangle bounded by $y = 0$, $y = b$, $x = M$, $x = -M$, with $M \to \infty$.

47. For $0 \leqq A \leqq \pi/4$, t real and varying from 0 to ∞, the integral of $e^{-z^2} \, dz$ with $z = te^{iA}$ is independent of A. From the value $\dfrac{\sqrt{\pi}}{2}$ for $A = 0$, deduce two real integrals, and in particular $\displaystyle\int_0^\infty \cos x^2 \, dx = \int_0^\infty \sin x^2 \, dx = \frac{\sqrt{2\pi}}{4}$.

Hint: Integrate around a sector bounded by the lines for two values of A and a circle about the origin of radius M, with $M \to \infty$. On the arc use equation (210) as for (211). This and problem 46 illustrate how contour integration sometimes enables us to deduce one definite integral from another.

48. Prove that $\cos z = \displaystyle\prod_{n=1}^{\infty} \left[1 - \frac{4z^2}{(2n - 1)^2 \pi^2} \right]$. *Hint:* Justify the regrouping in the product for $\sin (z + \pi/2)$.

49. Prove that $\cos\dfrac{z}{2}\cos\dfrac{z}{2^2}\cos\dfrac{z}{2^3}\cdots = \dfrac{\sin z}{z}.$ *Hint:* Use problem 48, or

$\sin z = 2\sin\dfrac{z}{2}\cos\dfrac{z}{2}$ and $\dfrac{2^n}{z}\sin\dfrac{z}{2^n}\rightarrow 1.$

50. $\dfrac{1}{2}\tan\dfrac{z}{2}+\dfrac{1}{2^2}\tan\dfrac{z}{2^2}+\dfrac{1}{2^3}\tan\dfrac{z}{2^3}+\cdots = \dfrac{1}{z}-\cot z.$ *Hint:* Use problem 49, take logarithms, and differentiate.

51. If $0 < |z| < \pi$, and $H_{2k} = 1 + \dfrac{1}{2^{2k}}+\dfrac{1}{3^{2k}}+\cdots$, prove that:

$$\log\frac{z}{\sin z} = H_2\frac{z^2}{\pi^2}+\frac{1}{2}H_4\frac{z^4}{\pi^4}+\frac{1}{3}H_6\frac{z^6}{\pi^6}+\cdots,$$

and $\qquad\cot z - \dfrac{1}{z} = -2H_2\dfrac{z}{\pi^2}-2H_4\dfrac{z^3}{\pi^4}-2H_6\dfrac{z^5}{\pi^6}-\cdots.$

It will be shown in section 320 that $\dfrac{-2H_{2k}}{\pi^{2k}} = \dfrac{(-1)^k\,2^{2k}}{(2k)\,!}B_{2k}$, where the B_{2n} are Bernoulli numbers. Compare problems 3 and 8 of Exercises XVI.

52. If $u+iv$ is an analytic function of $z = x+iy$ at $z_0 = x_0+iy_0$, then u and v are each analytic functions of the two variables x and y for $x = x_0$, $y = y_0$. *Hint:* Put $(z - z_0) = (x - x_0) + i(y - y_0)$ in the series in powers of $(z - z_0)$ and deduce convergent power series in powers of $(x - x_0)$, $(y - y_0)$.

53. If, for f, x,y real, $f(x,y)$ is a solution of Laplace's equation of problem 1 in some two dimensional region including x_0,y_0 as an interior point, $f(x,y)$ is an analytic function of x and y at x_0,y_0. Hence it has partial derivatives of all orders and a power series representation about this point. *Hint:* Use problems 2 and 52.

54. Let $u(x,y)$ and $v(x,y)$ be each real for x and y real and analytic in x and y for $x = x_0$, $y = y_0$. If $w = u + iv$, the equations $z = x + iy$ and $\bar{z} = x - iy$ or $x = (z + \bar{z})/2$, $y = (z - \bar{z})/2i$ determine w as an analytic function of z and $\bar{z}$. This will be a function of z alone if $\partial w/\partial\bar{z} = 0$. Show that, for real values of x and y this condition is equivalent to the Cauchy-Riemann differential equations (8).

CHAPTER XIV

FOURIER SERIES AND INTEGRALS

On any circle inside and concentric with the circle of convergence of a power series, the real and imaginary components of the analytic function represented by the series are each real, periodic functions of the angular coördinate. On such a circle, the power series representation of the analytic function leads to a series expansion for each of these periodic functions in terms of sines and cosines of multiples of the angular coördinate. This suggests the possibility of expanding other periodic functions in a series of sines and cosines, or in a Fourier series. We shall study this question, and derive a few of the simpler sufficient conditions for a function to admit of such a representation.

The Fourier series may be thought of as representing a given periodic function for all values, or in any interval of length one period as representing a function merely given in that period. There is an analogous representation for functions given on an infinite interval, involving an integral in place of a sum, the Fourier integral. We derive a sufficient condition for this representation, applicable to functions which approach zero at infinity in a suitable way.

287. Fourier Series of Periodic Functions. If the power series $\sum a_n z^n$ converges for all z with $|z| = r$ and the sum function is $F(z)$, we have:

$$F(re^{i\theta}) = \sum_{n=0}^{\infty} a_n (re^{i\theta})^n. \tag{1}$$

If we decompose the function on the left and the coefficients a_n into their real and imaginary parts,

$$F(re^{i\theta}) = P(\theta) + iQ(\theta) \quad \text{and} \quad a_n = p_n + iq_n, \tag{2}$$

we find as a consequence of equation (1) that:

$$P(\theta) = \sum_{n=0}^{\infty} (p_n r^n \cos n\theta - q_n r^n \sin n\theta), \tag{3}$$

and

$$Q(\theta) = \sum_{n=0}^{\infty} (q_n r^n \cos n\theta + p_n r^n \sin n\theta). \tag{4}$$

The functions $P(\theta)$ and $Q(\theta)$ are each real functions of θ, of period 2π and the equations just written show that certain periodic functions of a

475

special nature admit of a representation by a series of sines and cosines of multiples of the variable. Similar expansions may be derived from Laurent series, containing negative powers, as in problem 13 of Exercises XIV. The question naturally arises whether periodic functions of more general character admit of such expansions.

If we use the period T, instead of 2π, we must form the series from the terms $\cos n(2\pi/T)x$ and $\sin n(2\pi/T)x$, since each of these has the period T. In fact any finite sum or convergent series

$$A + \sum_{n=1}^{\infty} \left(A_n \cos \frac{2\pi nx}{T} + B_n \sin \frac{2\pi nx}{T} \right) \tag{5}$$

will represent a function of period T.

Now let us start with a function $f(x)$, of period T and assume that it can be expressed as the sum of a series of the form (5). If it is permissible to integrate the series termwise, we must have:

$$\int_0^T f(x) \, dx = AT, \quad \text{and} \quad A = \frac{1}{T} \int_0^T f(x) \, dx, \tag{6}$$

since for n a positive integer,

$$\int_0^T \cos \frac{2\pi nx}{T} \, dx = 0 \quad \text{and} \quad \int_0^T \sin \frac{2\pi nx}{T} \, dx = 0. \tag{7}$$

Next let us multiply each term of the series (5) by $\cos n(2\pi x/T)$. Then if this series may be integrated termwise, it follows that:

$$A_n = \frac{2}{T} \int_0^T f(x) \cos \frac{2\pi nx}{T} \, dx, \tag{8}$$

since, for m and n each a positive integer,

$$\int_0^T \sin \frac{2\pi mx}{T} \cos \frac{2\pi nx}{T} \, dx = 0, \tag{9}$$

$$\int_0^T \cos \frac{2\pi mx}{T} \cos \frac{2\pi nx}{T} \, dx = 0, \quad m \neq n, \tag{10}$$

but

$$\int_0^T \cos^2 \frac{2\pi nx}{T} \, dx = \frac{T}{2}. \tag{11}$$

Similarly, if the series obtained by multiplication by $\sin n(2\pi x/T)$ may be integrated termwise, it follows that:

$$B_n = \frac{2}{T} \int_0^T f(x) \sin \frac{2\pi nx}{T} \, dx, \tag{12}$$

in view of equation (9) together with

$$\int_0^T \sin\frac{2\pi m x}{T} \sin\frac{2\pi n x}{T}\, dx = 0,\ m \neq n, \tag{13}$$

$$\int_0^T \sin^2\frac{2\pi n x}{T}\, dx = \frac{T}{2}, \tag{14}$$

where m and n are each a positive integer.

For any function $f(x)$, of period T, for which the integrals exist, we define the constants A, A_n, B_n given by equations (6), (8) and (12) as the *Fourier coefficients* of the function $f(x)$. We write:

$$f(x) \sim A + \sum_{n=1}^{\infty}\left(A_n \cos\frac{2\pi n x}{T} + B_n \sin\frac{2\pi n x}{T}\right), \tag{15}$$

and speak of the right member as the *Fourier series* for $f(x)$, whether the series converges or not. If the series is known to converge to $f(x)$, we may replace the sign of equivalence, $\sim$, by the equality sign.

We also form the finite sums:

$$S_n = A + \sum_{k=1}^{n-1}\left(A_k \cos\frac{2\pi k x}{T} + B_n \sin\frac{2\pi k x}{T}\right), \tag{16}$$

which we call the partial sums of the Fourier series for $f(x)$.

We note that for a function of period T, we may use any interval of length T, as a to $a + T$, in place of 0, T in calcuating the integrals which appear in the formulas for the coefficients. Thus these coefficients may be defined by

$$A = \text{the average of } f(x),$$

$$A_n = \text{twice the average of } f(x) \cos\frac{2\pi n x}{T},$$

$$\tag{17}$$

$$B_n = \text{twice the average of } f(x) \sin\frac{2\pi n x}{T},$$

with all averages taken over any interval of length T.

288. Functions of Period 2π. When the period T is 2π, the factor $2\pi/T$ is unity and so may be omitted. Moreover, there is no real loss of generality in restricting ourselves to this case, since if we have any function $f(x)$ of period T, and we write:

$$X = \left(\frac{2\pi}{T}\right)x,\ \ f(x) = f\left(\frac{TX}{2\pi}\right) = F(X), \tag{18}$$

the function $F(X)$ is of period 2π. Also the Fourier coefficients of the function $F(X)$, regarded as a function of period 2π are the same as the Fourier coefficients of the function $f(x)$ regarded as a function of period T, since averages are not changed by a change of scale. Consequently,

$$F(X) \sim A + \sum_{n=1}^{\infty} (A_n \cos nX + B_n \sin nX), \tag{19}$$

is equivalent to the relation (15), and the series of (15) will converge to $f(x)$ if the series of (19) converges to $F(X)$.

Accordingly, to simplify the writing, from now on we shall consider $T = 2\pi$, but shall continue to use x as the variable and $f(x)$ as the function.

289. The Partial Sums. The partial sums are:

$$S_n = A + \sum_{k=1}^{n-1} (A_k \cos kx + B_k \sin kx). \tag{20}$$

Using the definition (17), we may consider the coefficients defined by:

$$A = \frac{1}{2\pi} \int_{-\pi+x}^{\pi+x} f(t) \, dt, \tag{21}$$

$$A_n = \frac{1}{\pi} \int_{-\pi+x}^{\pi+x} f(t) \cos nt \, dt, \tag{22}$$

$$B_n = \frac{1}{\pi} \int_{-\pi+x}^{\pi+x} f(t) \sin nt \, dt. \tag{23}$$

In these equations we think of x as a particular value under consideration and to avoid confusion we have replaced the dummy variable of integration by t.

We find:

$$A_k \cos kx + B_k \sin kx$$
$$= \frac{1}{\pi} \int_{-\pi+x}^{\pi+x} f(t) \, (\cos kt \cos kx + \sin kt \sin kx) \, dt$$
$$= \frac{1}{\pi} \int_{-\pi+x}^{\pi+x} f(t) \, \cos k(t - x) \, dt. \tag{24}$$

Consequently,

$$S_n = \frac{1}{\pi} \int_{-\pi+x}^{\pi+x} \left[\frac{1}{2} + \sum_{k=1}^{n-1} \cos k(t - x) \right] f(t) \, dt. \tag{25}$$

If we change the variable by putting $t = x + u$, this becomes

$$S_n = \frac{1}{\pi} \int_{-\pi}^{\pi} s_n(u) f(x + u) \, du, \tag{26}$$

where

$$s_n(u) = \frac{1}{2} + \sum_{k=1}^{n-1} \cos ku = \frac{\sin\left(n - \frac{1}{2}\right)u}{2\sin\frac{u}{2}}. \tag{27}$$

That the last term is the sum of the series follows by mathematical induction from the identity:

$$\sin\left(k + \frac{1}{2}\right)u - \sin\left(k - \frac{1}{2}\right)u = 2\sin\frac{u}{2}\cos ku. \tag{28}$$

Since the function $s_n(u)$ is an even function, we find on separating the range $-\pi$ to π into $-\pi$ to 0 and 0 to π that:

$$S_n = \frac{1}{\pi}\int_0^\pi s_n(u)[f(x + u) + f(x - u)]\,du. \tag{29}$$

From the sum for $s_n(u)$ in equation (27), we may deduce that

$$\frac{1}{\pi}\int_0^\pi s_n(u)\,du = \frac{1}{2}. \tag{30}$$

290. A Transformation of the Limit.   We shall write:

$$f(x_1+) = \lim_{x \to x_1+} f(x) \quad \text{and} \quad f(x_1-) = \lim_{x \to x_1-} f(x), \tag{31}$$

to denote the right- and left-hand limits introduced in section 30 and shall confine our attention to points for which both these limits exist. At such points we seek a condition for the Fourier series of the function to converge to

$$g(x) = \tfrac{1}{2}[f(x+) + f(x-)]. \tag{32}$$

In particular, at a point where $f(x)$ is continuous,

$$f(x+) = f(x-) = f(x), \quad \text{and} \quad g(x) = f(x), \tag{33}$$

so that the condition will be one for the convergence of the series to $f(x)$ if x is a point of continuity of the function.

From the definition of a partial sum, the series will converge to $g(x)$ if

$$g(x) = \lim_{n \to \infty} S_n = \lim_{n \to \infty} \frac{1}{\pi}\int_0^\pi s_n(u)[f(x + u) + f(x - u)]\,du. \tag{34}$$

But, in consequence of the relation (30), we have:

$$g(x) = \lim_{n \to \infty} \frac{1}{\pi}\int_0^\pi s_n(u)2g(x)\,du. \tag{35}$$

Thus the series will converge to $g(x)$ if, and only if,

$$\lim_{n \to \infty} \int_0^\pi s_n(u)[f(x+u) + f(x-u) - 2g(x)]\,du = 0. \qquad (36)$$

291. Riemann's Theorem. In those cases where we can prove that the integral just written approaches zero, we make use of the presence of the factor $\sin(n - 1/2)u$ in $s_n(u)$. This factor enables us to simplify our problem because of the fact that, *if $F(x)$ is a function possessing a finite proper or absolutely convergent improper Riemann integral, then for m real but not necessarily an integer.*

$$\lim_{m \to \infty} \int_a^b F(x) \sin mx\,dx = 0. \qquad (37)$$

We devote this section to proving this theorem, originally due to Riemann and generalized for the improper case by Lebesgue.

We first observe that the relation is true if $F(x)$ is a constant, since

$$\left| \int_a^b K \sin mx\,dx \right| = \left| K \frac{\cos ma - \cos mb}{m} \right| \le \frac{2|K|}{m}. \qquad (38)$$

Consider next a step function, $S(x)$, in the interval a,b; that is a function constant in each of a finite number of subintervals which, like those used in defining the Riemann integral, make up the entire interval a,b. The function is constant in the open intervals. Its value at the end points is of no consequence since these are finite in number and will not affect the integral of the function. If the function $S(x)$ is such that M is a bound for $|S(x)|$ and there are k steps, it follows from equation (38), applied to each subinterval, that:

$$\int_a^b S(x) \sin mx\,dx \le \frac{2kM}{m}. \qquad (39)$$

This approaches zero when $m \to \infty$, so that the result holds for a step function.

Finally, we note that for any proper Riemann integral, $\int F(x)\,dx$, the method of defining the integral shows that there is a step function $S(x)$ such that

$$\int_a^b |F(x) - S(x)|\,dx < \epsilon. \qquad (40)$$

In fact, for a step function used in a lower sum, the integral just written reduces to the excess of the Riemann integral over the lower sum.

The same result holds for an absolutely convergent improper Riemann integral, since such an integral may have its range of integration separated into that for a proper integral and a number of intervals on which $F(x)$ is unbounded, but such that the integral of $|F(x)|$ over these integrals is arbitrarily small, say $< \epsilon$. Thus we may take $S(x)$ as in equation (40) for the range of the proper integral and $S(x) = 0$ on the remaining intervals. It will result that:

$$\int_a^b |F(x) - S(x)| \, dx < 2\epsilon. \tag{41}$$

If we start with $\epsilon/2$ in place of ϵ, this is the relation (40).

Now consider

$$\left| \int_a^b F(x) \sin mx \, dx - \int_a^b S(x) \sin mx \, dx \right|$$

$$= \left| \int_a^b [F(x) - S(x)] \sin mx \, dx \right|$$

$$\leqq \int_a^b |F(x) - S(x)| \cdot |\sin mx| \, dx$$

$$\leqq \int_a^b |F(x) - S(x)| \, dx \leqq \epsilon. \tag{42}$$

By the relation (39), for m sufficiently large,

$$\left| \int_a^b S(x) \sin mx \, dx \right| < \epsilon, \quad m > m_0. \tag{43}$$

Consequently, from the last two relations,

$$\left| \int_a^b F(x) \sin mx \, dx \right| < 2\epsilon, \quad \text{for} \quad m > m_0. \tag{44}$$

This proves that, as $m \to \infty$ the integral approaches zero, as stated in equation (37).

With the same conditions on $F(x)$ and m, the argument shows that:

$$\lim_{m \to \infty} \int_a^b F(x) \cos mx \, dx = 0. \tag{45}$$

292. Conditions for Convergence. In equation (36), the factor

$$s_n(u) = \sin\left(n - \frac{1}{2}\right) u \frac{1}{2 \sin \dfrac{u}{2}}. \tag{46}$$

If δ is any positive number less than π, the function $1/\sin(u/2)$ is continuous and bounded in the interval δ,π. Hence

$$F(u) = [f(x + u) + f(x - u) - 2g(x)]\,\frac{1}{2\sin\dfrac{u}{2}} \qquad (47)$$

will have a proper, or absolutely convergent improper, integral with respect to u on the interval δ,π if, as we shall assume, $f(u)$ has an integral of this type on any finite interval.

Hence we may apply the Riemann theorem of the last section to prove that:

$$\lim_{n\to\infty} \int_\delta^\pi s_n(u)[f(x + u) + f(x - u) - 2g(x)]\,du$$
$$= \lim_{n\to\infty} \int_\delta^\pi F(u)\sin\left(n - \frac{1}{2}\right)u\,du = 0. \qquad (48)$$

This enables us to reduce the investigation of the integral of equation (36) to that for the interval $0,\delta$.

Again, we have:

$$\frac{\sin\left(n - \dfrac{1}{2}\right)u}{\sin\dfrac{u}{2}} = \sin nu \cot \frac{u}{2} - \cos nu, \qquad (49)$$

and in the interval $0,\delta$ we may apply equation (45) with

$$2F(u) = f(x + u) + f(x - u) - 2g(x), \qquad (50)$$

so that the part of the integral involving $\cos nu$ has a limit zero and the expression to be investigated is:

$$\lim_{n\to\infty} \frac{1}{2} \int_0^\delta \sin nu \cot \frac{u}{2} [f(x + u) + f(x - u) - 2g(x)]\,du. \qquad (51)$$

For $0 < u < 2\pi$, the factor $\cot u/2$ is analytic and

$$\cot \frac{u}{2} = \frac{\cos\dfrac{u}{2}}{\sin\dfrac{u}{2}} = \frac{1 - \dfrac{u^2}{8}\cdots}{\dfrac{u}{2} - \dfrac{u^3}{48}\cdots} = \frac{2}{u} - \frac{u}{6} + Au^3 + \cdots, \qquad (52)$$

the Laurent expansion of section 276. Hence the function

$$\cot \frac{u}{2} - \frac{2}{u} \to 0, \quad \text{as} \quad u \to 0, \qquad (53)$$

and if we use this limiting value at 0, the function is continuous for $0 \leq u < 2\pi$. Consequently, for the interval $0 \leq u \leq \delta$,

$$F(u) = \left[\cot \frac{u}{2} - \frac{2}{u} \right] [f(x + u) + f(x - u) - 2g(x)] \qquad (54)$$

will have a proper, or absolutely convergent improper integral and by equation (37),

$$\lim_{n \to \infty} \int_0^\delta \sin nu \, F(u) \, du = 0. \qquad (55)$$

Since the value, or indeterminate nature, of an integrand at a single point does not affect the integral, we may subtract this integral from the integral in the expression (51), and write the result:

$$\lim_{n \to \infty} \int_0^\delta \frac{\sin nu}{u} [f(x + u) + f(x - u) - 2g(x)] \, du. \qquad (56)$$

The relation (36) will hold if this limit is zero. If $f(x)$ is of period 2π and has a proper or absolutely convergent improper integral on the interval $0,2\pi$, it will have an integral of this type on any finite interval. Also the integrals defining the Fourier coefficients will necessarily exist. Our discussion shows that, for such a function, *a necessary and sufficient condition for its Fourier series to converge to the value $g(x)$ is that for some positive number δ, the limit* (56) *exists and equals zero.* The limit zero for any δ implies convergence, while convergence implies the limit zero for all positive δ.

293. Sufficient Conditions. Let us now seek a sufficient condition for the limit (56) to be zero, where $g(x)$ has the form given in equation (32). If we require that

$$\lim_{n \to \infty} \int_0^\delta \frac{\sin nu}{u} [f(x + u) - f(x+)] \, du = 0, \qquad (57)$$

and

$$\lim_{n \to \infty} \int_0^\delta \frac{\sin nu}{u} [f(x - u) - f(x-)] \, du = 0, \qquad (58)$$

it will follow by addition that the expression (56) approaches zero. In particular, if

$$|f(x+u) - f(x+)| \leq Ku^p, \quad \text{where} \quad p > 0, \quad \text{for} \quad 0 < u < u_0, \qquad (59)$$

we shall have, for $h < u_0$,

$$\left| \int_0^h \frac{\sin nu}{u} [f(x + u) - f(x)] \, du \right| \leqq \int_0^h \frac{|\sin nu|}{u} |f(x + u) - f(x+)| \, du$$

$$\leqq \int_0^h K u^{p-1} \, du \leqq \frac{K}{p} h^p. \tag{60}$$

In the interval h to δ, the integral of equation (57) approaches zero by the Riemann theorem.   Thus we have:

$$\overline{\lim_{n \to \infty}} \left| \int_0^\delta \frac{\sin nu}{u} [f(x + u) - f(x+)] \, du \right| \leqq \frac{K}{p} h^p. \tag{61}$$

Since K and p are fixed and p is positive, this may be made arbitrarily small by taking h sufficiently small.   Thus the upper limit, being positive or zero, must be zero; and the limit is zero as we wished to prove.

The relation (59) is described as a Lipschitz condition to the right of order p.   Similarly the condition

$$|f(x - u) - f(x-)| \leqq K u^p, \quad \text{where} \quad p > 0, \quad \text{for} \quad 0 \leqq u \leqq u_0, \tag{62}$$

is described as a Lipschitz condition to the left of order p.   If this holds, the reasoning just used shows that equation (58) will follow.   If the function is continuous, and such conditions hold on both sides, we have

$$|f(x + u) - f(x)| \leqq K |u|^p, \quad \text{where} \quad p > 0, \quad \text{for} \quad -u_0 \leqq u \leqq u_0, \tag{63}$$

and we say that the function satisfies a Lipschitz condition of order p at the point x.

The most important case is that when $p = 1$, in equation (63), to which we have already referred in sections 128 and 255, where the condition held at all points of an interval.   From the definition of a derivative as a limit, it follows that the condition (63) holds with $p = 1$, whenever $f(x)$ has a finite derivative at x.   This leads us to our first sufficient condition for the convergence of a Fourier series:

The Fourier series converges to the function $f(x)$ at any point where $f(x)$ has a finite derivative.

More generally, the series converges to $[f(x+) + f(x-)]/2$ if $f(x)$ has a finite right-hand and a finite left-hand derivative, or satisfies a Lipschitz condition to the right and to the left of any positive order.

To develop a second condition, suppose that $f(x)$ is monotonically decreasing in the interval x to $x + u_0$.   Then the function

$$\phi(u) = -f(x + u) + f(x+) \tag{64}$$

approaches zero for $u \to 0$ and monotonically increases in the interval 0 to h, $h < u_0$, so that it is positive in this interval. Thus we may apply the Bonnet mean value theorem of section 198 to obtain:

$$\int_0^h \phi(u) \frac{\sin nu}{u} \, du = \phi(h) \int_\xi^h \frac{\sin nu}{u} \, du, \tag{65}$$

for a suitably chosen value of ξ in the interval $0,h$.

From the properties of $\sin nu$ and the decreasing character of $1/u$, it follows that the series:

$$\int_0^{\pi/n} \frac{\sin nu}{u} \, du + \int_{\pi/n}^{2\pi/n} \frac{\sin nu}{u} \, du + \cdots \tag{66}$$

is an alternating series and so the sum of this series to any number of terms never exceeds the first term in numerical value. In fact, since each of the integrands preserves its sign in the interval corresponding to any one term, for any two positive numbers ξ and h,

$$\left| \int_\xi^h \frac{\sin nu}{u} \, du \right| \leqq \int_0^{\pi/n} \frac{\sin nu}{u} \, du \leqq \int_0^\pi \frac{\sin v}{v} \, dv. \tag{67}$$

Thus the integral in the right member of equation (65) admits a bound independent of n and h. Since it is multiplied by $\phi(h)$, which $\to 0$ when $h \to 0$, the product may be made small by taking h small. Hence the integral in the left member of equation (65) is numerically small, for h sufficiently small. By combining this fact with the Riemann theorem and using upper limits as we did for equation (61), we may prove that under the conditions stated, the limiting relation (57) holds.

For $f(x)$ monotonically increasing, we may use the same argument with $f(x)$ replaced by its negative in the equation which defines $\phi(u)$. The reasoning also applies to the relation (58), if the function is monotonic in the interval $x - u_0$ to x. Thus the Fourier series converges at any point which separates two open intervals in each of which $f(x)$ is monotonic and bounded. The Fourier series will converge for the sum of two functions if it converges for each of them. Since we proved in section 159 that any function of bounded variation in an interval can be decomposed into the sum of two monotonic functions, it follows that:

The Fourier series for a function $f(x)$ will converge to

$$\tfrac{1}{2}[f(x+) + f(x-)]$$

for any value x, in some interval in which the function $f(x)$ is of bounded variation. (Jordan.)

294. Uniform Convergence. Since each of the terms of a Fourier series is a continuous function, if the series converges uniformly for all values, or for all values in some interval, the sum function $f(x)$ will have to be continuous for all values, or for all values in the interval.

If the sum function $f(x)$ is of bounded variation throughout an interval and is continuous throughout this interval, then the Fourier series will converge uniformly in any subinterval of this interval. Again, if the sum function $f(x)$ has a finite derivative, uniformly bounded at all points of an interval, the Fourier series will converge uniformly in any subinterval of this interval. A similar result follows if a Lipschitz condition of positive order p holds at all points of an interval, with the same constants K and u_0 for all points of the interval. This results from the fact, that the number of terms necessary to achieve a given degree of approximation depends on the Riemann theorem and on the magnitude of h in such formulas as (61) and (65) necessary to make these terms small. When the function is continuous in a closed subinterval, as follows from any of the conditions stated, it results from the uniform continuity that the size of h can be fixed so as to do for all the points of this subinterval. This leads to a minimum value of h, so that the functions $F(x)$ to which we apply the Riemann theorem have the form $f(x + u)/u$, for an interval h to b, or at least may be made up of a sum of such terms. The function $f(x)$ may be approximated by a step function $S(x)$ in such a way that the relation (40) holds for the interval 0 to 2π, or, from the periodicity, for any interval of length less than 2π. Again, in the interval h to b, the function $1/u$ is continuous and may be approximated uniformly by a second step function $T(u)$. If $S(x)$ has s steps in the interval $0 \leqq x \leqq 2\pi$, and $T(u)$ has t steps, the function $S(x + u)T(u)$ will have at most st steps for $h \leqq u \leqq b$. Hence the factor k in equation (39), due to the number of steps, will not exceed st and so will not disturb the uniformity. Similarly, the factor $\cot u/2 - 2/u$ is uniformly continuous for $0 \leqq u \leqq \pi$ and hence for $h \leqq u \leqq b$, so that its presence in equation (54) will not disturb the uniformity.

295. The Fejér Theorem. While continuity of itself is not a sufficient condition for the convergence of a Fourier series, there is a generalized process of summation by which we may get back the function from the partial sums. If, in place of the partial sums of a series, we use the first Cesàro sums:

$$C_1 = S_1, \quad C_2 = \frac{S_1 + S_2}{2}, \quad C_n = \frac{1}{n} \sum_{k=1}^{n} S_k, \tag{68}$$

we say that the series is summable to a value $f(x)$ in the sense of Cesàro, or summable $(C1)$, if

$$f(x) = \lim_{n \to \infty} C_n. \tag{69}$$

We note that if a series is convergent, it is summable in this sense. For, if L is the sum, for any positive ϵ there is an N such that if $k > N$, all the sums S_k will be between $L - \epsilon$ and $L + \epsilon$. Thus, for $n = N + m$, we shall have:

$$NC_N + mL - m\epsilon \leqq (N + m)C_n \leqq NC_N + mL + m\epsilon. \tag{70}$$

If we divide all the terms by m and let $m \to \infty$, we may conclude from this that:

$$L - \epsilon \leqq \overline{\lim} \, C_n \leqq L + \epsilon, \tag{71}$$

with a similar relation for $\underline{\lim}$. From this and the fact that ϵ is arbitrary, we have:

$$\lim C_n = L. \tag{72}$$

This proves that *a convergent series is summable in the sense of Cesàro to the sum to which it converges.*

However, a series may be summable in the sense of Cesàro without being convergent. Thus, for

$$1 - 1 + 1 - 1 + \cdots, \tag{73}$$

the sums are:

$$S_i = 1, 0, 1, 0, \cdots, 1, 0, \cdots \tag{74}$$

and

$$C_i = 1, \frac{1}{2}, \frac{2}{3}, \frac{1}{2}, \frac{3}{5}, \cdots, \frac{n}{2n-1}, \frac{1}{2}, \cdots \tag{75}$$

so that the series is summable ($C1$) to $1/2$.

Let us now apply the process of Cesàro summation to a Fourier series, where we regard the $(n + 1)$st term as $(A_n \cos nx + B_n \sin nx)$, so that the sum of the first n terms is the S_n given by equation (20), or (29):

$$S_n = \frac{1}{\pi} \int_0^\pi s_n(u)[f(x + u) + f(x - u)] \, du, \tag{76}$$

with

$$s_n(u) = \frac{\sin (n - \frac{1}{2}) u}{2 \sin \dfrac{u}{2}} = \frac{1}{2} + \sum_{k=1}^{n-1} \cos ku. \tag{77}$$

We wish to calculate

$$C_n = \frac{1}{n} \sum_{k=1}^n S_k. \tag{78}$$

We begin by evaluating the sum for the only factor involving k,

$$\sum_{k=1}^n \sin (k - \tfrac{1}{2}) u = \frac{1 - \cos nu}{2 \sin \dfrac{u}{2}} = \frac{\sin^2 \dfrac{nu}{2}}{\sin \dfrac{u}{2}}. \tag{79}$$

The first form is proved by mathematical induction and the use of the identity:

$$-\cos(k+1)u + \cos ku = 2\sin\left(k+\frac{1}{2}\right)u \sin\frac{u}{2}. \qquad (80)$$

It follows from the second form that

$$C_n = \frac{1}{n\pi} \int_0^\pi \frac{\sin^2\dfrac{nu}{2}}{\sin^2\dfrac{u}{2}}\left[\frac{f(x+u)+f(x-u)}{2}\right]du. \qquad (81)$$

We also note, from the last expression of equation (77) and equation (79) that:

$$\frac{\sin^2\dfrac{nu}{2}}{2\sin^2\dfrac{u}{2}} = \frac{n}{2} + \sum_{k=1}^{n-1}(n-k)\cos ku, \qquad (82)$$

so that

$$\frac{1}{n\pi}\int_0^\pi \frac{\sin^2\dfrac{nu}{2}}{\sin^2\dfrac{u}{2}}\,du = 1. \qquad (83)$$

Now consider a function $f(x)$, of period 2π and continuous for all values. For any positive ϵ, there is a δ such that

$$|f(x+u) - f(x)| < \epsilon, \quad \text{if} \quad |u| \leqq \delta. \qquad (84)$$

From equations (81) and (83), we have:

$$C_n - f(x) = \frac{1}{n\pi}\int_0^\pi \frac{\sin^2\dfrac{nu}{2}}{\sin^2\dfrac{u}{2}}\left[\frac{f(x+u)+f(x-u)}{2} - f(x)\right]du. \qquad (85)$$

Let us separate the interval of integration $0,\pi$ into $0,\delta$ and δ,π. In the first interval, by equation (84), the last factor is numerically less than ϵ, so that the contribution to the expression on the right for this interval does not exceed:

$$I_1 = \frac{\epsilon}{n\pi}\int_0^\delta \frac{\sin^2\dfrac{nu}{2}}{\sin^2\dfrac{u}{2}}\,du. \qquad (86)$$

Since the integrand is positive, this is less than the result when we replace the upper limit by π. Thus, in view of equation (83), we find:

$$I_1 < \epsilon. \tag{87}$$

In the interval δ, π we have $\sin^2{(nu/2)}$ is at most unity, and

$$\sin^2 \frac{u}{2} > \sin^2 \frac{\delta}{2}. \tag{88}$$

Thus, if M is such that

$$|f(x)| \leqq M, \quad \text{for all } x, \tag{89}$$

we have for the contribution from the second interval a quantity numerically at most:

$$I_2 = \frac{1}{n\pi} \int_0^\pi \frac{2M}{\sin^2 \dfrac{\delta}{2}} \, du \leqq \frac{K}{n}, \tag{90}$$

where K is a constant independent of n.

This proves that:

$$|C_n - f(x)| < \epsilon + \frac{K}{n}. \tag{91}$$

For $n > K/\epsilon$, the right member is less than 2ϵ, and hence:

$$\lim C_n = f(x). \tag{92}$$

Since a function continuous on the closed interval $0, 2\pi$ is uniformly continuous, the quantity δ may be chosen independently of x, so that the same is true of K and hence K/ϵ. This proves that the convergence of the sequence C_n is uniform.

We have proved one form of Fejér's theorem:

The first Cesàro sums for the Fourier series of a continuous periodic function converge uniformly to the function.

296. The Weierstrass Approximation Theorem. This theorem asserts that any function, continuous on a closed interval, may be uniformly approximated in this interval by a polynomial. We may easily deduce it from the theorem just proved. For, by a change of scale, the interval may be made less than 2π. And, by combining the function with a suitable first degree function joining the point b, $f(b)$ with $a + 2\pi$, $f(a)$, we may define a function $c(x)$, continuous and of period 2π, which equals $f(x)$ in the interval $a \leqq x \leqq b$. Then, by the Fejér theorem, there is a Cesàro sum C_n such that:

$$|c(x) - C_n(x)| < \epsilon, \tag{93}$$

for all x.

But the sum $C_n(x)$ was obtained from sums $S_n(x)$, each of which was a combination of constants and terms of the form $\sin kx$ and $\cos kx$, with k at most $n - 1$. Thus the sum $C_n(x)$ has the form:

$$C_n(x) = A_n' + \sum_{k=1}^{n-1} (A_{n,k}' \cos kx + B_{n,k}' \sin kx). \qquad (94)$$

There are $2n - 2 < 2n$ trigonometric terms. If G is an upper bound for the numerical value of the coefficients, we may approximate each trigonometric function by a polynomial to within $\epsilon/2Gn$. In fact, the Taylor's series for $\sin kx$ and $\cos kx$ converge for all values of x and uniformly on any finite interval, $a \leq x \leq b$. Hence we may carry out these series to a point where the partial sums furnish an approximation to the desired accuracy. When this is done with all the terms and these polynomials are combined, we have a polynomial $P(x)$ such that

$$|C_n(x) - P(x)| < \epsilon, \quad a \leq x \leq b. \qquad (95)$$

In view of the relations (93) and (95),

$$|c(x) - P(x)| < 2\epsilon, \quad a \leq x \leq b. \qquad (96)$$

This shows the existence of a polynomial uniformly approximating $c(x)$ to within 2ϵ, an arbitrary positive quantity.

297. Convergence in the Mean. Let $f(x)$ be a real periodic function for which the Fourier coefficients exist, and let the function $[f(x)]^2$ be integrable in the interval 0 to 2π. Now consider any trigonometric sum of order $n - 1$:

$$T_n(x) = a + \sum_{k=1}^{n-1} (a_k \cos kx + b_k \sin kx). \qquad (97)$$

If we regard $T_n(x)$ as an approximation to $f(x)$, we may use the integral of the square of the error, or

$$E = \int_0^{2\pi} |f(x) - T_n(x)|^2 \, dx, \qquad (98)$$

as a measure of the degree of the approximation, as in section 249. If we replace $T_n(x)$ by its expansion, multiply out, and recall the definition of the Fourier coefficients, as well as the values of the integrals of the trigonometric functions and their squares and products given in section 287, we find:

$$E = \int_0^{2\pi} [f(x)]^2 \, dx - 4\pi aA - 2\pi \sum_{k=1}^{n-1} (a_k A_k + b_k B_k) + 2\pi a^2$$
$$+ \pi \sum_{k=1}^{n-1} (a_k^2 + b_k^2) \quad (99)$$

$$= \int_0^{2\pi} [f(x)]^2 - 2\pi A^2 - \pi \sum_{k=1}^{n-1} (A_k^2 + B_k^2)$$
$$+ 2\pi (A - a)^2 + \pi \sum_{k=1}^{n-1} [(A_k - a_k)^2 + (B_k - b_k)^2]. \quad (100)$$

Since the squares are positive or zero, the second form shows that E is larger for any sum with one or more coefficients differing from the Fourier coefficients than for the sum formed with Fourier coefficients, that is $T_n = S_n$. This proves that:

Of all trigonometric sums of a given order, the one formed with Fourier coefficients makes the integral of the square of the error least.

For the sum with Fourier coefficients, we have:

$$\frac{1}{2\pi} \int_0^{2\pi} [f(x) - S_n(x)]^2 \, dx = \frac{1}{2\pi} \int_0^{2\pi} f(x)^2 \, dx$$
$$- A^2 - \frac{1}{2} \sum_{k=1}^{n-1} (A_k^2 + B_k^2). \quad (101)$$

Since the left-hand side is greater than or equal to zero, the same is true of the right, and we have:

$$\frac{1}{2\pi} \int_0^{2\pi} [f(x)]^2 \, dx \geqq A^2 + \frac{1}{2} \sum_{k=1}^{n-1} (A_k^2 + B_k^2). \quad (102)$$

This is known as *Bessel's inequality*. The infinite series whose partial sums appear on the right of such relations converges, since it is a series of positive terms whose sum is bounded.

We may show that it converges to the integral on the left as follows. By reasoning similar to that of section 291, if the integral of $[f(x)]^2$ exists as a proper or improper integral, we may find a step function $S(x)$ such that:

$$\int_0^{2\pi} |f(x) - S(x)|^2 \, dx < \epsilon. \quad (103)$$

By changing the step function to a linear function in sufficiently small intervals including the points of discontinuity, we may find a continuous periodic function $c(x)$, such that:

$$\int_0^{2\pi} |S(x) - c(x)|^2 \, dx < \epsilon. \tag{104}$$

By the result of section 295, the first Cesàro sums for the Fourier series of $c(x)$ approach this function uniformly. Hence we may find one of these sums, say $C_n(x)$ such that:

$$|c(x) - C_n(x)| \leq \epsilon, \tag{105}$$

and hence:

$$\int_0^{2\pi} |c(x) - C_n(x)|^2 \, dx \leq \epsilon^2 \, 2\pi. \tag{106}$$

Finally, by a double application of the inequality (130) of section 252, and the relations (103), (104), and (106), we find:

$$\int_0^{2\pi} |f(x) - C_n(x)|^2 \, dx \leq [\epsilon^{\frac{1}{2}} + \epsilon^{\frac{1}{2}} + (2\pi)^{\frac{1}{2}}\epsilon]^2. \tag{107}$$

Since ϵ is arbitrary, this shows that there is a trigonometric sum, $C_n(x)$, for which the integral on the left is arbitrarily small. But, if we form $S_n(x)$, the partial sum of the Fourier series for $f(x)$ of the same order as $C_n(x)$, this will make the integral on the left less than or equal to its previous value, and the integral cannot be larger for any partial sum of a higher order. This proves that:

$$\lim \int_0^{2\pi} [f(x) - S_n(x)]^2 \, dx = 0, \tag{108}$$

and, *if the integral of $[f(x)]^2$, and the integrals defining the Fourier coefficients exist, the Fourier series for $f(x)$ converges in the mean to $f(x)$.* The equality obtained by combining relations (108) and (101), or letting $n \to \infty$ in (102), is called *Parseval's theorem.*

Since the series converges in the mean, by section 253, it may be integrated termwise and under the conditions just stated: *The series obtained from the Fourier development of $f(x)$ by termwise integration converges to the integral of the function.*

298. Modified Fourier Series. So far we have considered our functions as of period 2π, and the Fourier series as corresponding to the function for all values of x and converging to it for any value of x for which the sufficient conditions were met. We may, however, confine our attention to any interval of length 2π, for example the interval $0,2\pi$ or $-\pi,\pi$. In this case the Fourier coefficients computed for the fundamental interval of integration will lead to a series convergent, or convergent in the mean, to the original function if the appropriate conditions are met for values of x in the fundamental interval.

If we take as our fundamental interval $-\pi,\pi$, and consider a function defined in this interval and *odd*, that is, one for which $f(-x) = -f(x)$, the constant and cosine coefficients will all be zero, and we will have a series of sines only. Similarly, if we consider a function as defined in this interval and *even*, that is, one for which $f(-x) = f(x)$, the sine coefficients will all be zero, and we shall have a constant term and a series of cosines only. Since the function may be arbitrarily given in the interval $0,\pi$ and then defined in the interval $-\pi,0$ so as to be odd or even, we see that for the restricted interval $0,\pi$ any function with $f(x)$ and $|f(x)|$ integrable will have a Fourier sine development and a Fourier cosine development. If in addition $f(x)$ has an integrable square, each of these developments will converge in the mean to the function.

If at x and $-x$ one of the conditions of section 293 is met, the condition will be satisfied for each of the functions

$$\frac{f(x) + f(-x)}{2} \quad \text{and} \quad \frac{f(x) - f(-x)}{2}. \tag{109}$$

The first of these is even and the second odd, while $f(x)$ is equal to the sum of these two functions. Hence the constant and cosine terms for $f(x)$ will be the same as those for the first function, while the sine terms will be the same as those for the second function. Thus under the condition stated the sine terms will converge by themselves, and the constant and cosine terms will converge by themselves.

By using the change of scale inverse to that introduced in section 288, we obtain developments in terms of $\sin (2\pi nx/T)$ and $\cos (2\pi nx/T)$, for any function given in any interval of length T. Similarly, we may obtain developments in terms of sines alone, or of a constant and cosines alone, for a function given in any interval of length $T/2$.

299. The Fourier Integral Theorem. If a function $f(x)$ is defined on the interval $-P,P$ and the integrals for the coefficients exist, its Fourier partial sum may be written in the form

$$\frac{1}{P} \int_{-P}^{P} \left[\frac{1}{2} + \sum_{k=1}^{n} \cos \frac{k(x - t)\pi}{P} \right] f(t) \, dt, \tag{110}$$

analogous to equation (25).

If we express the cosine in terms of exponentials,

$$\cos \frac{k(x - t)\pi}{P} = \frac{1}{2} \left[e^{ik(x-t)\frac{\pi}{P}} + e^{-ik(x-t)\frac{\pi}{P}} \right], \tag{111}$$

we may use the more symmetrical expression:

$$\frac{1}{2P} \int_{-P}^{P} \left[\sum_{k=-n}^{n} e^{ik(x-t)\frac{\pi}{P}} \right] f(t) \, dt. \tag{112}$$

If we now put:

$$\frac{k\pi}{P} = u_k, \quad \Delta u_k = \frac{\pi}{P}, \tag{113}$$

this may be written:

$$\frac{1}{2\pi} \sum_{k=-n}^{n} \Delta u_k \int_{-P}^{P} e^{iu_k(x-t)} f(t) \, dt. \tag{114}$$

If we put $n = AP/\pi$ and let P become infinite, since $\Delta u_k \to 0$, this suggests an integral, namely,

$$\frac{1}{2\pi} \int_{-A}^{A} du \int_{-\infty}^{\infty} e^{iu(x-t)} f(t) \, dt. \tag{115}$$

In fact, if we let n and P increase in such a way that $A = n/P$ remained constant, the expression (114) would approach this repeated integral as a limit.

We know that, under certain conditions, the limit of the expression (110) as $n \to \infty$ with P fixed is $f(x)$ in the interval $-P$ to P. Since this makes $n/P \to \infty$, we are led to take the limit of the expression (115) as $A \to \infty$.

So far the procedure of this section has merely been heuristic, to help us guess the proper expression to use. We shall now prove that, with suitable restrictions, the limit of the expression (115) as $A \to \infty$ is $f(x)$.

Let us assume that $f(x)$ is integrable in any finite interval, and that:

$$\int_{-\infty}^{\infty} |f(x)| \, dx = \lim_{\substack{M \to \infty \\ N \to \infty}} \int_{-M}^{N} |f(x)| \, dx \tag{116}$$

exists. Then, since

$$|e^{iu(x-t)}| = 1, \tag{117}$$

the integral

$$\int_{-\infty}^{\infty} e^{iu(x-t)} f(t) \, dt \tag{118}$$

converges uniformly in u. Hence we may integrate from $-A$ to A and interchange the order of integration, and so find:

$$I = \int_{-A}^{A} du \int_{-\infty}^{\infty} e^{iu(x-t)} f(t) \, dt$$

$$= \int_{-\infty}^{\infty} dt \int_{-A}^{A} e^{iu(x-t)} f(t) \, du. \tag{119}$$

But

$$\int_{-A}^{A} e^{iu(x-t)} \, du = \frac{e^{iu(x-t)}}{i(x-t)} \bigg|_{-A}^{A} = \frac{2 \sin A (x-t)}{x-t}, \qquad (120)$$

so that

$$I = \int_{-\infty}^{\infty} \frac{2 \sin A (x-t)}{x-t} f(t) \, dt. \qquad (121)$$

To discuss the behavior of this integral as $A \to \infty$, we shall separate the interval of integration into the following ranges:

$$-\infty, -B; \quad -B, x - \delta; \quad x - \delta, x + \delta; \quad x + \delta, B; \quad B, \infty. \qquad (122)$$

We choose B so large that:

$$\int_{-\infty}^{-B} |f(x)| \, dx < \epsilon, \int_{B}^{\infty} |f(x)| \, dx < \epsilon, B > x + 2, \ -B < x - 2. \quad (123)$$

The first two conditions may be realized in view of the assumption that the integral of equation (116) converges. For t in the ranges $-\infty, -B$ and B, ∞, the last conditions make $|x - t| > 2$. Since $\sin A (x - t)$ does not exceed unity, the integrand of I is dominated by $|f(t)|$ in these ranges. Thus, by the first conditions (123), the contribution to I from these two intervals may be written:

$$2\theta' \epsilon, \quad |\theta'| < 1. \qquad (124)$$

Next assume that, for values of the variable near x, the function satisfies one of the sufficient conditions given in section 293, or is such that the equation (56) holds for some positive δ. Thus

$$\lim_{n \to \infty} \int_{0}^{\delta} \frac{\sin nu}{u} [f(x + u) + f(x - u) - 2g(x)] \, du = 0. \quad (125)$$

By using equations (35) and (53), and reasoning as in section 292, we may show that:

$$g(x) = \lim_{n \to \infty} \frac{2}{\pi} \int_{0}^{\delta} \frac{\sin nu}{u} g(x) \, du. \qquad (126)$$

Also, by putting $u = t - x$ for the term in $f(x + u)$, and $u = -t + x$ for the term in $f(x - u)$, we find:

$$\int_{0}^{\delta} \frac{\sin nu}{u} [f(x + u) + f(x - u)] \, du$$
$$= \int_{x-\delta}^{x+\delta} \frac{\sin n(x - t)}{x-t} f(t) \, dt. \quad (127)$$

We may conclude from the last three equations that:

$$\lim_{n \to \infty} \int_{x-\delta}^{x+\delta} \frac{2 \sin n(x-t)}{x-t} f(t) \, dt = 2\pi g(x). \tag{128}$$

If we take the δ which defines the middle interval (122) as a δ for which equation (125), and hence (128) holds, we see that for A sufficiently large, say $>A'$, the contribution to I from the middle interval may be written in the form:

$$2\pi g(x) + \theta''\epsilon, \quad |\theta''| < 1. \tag{129}$$

Finally, for the two intervals $-B, x - \delta$ and $x + \delta, B$, we may use the Riemann theorem, and reason as in section 292 to show that the contribution to I from each of these intervals approaches zero as A becomes infinite. Thus, for $A > A''$, it may be written

$$2\theta'''\epsilon, \quad |\theta'''| < 1. \tag{130}$$

On combining the contributions to I from the separate ranges as listed in the expressions (124), (129) and (130), we see that

$$|I - 2\pi g(x)| < 5\epsilon, \quad \text{for} \quad A > A', A''. \tag{131}$$

This shows that the limit of I as A becomes infinite is $2\pi g(x)$, and:

$$\lim_{A \to \infty} \frac{1}{2\pi} \int_{-A}^{A} du \int_{-\infty}^{\infty} e^{iu(x-t)} f(t) \, dt = g(x), \tag{132}$$

at any point where the condition (125) holds. Thus this limit is $[f(x+) + f(x-)]/2$ whenever any of the conditions of section 293 hold and in particular:

If $f(x)$ and $|f(x)|$ are each integrable from $-\infty$ to ∞, for any value of x where $f(x)$ is continuous and one of the sufficient conditions of section 293 holds,

$$\lim_{A \to \infty} \frac{1}{2\pi} \int_{-A}^{A} du \int_{-\infty}^{\infty} e^{iu(x-t)} f(t) \, dt = f(x). \tag{133}$$

This expression is known as a Fourier integral and this is one form of the *Fourier integral theorem*.

300. Other Fourier Integrals. If the conditions of the preceding section are satisfied, and we have convergence for all values of x, we may define a function:

$$F(u) = \lambda \int_{-\infty}^{\infty} e^{-iut} f(t) \, dt, \tag{134}$$

where λ is any positive constant. Then, from equation (133),

$$f(x) = \lim_{A \to \infty} \mu \int_{-A}^{A} e^{iux} F(u) \, du, \quad \text{if } \lambda\mu = \frac{1}{2\pi}. \tag{135}$$

The function $F(u)$ is known as the *Fourier transform* of $f(x)$. The formulas become symmetrical if $\lambda = \mu = (1/\sqrt{2\pi})$, but it is often convenient to take $\lambda = 1$, or $\mu = 1$.

The equations (133), (134) and (135) hold if $f(x)$ is a complex function of a real variable, whose real and imaginary components satisfy the conditions previously imposed on the real function $f(x)$.

If the function $f(x)$ is real, the Fourier integral may be written:

$$\lim_{A \to \infty} \frac{1}{\pi} \int_{0}^{A} du \int_{-\infty}^{\infty} \cos u(x - t) f(t) \, dt = f(x), \tag{136}$$

since the imaginary part of the expression in equation (133) must be zero, and we may replace the integral from $-A$ to A by twice that from 0 to A since the first integral is an even function of u.

If $f(t)$ is real and even, we may take symmetrical intervals $-M$ to M in calculating the first integral, and so have:

$$\lim_{A \to \infty} \frac{2}{\pi} \int_{0}^{A} du \int_{0}^{\infty} \cos ux \cos ut \, f(t) \, dt = f(x). \tag{137}$$

This leads to the formulas for the transform of an even function:

$$F(u) = 2\lambda \int_{0}^{\infty} \cos ut \, f(t) \, dt, \tag{138}$$

and

$$f(x) = 2\mu \int_{0}^{\infty} \cos ux \, F(u) \, du, \quad \lambda\mu = \frac{1}{2\pi}. \tag{139}$$

Similarly, if $f(t)$ is real and odd, we find:

$$\lim_{A \to \infty} \frac{2}{\pi} \int_{0}^{A} du \int_{0}^{\infty} \sin ux \sin ut \, f(t) \, dt = f(x), \tag{140}$$

and for the transforms:

$$F(u) = -2\lambda i \int_{0}^{\infty} \sin ut \, f(t) \, dt, \tag{141}$$

$$f(x) = 2\mu i \int_{0}^{\infty} \sin ux \, F(u) \, du, \quad \lambda\mu = \frac{1}{2\pi}. \tag{142}$$

301. Convolution. If

$$h(x) = \int_{-\infty}^{\infty} f_1(y)f_2(x - y)\, dy, \tag{143}$$

the function $h(x)$ is called the *convolution** of the two functions $f_1(x)$ and $f_2(x)$. It is defined for any value of x for which the integral on the right converges.

If we reverse the rôles of $f_1(x)$ and $f_2(x)$ and make the change of variable

$$y = x - z, \quad z = x - y, \tag{144}$$

we find:

$$\int_{-\infty}^{\infty} f_2(y)f_1(x - y)\, dy = \int_{-\infty}^{\infty} f_2(x - z)f_1(z)\, dz = h(x), \tag{145}$$

since we may replace the dummy variable of integration z by y. This shows that the convolution of a pair of functions does not depend on which of them we consider $f_1(x)$ and which $f_2(x)$.

We may use equation (134) to define the Fourier transforms of each of the three functions $f_1(x), f_2(x), h(x)$. They are:

$$F_1(u) = \lambda \int_{-\infty}^{\infty} e^{-iut}f_1(t)\, dt, \; F_2(u) = \lambda \int_{-\infty}^{\infty} e^{-iut}f_2(t)\, dt, \tag{146}$$

$$H(u) = \lambda \int_{-\infty}^{\infty} e^{-iut}h(t)\, dt. \tag{147}$$

If the functions $f_1(x)$, $f_2(x)$ and $h(x)$ are all integrable and absolutely integrable over the range $-\infty$ to ∞, the integrals defining the transforms will all exist. Also, from the assumed convergence of the integral which defines the convolution, $h(x)$,

$$H(u) = \lim_{\substack{M' \to \infty \\ N' \to \infty}} \lim_{\substack{M \to \infty \\ N \to \infty}} \lambda \int_{-M'}^{N'} dt \int_{-M}^{N} e^{-iut}f_1(y)f_2(t - y)\, dy. \tag{148}$$

The integrand of this repeated integral has its numerical value

$$|e^{-iut}f_1(y)f_2(t - y)| = |f_1(y)f_2(t - y)|. \tag{149}$$

But, on putting $z = t - y, t = z + y$,

$$\int_{-M}^{N} dy \int_{-M'}^{N'} dt |f_1(y)f_2(t - y)| = \int_{-M}^{N} dy |f_1(y)| \int_{-M'-y}^{N'-y} dz |f_2(z)|$$

$$\leqq \int_{-\infty}^{\infty} |f_1(y)|\, dy \int_{-\infty}^{\infty} |f_2(z)|\, dz. \tag{150}$$

---

* Composition and the German " Faltung " are sometimes used.

Thus, by the remark made in section 244, the limit of the right member of equation (148) will be the same if we reverse the order of integration and let M', N' become infinite, before letting M, N become infinite. Also, on putting $z = t - y$, $t = z + y$,

$$\int_{-\infty}^{\infty} e^{-iut} f_2(t - y)\, dt = \int_{-\infty}^{\infty} e^{-iuz} e^{-iuy} f_2(z)\, dz, \qquad (151)$$

so that:

$$H(u) = \lim_{\substack{M \to \infty \\ N \to \infty}} \lambda \int_{-M}^{N} dy\, f_1(y) e^{-iuy} \int_{-\infty}^{\infty} e^{-iuz} f_2(z)\, dz$$

$$= \lambda \int_{-\infty}^{\infty} f_1(y) e^{-iuy}\, dy \int_{-\infty}^{\infty} f_2(z) e^{-iuz}\, dz$$

$$= \frac{1}{\lambda} F_1(u) F_2(u), \qquad (152)$$

in view of equation (146).

We note that if $h(x)$ is integrable over all finite ranges, $h(x)$ must be integrable from $-\infty$ to ∞, from equation (150) and the relation:

$$\int_{-M'}^{N'} |h(t)|\, dt \leqq \int_{-M'}^{N'} dt \int_{-\infty}^{\infty} dy\, |f_1(y) f_2(t - y)|. \qquad (153)$$

Thus we have proved that: *If $|f_1(x)|$ and $|f_2(x)|$ are integrable from $-\infty$ to ∞, while $f_1(x)$, $f_2(x)$ and their convolution $h(x)$ are integrable over all finite ranges, then the product of the Fourier transforms of $f_1(x)$ and $f_2(x)$, formed with constant λ, is λ times the transform of their convolution,*

$$F_1(u) F_2(u) = \lambda H(u). \qquad (154)$$

302. Functions of Integrable Square. It is desirable to have conditions on the functions $f_1(x)$ and $f_2(x)$ which insure the proper behavior of their convolution.

Let us assume first that the functions are $c_1(x)$ and $c_2(x)$, each continuous for all values of x and zero for $|x| > M$. Then the convolution of these functions is given by

$$h(x) = \int_{-\infty}^{\infty} c_1(y) c_2(x - y)\, dy = \int_{-M}^{M} c_1(y) c_2(x - y)\, dy, \qquad (155)$$

since the integrand is zero outside of this range. Then the integrand is a continuous function of the two variables x and y, for all values, so that the proper integral is a continuous function of x.

Next assume that each of our functions is integrable over all finite ranges, and each has a square absolutely integrable over the infinite interval. Thus

$$\int_{-\infty}^{\infty} |f_1(x)|^2\,dx \quad \text{and} \quad \int_{-\infty}^{\infty} |f_2(x)|^2\,dx \tag{156}$$

each exist.

Then we may choose M so large that the integral of $|f_1(x)|^2$ is less than ϵ, for the part of the infinite range with $|x| \geqq M$. Also, on the range $-M \leqq x \leqq M$ we may find a continuous function $c_1(x)$, zero for $x = -M$ and $x = M$, such that

$$\int_{-M}^{M} |f_1(x) - c_1(x)|^2\,dx < \epsilon, \tag{157}$$

by the construction used in section 297. If we define $c_1(x)$ as zero for $|x| > M$, we have a function of the type first referred to. We proceed similarly to find a function $c_2(x)$, continuous for all values of x, and zero for $|x| > M$ and such that

$$\int_{-M}^{M} |f_2(x) - c_2(x)|^2\,dx < \epsilon, \tag{158}$$

Next take a series of values of ϵ_n approaching zero. For each value we may find two functions $c_{1,n}(x)$ and $c_{2,n}(x)$. Then, as n becomes infinite, these give rise to two sequences of functions converging in the mean to $f_1(x)$ and $f_2(x)$. If $h_n(x)$ is the convolution of $c_{1,n}(x)$ and $c_{2,n}(x)$, it will be continuous for all values of x. But, from the convergence in the mean of $c_{1,n}(y)$ to $f_1(y)$ and $c_2(x - y)$ to $f_2(x - y)$ for fixed x, it follows from section 251 that $h_n(x)$ approaches $h(x)$, the convolution of $f_1(x)$ and $f_2(x)$. Moreover, since the integral

$$\int_{-\infty}^{\infty} |f_2(x - y) - c_{2,n}(x - y)|^2\,dy < \epsilon_n, \tag{159}$$

the argument used in section 251 shows that the function $h_n(x)$ approaches $h(x)$ uniformly in x, so that the limiting function $g(x)$ is continuous.

This proves that: *If $f_1(x)$ and $f_2(x)$ are each integrable over all finite ranges, while $|f_1(x)|^2$ and $|f_2(x)|^2$ are integrable from $-\infty$ to ∞, then $h(x)$, the convolution of $f_1(x)$ and $f_2(x)$ is continuous for all values of x.*

If, in addition, $|f_1(x)|$ and $|f_2(x)|$ are each integrable from $-\infty$ to ∞, the transforms of $f_1(x)$, $f_2(x)$ and $h(x)$ exist, with

$$F_1(u)F_2(u) = \lambda H(u). \tag{160}$$

The last remark follows from the results of the preceding section.

Note that, on the infinite range, we may have $|f(x)|^2$ integrable, without $|f(x)|$ integrable. An example is:

$$f(x) = 0, \ |x| < 1, \ f(x) = \frac{1}{x}, \ 1 < |x|. \tag{161}$$

303. Generalized Transforms. The restriction that our functions should be absolutely integrable or have absolutely integrable squares may be satisfied in certain cases by using in place of given functions, other functions obtained from them by multiplication by a factor. For example, if $f(x)e^{-kx^2}$ has a transform, $F_k(x)$, and when k approaches zero $F_k(x)$ approaches a limiting function, we might use this as a type of generalized transform of $f(x)$.

In one large class of applications, the functions are zero up to a certain point, and are either bounded, or at least dominated by a power of x for large positive values.

In such cases we may use e^{-kx} as a convergence factor. To be more specific, let

$$f(x) = 0, x < 0 \quad \text{and} \quad |f(x)| < e^{ax} \quad \text{for} \quad x > x_1, \ a > 0. \tag{162}$$

Let $f(x)$ be integrable on all finite ranges. Then the function

$$f(x)e^{-kx}, \quad \text{for} \quad k > a, \tag{163}$$

is integrable, and together with its square absolutely integrable from $-\infty$ to ∞. Consequently, it has a transform:

$$F_k(u) = \lambda \int_{-\infty}^{\infty} e^{-iut}f(t)e^{-kt} \, dt. \tag{164}$$

$$= \lambda \int_{0}^{\infty} e^{-iut}f(t)e^{-kt} \, dt. \tag{165}$$

We also note that, by equation (160), if $F_{k,1}(u)$ and $F_{k,2}(u)$ are the transforms of $f_1(x)e^{-kx}$ and $f_2(x)e^{-kx}$, then

$$\lambda H_k(u) = F_{k,1}(u)F_{k,2}(u), \tag{166}$$

where $H_k(u)$ is the transform of the convolution:

$$h_k(x) = \int_{-\infty}^{\infty} f_1(y)e^{-ky}f_2(x-y)e^{-k(x-y)} \, dy$$

$$= \int_{0}^{x} f_1(y)f_2(x-y)e^{-kx} \, dy = e^{-kx}h(x), \tag{167}$$

since the integrand is zero unless $0 \leqq y \leqq x$. It follows that $h_k(x)$ and $h(x)$ are 0 for $x < 0$.

Also, when the conditions of section 300 are satisfied,

$$f(x)e^{-kx} = \lim_{A \to \infty} \mu \int_{-A}^{A} e^{iux}F_k(u) \, du. \tag{168}$$

We shall now prove that if $z = k + iu$, $F_k(u)$ is an analytic function of z, for $k > a$. We begin with the special transform $C_k(u)$, obtained from a function $c(x)$ which is continuous for all values of x and is zero for $x < 0$, and $x > M$. Thus:

$$C_k(u) = \int_0^{\infty} e^{-iut}c(t)e^{-kt} \, dt = \int_0^{M} c(t)e^{-zt} \, dt. \tag{169}$$

This is analytic for all z, by section 275, since the integrand is analytic in z and continuous in z and t.

Next consider any function $f(x)$ satisfying the conditions (162), and any number $b > a$. Then we may approximate $f(x)e^{-bx}$ in the mean by a function $c(x)$, of the type just used, by the construction used in section 302. Furthermore, we may take a series of values of ϵ_n approaching zero, and for each ϵ_n determine a function $c_n(x)$ of the special type such that:

$$\int_0^{\infty} |f(x)e^{-bt} - c_n(x)|^2 \, dx < \epsilon_n. \tag{170}$$

Then the $c_n(t)$ converge in the mean to $f(t)e^{-bt}$. Also,

$$\int_0^{\infty} |e^{-iut-rt}|^2 \, dt = \int_0^{\infty} e^{-2rt} \, dt < \frac{1}{2s}, \quad \text{if} \quad r > s > 0,$$

so that $e^{-iut-rt}$ has a square absolutely integrable from 0 to ∞. Hence:

$$\int_0^{\infty} e^{-iut}c_n(t)e^{-rt} \, dt \text{ approaches } \int_0^{\infty} e^{-iut}f(t)e^{-bt}e^{-rt} \, dt, \tag{171}$$

uniformly in r for $r \geqq s$, by the reasoning of section 251. But each integral of the sequence has the form of that in equation (169), and so is an analytic function of $r + iu$. Hence, by section 273, the limiting integral is an analytic function of $r + iu$ in the two-dimensional open region $r > s$. But, if $k = b + r$, the limiting integral is that used to define $F_k(u)$ in equation (165). And an analytic function of $r + iu$ is an analytic function of $b + (r + iu)$ or $z = k + iu$. Moreover, for any number $k > a$, we may write:

$$s = \frac{k-a}{3}, \quad b = a + s, \quad r = 2s, \tag{172}$$

so that $F_k(u)$ is an analytic function of $z = k + iu$, for $k > a$, as we stated.

304. Laplace Transforms. When $f(x)$ is integrable on any finite range and satisfies the conditions:

$$f(x) = 0,\ x < 0 \quad \text{and} \quad |f(x)| < e^{ax} \quad \text{for} \quad x > x_1,\ a > 0, \quad (173)$$

we call the function defined by

$$L(p) = \int_0^\infty e^{-pt} f(t)\, dt \quad (174)$$

the *Laplace transform* of the function $f(x)$. It is analytic for all complex values of p with $\mathbf{R}p > a$, or

$$p = k + iu, \quad \text{with} \quad k > a, \quad (175)$$

as we proved at the end of the last section.

We note that $L(p)$ may be derived from $F_k(u)$ of equation (165) by putting $\lambda = 1$, and replacing $k + iu$ by p. For the convolution of the two functions $f_1(x)$ and $f_2(x)$, each 0 for $x < 0$, we have

$$h(x) = \int_0^x f_1(y) f_2(x - y)\, dy. \quad (176)$$

For the Laplace transform of $h(x)$, we find:

$$\int_0^\infty e^{-pt} h(t)\, dt = \int_0^\infty e^{-kt - iut} h(t)\, dt = \int_0^\infty e^{-iut} h_k(t)\, dt$$
$$= H_k(u) = L_1(p) L_2(p), \quad \lambda = 1, \quad (177)$$

by equations (167) and (166). Thus, for functions of the type here considered, *the Laplace transform of the convolution of two functions is the product of their Laplace transforms.*

We also note that if the function $f(x)$ has a derivative, $f'(x)$, which satisfies the conditions imposed on $f(x)$, then the Laplace transform of $f'(x)$ is

$$\int_0^\infty e^{-pt} f'(t)\, dt. \quad (178)$$

Since it has a derivative for all $x > 0$, $f(x)$ is continuous for such values and we may integrate by parts to obtain:

$$\int_0^M e^{-pt} f'(t)\, dt = e^{-pt} f(t) \Big|_0^M + \int_0^M p e^{-pt} f(t)\, dt. \quad (179)$$

By the condition (173), for values of p with $k > a$, the limit of the integrated part is zero for $M \to \infty$. Thus we find:

$$\int_0^\infty e^{-pt} f'(t)\, dt = f(0+) + p \int_0^\infty e^{-pt} f(t)\, dt. \quad (180)$$

If the derivative is continuous for $x = 0$, since it is zero for $x < 0$, we must have $f(0+) = 0$, and the Laplace transform of the derivative is the transform of the function multiplied by p. Otherwise the additional term appears.

This relation of differentiation to multiplication by a variable in the transform is the basis for the use of Laplace transforms in solving differential equations.

Before giving further details, we must find out in what sense the function is determined by the transform. For functions having a finite derivative at all except a finite number of isolated points, the equation (135), or (168) applies, except at the isolated points. For other values of x we have equation (168) with $\mu = 1/2\pi$ since $\lambda = 1$ and $\lambda\mu = 1/2\pi$. Hence:

$$f(x) = \lim_{A \to \infty} \frac{1}{2\pi} \int_{-A}^{A} e^{iux+kx} F_k(u) \, du$$

$$\lim_{A \to \infty} \frac{1}{2\pi} \int_{-A}^{A} e^{px} L(p) \, du. \tag{181}$$

Since $p = k + iu$, $dp = i \, du$, and this may be written:

$$f(x) = \lim_{A \to \infty} \frac{1}{2\pi i} \int_{k-iA}^{k+iA} e^{px} L(p) \, dp. \tag{182}$$

Thus, except at the isolated points, the function is determined by the value of the Laplace transform.

In the applications we shall make, the function will be smooth except perhaps for $x = 0$, so that except at this single value, the function will be determined by its transform.

305. Operational Solution of Differential Equations. Consider any linear differential equation with constant coefficients, which we write:

$$\sum_{k=0}^{n} a_k \frac{d^k y}{dx^k} = b(x). \tag{183}$$

Here the a_k are constants and b is a function of x. Suppose the initial conditions are that y and its derivatives up to the $(n-1)$st order are zero for $x = 0$. Suppose also that the problem has a solution which, together with its derivatives up to the nth order satisfies the conditions imposed on $f(x)$ in the last section. Let $b(x)$ also satisfy these conditions. Then we may take the transforms of both sides of the equation. From the choice of our initial conditions, the integrated term in equation (180) and the similar terms for the higher derivatives are all zero, and the transform of each derivative is obtained by multiplying the transform of the function by a suitable power of p. Thus we find:

$$\sum_{k=0}^{n} a_k p^k Y = B, \quad \text{or} \quad P(p)Y = B, \tag{184}$$

where Y is the Laplace transform of y and B is that of $b(x)$. Then we have:

$$Y = \frac{1}{P(p)} B = \sum_{k=1}^{n} \frac{A_k}{p - r_k} B, \tag{185}$$

where we have used a partial fraction decomposition of the rational function $1/P(p)$, and for simplicity only consider the case when all the roots are simple. For the multiple root case compare problems 50 and 51 of Exercises XIV.

Then, since

$$\int_0^{\infty} e^{rt} e^{-pt}\, dt = \frac{1}{p - r}, \quad \mathbf{R}p > \mathbf{R}r \tag{186}$$

we see that the fraction in the sum in equation (185) is the Laplace transform of $A_k e^{r_k x}$, and by the theorem on convolutions, the product of the fraction by B is the Laplace transform of the convolution of $A_k e^{r_1 x}$ and $b(x)$, or

$$\int_0^x b(y) A_k e^{r_1(x-y)}\, dy = A_k e^{r_1 x} \int_0^x b(y) e^{-r_1 y}\, dy. \tag{187}$$

The solution of the problem is the sum of terms of this form.

The Laplace transform may also be applied to certain partial differential equations with constant coefficients, reducing a problem originally containing partial derivatives with respect to two variables to a problem algebraic in one of the variables, and therefore capable of treatment as an ordinary differential equation in the other variable.

EXERCISES XIV

1. Show that the definite integrals of sines, cosines and their products used in section 287 may be derived from $\int_0^{2\pi} e^{imx} e^{inx}\, dx = 0$ if $m \neq -n$ and 2π if $m = -n$, where m and n are integral, and that this is equivalent to $\int_C z^{m+n-1}\, dz = 0$ if $m \neq -n$ and $2\pi i$ if $m = -n$, with C a circle with center at the origin.

2. If a series of the form (5) of section 287 converges to $f(x)$ either uniformly, or in the mean, then this series is the Fourier series for $f(x)$. In the uniform case, $f(x)$ is necessarily continuous, in the case of mean convergence we assume $f(x)$ and $|f(x)|^2$, implying $|f(x)|$, integrable over the fundamental interval.

3. If $f(x)$ and $|f(x)|$ are integrable over the fundamental interval, the Fourier coefficients exist and A_n and B_n each approach zero as $n \to \infty$. *Hint:* Use Riemann's theorem.

4. If for *all* values of x the *periodic* function $f(x)$ has a kth derivative, with $f^{(k)}(x)$ and $|f^{(k)}(x)|$ integrable over the fundamental interval, then $n^k A_n$ and $n^k B_n$ each approach zero as $n \to \infty$. *Hint:* Integrate the integrals defining the coefficients by parts k times, noting that the integrated part vanishes by the periodicity, and apply problem 3 to $f^k(x)$.

5. Show that if, for a particular x, the limit (56) of section 292 is zero for one positive δ, it is zero for all positive δ.

6. Show that

$$\frac{r \sin \theta}{1 - 2r \cos \theta + r^2} = \sum_{n=1}^{\infty} r^n \sin n\theta$$

and

$$\frac{1 - r \cos \theta}{1 - 2r \cos \theta + r^2} = 1 + \sum_{n=1}^{\infty} r^n \cos n\theta, \quad |r| < 1.$$

Hint: Use section 287, with $F(z) = 1/(1 - z)$.

7. Show that

$$\frac{1}{2} \log (1 - 2r \cos \theta + r^2) = - \sum_{n=1}^{\infty} \frac{r^n}{n} \cos n\theta$$

and

$$\tan^{-1} \left[\frac{r \sin \theta}{1 - r \cos \theta} \right] = \sum_{n=1}^{\infty} \frac{r^n}{n} \sin n\theta,$$

$|r| < 1$ and, for real r, θ, the inverse tangent between $-\pi/2$ and $\pi/2$. *Hint:* Use section 287, with $F(z) = \log(1 - z)$.

8. Let $f(x)$ have a Fourier series uniformly convergent for all real x in consequence of one of the conditions of section 294. If we replace x in the series by a complex variable z, the uniform convergence cannot hold in any two dimensional region including an interval of one period on the real axis in its interior, unless the periodic function $f(x)$ is analytic for all values of x.

9. For any fixed real or complex r with $|r| < 1$, and θ complex, the expansions of problems 6 and 7 are valid and converge uniformly for θ in some two dimensional strip of the complex plane including the real axis in its interior. A suitable branch of the inverse tangent must be used.

10. Show that

$$\frac{1}{2} \tan^{-1} \left[\frac{2r \sin \theta}{1 - r^2} \right] = \sum_{n=1}^{\infty} \frac{r^{2n-1}}{2n-1} \sin(2n-1)\theta,$$

$|r| < 1$, and, for real r, θ, the $\tan^{-1}$ between $-\pi/2$ and $\pi/2$. *Hint:* Use section 287, with $F(z) = \log (1 - z) - \log (1 + z)$.

11. The sine series of period $2p$ which represents $ax + b$ in the interval $0 < x < p$ is $\dfrac{1}{\pi} \displaystyle\sum_{n=1}^{\infty} P_n \sin \dfrac{n\pi x}{p}$ with $P_n = \dfrac{4b + 2ap}{n}$ for n odd, and $P_n = - \dfrac{2ap}{n}$

for n even.   *Hint:* First verify the special cases, for $0 < x < \pi$,

$$1 = \frac{4}{\pi}\left(\sin x + \frac{1}{3}\sin 3x + \frac{1}{5}\sin 5x + \cdots\right)$$

and

$$x = 2\left(\sin x - \frac{1}{2}\sin 2x + \frac{1}{3}\sin 3x + \cdots\right).$$

12. The cosine series of period $2p$ which represents $ax + b$ in the interval

$$0 \leqq x \leqq p \text{ is } b + \frac{ap}{2} - \frac{4ap}{\pi^2}\sum_{n=1}^{\infty}\frac{\cos\dfrac{(2n-1)\pi x}{p}}{(2n-1)^2}.$$

13. If $f(z)$ is single-valued and analytic in the ring $r_1 < |z| < r_2$, and $r_1 < r < r_2$ the Fourier series for $f(re^{i\theta})$, regarded as a periodic function of θ, may be obtained from the Laurent series for $f(z)$ described in problem 27 of Exercises XIII.

14. If $F(w)$ is of period $2p$ and analytic for all $w = u + iv$ with $|v| < h$, where $h > 0$, the Fourier series for $F(u)$ may be obtained by taking

$$f(z) = F\left(\frac{p \log z}{\pi i}\right)$$

and $r = 1$ in problem 13.

15. Illustrate problem 14 for $F(w) = \dfrac{1 - b^2}{1 - 2b\cos w + b^2}$, $|b| < 1$.

Here $p = \pi$, $r_1 = |b|$, $r_2 = 1/|b|$.   Hence

$$f(z) = \frac{(b^2 - 1)z}{bz^2 - (1 + b^2)z + b} = \frac{b}{z - b} + \frac{-\dfrac{1}{b}}{z - \dfrac{1}{b}} = 1 + \sum_{n=1}^{\infty} b^n(z^n + z^{-n}),$$

by problem 28 of Exercises XIII, and the series for $F(u)$ is $1 + \displaystyle\sum_{n=1}^{\infty} 2b^n \cos nu$. This checks with problems 6 and 9.   Whenever, as in problems 6, 7, and 10, the expansion can be found from a Taylor's series this is simpler than the procedure of problem 14.

16. Let $f(x)$ be of period $2p$, and $f(x)$ and $|f(x)|$ integrable over some interval of length $2p$.   Prove that formal termwise integration of the Fourier series for $f(x)$ yields a series which converges to the integral of $f(x)$ on any finite interval. *Hint:* By a change of scale we may take $p = \pi$.   The variation of $\displaystyle\int_a^x f(t)\,dt$ on any interval a,b is at most $\displaystyle\int_a^b |f(t)|\,dt$.   Also, the first integral increases by $2\pi A$ when x is increased by 2π.   Hence $g(x) = \displaystyle\int_a^x f(t)\,dt - Ax$ is periodic, continuous and of bounded variation so that its Fourier series converges to it for all values, in particular x and a. Subtracting these two series gives

$$\int_a^x f(t)\, dt - A(x - a) = \frac{1}{\pi} \sum_{n=1}^\infty \int_0^{2\pi} [\cos n(t - x) - \cos n(t - a)]\, g(t)\, dt.$$

But, since the Fourier series for $f(t)$ and $h(t) = f(t) - A$ only differ in the constant terms, we have $A_n \cos nx + B_n \sin nx = \dfrac{1}{\pi} \int_0^{2\pi} \cos n(t - x) h(t)\, dt.$ Integrate from a to x, and invert the order of integration to obtain

$$-\frac{1}{n\pi} \int_0^{2\pi} [\sin n(t - x) - \sin n(t - a)]\, h(t)\, dt.$$

An integration by parts (problem 27 of Exercises VIII) gives:

$$-\frac{1}{n\pi} [\sin n(t - x) - \sin n(t - a)]\, g(t) \,\Big|_0^{2\pi}$$

$$+ \frac{1}{\pi} \int_0^{2\pi} [\cos n(t - x) - \cos n(t - a)]\, g(t)\, dt.$$

The integrated part is zero by the periodicity, and the other part is one term of the series shown to equal the integral of $f(x)$ minus the integral of the constant term.

17. Show that, for $0 < x < \pi$,

$$\frac{\pi}{4} = \sin x + \frac{\sin 3x}{3} + \frac{\sin 5x}{5} + \frac{\sin 7x}{7} + \cdots,$$

$$-\frac{\pi x}{4} + \frac{\pi^2}{8} = \cos x + \frac{\cos 3x}{3^2} + \frac{\cos 5x}{5^2} + \cdots,$$

$$-\frac{\pi x^2}{8} + \frac{\pi^2 x}{8} = \sin x + \frac{\sin 3x}{3^3} + \frac{\sin 5x}{5^3} + \cdots.$$

Hint: Use problem 11 for the first series, and integration, valid by section 297 or problem 16, for the others. The constants are determined by equating the integral of the left member from 0 to π to zero, for the cosine series; and using the validity of the series at zero for the sine series.

18. Show that, for $0 < x < \pi$,

$$-\frac{x}{2} + \frac{\pi}{4} = \frac{\sin 2x}{2} + \frac{\sin 4x}{4} + \frac{\sin 6x}{6} + \cdots,$$

$$\frac{x^2}{4} - \frac{\pi x}{4} + \frac{\pi^2}{24} = \frac{\cos 2x}{2^2} + \frac{\cos 4x}{4^2} + \frac{\cos 6x}{6^2} + \cdots,$$

$$\frac{x^3}{12} - \frac{\pi x^2}{8} + \frac{\pi^2 x}{24} = \frac{\sin 2x}{2^3} + \frac{\sin 4x}{4^3} + \frac{\sin 6x}{6^3} + \cdots.$$

See hint to problem 17.

19. Let $f(x)$ be periodic and continuous, and such that $f(x) = \int_a^x \phi(x)\, dx$,
where $|\phi(x)|$ is integrable over any finite range. Then the Fourier series for $\phi(x)$ may be obtained from that for $f(x)$ by termwise differentiation. At any x where $\phi(x)$ satisfies one of the conditions of section 293, the series will converge to it. *Hint:* Use problem 16. Problems 17 and 18 furnish examples.

20. The series obtained by differentiating the first series of problem 17, or of problem 18, termwise, does not converge for any real value of x. *Hint:* Show that the terms do not approach zero, reasoning as for problem 23 of Exercises III. In each case, for x not a multiple of π, $f'(x)$ exists and is constant. However, in an interval including a discontinuity of the periodic function $f(x)$, $f(x)$ is not the integral of $f'(x)$, and the argument of problem 19 does not apply.

21. If $-\pi < x < \pi$, and $e^{ax} = A + \sum_{n=1}^{\infty} [A_n \cos nx + B_n \sin nx]$, by the method used for problem 17,

$$\frac{e^{ax}}{a} - \frac{A}{a} = Ax + \sum_{n=1}^{\infty} \frac{A_n \sin nx - B_n \cos nx}{n}.$$

Replacing Ax by $2A(\sin x - \sin 2x/2 + \sin 3x/3 - \cdots)$, found from problem 11, and comparing coefficients with the first relation determines A_n and B_n in terms of A. A may be directly calculated, so that, for $-\pi < x < \pi$:

$$e^{ax} = \frac{2 \sinh a\pi}{\pi} \left[\frac{1}{2a} + \sum_{n=1}^{\infty} (-1)^n \frac{a \cos nx - n \sin nx}{a^2 + n^2} \right].$$

22. Show that

$$\sinh ax = \frac{2 \sinh a\pi}{\pi} \left[\frac{\sin x}{1^2 + a^2} - \frac{2 \sin 2x}{2^2 + a^2} + \frac{3 \sin 3x}{3^2 + a^2} - \cdots \right]$$

and

$$\cosh ax = \frac{2a \sinh a\pi}{\pi} \left[\frac{1}{2a^2} - \frac{\cos x}{1^2 + a^2} + \frac{\cos 2x}{2^2 + a^2} - \frac{\cos 3x}{3^2 + a^2} + \cdots \right]$$

for $-\pi < x < \pi$. *Hint:* Use the result of problem 21.

23. Show that

$$\sin ax = \frac{2 \sin a\pi}{\pi} \left[\frac{\sin x}{1^2 - a^2} - \frac{2 \sin 2x}{2^2 - a^2} + \frac{3 \sin 3x}{3^2 - a^2} - \cdots \right]$$

and

$$\cos ax = \frac{2a \sin a\pi}{\pi} \left[\frac{1}{2a^2} + \frac{\cos x}{1^2 - a^2} - \frac{\cos 2x}{2^2 - a^2} + \frac{\cos 3x}{3^2 - a^2} - \cdots \right]$$

for $-\pi < x < \pi$. *Hint:* For x real and fixed, and a complex in a closed region of the plane excluding poles of the terms, the series of problem 22 converge uniformly and so are analytic functions of a. Hence they are valid for $a = bi$, b real.

24. Deduce the partial fraction expansions for $\csc z$ and $\cot z$ of section 284 from problem 23. *Hint:* Put $x = 0$, and $x = \pi$ in the second expansion, and $a = z/\pi$.

25. As an example where $f(x)$ is integrable, but unbounded, we have:

$$\log \left| \sin \frac{x}{2} \right| = -\log 2 - \frac{\cos x}{1} - \frac{\cos 2x}{2} - \frac{\cos 3x}{3} - \cdots$$

and

$$\log \left| \cos \frac{x}{2} \right| = -\log 2 + \frac{\cos x}{1} - \frac{\cos 2x}{2} + \frac{\cos 3x}{3} - \cdots,$$

for any x which makes the left member finite. *Hint:* By equations (27), (30) and (49) we find: $\dfrac{1}{\pi} \displaystyle\int_0^\pi \sin nu \cot \dfrac{u}{2}\, du = 1$. From this, by integrating by parts, $\dfrac{2}{\pi} \displaystyle\int_0^\pi \log \sin \dfrac{u}{2} \cos nu\, du = -\dfrac{1}{n}$. This shows that

$$\log \left| \sin \frac{x}{2} \right| = A - \sum_{n=1}^\infty \frac{\cos nx}{n}.$$

Replacing x by $\pi - x$, $\log \left| \cos \dfrac{x}{2} \right| = A + \displaystyle\sum_{n=1}^\infty (-1)^{n+1} \dfrac{\cos nx}{n}$. To determine A, put $2x$ in place of x in the first series, and deduce from $\log |\sin x| = \log 2 + \log |\sin x/2| + \log |\cos x/2|$ that $A = \log 2 + 2A$, or $A = -\log 2$.

26. Deduce from problem 25 that, when $\log |\tan x/2|$ is finite, $\log |\tan x/2| = -2 \left(\cos x/1 + \cos 3x/3 + \cos 5x/5 + \cdots \right)$. Hence, by the method of problem 17, show that for all x,

$$\int_0^x \log \left| \tan \frac{u}{2} \right| du = -2 \left[\frac{\sin x}{1^2} + \frac{\sin 3x}{3^2} + \frac{\sin 5x}{5^2} + \cdots \right]$$

and

$$\int_0^x dv \int_0^v \log \left| \tan \frac{u}{2} \right| du - \frac{1}{\pi} \int_0^\pi dw \int_0^w dv \int_0^v \log \left| \tan \frac{u}{2} \right| du =$$
$$2 \left[\frac{\cos x}{1^3} + \frac{\cos 3x}{3^3} + \frac{\cos 5x}{5^3} + \cdots \right].$$

27. Show that, if $f(x)$ and $|f(x)|$ are integrable over the fundamental interval, the Fourier series is summable $(C1)$ to $[f(x+) + f(x-)]/2$ at any point where these limits both exist. *Hint:* Use the reasoning of section 295, with the factor $[f(x + u) + f(x - u) - 2f(x)]$ replaced by the sum of $[f(x + u) - f(x+)]$ and $[f(x + u) - f(x-)]$.

28. By problem 11, the sine series equal to 1 for $0 < x < \pi$ is: $4/\pi$ ($\sin x/1 + \sin 3x/3 + \sin 5x/5 + \cdots$). Its sum is -1 for $-\pi < x < 0$, and 0 at 0, $-\pi$ and π. Let $m = 2n - 1$, and $S_m(x)$ be the sum to m terms. Show that, near zero, the approximating curves $S_m(x)$ tend to approximate the three line segments $y = -1$, $x < 0$, $y = 1$, $x > 0$ and $-K \leqq y \leqq K$, $x = 0$, where $K = \dfrac{2}{\pi} \displaystyle\int_0^\pi \dfrac{\sin t}{t}\, dt$, approximately 1.18. (Gronwall.) As this exceeds 1, the third segment extends beyond the other two. *Hint:* For the derivative, $\pi/4\, S'_m(x) = \cos x + \cos 3x + \cdots + \cos(2n-1)x = \sin 2nx/(2\sin x)$. Hence, for $0 < x < \pi/2$, $S_m(x)$ has a maximum for $2nx = \pi$, or an odd multiple of π. Moreover $S_m(x) = \dfrac{2}{\pi} \displaystyle\int_0^x \dfrac{\sin 2nx}{\sin x}\, dx$. Since $\sin x$ increases, by reasoning similar to that for equation (67) in section 293, the biggest maximum is at $x = \pi/2n$. Now interpret the sum for $S_m(\pi/2n)$ as a Riemann sum approximating the integral $\dfrac{2}{\pi} \displaystyle\int_0^\pi \dfrac{\sin t}{t}\, dt$, with $\Delta x = \pi/n$, and thus show that the limit as m, or $n \to \infty$ is the integral. The numerical value may be found by Simpson's rule, section 145, or by expanding $\sin t$ in a power series.

29. *Gibbs' phenomenon:* Let $f(x)$ be of bounded variation in some interval $x_0 - h$, $x_0 + h$, where x_0 is a point of discontinuity, so that $f(x_0-) \neq f(x_0+)$, but for $x_0 - h < x < x_0$ or $x_0 < x < x_0 + h$ let $f(x)$ be continuous. Assume also that $f(x)$ and $|f(x)|$ are integrable over the fundamental interval. Then the approximating curves of the Fourier partial sums, $S_n(x)$, near x_0, tend to approximate a graph made up of two continuous pieces representing $f(x)$ in the open intervals $x_0 - h < x < x_0$ and $x_0 < x < x_0 + h$, together with the segment obtained by extending that joining $x_0, f(x_0-)$ and $x_0, f(x_0+)$ equally in each direction to a length K times the original length. $K = \dfrac{2}{\pi} \displaystyle\int_0^\pi \dfrac{\sin t}{t}\, dt$, approximately 1.18. That the approximations tend to this *increased* segment is known as Gibbs' phenomenon. *Hint:* If $\phi(x)$ is the function of problem 28, the function $f(x) - \phi(x - x_0)[f(x_0+) - f(x_0-)]/2$ is continuous at x_0, and for $h_1 < h$ and $x_0 - h_1 < x < x_0 + h_1$, its Fourier series converges uniformly.

30. The behavior of the Fejér sums of the function of problem 28, for fixed x, is given by problem 27. Show that the Fejér sums for this function, $C_n(x)$, near zero tend to approximate the three line segments $y = -1$, $x < 0$; $y = 1$, $x > 0$ and $-1 \leqq y \leqq 1$, $x = 0$. *Hint:* As $C_n(x)$ is a weighted average of values of the function with a positive weighting factor, its values must lie between -1 and 1. The result then follows from problem 27, for fixed x near x_0, and the fact that $C_n(x)$ is continuous for all x.

31. The Fejér sums for the function $f(x)$ of problem 29 do not exhibit Gibbs' phenomenon, that is, the vertical segment is that joining $x_0, f(x_0-)$ and x_0, $f(x_0)$. *Hint:* Reason as in problem 29, using the property of $\phi(x)$ proved in problem 30.

32. Deduce the result of problem 45, Exercises XIII from problems 7 and 25. *Hint:* The constant term of problem 7 gives the integral for $|p| < 1$, those of problem 25 for $p = 1$ or -1; for $|p| > 1$, put $p = 1/q$ as in problem 45, Exercises XIII.

33. If $f(x)$ and $|f(x)|$ are integrable from 0 to 2π, A, A_n, and B_n are its Fourier coefficients, and $|r| < 1$,

$$A + \sum_{n=1}^{\infty} (A_n \cos n\theta + B_n \sin n\theta) r^n = \frac{1}{2\pi} \int_0^{2\pi} \frac{1 - r^2}{1 - 2r\cos(\theta - t) + r^2}\, f(t)\, dt.$$

Hint: The series of problem 15 converges uniformly for u real and any $|b| < 1$. Put $b = r$, $u = \theta - t$, multiply by $f(t)$, and integrate termwise.

34. If $f(x)$ is of period 2π, and continuous for all values, and r is real and less than 1,

$$\lim_{r \to 1-} \frac{1}{2\pi} \int_0^{2\pi} \frac{1 - r^2}{1 - 2r \cos(\theta - t) + r^2} f(t)\, dt = f(\theta).$$

Hint: Reason as in section 295, noting that the fraction multiplying $f(t)$ is positive, and its integral from 0 to 2π is 2π, by putting $f(t) = 1$ and $A = 1$, $A_n = B_n = 0$, in problem 33. And $|f(t) - f(\theta)| < \epsilon$ when $\cos(\theta - t) > 1 - \delta$.

35. Prove that for any particular θ for which the Fourier series for $f(\theta)$ converges to $g(\theta)$, the limit in problem 34 is $g(\theta)$. *Hint:* Use problem 33, and Abel's theorem of problem 15, Exercises XIII. An example is found by comparing problems 25 and 7.

36. If $f(x)$ and $|f(x)|$ are integrable from 0 to 2π, the limit in problem 34 is $[f(\theta+) + f(\theta-)]/2$, at any point where both limits exist. *Hint:* Reason as in problems 34 and 27.

37. The integral of problems 33, 34, 35 and 36 is called *Poisson's integral.* It enables us to find a function which satisfies Laplace's equation, problem 1 of Exercises XIII, inside the unit circle, and takes given values $f(\theta)$ on the boundary whenever the relation of problem 34 holds. *Hint:* With $z = x + iy = re^{i\theta}$, $(A_n \cos n\theta + B_n \sin n\theta)r^n$ is $\mathbf{R}(A_n z^n - iB_n z^n)$, so that by problem 33 the integral is the real part of an analytic function inside the circle.

38. If $S_n = u_1 + u_2 + \cdots + u_n$ is the partial sum to n terms of an infinite series which is summable $(C1)$, and $t_n = u_1 + 2u_2 + \cdots + nu_n$, a necessary and sufficient condition for the ordinary convergence of the series is that $t_n/n \to 0$. *Hint:* $t_n = (n + 1)S_n - nC_n$; $t_n/n \to \lim(S_n - C_n) = L - L$ if $\sum u_n$ is convergent. And $S_n \to \lim C_n$ if $t_n/n \to 0$.

39. A necessary and sufficient condition for any series $\sum u_n$ to be summable $(C1)$ is that $\sum \dfrac{t_n}{n(n + 1)}$, where $t_n = u_1 + 2u_2 + \cdots + nu_n$, be convergent. *Hint:* $t_n = (n + 1)S_n - nC_n$; $S_n = nC_n - (n - 1)C_{n-1}$ so that

$$\frac{t_n}{n(n + 1)} = \frac{n}{n + 1} C_n - \frac{n - 1}{n} C_{n-1} \quad \text{and} \quad \sum_{k=1}^{n} \frac{t_k}{k(k + 1)} = \frac{n}{n + 1} C_n.$$

40. If $\sum u_n$ is summable $(C1)$, and $u_n = O(1/n)$, then $\sum u_n$ is convergent. (Hardy.) *Hint:* If $\sum u_n$ is not convergent, by problem 38, t_n/n is either $> a$, or $< -a$ for an infinite number of values of n, say $n = m$, for some $a > 0$. In the second case, replace u_n by $-u_n$. Again $t_{n+1} = t_n + (n + 1)u_{n+1} > t_n - K$, for some positive K, and $n > n'$, by the definition of $u_n = O(1/n)$ in section 81. Hence, for any $m > n'$, $t_{m+k} > am/2$ if $0 \leq k \leq k'$, where $am/2K - 1 < k' \leq am/2K$.

Hence $\displaystyle\sum_{n=m}^{m+k'} \frac{t_n}{n(n + 1)} > \frac{am/2[(am/2K) - 1]}{(m + am/2K)^2}$. As this approaches a positive limit for $m \rightarrow \infty$, by the Cauchy criterion the series $\sum \dfrac{t_n}{n(n+1)}$ cannot converge. By problem 39 this contradicts the assumption that $\sum u_n$ is summable $(C1)$.

41. If $f(x)$ and $|f(x)|$ are integrable from 0 to 2π, and $A_n = O(1/n)$, $B_n = O(1/n)$, the Fourier series converges to $[f(x+) + f(x-)]/2$ at any point where both limits exist. *Hint:* Use problems 27 and 40. Some of the conditions of section 293 may be proved from this point of view if they hold over the entire interval.

42. An example of a continuous periodic function whose Fourier series fails to

converge for $x = 0$ is $f(x) = \displaystyle\sum_{n=1}^{\infty} \dfrac{1}{n^2} T(P_n, Q_n, x)$, where $P_n = n^{n^2}$,

$$Q_n = 2(P_1 + P_2 + \cdots + P_{n-1}),$$

and for integral P, Q,

$$T(P,Q,x) = \dfrac{\cos (Q+1)x}{2P-1} + \dfrac{\cos (Q+2)x}{2P-3} + \cdots + \dfrac{\cos (Q+P)x}{1}$$

$$- \dfrac{\cos (Q+P+1)x}{1} - \dfrac{\cos (Q+P+2)x}{3} - \cdots - \dfrac{\cos (Q+2P)x}{2P-1}. \quad \text{(Fejér)}$$

Hint: By grouping the terms with the same denominators,

$$T(P,Q,x) = 2 \sin\left(Q + P + \dfrac{1}{2}\right) x \sum_{k=1}^{P} \dfrac{\sin (2k-1)\dfrac{x}{2}}{2k-1}.$$

Hence, by problem 28, $T(P,Q,x)$ is bounded. Thus the series defining $f(x)$ converges uniformly, and $f(x)$ is continuous for all x. Also, the Fourier coefficients of $f(x)$ may be obtained from this by termwise integration, and the choice of P_n and Q_n is such that a term $\cos mx$ appears in only one $T(P_n, Q_n, x)$ and its coefficient, divided by n^2 will be A_n. A and all the B_n will be zero. Thus, when the T are decomposed, the series is the Fourier series for $f(x)$. But, at 0, the particular sum to $Q_n + P_n$ terms is $1/n^2[1/(2P_n - 1) + 1/(2P_n - 3) + \cdots + 1/3 + 1] >$ $(\log n)/2$, since $2[1 + 1/3 + 1/5 + \cdots + 1/(2P-1)] > 1 + 1/2 + 1/3 + \cdots$ $+ 1/P > \displaystyle\int_1^P \dfrac{dt}{t} \geqq \log P$, and $\log P_n = n^2 \log n$. Thus the Fourier series diverges at 0, since for one sequence of integers, $m = (Q_n + P_n) \rightarrow \infty$ as $n \rightarrow \infty$, the sums $S_m \rightarrow \infty$. Note that for $m' = Q_n$, $\lim S_{m'} = f(0) = 0$, so that removing parentheses renders a convergent series divergent, as remarked in section 187.

43. Using the definitions of P_n, Q_n and $T(P,Q,x)$ given in problem 42, show

that $F(x) = \displaystyle\sum_{n=1}^{\infty} \dfrac{1}{n^2} T(P_n, Q_n, n \, ! \, 2\pi x)$ is periodic with period 1, continuous for all

x, and has a Fourier series divergent for all rational values of x.

44. Verify that if $f(x) = c$, $a < x < b$ and $f(x) = 0$, $x < a$ or $x > b$, the Fourier transform $F(u) = \lambda c(e^{-iua} - e^{-iub})/iu$. Also that

$$\lim_{A \to \infty} \mu \int_{-A}^{A} e^{iux} F(u)\, du = \frac{c}{\pi} \int_{0}^{\infty} \left[\frac{\sin u(x - a)}{u} - \frac{\sin u(x - b)}{u} \right] du = \frac{c}{2}$$

if $x = a$ or b and otherwise equals $f(x)$. *Hint:* Use problem **31** of Exercises XII. $F(u)$ is replaced by zero. *Hint:* Use problem **31 of Exercises XII**.

45. If $f_1(x)$ and $f_2(x)$ are functions of the type defined in problem 44, using constants a, b, c and a', b', c', with $a < a' < b' < b$, calculate the convolution $h(x)$, and verify that its graph is polygonal, with vertices at $x = a + a'$, $a + b'$, $a' + b$, $b + b'$. And $h(x) = 0$ for $x < a + a'$ or $x > b + b'$.

46. If $F(u)$ is the transform of $f(x)$, and $a > 0$, then $(1/a)F(u/a)$ is the transform of $f(ax)$.

47. The transform of $f(x) = e^{-x^2}$ is $F(u) = \lambda\sqrt{\pi}e^{-u^2/4}$, and the transform of $f(x) = e^{-x^2/2}$ is $F(u) = \lambda\sqrt{2\pi}e^{-u^2/2}$. *Hint:* Use problem 46 of Exercises XIII.

48. For some pair of numbers a,b let $f(x)$ be the difference of two monotonic functions for $x \leq a$, and for $x \geq b$, where each monotonic function is integrable on the semi-infinite range $-\infty$, a or b,∞ on which it is defined. Let $f(x)$ be of bounded variation for $a \leq x \leq b$. Define $g(x) = [f(x+) + f(x-)]/2$, so that $f(x) = g(x)$ at all points of continuity and has the same transform $F(u) = G(u)$. Then:

$$\sum_{k=-\infty}^{\infty} g(2\pi k) = \mu \sum_{n=-\infty}^{\infty} F(n)$$

and

$$\sum_{n=-\infty}^{\infty} F\left(\frac{2\pi n}{a}\right) = a\lambda \sum_{k=-\infty}^{\infty} g(ak), \quad a > 0.$$

These formulas, and in particular the special case given in problem 49, are known as the *Poisson formula*. *Hint:* A monotonic function integrable on b, ∞ is either positive and decreasing to zero or negative and increasing to zero. Reversing the sign of the function converts the second case to the first, while reversing the sign of x reduces the range $-\infty$, a to $-a,\infty$. Hence, by section 192, the series $\sum_{k=-\infty}^{\infty} g(x + 2\pi k) = \phi(x)$ converges, for all x. From its form, the series is of period 2π. For x on any finite range, the convergence is uniform, and $\phi(x)$ is of bounded variation, since an infinite series of monotonic terms is monotonic, and a finite sum of functions of bounded variation is of bounded variation. Also $[\phi(x+) + \phi(x-)]/2 = \phi(x)$, since $g(x)$ has this property. Hence, by section 293 the Fourier series for $\phi(x)$ converges to it for all x. In particular, for $x = 0$,

$$\sum_{k=-\infty}^{\infty} g(2\pi k) = \phi(0) = \lim_{N \to \infty} \frac{1}{2\pi} \int_{-\pi}^{\pi} \left(1 + \sum_{n=1}^{N} 2 \cos nt\right) \phi(t)\, dt. \quad \text{Again, for}$$

n, an integer, $\dfrac{F(n)}{\lambda} = \dfrac{G(n)}{\lambda} = \displaystyle\int_{-\infty}^{\infty} g(t)e^{-int}\, dt = \sum_{k=-\infty}^{\infty} \int_{-\pi}^{\pi} g(t + 2\pi k)e^{-int}\, dt$

$= \displaystyle\int_{-\pi}^{\pi} \phi(t)e^{-int}\, dt$. Here the interval $-\infty,\infty$ is decomposed into intervals

$2\pi(k-1)$, $2\pi(k+1)$, the variable changed by $t_1 = t + 2\pi k$, and use made of $e^{-in(2\pi k)} = 1$, for n,k integral. The integration of $\phi(t)e^{-int}$ by termwise integration of the series is justified by the uniform convergence. Finally

$$\mu \sum_{n=-N}^{N} F(n) = \lambda\mu \sum_{n=-N}^{N} \int_{-\pi}^{\pi} \phi(t)e^{-int}\,dt = \frac{1}{2\pi}\int_{-\pi}^{\pi} \phi(t)\left(1 + \sum_{n=1}^{N'} 2\cos nt\right) dt.$$

Letting $N \to \infty$ and noting that the limit is that shown to be $\phi(0)$ gives the first relation. The second relation follows from the first by problem 46.

49. For x real and positive, and the square root positive:

$$\sum_{n=-\infty}^{\infty} e^{-n^2\pi x} = \frac{1}{\sqrt{x}} \sum_{n=-\infty}^{\infty} e^{-n^2\frac{\pi}{x}}$$

or

$$\frac{1}{2} + \sum_{n=1}^{\infty} e^{-n^2\pi x} = \frac{1}{\sqrt{x}}\left[\frac{1}{2} + \sum_{n=1}^{\infty} e^{-n^2\frac{\pi}{x}}\right].$$

Hint: Use the Poisson formula of problem 48, and problem 47. Whenever the functions are even, the double sums can be replaced by single sums as is done in the second form.

50. The Laplace transform of $\dfrac{x^k}{k\,!}\,e^{rx}$ is $\dfrac{1}{(p-r)^{k+1}}$, for $\mathbf{R}p > \mathbf{R}r$. *Hint:* Differentiate equation (186) of section 305 with respect to r k times.

51. Verify the relation of equation (182) for the Laplace transform of problem 50. *Hint:* Close the contour by a large semicircle of radius A to the left of the line joining $k - iA$ and $k + iA$, and calculate the residue at r. This is often the simplest method of finding the function which has a given $L(p)$ as its transform, even when $L(p)$ is rational. For the semicircle argue as in section 281.

52. Prove that the Laplace transform of $J_0(bx)$, where the Bessel's function is defined in problem 10 of Exercises XIII, is given by

$$\int_0^{\infty} e^{-pt} J_0(bt)\,dt = \frac{1}{\sqrt{p^2 + b^2}}, \quad \text{for} \quad \mathbf{R}p > b > 0.$$

Hint: Use problem 18 of Exercises XIII for p real.

CHAPTER XV

DIFFERENTIAL EQUATIONS

In this chapter we prove certain existence theorems for ordinary differential equations, as well as one for a special type of partial differential equation.

We also discuss certain theorems on envelopes, which are related to these existence theorems.

306. The First Order Analytic Equation. We begin by proving that:

There is a unique function $y(x)$, analytic for all values of the complex variable x sufficiently near x_0, $|x - x_0| < h$, and such that $y(x_0) = y_0$, which satisfies the first-order differential equation

$$\frac{dy}{dx} = f(x,y), \tag{1}$$

provided that the function $f(x,y)$ is an analytic function of the two complex variables x,y at x_0,y_0.

Since $f(x,y)$ is analytic, by section 286, it has an expansion:

$$f(x,y) = \sum_{k=0}^{\infty} \sum_{j=0}^{k} a_{j,k-j}(x - x_0)^j (y - y_0)^{k-j}, \tag{2}$$

convergent for all x and y such that $|x - x_0| < H$, $|y - y_0| < K$. To simplify the writing, we select H', $0 < H' < \min (H,K)$, and make the change of variable:

$$X = \frac{x - x_0}{H'}, \quad Y = \frac{y - y_0}{H'}. \tag{3}$$

This reduces the theorem to the case for which the initial values are 0,0 and the power series converges for all values numerically at most unity. Using the original notation for this case, we have to solve:

$$\frac{dy}{dx} = f(x,y); \quad y(0) = 0, \tag{4}$$

where

$$f(x,y) = a_{00} + a_{10}x + a_{01}y + a_{20}x^2 + a_{11}xy + a_{02}y^2 + \cdots. \tag{5}$$

If the problem has an analytic solution, we must have:

$$y = c_1 x + c_2 x^2 + c_3 x^3 + \cdots, \tag{6}$$

516

where the series has no constant term, since $y(0) = 0$. Inside any circle of uniform convergence for this series, we may differentiate termwise, so that:

$$\frac{dy}{dx} = c_1 + 2c_2 x + 3c_3 x^2 + 4c_4 x^3 + \cdots . \tag{7}$$

Again, for sufficiently small values of x, by the results of sections 274 and 286, the function of x defined by equations (5) and (6) will be analytic and have an expansion:

$$\begin{aligned}
f(x,y) = {}& a_{00} + a_{10}x + a_{01}(c_1 x + c_2 x^2 + c_3 x^3 + \cdots) + a_{20}x^2 \\
& + a_{11}(c_1 x^2 + c_2 x^3 + \cdots) + a_{02}(c_1^2 x^2 + 2c_1 c_2 x^3 + \cdots) \\
& + a_{30}x^3 + a_{21}(c_1 x^3 + \cdots) + a_{12}(c_1^2 x^3 + \cdots) \\
& + a_{03}(c_1^3 x^3 + \cdots) + \cdots . \tag{8}
\end{aligned}$$

By equating coefficients in the expansions (7) and (8), in accordance with equation (4), we find:

$$\begin{aligned}
c_1 &= a_{00}, \\
2c_2 &= a_{10} + a_{01}c_1, \\
3c_3 &= a_{01}c_2 + a_{20} + a_{11}c_1 + a_{02}c_1^2, \\
4c_4 &= a_{01}c_3 + a_{11}c_2 + 2a_{02}c_1 c_2 + a_{30} + a_{21}c_1 + a_{12}c_1^2 + a_{03}c_1^3. \tag{9}
\end{aligned}$$

These equations enable us to determine the coefficients, since at each stage the subscripts of the c_i on the right are less than that of the c_i in the left member. The c_i so determined will lead to an expansion (6) for a function which satisfies all the conditions in any region where it converges.

To show that the expansion so obtained does have a positive radius of convergence, we proceed as follows. From the choice of H', the series (5) converges absolutely for $x = 1, y = 1$. Hence the series

$$|a_{00}| + |a_{10}| + |a_{01}| + |a_{20}| + |a_{11}| + |a_{02}| + \cdots \tag{10}$$

converges. Thus the terms approach zero, and there is some point beyond which all are less than unity. Let M be a number greater than all the terms preceding this point, and also greater than unity. Then in the sense of numerical values of the terms, the series

$$M(1 + x + y + x^2 + xy + y^2 + \cdots) \tag{11}$$

dominates the series (5), since $|a_{ij}x^i y^j| < |Mx^i y^j|$. But this series is:

$$M(1 + x + x^2 + \cdots)(1 + y + y^2 + \cdots) = \frac{M}{(1 - x)(1 - y)}. \tag{12}$$

Now consider the differential equation

$$\frac{dy}{dx} = \frac{M}{(1-x)(1-y)},$$ (13)

which, by the procedure of section 134, may be written:

$$(1-y)\,dy = \frac{M\,dx}{(1-x)}.$$ (14)

This will be satisfied if:

$$y - \frac{y^2}{2} = -M \log (1-x) + K.$$ (15)

To make $y(0) = 0$, we must take $K = 0$, and use the root of the quadratic equation

$$y = 1 - \sqrt{1 + 2M \log (1-x)},$$ (16)

which makes the radical 1 when $x = 0$. Since the branch of the function (16) determined by these conditions is analytic for $x = 0$, it has a power series expansion

$$y = C_1 x + C_2 x^2 + C_3 x^3 + \cdots,$$ (17)

and $|y| < 1$ for sufficiently small values of x, say

$$|x| < h'.$$ (18)

Since the expansion (17) comes from an analytic function which solves the differential equation (13) with $y(0) = 0$, its coefficients will solve the equations obtained from (9) by replacing all the a_{ij} by M, and the c_i by C_i. Since all the algebraic signs in equations (9) are positive, we see that all the C_i will be positive. Moreover, since M exceeds all the $|a_{ij}|$, the first and hence all following C_i will exceed the $|c_i|$. Thus the series (6), with coefficients found from the equations (9) will be dominated by the series (17), and hence converge for $|x| < h'$.

This proves the existence of a solution, as stated. Since the coefficients were uniquely determined, there is no other analytic solution satisfying the initial conditions. By section 282 the expansion or any function obtained from it by analytic continuation will be a solution of the differential equation, provided that $f(x,y)$ remains analytic along the path of continuation.

307. Systems of Equations. A single differential equation of higher order than the first, say the nth,

$$y^{(n)} = f[x,y,y',y'', \cdots y^{(n-1)}]$$ (19)

is equivalent to a system of equations of the first order, obtained by writing:

$$y = u_1, \; y' = u_2, \; y'' = u_3, \; \cdots, \; y^{(n-1)} = u_n. \tag{20}$$

The system then is:

$$\frac{du_1}{dx} = u_2, \frac{du_2}{dx} = u_3, \; \cdots, \frac{du_{n-1}}{dx} = u_n,$$

and

$$\frac{du_n}{dx} = f(x, u_1, u_2, u_3, \cdots, u_n) . \tag{21}$$

A similar device may be used to reduce a system of p differential equations, of various orders, involving p independent variables to a system of equations of the first order, if certain algebraic conditions enabling us to solve for the highest derivatives of each variable are satisfied.

As initial conditions for the higher order case, we may prescribe the value of each variable, and its derivatives up to an order one less than the highest order which appears. For the system of the first order this corresponds to prescribing the initial value of each variable. A theorem similar to that of the preceding section may be proved for any system:

$$\frac{dy_k}{dx} = F_k(x, y_1, y_2, \cdots, y_n), \quad k = 1, 2, 3, \cdots, n. \tag{22}$$

If each of the n functions $F_k(x, y_i)$ is an analytic function of the $n + 1$ variables, there is a uniquely defined set of solutions, analytic for $|x - x_0| < h$, and such that $y_i(0) = y_{i,0}$. This theorem is proved by reasoning similar to that just given. We first make a change of variables of the form (3), here

$$X = \frac{x - x_0}{H'}, \quad Y_i = \frac{y_i - y_{i,0}}{H'}, \tag{23}$$

which reduces the problem to one in which the initial values are all zero, and the expansions for the functions $F_k(x, y_i)$ all converge absolutely for the values $x = y_i = 1$.

We then find formal series expansions which will represent the solution if they converge. These series are dominated by the series for the solution of the system:

$$\frac{dy_k}{dx} = \frac{M}{(1 - x) \displaystyle\prod_{i=1}^{n} (1 - y_i)} . \tag{24}$$

But this system may be solved, for the given initial values, by putting

$$y_i = y, \quad \text{where} \quad y(0) = 0,$$

and
$$\frac{dy}{dx} = \frac{M}{(1-x)(1-y)^n}. \tag{25}$$

A solution of this problem is found from
$$1 - (1-y)^{n+1} = -(n+1)M \log (1-x), \tag{26}$$
to be
$$y = 1 - [1 + (n+1)M \log (1-x)]^{\frac{1}{(n+1)}}. \tag{27}$$

This is analytic for the branch with $y = 0$ at $x = 0$, so that the formal expansions do have a positive radius of convergence.

308. Parameters. If the functions on the right for a single equation, or a system of equations, are not only analytic in the set of $n + 1$ variables x, y_i but also in the set of $n + k + 1$ variables x, y_i, p_j where the p_j are k parameters, then the solutions are analytic in the $k + 1$ variables x, p_j. For, if p is a parameter, we may introduce an additional variable with the conditions:
$$\frac{du}{dx} = 0, \quad u(x_0) = p. \tag{28}$$

These make $u(x) = p$ for all x, so that we may replace p wherever it occurs by u, and regard u as one of the variables.

Again, the solution remains analytic if we consider the initial values as variables. For on making the change of variables indicated by equations (3) or (23), the initial conditions become fixed, the functions in the differential equations are analytic in x, y_i, x_0, $y_{i,0}$ and the values x_0, y_0 or $y_{i,0}$ now appear as parameters, in which the functions are analytic.

309. The Continuous Case. If we consider only real functions of real variables, and merely require the functions on the right of equations (1) or (19) to be continuous, we may show that the problems previously considered admit continuous solutions. We proceed at once to the system:
$$\frac{dy_k}{dx} = f_k(x, y_1, y_2, \cdots, y_n), \ k = 1, 2, 3, \cdots, n. \tag{29}$$

As before, we may consider the problem reduced to the case where the initial conditions are $y_k(0) = 0$.

We begin with an approximate solution defined by
$$y_{k,h}(x) = 0, \ -h \le x \le 0$$
and
$$y_{k,h}(x) = \int_0^x f_k[t, y_{i,h}(t - h)] \, dt, \ x > 0. \tag{30}$$

With the notation here used, we assume the functions $f_k(x,y_i)$ are continuous in all $n + 1$ variables in some closed $n + 1$ dimensional region including the origin. From the definition, the functions $y_{k,h}$ are all continuous and so for sufficiently small values of x, say $|x| < H$, they will have values for which the integrand of equation (30) is in the region of continuity. For such values, the functions will all be bounded, say:

$$|f_k(x,y_i)| \leqq M. \tag{31}$$

Hence, for any two values of x, x_1 and x_2, with

$$0 < x_1 < H, \quad 0 < x_2 < H \tag{32}$$

we shall have:

$$|y_{k,h}(x_2) - y_{k,h}(x_1)| = \left| \int_{x_1}^{x_2} f_k[t, y_{i,h}(t - h)] \, dt \right|$$

$$\leqq M|x_2 - x_1|. \tag{33}$$

By taking an enumerable set of values of h decreasing to zero, for each value of k we obtain an enumerable set of functions. This set $y_{k,h}(x)$ is equi-continuous, by equation (33). Hence by the theorem of Ascoli proved in section 254 we may select a subset of these functions approaching a limiting function. By doing this for $k = 1$, then, using only the corresponding values of h in $y_{2,h}(x)$, and so on we may find an enumerable subset of values of h, say h_m such that:

$$\lim_{m \to \infty} y_{k,h_n}(x) = \bar{y}_k(x), \tag{34}$$

uniformly in x for all k. Thus the limiting functions will be continuous. Also, from the uniformity, and the fact that $h_n \to 0$, equation (30) implies that:

$$\bar{y}_k(x) = \int_0^x f_k[t,\bar{y}_i(t)] \, dt. \tag{35}$$

Since the integrand of this equation is a continuous function of t, we have:

$$\frac{d\bar{y}_k}{dx} = f_k[x,\bar{y}_i(x)], \tag{36}$$

while from the form of equation (35) we see that $\bar{y}_k(0) = 0$. Thus the existence of continuous functions which are solutions of our problem is established. A similar argument holds for $-H < x < 0$.

310. Uniqueness. If the functions are merely required to be continuous, there is not necessarily a unique continuous solution. For example, if we seek to solve

$$\frac{dy}{dx} = 3y^{\frac{2}{3}}, \quad \text{with} \quad y(0) = 0, \tag{37}$$

the solution found by the process of the preceding section is

$$y = 0. \tag{38}$$

However, the function

$$y = x^3 \tag{39}$$

or any of the functions:

$$y = (x + b)^3, \ x < -b < 0; \quad y = 0, \ -b < x < a;$$
$$y = (x - a)^3, \ 0 < a < x; \tag{40}$$

defined by a particular pair of positive numbers a and b are also continuous solutions of the problem.

If we require the functions $f_k(x, y_i)$, as functions of the y_i to satisfy a Lipschitz condition of the first order, or to have bounded partial derivatives with respect to the y_i, then the solution is necessarily unique, as we shall now prove.

For a function of k variables, the Lipschitz condition is

$$|f_k(x, y_i) - f_k(x, \bar{y}_i)| \leqq K \sum_{i=1}^{n} |y_i - \bar{y}_i|, \quad \text{for} \quad |y_i - \bar{y}_i| < h. \tag{41}$$

If this condition is satisfied for all the k, then for $|x| < L$,

$$\left| \int_0^x [f_k(x, y_i) - f_k(x, \bar{y}_k)] \, dx \right| \leqq LKn \max |y_i - \bar{y}_i|. \tag{42}$$

Now consider two solutions, y_k and $\bar{y}_k$ each of which satisfies the differential equations (36), and the initial conditions $y_k(0) = 0$. Then each of these satisfies the equations (35), so that by the relation (42),

$$|y_k(x) - \bar{y}_k(x)| \leqq LKn \max |y_i - \bar{y}_i|. \tag{43}$$

Now take $L_1 = 1/(2nK)$, and let Q be the maximum value of $|y_i - \bar{y}_i|$ for all x in the interval $|x| \leqq L_1$, and $i = 1, 2, \cdots, n$. Then we find from the equation just written

$$|y_k(x) - \bar{y}_k(x)| \leqq \frac{Q}{2} \quad \text{and hence} \quad 0 \leqq Q \leqq \frac{Q}{2}. \tag{44}$$

This proves that $Q = 0$, and the two solutions are identical in a finite interval including the initial point. Hence, for $|x| \leqq L_1$, the solution is uniquely determined.

311. Extension of the Solution. If the functions $f_k(x, y_i)$ are continuous in a closed region, R, and the minimum distance of the initial point to the boundary exceeds D, then as long as x and all the y_i do not differ by more than $D/\sqrt{n+1}$ from their initial values, the point will be in this region. Thus, if M in equations (31) and (33) exceeds unity, for $|x - x_0| < D/(M\sqrt{n+1})$ the argument of section 309 will give a solution. If, for $x_1 = x_0 + D/(M\sqrt{n+1})$ the values of $y_k(x_1)$ are such that the point is again at least a distance D from the boundary, the process may be repeated. Since R is closed, for some N any point with $|x - x_0| > ND$ will lie outside R. Thus the solution may not be extended in R for x increasing indefinitely, and there is a greatest x' such that, for $x_0 < x < x'$ the solution may be extended with $x,y_k(x)$ remaining in R. If we took a new region R' including R in its interior, and defined the $f_k(x,y_i)$ outside of R so as to be continuous in R', the solution could be extended in R' for x beyond x'. This shows that as $x \to x'$, the point x,y_k approaches a limiting point, necessarily on the boundary of R.

If the functions $f_k(x,y_i)$ are continuous in an open region, R_0, either the solutions may be extended for $x_0 < x < \infty$, or there is a greatest x' such that the solutions may be extended for $x_0 < x < x'$, where in each case the solutions are continuous and remain in R_0. As $x \to x'$, the point x,y_k need not approach a limiting point, but if it does this point cannot be in R_0, and must be a boundary point.

The extended solutions are unique if the Lipschitz condition holds for all points of some open region including all x,y_k of the solution.

Whenever the functions $f_k(x,y_i)$ are analytic in their arguments throughout a closed region R, they possess partial derivatives which are bounded in R. Hence the functions satisfy a Lipschitz condition and the continuous solution of the differential equation is unique. Consequently, at each point it must agree with the analytic solution shown to exist in section 307. In this case the continuous solution is analytic throughout its extension in R.

312. Differentiability. The argument of section 308 shows that if the functions $f_k(x,y_i)$ are continuous, the solutions are continuous functions of the initial values $x_0,y_{i,0}$. It also shows that if the functions contain any parameter, a, and the functions are continuous in the $n+2$ variables x, a and the y_k taken together, then there are solutions continuous in the parameter. Thus, if a Lipschitz condition is satisfied in all variables, this is the only solution, and the solution is continuous in the parameter.

We may apply this fact to prove that, if the functions $f_k(x,y_i)$ possess continuous partial derivatives with respect to all the variables, the solution is a differentiable function of x_0 and $y_{i,0}$. Since the solutions are continuous functions of x_0 and $y_{i,0}$, for a sufficiently small interval D, with $|\Delta x_0| < D$, $|\Delta y_0| < D$ and $|x - x_0| < D$, the solutions x,y_k for initial values $x_0,y_{k,0}$ and $x + \Delta x$, $y_k + \Delta y_k$ for initial conditions $x_0 + \Delta x_0$, $y_{k,0} + \Delta y_{k,0}$ will all lie inside R, the region of differentiability of the functions $f_k(x,y_i)$. In consequence of this, by the mean value theorem of section 215,

$$\Delta f_k = f_k(x + \Delta x, y_i + \Delta y_i) - f_k(x,y_i)$$

$$= \Delta x \left.\frac{\partial f_k}{\partial x}\right|_\theta + \sum_{i=1}^n \Delta y_i \left.\frac{\partial f_k}{\partial y_i}\right|_\theta , \qquad (45)$$

where $|_\theta$ indicates that the partial derivatives are to be evaluated at $x = x + \theta \Delta x, y_i = y_i + \theta \Delta y_i$, with a suitable value of θ, $0 < \theta < 1$.

Now let us temporarily confine ourselves to partial derivatives with respect to x_0. We write:

$$z_0 = \frac{\Delta x}{\Delta x_0} , \quad z_k = \frac{\Delta y_k}{\Delta x_0}, \qquad (46)$$

and form the equations:

$$\frac{dz_k}{dx} = \frac{\Delta f_k}{\Delta x_0} = z_0 \left.\frac{\partial f_k}{\partial x}\right|_\theta + \sum_{i=1}^n z_i \left.\frac{\partial f_k}{\partial y_i}\right|_\theta . \qquad (47)$$

For any value of $\Delta x_0 \neq 0$, we may consider equations (47), together with

$$\frac{dy_k}{dx} = f_k(x,y_i) \qquad (48)$$

as a system of equations, and find a solution with the initial conditions

$$x = x_0, \ y_k = y_{k,0}, \ z_0 = 1, \ z_k = 0. \qquad (49)$$

If, for $\Delta x_0 = 0$, we replace the system of equations (47) by

$$\frac{dZ_k}{dx} = Z_0 \frac{\partial f_k}{\partial x} + \sum_{i=1}^n Z_i \frac{\partial f_k}{\partial y_i}, \qquad (50)$$

where the partial derivatives are evaluated at x,y_k, we may regard the extended system as containing a parameter, Δx_0, and the right members as being continuous in the variables together with the parameter. Thus there is a solution such that:

$$\lim z_k = Z_k, \quad \text{when} \quad \Delta x_0 \to 0. \qquad (51)$$

But, for $\Delta x_0 \neq 0$, the solution of the system is unique, since the $f_k(x,y_i)$ possess continuous partial derivatives and hence for any fixed Δx_0, the functions $\Delta f_k/\Delta x_0$ satisfy a Lipschitz condition. And, for

$\Delta x_0 = 0$, the solution of the system is unique, since equations (48) have a unique solution, and since the partial derivatives of the $f_k(x,y_i)$ are bounded the right member of each equation (50) satisfies a Lipschitz condition in the Z_k.

Finally, we note from its construction, if x,y_k are the solutions of the original system of equations, (48), with initial values $x = x_0$, $y_k = y_{k,0}$, then the solutions of the extended system for $\Delta x_0 \neq 0$ are given by the equations (46). This proves that:

$$\lim_{x_0 \to 0} \frac{\Delta x}{\Delta x_0} = \lim z_0 = Z_0 \quad \text{and} \quad \lim_{x_0 \to 0} \frac{\Delta y_k}{\Delta x_0} = \lim z_k = Z_k. \quad (52)$$

Thus the partial derivatives $\partial x/\partial x_0$ and $\partial y_k/\partial x_0$ exist and satisfy the *equations of variation,*

$$\frac{d\left(\dfrac{\partial y_k}{\partial x_0}\right)}{dx} = \frac{\partial x}{\partial x_0}\frac{\partial f_k}{\partial x} + \sum_{i=1}^{n} \frac{\partial y_i}{\partial x_0}\frac{\partial f_k}{\partial y_i}, \quad (53)$$

formally obtained by differentiating the original equations partially with respect to x_0.

A similar argument proves that the partial derivatives with respect to $y_{k,0}$ exist and satisfy similar equations.

Also, by the device used in section 308, we may show that the solution may be differentiated with respect to a parameter, if the solutions have partial derivatives with respect to the variables and the parameter, continuous in all $n + 2$ variables.

313. Envelopes of Curves. Let the equation of a family of curves in a plane containing a parameter be

$$F(x,y,a) = 0, \quad (54)$$

and suppose the function possesses partial derivatives with respect to x,y and a of the first two orders, continuous in these variables. The derivative, or slope of the tangent for any one curve of the family will satisfy the equation:

$$F_x + F_y \frac{dy}{dx} = 0. \quad (55)$$

If, for a particular value of x,y,a which satisfies equation (54) we have:

$$F_a \neq 0, \quad (56)$$

we may, by the theorem on implicit functions of section 217, solve the equation for a in terms of x and y,

$$a = g(x,y), \quad (57)$$

for values of x and y sufficiently near this value, and insert this function in place of a in the partial derivatives of equation (55). Suppose further that, for the particular choice of x,y,a,

$$F_y(x,y,a) \quad \text{or} \quad F_y[x,y,g(x,y)] \neq 0. \tag{58}$$

Then we shall have:

$$\frac{dy}{dx} = -\frac{F_x[x,y,g(x,y)]}{F_y[x,y,g(x,y)]}. \tag{59}$$

Our assumptions about the second derivatives of F make the right member of this equation differentiable near the x,y considered. Hence this differential equation has a unique solution. But the equation (59) is the condition that a curve should be tangent at a point to the unique curve of the family through the point. Thus in this case the unique solution must be the curve of the family itself. Consequently, when the conditions stated hold, there can be no envelope.

If $F_y(x,y,a) = 0$, but $F_x(x,y,a) \neq 0$, we could reverse the rôles of x and y, and again show that there is no envelope.

Suppose next that the family of curves (54) has an envelope, or curve tangent at each of its points to the curve of the family through the point, which curve has a parameter a varying smoothly as we move along the envelope. Then we may take a as the parameter for the envelope, and write its parametric equations:

$$x = x(a), \quad y = y(a), \tag{60}$$

where each of these functions is differentiable.

Then, since the point x,y is on the curve of the family with the parameter a, we have:

$$F(x,y,a) = 0. \tag{61}$$

As this must be identically satisfied when the equations (60) hold, we find on differentiating with respect to a,

$$F_x \frac{dx}{da} + F_y \frac{dy}{da} + F_a = 0. \tag{62}$$

This equation shows that we cannot have

$$F_a \neq 0, \quad \text{and} \quad F_x = 0, \; F_y = 0. \tag{63}$$

It follows from our discussion that:

A necessary condition for the family of curves defined by

$$F(x,y,a) = 0, \tag{64}$$

where $F(x,y,a)$ is twice differentiable, to have an envelope, is that the points of the envelope satisfy

$$F_a(x,y,a) = 0, \tag{65}$$

as well as equation (64).

If, for values of x,y,a the Jacobian of the functions on the left in equations (64) and (65) with respect to x and y is different from zero, these equations may be solved in the form:

$$x = x(a), \quad y = y(a). \tag{66}$$

Also, since the function $F(x,y,a)$ is twice differentiable, the function $F_a(x,y,a)$ is differentiable, and the functions of equation (66) each have first derivatives. These satisfy:

$$F_x x'(a) + F_y y'(a) + F_a = 0,$$
$$F_{ax} x'(a) + F_{ay} y'(a) + F_{aa} = 0. \tag{67}$$

If the function $F_{aa} \neq 0$, it follows from the second equation that $x'(a)$ and $y'(a)$ are not both zero, so that the curve defined by equations (66) has a tangent whose direction ratio is that of these two numbers. And, by equation (65) and the first of equations (67) we have:

$$F_x x'(a) + F_y y'(a) = 0. \tag{68}$$

By our assumption on the Jacobian, F_x and F_y are not both zero for the particular x,y,a considered. Hence the equation

$$F_x \, dx + F_y \, dy = 0 \tag{69}$$

determines the direction ratio of the tangent to the curve of the family through the point considered, or equation (64) with a kept constant. A comparison of equations (68) and (69) shows that this ratio is the same as that for the curve (66).

The discussion shows that:

A sufficient condition for the family of curves defined by

$$F(x,y,a) = 0, \tag{70}$$

where $F(x,y,a)$ is twice differentiable, to have an envelope near a set of values x,y,a is that:

$$F(x,y,a) = 0, \quad F_a(x,y,a) = 0, \tag{71}$$

and

$$\frac{\partial(F,F_a)}{\partial(x,y)} = \begin{vmatrix} F_x & F_y \\ F_{ax} & F_{ay} \end{vmatrix} \neq 0, \quad F_{aa} \neq 0. \tag{72}$$

From the continuity of the derivatives, the conditions (72) hold throughout some interval including the given value of a, and the **first** condition insures that in a subinterval the pair of equations (71) have a solution which gives the envelope.

Note that there may be an envelope even when the sufficient conditions are not satisfied. Thus, if

$$(x - a)^4 + y^2 - 1 = 0, \tag{73}$$

the necessary condition for an envelope is

$$F_a = -4(x - a)^3 = 0, \quad \text{or} \quad x = a, \tag{74}$$

so that if there is an envelope it must be

$$y = 1, \quad \text{or} \quad -1. \tag{75}$$

These straight lines are in fact envelopes. However, the condition $F_{aa} \neq 0$ is not satisfied. We may dispense with this condition, which we used only to show that $x'(a)$ and $y'(a)$ were not both zero, whenever, as here, we can show this directly.

As a second example, consider:

$$(x - a)^2 - y^2 = 0. \tag{76}$$

Here

$$F_a = -2(x - a) = 0, \quad x = a, \quad \text{and} \quad y = 0 \tag{77}$$

is the only possibility. However, this is not an envelope. Here the Jacobian is $4y$, which is zero when the last of equations (77) holds.

314. Partial Differential Equations of the First Order. We wish to prove an existence theorem for a partial differential equation of the first order. We consider the case of one dependent and two independent variables. We shall reserve subscripts for other purposes, and use the abbreviations:

$$p = \frac{\partial z}{\partial x}, \; q = \frac{\partial z}{\partial y}, \; r = \frac{\partial^2 z}{\partial x^2}, \; s = \frac{\partial^2 z}{\partial x \partial y}, \; t = \frac{\partial^2 z}{\partial y^2}. \tag{78}$$

Then the partial differential equation we seek to solve is

$$F(x,y,z,p,q) = 0. \tag{79}$$

We assume that this function is twice differentiable.

We wish a solution containing the given curve:

$$x = x_0(u), \; y = y_0(u), \; z = z_0(u). \tag{80}$$

Suppose that we are given the values of p and q at one point of this curve, determined by $u = \bar{u}$,

$$\bar{x}_0, \bar{y}_0, \bar{z}_0, \bar{p}_0, \bar{q}_0 \quad \text{where} \quad F(\bar{x}_0, \bar{y}_0, \bar{z}_0, \bar{p}_0, \bar{q}_0) = 0. \tag{81}$$

Usually if one of these values is given, the equation will determine the other. In any case we have a pair satisfying this equation.

Since, for any point in a surface,

$$z = f(x,y), \quad dz = \frac{\partial f}{\partial x}\, dx + \frac{\partial f}{\partial y}\, dy, \tag{82}$$

and our solution must contain the curve (80), we must have

$$\frac{dz_0}{du} = p_0 \frac{dx_0}{du} + q_0 \frac{dy_0}{du}. \tag{83}$$

Also, if we regard the surface which represents the solution sought as given in terms of the parameters u and v, we shall have, for $v = 0$,

$$F(x_0,y_0,z_0,p_0,q_0) = 0. \tag{84}$$

The equations (83) and (84) can be solved for p_0 and q_0 in terms of u, for values near $\bar{p}_0, \bar{q}_0$, if the Jacobian:

$$\begin{vmatrix} P_0 & Q_0 \\ \dfrac{dx_0}{du} & \dfrac{dy_0}{du} \end{vmatrix} \neq 0, \tag{85}$$

where P and Q denote the partial derivatives of F with respect to p and q. If the condition (85) holds, equations (83) and (84) will determine functions:

$$p_0 = p_0(u) \quad \text{and} \quad q_0 = q_0(u), \tag{86}$$

which reduce to $\bar{p}_0$ and $\bar{q}_0$ for $u = \bar{u}$.

We shall now define the parameter v more precisely, by using the curves defined by

$$\frac{dx}{P} = \frac{dy}{Q} \tag{87}$$

as the projections on the x,y plane of the curves $u = $ constant, and introducing v by equating each of these to dv,

$$dv = \frac{dx}{P} = \frac{dy}{Q}. \tag{88}$$

From the relation

$$dz = p\, dx + q\, dy, \tag{89}$$

we find

$$dz = dv(pP + qQ) \quad \text{and} \quad \frac{dz}{pP + qQ} = dv, \tag{90}$$

the value of the fractions in equation (88).

Again, differentiating the function F partially with respect to x and y,

and using capital letters to denote the derivatives of F with respect to the corresponding small letters, as well as the abbreviations already defined in equation (78), we find:

$$X + pZ + rP + sQ = 0, \tag{91}$$

$$Y + qZ + sP + tQ = 0. \tag{92}$$

But,

$$dp = r\,dx + s\,dy, \quad dq = s\,dx + t\,dy \tag{93}$$

so that:

$$dp = (rP + sQ)\,dv = -(X + pZ)\,dv \quad \text{or} \quad \frac{dp}{-(X + pZ)} = dv, \tag{94}$$

and

$$dq = (sP + tQ)\,dv = -(Y + qZ)\,dv \quad \text{or} \quad \frac{dq}{-(Y + qZ)} = dv. \tag{95}$$

On combining equations (88), (90), (94) and (95) we find:

$$dv = \frac{dx}{P} = \frac{dy}{Q} = \frac{dz}{pP + qQ} = \frac{dp}{-(X + pZ)} = \frac{dq}{-(Y + qZ)} \cdot \tag{96}$$

This may be regarded as a system of five ordinary differential equations of the first order with v as the independent variable, namely,

$$\frac{dx}{dv} = P, \frac{dy}{dv} = Q, \frac{dz}{dv} = pP + qQ,$$

$$\frac{dp}{dv} = -X - pZ, \frac{dq}{dv} = -Y - qZ. \tag{97}$$

Let us now attempt to find a solution of equation (79), which includes the values given by equations (80) and (86). We proceed as follows: For any fixed value of u, the equations (80) and (86) will determine values of the five variables which we may associate with the value $v = 0$, and take as initial conditions for the system (97). Since the function F was twice differentiable, the right members of the equations (97) are differentiable, so that the system has a unique solution for these initial conditions in some restricted region. We now regard x,y,z,p,q as five dependent variables, unrelated except through the system (97). This determines five functions of the variable v for any fixed u, that is five functions of u and v. If the Jacobian of the first two functions with respect to u and v is distinct from zero, for any value of u and v, then

$$\frac{\partial(x,y)}{\partial(u,v)} = \begin{vmatrix} \dfrac{\partial x}{\partial u} & \dfrac{\partial x}{\partial v} \\[2mm] \dfrac{\partial y}{\partial u} & \dfrac{\partial y}{\partial v} \end{vmatrix} \neq 0, \tag{98}$$

and the first two equations

$$x = x(u,v), \quad y = y(u,v), \tag{99}$$

can be solved for u and v in terms of x and y in the neighborhood of the particular values. For $v = 0$, the Jacobian of equation (98) reduces to

$$\begin{vmatrix} \dfrac{dx_0}{du} & P_0 \\ \dfrac{dy_0}{du} & Q_0 \end{vmatrix} = - \begin{vmatrix} P_0 & Q_0 \\ \dfrac{dx_0}{du} & \dfrac{dy_0}{du} \end{vmatrix} \tag{100}$$

in view of the equations (80) and the first two of equations (97). This will be different from zero if the relation (85) holds. Hence for the values of u considered, and any value of v sufficiently near zero, the equations (99) have solutions of the form

$$u = u(x,y), \quad v = v(x,y). \tag{101}$$

Using these equations, and the equations that give z, p and q in terms of u and v, we may express z, p and q in terms of x and y. We wish to show that the first of these relations actually gives a solution of the equation (79).

We begin by showing that p and q, as determined here from the system (97) are actually equal to the partial derivatives of z. For the partial derivatives we have:

$$\frac{\partial z}{\partial v} = \frac{\partial z}{\partial x}\frac{\partial x}{\partial v} + \frac{\partial z}{\partial y}\frac{\partial y}{\partial v} \quad \text{and} \quad \frac{\partial z}{\partial u} = \frac{\partial z}{\partial x}\frac{\partial x}{\partial u} + \frac{\partial z}{\partial y}\frac{\partial y}{\partial u}. \tag{102}$$

Regarded as first degree equations in the partial derivatives $\partial z/\partial x$ and $\partial z/\partial y$, these determine the values uniquely, since the determinant of the coefficients is not zero, being the Jacobian of the relation (98). Thus we may identify these derivatives with p and q if we show that the same equations are satisfied by p and q.

Since we kept u constant in solving the system (97), the derivatives may be regarded as partial derivatives with respect to v, and from the first three equations (97) we find:

$$\frac{\partial z}{\partial v} = p\frac{\partial x}{\partial v} + q\frac{\partial y}{\partial v}, \tag{103}$$

which is identical in form with the first equation (102). We shall establish the analogue of the second equation by showing that the function

$$U(x,y,z) = p\frac{\partial x}{\partial u} + q\frac{\partial y}{\partial u} - \frac{\partial z}{\partial u} \tag{104}$$

is zero. By equation (83), $U = 0$ for $v = 0$. To show that it vanishes for other values, we differentiate with respect to v and use subscripts to denote differentiation in this part of the argument. Then:

$$U = px_u + qy_u - z_u, \tag{105}$$

$$U_v = px_{uv} + qy_{uv} + p_v x_u + q_v x_u - z_{uv}. \tag{106}$$

Since the equation (84) holds for $v = 0$, we may differentiate it partially with respect to u, and obtain:

$$F_u = Xx_u + Yy_u + Zz_u + Pp_u + Qq_u = 0. \tag{107}$$

We may also differentiate the equation (103) and obtain:

$$z_{uv} = px_{uv} + qy_{uv} + p_u x_v + q_u y_v. \tag{108}$$

By eliminating z_{uv} from equations (106) and (108) we find:

$$U_v = p_v x_u + q_v y_u - p_u x_v - q_u y_v. \tag{109}$$

We may eliminate x_v, y_v, p_v and q_v by using the equations

$$x_v = P, \; y_v = Q, \; p_v = -X - pZ, \; q_v = -Y - qZ, \tag{110}$$

of the system (97). The result is:

$$-U_v = (X + pZ)x_u + (Y + qZ)y_u + p_u P + q_u Q. \tag{111}$$

By equations (107) and (105) this may be written:

$$-U_v = pZx_u + qZy_u - Zz_u = ZU. \tag{112}$$

Consequently, for u fixed, regarded as a function of v alone, U satisfies the differential equation:

$$\frac{dU}{dv} = -ZU. \tag{113}$$

This has a unique solution which is zero for $v = 0$, namely $U = 0$. Since we know that $U = 0$ for $v = 0$ for all values of u considered, it follows that, for all the values of u and v considered,

$$U(x,y,z) = 0 \quad \text{and} \quad \frac{\partial z}{\partial u} = p\,\frac{\partial x}{\partial u} + q\,\frac{\partial y}{\partial u}. \tag{114}$$

Equations (103) and (114), together with (102) show that:

$$p = \frac{\partial z}{\partial u}, \quad \text{and} \quad q = \frac{\partial z}{\partial u}. \tag{115}$$

We must now show that the values of x, y, z, p and q, where the last two are now identified with $\partial z/\partial x$ and $\partial z/\partial y$, satisfy the relation $F = 0$, equation (79).   By equation (84) we already know that this is satisfied for $v = 0$.   And, if we differentiate F with respect to v, we find:

$$F_v = Xx_v + Yy_v + Zz_v + Pp_v + Qq_v. \tag{116}$$

Since the system (97) is satisfied,

$$x_v = P, y_v = Q, z_v = pP + qQ, p_v = -X - pZ, q_v = -Y - qZ, \tag{117}$$

and

$$F_v = XP + YQ + Z(pP + qQ) - P(X + pZ) - Q(Y + qZ) = 0. \tag{118}$$

Consequently, since $F = 0$ for $v = 0$, it is zero for all values of u and v considered.   Thus we have established the existence of a solution of the partial differential equation.

We may formulate the result in the theorem:

Let there be given a curve whose equation is:

$$x = x_0(u), \ y = y_0(u), \ z = z_0(u), \tag{119}$$

and along it two functions

$$p = p_0(u), \quad q = q_0(u), \tag{120}$$

such that

$$\frac{dz_0}{du} = p_0 \frac{dx_0}{du} + q_0 \frac{dy_0}{du} \tag{121}$$

and

$$F(x_0, y_0, z_0, p_0, q_0) = 0, \tag{122}$$

while

$$\begin{vmatrix} P_0 & Q_0 \\ \dfrac{dx_0}{du} & \dfrac{dy_0}{du} \end{vmatrix} \neq 0, \tag{123}$$

where $F(x,y,z,p,q)$ is a function of the five variables having continuous second partial derivatives, and capital letters denote first partial derivatives with respect to the small letters on the assumption that all five variables are independent.

Then the partial differential equation:

$$F\left(x, y, z, \frac{\partial z}{\partial x}, \frac{\partial z}{\partial y}\right) = 0 \tag{124}$$

has a unique solution

$$z = f(x,y), \tag{125}$$

for which

$$z_0 = f(x_0, y_0). \tag{126}$$

The solution may be expressed parametrically in terms of u, the parameter of the curve, and v, for sufficiently small values of v, by solving the system of ordinary differential equations:

$$\frac{dx}{P} = \frac{dy}{Q} = \frac{dz}{pP + qQ} = \frac{-dp}{X + pZ} = \frac{-dq}{Y + qZ} = dv. \qquad (127)$$

We note that the values of $p_0(u)$ and $q_0(u)$ along the curve are determined by their values at one point, by the conditions (121) and (122) in view of the condition (123).

315. Other Partial Differential Equations of the First Order. A similar theorem may be formulated and proved for a partial differential equation in more than two variables, say

$$x_1, \ x_2, \ \cdots, \ x_n, \ \text{with} \ \frac{\partial z}{\partial x_i} = p_i, \qquad (128)$$

so that the equation is:

$$F(z, x_i, p_i) = 0. \qquad (129)$$

In this case the auxiliary system of ordinary differential equations is:

$$dv = \frac{dx_i}{P_i} = \frac{dz}{\sum_{k=1}^{n} p_k P_k} = \frac{-dp_i}{X_i + p_i Z}, \quad i = 1, 2, \cdots, n \qquad (130)$$

to be solved for initial conditions $v = 0$, and

$$z_0(u_j), \ x_{i0}(u_j), \ p_{i0}(u_j), \ j = 1, 2, \cdots, n - 1. \qquad (131)$$

These values must be such that:

$$\frac{\partial z_0}{\partial u_j} = \sum_{i=1}^{n} p_i \frac{\partial x_{i0}}{\partial u_j}, \quad j = 1, 2, \cdots, n - 1 \qquad (132)$$

and

$$F(z_0, x_{i0}, p_{i0}) = 0. \qquad (133)$$

The condition that insures the existence of a solution is the non-vanishing of the determinant:

$$\begin{vmatrix} P_1 & P_2 & \cdots & P_n \\ \dfrac{\partial x_{10}}{\partial u_1} & \dfrac{\partial x_{20}}{\partial u_1} & \cdots & \dfrac{\partial x_{n0}}{\partial u_1} \\ \cdot & \cdot & & \cdot \\ \cdot & \cdot & & \cdot \\ \cdot & \cdot & & \cdot \\ \dfrac{\partial x_{10}}{\partial u_{n-1}} & \dfrac{\partial x_{20}}{\partial u_{n-1}} & \cdots & \dfrac{\partial x_{n0}}{\partial u_{n-1}} \end{vmatrix} \neq 0. \qquad (134)$$

This enables us, by reasoning similar to that for the two variable case, to identify the p_i obtained from the system (130) with the derivatives $\partial z/\partial x_i$. It is then possible to prove as before that the equation (129) is satisfied.

In view of the equations (132) and (133), and the condition (134), the values of $p_{i0}(u_j)$ are determined by their values for a particular set of $u_j, \bar{u}_1, \bar{u}_2, \cdots, \bar{u}_{n-1}$.

When the function F contains the derivatives p_i only in terms of the first degree, the equation $F = 0$ may be written

$$\sum_{i=1}^{n} A_i(z,x_k)\,\frac{\partial z}{\partial x_i} = C(z,x_k), \tag{135}$$

where A_i and C are functions of z and the n x_k. Since

$$F = \sum_{i=1}^{n} A_i p_i - C; \quad P_i = A_i \quad \text{and} \quad \sum_{i=1}^{n} p_i P_i = C + F. \tag{136}$$

As the solutions of the system (130) which we seek make $F = 0$, they satisfy:

$$dv = \frac{dx_i}{P_i} = \frac{dz}{C}, \quad i = 1, 2, \cdots, n. \tag{137}$$

Since the p_i do not occur in this set of equations, the remaining terms in equation (130) may be omitted, and we may use the simplified system (137) instead of (130) for the special equation (135).

316. Envelopes of Surfaces. Let the equation of a family of surfaces in space, containing a parameter, be

$$f(x,y,z,a) = 0, \tag{138}$$

and suppose that the function possesses partial derivatives with respect to all four variables of the first three orders. Then the partial derivatives as determined from this relation will satisfy:

$$f_x p + f_y q + \frac{f_x^2 + f_y^2}{f_z} = 0, \quad f_z \neq 0. \tag{139}$$

Suppose that for a particular set of values of x,y,z and a for which equation (138) holds, the derivative

$$f_a(x,y,z,a) \neq 0. \tag{140}$$

Then we may solve the equation (138) for a in terms of x, y and z for values near the particular set, and by substituting in the equation (139), obtain an equation:

$$A(x,y,z)p + B(x,y,z)q - C(x,y,z) = 0. \tag{141}$$

Now consider a curve:

$$x = x_0(u), \quad y = y_0(u), \quad z = z_0(u) \tag{142}$$

which lies on the surface of the family with $a = a_0$,

$$f(x,y,z,a_0) = 0. \tag{143}$$

This equation will determine a value of p and q, $p_0(u)$ and $q_0(u)$, for each point of the curve. These values will satisfy:

$$\frac{dz_0}{du} = p_0 \frac{dx_0}{du} + q_0 \frac{dy_0}{du} \quad \text{and} \quad A_0 p_0 + B_0 q_0 - C_0 = 0, \tag{144}$$

where $A_0 = A(x_0,y_0,z_0)$, and similarly for B_0 and C_0.

If, further,

$$\begin{vmatrix} A_0 & B_0 \\ \dfrac{dx_0}{du} & \dfrac{dy_0}{du} \end{vmatrix} \neq 0, \quad \text{or} \quad \frac{dx}{du}\Big/ f_x \Big|_0 \neq \frac{dy}{du}\Big/ f_y \Big|_0, \tag{145}$$

the partial differential equation (141) will have a unique solution for the initial values x_0, y_0, z_0, p_0, q_0, which must be the surface given by equation (143), since this is such a solution. Thus there can be no envelope through a curve of the type described.

Since the problem of an envelope is geometrical, the axes may be permuted, and the curve (142) can only lie on an envelope if

$$\frac{dx}{du}\Big/ f_x = \frac{dy}{du}\Big/ f_y = \frac{dz}{du}\Big/ f_z. \tag{146}$$

But, since the curve lies on the surface given by equation (143), we may differentiate this relation with respect to u to obtain:

$$f_x \frac{dx}{du} + f_y \frac{dy}{du} + f_z \frac{dz}{du} = 0. \tag{147}$$

It follows from the last two equations that:

$$f_x^2 + f_y^2 + f_z^2 = 0. \tag{148}$$

For real functions, this implies

$$f_x = f_y = f_z = 0, \tag{149}$$

so that the surface (143) can not have a uniquely defined tangent plane. If we exclude this case, we have shown that there can be no envelope whenever the condition (140) holds.

The discussion shows that:

A necessary condition for the family of surfaces

$$f(x,y,z,a) = 0 \tag{150}$$

to have an envelope is that

$$f_a(x,y,z,a) = 0, \tag{151}$$

if the function $f(x,y,z,a)$ has continuous partial derivatives of the first three orders, and the equation (150) determines a unique tangent plane at the points of contact.

We shall now prove the following result:

If, for a particular set of values of x,y,z,a, satisfying the equations (150) and (151), we have:

$$f_{aa} \neq 0, \tag{152}$$

and some one of the Jacobians:

$$\frac{\partial(f,f_a)}{\partial(y,z)}, \frac{\partial(f,f_a)}{\partial(z,x)}, \frac{\partial(f,f_a)}{\partial(x,y)}, \tag{153}$$

is distinct from zero, there will be an envelope near the particular set of values considered.

For example, suppose that

$$\frac{\partial(f,f_a)}{\partial(y,z)} \neq 0. \tag{154}$$

Then, in the neighborhood of the particular set of values, we may solve the equations (150) and (151) for y and z in terms of x and a:

$$y = y(x,a) \quad \text{and} \quad z = z(x,a). \tag{155}$$

These equations determine a surface. A direction in the tangent plane to this surface will satisfy the equations obtained by differentiating equations (150) and (151) partially with respect to x and a, namely,

$$f_x + f_y y_x + f_z z_x = 0, \quad f_{ax} + f_{ay} y_x + f_{az} z_x = 0, \tag{156}$$

and

$$f_a + f_y y_a + f_z z_a = 0, \quad f_{aa} + f_{ay} y_a + f_{az} z_a = 0. \tag{157}$$

From the condition (154), these equations determine unique values of $y_x, z_x; y_a, z_a$. These give rise to directions in the tangent plane:

$$\frac{dx}{1} = \frac{dy}{y_x} = \frac{dz}{z_x}, \quad \text{and} \quad \frac{dx}{0} = \frac{dy}{y_a} = \frac{dz}{z_a}. \tag{158}$$

The first does not have all its components zero, because of the 1. The second does not have all its components zero, because of the condition that $f_{aa} \neq 0$, and the last equation (157).

These two directions, distinct because of the first components 0 and 1, determine uniquely the tangent plane to the surface given by equation (155). Again, by the condition (154), f_y and f_z can not both be zero, so that the surface given by equation (150) for a fixed value of a has a tangent plane, whose normal direction is

$$f_x, f_y, f_z. \tag{159}$$

The first direction (158) lies in this plane because of the first equation (156). And, in view of equation (151), the first equation (157) may be written:

$$f_x \cdot 0 + f_y y_a + f_z z_a = 0. \tag{160}$$

This shows that the second direction also lies in this plane. Consequently, for a given a and x, determining y and z by equations (155), the surfaces (155) and (150) have the same tangent plane at x,y,z. For a given a the surfaces have only a curve in common, so that they are distinct.

This proves that, under the conditions stated there is an envelope, obtainable from equations (150) and (151).

317. Complete Integrals. Let

$$F(x,y,z,p,q) = 0 \tag{161}$$

be a first-order partial differential equation, and let $f(x,y,z,a,b)$ be a function containing two independent parameters a and b. Then if, for each value of a and b in a restricted range,

$$f(x,y,z,a,b) = 0, \tag{162}$$

defines a particular solution of the partial differential equation (161), the relation (162) is called a *complete integral* of the equation.

If we regard b as a function of a,

$$b = g(a), \tag{163}$$

and if the conditions of the preceding section are met for the family:

$$f[x,y,z,a,g(a)] = 0, \tag{164}$$

then this family of surfaces will have an envelope given by

$$f_a + f_b g'(a) = 0, \tag{165}$$

combined with equation (164). Since this envelope, at each of its points, has the same value of x,y,z,p,q as one of the surfaces of the family (162), these values satisfy the equation (161), and the envelope is a solution of the differential equation.

In a limited region, the differential equation (161) may be thought of as determining at each point of space a set of values of p and q depending on one parameter, or a family of tangent planes enveloping a cone. In the process of section 314 we started out with a curve, associated at each of its points with a tangent plane touching a cone for that point. We chose this curve so that:

$$\begin{vmatrix} P & Q \\ \dfrac{\partial x}{\partial u} & \dfrac{\partial y}{\partial u} \end{vmatrix} \neq 0 \quad \text{or} \quad \dfrac{\dfrac{\partial x}{\partial u}}{P} \neq \dfrac{\dfrac{\partial y}{\partial u}}{Q}. \tag{166}$$

We then used this curve as the initial points of curves such that

$$\dfrac{\dfrac{\partial x}{\partial v}}{P} = \dfrac{\dfrac{\partial y}{\partial v}}{Q} = \dfrac{\dfrac{\partial z}{\partial v}}{pP + qQ}. \tag{167}$$

These latter curves are called the *characteristic curves* of the partial differential equation. The condition (166) on the initial curve is, essentially, that it should not be tangent to a characteristic curve. A characteristic curve, with its tangent planes, given by equation (97), is called a characteristic strip. Two solutions which are tangent along a curve not a characteristic curve at any of its points, must coincide, since such a curve may be taken as an initial curve. However, by varying the initial curve, but keeping one point and the tangent plane there fixed, we may obtain several solutions tangent along the same characteristic curve, or having a characteristic strip in common. Thus the characteristic curves may be distinguished as the curves where distinct solutions may be tangent.

But the surface given by equation (164) for a fixed a, and its envelope are two solutions of the differential equation tangent along the curve where equations (164) and (165) both hold. Consequently, this curve is a characteristic curve. Thus the surfaces given by equation (162) are built up of characteristic strips, and the process of taking the envelope amounts to recombining these characteristic strips to form new surfaces.

As an example, consider the partial differential equation:

$$\dfrac{p^2}{2} + \dfrac{q^2}{2} - z = 0. \tag{168}$$

Here the equations (97), or (127) become:

$$dv = \dfrac{dx}{p} = \dfrac{dy}{q} = \dfrac{dz}{p^2 + q^2} = \dfrac{dp}{p} = \dfrac{dq}{q}. \tag{169}$$

The solution in terms of initial values is:

$$p = p_0 e^v, \quad q = q_0 e^v, \quad x - x_0 = p_0(e^v - 1),$$
$$y - y_0 = q_0(e^v - 1), \quad z - z_0 = \tfrac{1}{2}(p_0^2 + q_0^2)(e^{2v} - 1). \tag{170}$$

Since the initial conditions must satisfy

$$z_0 = \tfrac{1}{2}(p_0^2 + q_0^2), \tag{171}$$

the characteristic curves are given parametrically by

$$x - x_0 + p_0 = p_0 e^v, \quad y - y_0 + q_0 = q_0 e^v, \quad z = z_0 e^{2v}. \tag{172}$$

The curves are parabolas lying in vertical planes.

The family

$$2z = (x - a)^2 + (y - b)^2$$

is seen to be a complete integral of the equation.

EXERCISES XV

1. If $f(x,y)$ is analytic in the two variables, $f(x_0,y_0) = 0$, and $\partial f/\partial y \neq 0$ at x_0,y_0, the implicit function $y = g(x)$ with $y_0 = g(x_0)$ defined by $f(x,y) = 0$ is analytic. *Hint:* It satisfies the differential equation $dy/dx = -f_x/f_y$, whose right member is analytic.

2. If the given functions are analytic, the implicit functions shown to exist in sections 217 and 218 are analytic. *Hint:* For $f(y,x_i) = 0$, the function is analytic in each x_i separately by problem 1, and continuous by section 217. For a system, the argument by induction proceeds as in section 218, with the added condition of analyticity.

3. A *separable* equation, $dy/dx = A(x)B(y)$ has a solution given by $\int_a^x A(x)\, dx = \int_b^y \dfrac{dy}{B(y)}$, with $y = b$ when $x = a$. This solution is unique if $A(x)$ and $B(y)$ are each continuous and of fixed sign, never zero. Compare section 134.

4. If in problem 3 $B(b) = 0$, the other conditions as before, the expression gives a solution if the integral of $1/B(y)$ exists. However, $y = b$ gives a second solution. Show that $B(y)$ does not satisfy a Lipschitz condition. *Hint:* Use section 310, or more directly note that if $|B(y) - B(b)| < K|y - b|$, since $B(b) = 0$, $1/|B(y)| > 1/[K|y - b|]$, and since $B(y)$ is of fixed sign, $1/B(y)$ is not integrable.

5. If $f(x,y)$ is homogeneous of degree zero in x and y, the equation $dy/dx = f(x,y)$ becomes separable (problem 3) if y is replaced by v where $y = vx$. *Hint:* $f(x,vx) = x^0 f(1,v) = f(1,v)$ and $dy/dx = x\, dv/dx + v$.

6. Show that $\dfrac{d}{dx}\left[\dfrac{y''^2}{(1 + y'^2)^3}\right] = 0$ is the differential equation of all circles in the plane. For the corresponding equations for parabolas and conics, see problems 13 and 14 of Exercises IV. *Hint:* Deduce successively:

$$y''(1 + y'^2)^{-3/2} = r^{-1}, \quad y'(1 + y'^2)^{-1/2} = (x - a)/r,$$
$$y' = (x - a)[r^2 - (x - a)^2]^{-1/2}, \quad (x - a)^2 + (y - b)^2 = r^2.$$

7. Prove that the evolute of a curve (see problem 12 of Exercises VIII) is the envelope of its normals.

8. Any plane curve is the envelope of its circles of curvature. It is *not* the locus of limiting real points of intersection, since along an arc where the radius of curvature increases, no two circles of curvature intersect! *Hint:* By problem 12 of Exercises VIII, the difference of the two radii equals the arc along the evolute between centers, and hence exceeds the chord joining the two centers.

9. If the family of curves obtained by solving a first order differential equation for different initial conditions has an envelope, this will be a solution. It is called a *singular* solution.

10. Let $G(c,x,y) = 0$ define a family of solutions of a differential equation $F(p,x,y) = 0$, $p = dy/dx$. Assume that the functions G and F are each twice differentiable in all three variables. If there is a singular solution, problem 9, it will satisfy $G(c,x,y) = 0$ and $G_c(c,x,y) = 0$, or the equation $C(x,y) = 0$ obtained by eliminating c. It will also satisfy the equation $P(x,y) = 0$, obtained by eliminating p between $F(p,x,y) = 0$ and $F_p(p,x,y) = 0$. This gives a practical method of finding possible singular solutions by testing those factors of the c-discriminant, $C(x,y)$, or the p-discriminant, $P(x,y)$ which equated to zero give solutions. *Hint:* Use section 313 and problem 9 for the c-discriminant. The other result follows from the fact that if $\partial F/\partial p \neq 0$, there is a unique differentiable function $p = f(x,y)$ with $p_0 = f(x_0,y_0)$ and such that $F(f,x,y) = 0$. Thus the solution is unique, and there is no singular solution.

11. As an example of problem 10, let $G(c,x,y) = y^{n-1} - \left[\dfrac{n-1}{n}(x - c)\right]^n$,

and $F(p,x,y) = p^n - y = 0$, with n a positive integer ≥ 2. The singular solution is $y = 0$. Note that if we write the equation $p - y^{1/n} = 0$, and the solution $n/(1 - n)\, y^{(n-1)/n} + (x - a) = 0$, it illustrates problem 4, but problem 10 may not be applied to these functions, since they are not differentiable for $y = 0$. In

problem 4, both $p - A(x)B(y)$ and $\displaystyle\int_a^x A(x)\,dx - \int_b^y \dfrac{dy}{B(y)}$ are not differentiable at $y = b$, since $B(y) = 0$ and fails to satisfy a Lipschitz condition at $y = b$.

12. *Clairaut's Equation*, $y = px + f(p)$, may be solved as follows. By differentiation, $dy/dx = p + [x + f'(p)]\,dp/dx$, and since $dy/dx = p$, $[x + f'(p)]\,dp/dx = 0$. If $dp/dx = 0$, $p = c$ and from the given equation $y = cx + f(c)$, a family of straight lines. If $x + f'(p) = 0$, $x = -f'(p)$ and by combining with the given equation $y = f(p) - pf'(p)$. Unless $f'(p)$ is a constant, when the lines pass through a point, the last two equations are the parametric equations of the envelope of the lines, and give the singular solution. In this case the c-discriminant and the p-discriminant of problem 10 are the same. Most simple examples of envelopes in elementary calculus and differential equations texts come under problem 4 or Clairaut's form, sometimes with a transformation of variables. In the Clairaut case, with new variables the family is $v(x,y) = cu(x,y) + f(c)$.

13. The linear homogeneous equation of the nth order is

$$L(y) = a_n y^{(n)} + a_{n-1} y^{(n-1)} + \cdots + a_1 y' + a_0 y = 0,$$

where the a_i are functions of x, and $a_n \neq 0$. If $u_1, u_2, \cdots, u_n$ are n functions of x such that $L(u_i) = 0$, and the Wronskian

$$W(u_1, u_2, \cdots, u_n) = \begin{vmatrix} u_1 & u_2 & \cdots & u_n \\ u_1' & u_2' & \cdots & u_n' \\ \cdot & \cdot & & \cdot \\ \cdot & \cdot & & \cdot \\ \cdot & \cdot & & \cdot \\ u_1^{(n-1)} & u_2^{(n-1)} & \cdots & u_n^{(n-1)} \end{vmatrix} \neq 0, \quad \text{for} \quad x = x_0,$$

constants c_i may be found such that $y = \sum_{i=1}^{n} c_i u_i$ is the solution of $L(y) = 0$ which equals y_0 and has $y^{(k)} = y_0^{(k)}$, $k = 1, 2, \cdots, n - 1$, when $x = x_0$.

14. A set of n functions $u_i(x)$ are *linearly dependent* if for some set of constants k_i, not all zero, $\sum_{i=1}^{n} k_i u_i = 0$ identically in x. If no such k_i exist, the functions are *linearly independent*. Show that if the $u_i(x)$ are linearly dependent, $W(u_1, u_2, \cdots, u_n) = 0$, identically where $W(u_i)$ is the Wronskian defined in problem 13. *Hint:* The k_i are solutions of the n linear equations obtained by differentiating the given relation $n - 1$ times.

15. The n solutions u_i of problem 13 are linearly independent, as defined in problem 14. *Hint:* By problem 46 of Exercises VI, $W \neq 0$ for any value of x, so that by problem 14 the functions are not linearly dependent in any range.

16. When the a_i of problem 13 are constants, the particular solutions may be found in the form $e^{m_i x}$, if m_i are the distinct roots of $a_n m^n + a_{n-1} m^{n-1} + \cdots + a_1 m + a_0 = 0$, by problem 31 of Exercises V. Show that for $x = 0$, the Wronskian reduces to $\prod (m_i - m_j)$, the product of differences of distinct roots, and so is $\neq 0$. Hence, by problem 15, these solutions are independent. For multiple roots solutions $x^k e^{m_i x}$ appear, and for $x = 0$ the Wronskian is a similar product, with higher powers of the factors $(m_i - m_j)$ if m_i or m_j is a multiple root. For the real form for complex roots see problem 32 of Exercises V.

17. If k linearly independent solutions, u_j, of the equation $L(y) = 0$ of problem 13 are known, the solution of the equation $L(y) = f(x)$ may be reduced to that of a similar equation of the $(n - k)$th order. Put $y = \sum_{j=1}^{k} v_j u_j$, and take $\sum_{j=1}^{k} \frac{dv_j}{dx} \left(\frac{d}{dx} \right)^r u_j = 0$ for $r = 0, 1, 2, \cdots, k - 2$. These conditions make the terms which contain dv_j/dx disappear from the expression for dy/dx, d^2y/dx^2, $\cdots$, $d^{k-1}y/dx^{k-1}$ found by successive differentiation of the first relation. Thus the highest derivative of the v_j appearing in $d^n y/dx^n$ is of order $n - k + 1$. To find the further conditions on the v_j which make $L(y) = f(x)$, substitute these expressions in this equation. The coefficient of v_j itself will be $L(u_j)$ which $= 0$. Hence, if we take $z = dv_1/dx$ as a new variable, we may solve the $k - 1$ assumed relations, linear in the dv_j/dx for $dv_2/dx, \cdots, dv_k/dx$ in terms of z, and express the derivatives of the v_j up to that of order $n - k + 1$ in terms of z and its derivatives up to order $n - k$, linearly. Thus the relation $L(y) = f(x)$ becomes $M(z) = f(x)$, where M is a linear differential operator of the $(n - k)$th order.

18. *Variation of Parameters.* If n linearly independent solutions of the equation $L(y) = 0$ are known, the solution of $L(y) = f(x)$ may be found by integrations. *Hint:* The method of problem 17 determines each dv_j/dx algebraically.

19. *First order linear equation.* The solution of $dy/dx + yP(x) = Q(x)$ is given by $y = uv$, where $u = e^{-Pdx}$ and $v = \int Qu^{-1}\, dx$. *Hint: $du/dx + Pu = 0$* is solvable by problem 3, and then problem 18, or 17 with no conditions, applies.

20. If $n - 1$ linearly independent solutions of $L(y) = 0$ are known, the equation $L(y) = f(x)$ may be solved by using problem 17 to reduce to a first order equation, solvable by problem 19.

21. If one solution of $L(y) = 0$ is known, where $L(y) = d^2y/dx^2 + A(x)dy/dx + B(x)y$ is of the second order, the equation $L(y) = f(x)$ may be solved by problem 20. This is one method of completing the solution of $L(y) = 0$ when one solution has been found in series form, as in problems 10, 11, and 12 of Exercises XIII. With $y = uv$, where $L(u) = 0$, and $dv/dx = z$, the linear equation in z is $u\, dz/dx + (2du/dx + Au)z = f(x)$.

22. In applying the method of variation of parameters of problem 18, if we write $v_j = \int_{x_0}^{x} (dv_j/dx)\, dx$ or determine the constants in each v_j so that $v_j(x_0) = 0$, the solution $y = \sum_{j=1}^{n} u_j v_j$ of $L(y) = f(x)$ is the one which, together with all its derivatives up to the $(n - 1)$st order is zero for $x = x_0$.

23. The solution of the linear equation with constant coefficients, $L(y) = f(x)$ obtained by the method of variation of parameters, problem 18, using $u_i = e^{m_i x}$ in the distinct root case of problem 16 reduces to the sum of the solutions found in problem 33 of Exercises V. If we use an x_0 as in problem 22, and take $x_0 = 0$, either of these solutions becomes that found in section 305.

24. The solution of any system of m equations in m variables y_i, where each equation is linear in the y_i and their derivatives $d^k y_i/dx^k$, $k \leq n$ may be reduced to the solution of a series of equations, each linear in one variable. *Hint:* If we regard $y_1, dy_1/dx, \cdots, d^n y/dx^n$ as algebraic variables and differentiate each of the equations, we increase the number of variables by 1, and the number of equations by m. Hence, if $m > 1$, after a sufficient number of differentiations, y_1 and its derivatives may be eliminated, and similarly for the other variables until only one is left.

25. A system of m linear equations in m variables with constant coefficients, by problem 24, leads to a series of equations in one variable with constant coefficients. These may be solved by problem 23. Or the method of section 305 may be applied directly to the system.

26. The equation $(ax + by + c) dx + (a'x + b'y + c') dy = 0$, or more generally the system $dx_1/L_1 = dx_2/L_2 = \cdots = dx_n/L_n$, where $L_i = \sum_{j=1}^{n} a_{ij}x_j + c_i$, is solvable explicitly. *Hint:* Put each fraction equal to dt, so that $dx_i/dt = L_i$, a system of linear equations with constant coefficients solvable by problem 25.

27. *Riccati's equation,* $dy/dx = P(x) + Q(x)y + R(x)y^2$, is reducible to a linear equation of the second order, $d^2u/dx^2 - (Q + R'/R) du/dx + PRu = 0$, by the substitution $y = -1/Ru \, du/dx$. The Riccati equation is solvable if one solution is known. The solution is a linear fractional function of c, the constant of integration. *Hint:* A known solution y_1 leads to a known solution u_1, and a second is found by problem 21. If $u = c_1u_1 + c_2u_2$, and $c = \dfrac{c_2}{c_1}$,

$$y = -\frac{u_1' + cu_2'}{Ru_1 + cRu_2}.$$

28. The general linear homogeneous second order equation,

$$\frac{d^2y}{dx^2} + A(x) \frac{dy}{dx} + B(x)y = 0$$

is reducible to a first order Riccati equation, $dz/dx + B + Az + z^2 = 0$ by the substitution $y = e^{\int z dx}$. This is less useful than the reverse procedure of problem 27.

29. If a family of solutions of a second-order equation can be found which has an envelope with the same second derivative at each of its points as the curves of the family, this will give a singular solution of the differential equation. If $G(x,y,a,b) = 0$ gives the solution, and the envelope is obtained by replacing a and b by functions of a parameter, the equation for y' will be unchanged if $G_a a' + G_b b' = 0$. This equation is $G' = 0$, where $G' = G_x + G_y y'$. Similarly, the equation for y'' will be unchanged if $G_a' a' + G_b' b' = 0$. Thus, assuming $G_y \neq 0$, a necessary condition for a singular solution is $G_a G_b' - G_b G_a' = 0$. As an example, $y = ae^x + be^{-x} + ab$ is the solution of $y''^2 + 4y'' - y'^2 - 4y = 0$, obtained by eliminating the constants a and b. If $G = ae^x + be^{-x} + ab - y$, $G' = ae^x - be^{-x} - y'$, and $G_a G_b' - G_b G_a' = -ae^x - be^{-x} - 2$. Putting each of these equal to zero, and eliminating a and b gives: $y'^2 + 4y + 4 = 0$. This is more readily found as the discriminant of the differential equation, regarded as a quadratic equation in y'', or eliminant between it and the partial with respect to y'', $2y'' + 4 = 0$. Compare the p-discriminant of problem 10. The general solution of $y'^2 + 4y + 4 = 0$ is $(x + k)^2 = -(1 + y)$. This is a singular solution of the second-order equation. The first-order equation also has the singular solution $y = -1$, which does not satisfy the second-order equation.

30. For the *linear partial differential equation,*

$$A(x,y,z) \frac{\partial z}{\partial x} + B(x,y,z) \frac{\partial z}{\partial y} = C(x,y,z),$$

the equations for the characteristics are, by section 315, $dv = dx/A = dy/B = dz/C$. In the discussion of section 317 applied to this case, the cones which the tangent planes must touch degenerate into lines, the tangents to the characteristic curves. Hence any surface through such a curve is a characteristic strip. If $f(x,y,z) = c_1$ and $g(x,y,z) = c_2$ are two independent integrals of the system $dx/A = dy/B = dz/C$, and if F is any differentiable function of two variables, $F(f,g) = 0$ defines a surface built up of characteristic curves and hence is a solution of the differential equation.

31. One complete integral of the Clairaut partial differential equation, $z = px + qy + f(p,q)$, is given by $z = ax + by + f(a,b)$.

32. In dynamics, Jacobi made use of the partial differential equation $\partial V/\partial t + H(q_i, \partial V/\partial q_i, t) = 0$. Here V is a function of t and the nq_i. With $p_i = \partial V/\partial q_i$, the equations (130) of section 315 are:

$$du_{n+1} = \frac{dt}{1} = \frac{dq_i}{\dfrac{\partial H}{\partial p_i}} = \frac{dV}{\dfrac{\partial V}{\partial t} + \sum_{j=1}^{n} p_j \dfrac{\partial H}{\partial p_j}} = \frac{-d\left(\dfrac{\partial V}{\partial t}\right)}{\dfrac{\partial H}{\partial t}} = \frac{-dp_i}{\dfrac{\partial H}{\partial q_i}}.$$

Thus, along a characteristic, the Hamiltonian equations:

$$\frac{dq_i}{dt} = \frac{\partial H}{\partial p_i} \quad \text{and} \quad \frac{dp_i}{dt} = -\frac{\partial H}{\partial q_i}, \quad \text{are satisfied.}$$

33. If u_1 and u_2 are two linearly independent solutions of the second order linear equation $L(y) = 0$ of problem 21, the zeros of u_1 separate those of u_2, in the sense that if $u_1(a) = u_1(b) = 0$, u_2 is not zero at a or b, but is zero at some point c between a and b. *Hint:* Use problems 14 and 15, and problem 9 of Exercises IV.

34. For a given function of five variables, $f(x,y,z,a,b)$, let J denote the Jacobian of f_a and f_b with respect to x and y, when z is considered a function of x and y, so that

$$J = \begin{vmatrix} f_{ax} + pf_{az}, & f_{bx} + pf_{bx} \\ f_{ay} + qf_{az}, & f_{by} + qf_{bz} \end{vmatrix}.$$

Show that, if $f_z \neq 0$ and $J \neq 0$ there is a partial differential equation $F(x,y,z,p,q) = 0$ of which $f(x,y,z,a,b) = 0$ is a complete integral. *Hint:* Since $f_z \neq 0$, the equation may be solved for z, and p and q are uniquely determined from $f_x + pf_z = 0$, $f_y + qf_z = 0$. Since $J \neq 0$, these equations may be solved ior a and b in terms of x,y,z,p,q, and substitution in f gives F. The function $f(x,y,z,a,b)$ contains two independent constants, since if it equalled $f(x,y,z,c)$ with $c = c(a,b), f_a = f_c c_a$ and $f_b = f_c c_b$ would imply $J = 0$.

CHAPTER XVI

THE GAMMA FUNCTION AND OTHER DEFINITE INTEGRALS

It is often desirable to use asymptotic expansions for functions which facilitate their computation for large values of the argument. We develop a general theorem on such expansions, the Euler-Maclaurin sum formula, after introducing the Bernoulli numbers and Bernoulli polynomials which are related to it.

We then apply the sum formula to the computation of Euler's constant, and to the development of Stirling's formula for the factorial function, as well as the Gamma function, $\Gamma(z)$. This function is first defined for positive real values of the argument by an integral between fixed limits containing the argument as a parameter. It is a generalization of the factorial function, since for a positive integer n, $\Gamma(n + 1) = n!$. We obtain some alternative expressions for the Gamma function. In particular, we find an expansion for the reciprocal of the Gamma function as an infinite product. This shows that $\Gamma(z)$ has simple poles when z is zero or a negative integer, and is analytic for all other finite values of z.

The Beta function is defined as a definite integral between fixed limits containing two parameters. It is expressible in terms of Gamma functions.

Finally we discuss briefly, and give asymptotic expansions for a few of the more common non-elementary integrals.

318. Bernoulli Periodic Functions. As a first step toward the study of the Bernoulli numbers and Bernoulli polynomials, which are important for certain theorems on expansions, we here define the Bernoulli periodic functions, $P_k(x)$. We begin by expanding the function $x - \frac{1}{2}$ in a Fourier series of period unity, which represents it in the interval $0 < x < 1$. The periodic function defined by this series is odd, so that the series is the sine series for $x - \frac{1}{2}$ for the interval $0 < x < \frac{1}{2}$, obtainable by problem 11 of Exercises XIV:

$$x - \tfrac{1}{2} = - \sum_{n=1}^{\infty} \frac{\sin 2n\pi x}{n\pi}, \quad 0 < x < 1. \tag{1}$$

Now define
$$P_1(x) = - \sum_{n=1}^{\infty} \frac{\sin 2n\pi x}{n\pi} \tag{2}$$

for all values of x. Then $P_1(x)$ is of period unity and is continuous for all values different from 0 or an integer. We have

$$P_1(1-) = \tfrac{1}{2}, \; P_1(1+) = P_1(0+) = -\tfrac{1}{2} \quad \text{and} \quad P_1(1) = 0. \quad (3)$$

Thus the function $P_1(x)$ has discontinuities at zero and all the integral points.

Next define $P_2(x)$ as the function equal to the trigonometric series obtained from the series (2) by formal termwise integration, with the constants of integration omitted, namely,

$$P_2(x) = \sum_{n=1}^{\infty} \frac{\cos 2n\pi x}{2n^2\pi^2}. \quad (4)$$

Repeat this process, defining the function $P_{k+1}(x)$ by the series obtained from that for $P_k(x)$ by integrating termwise, and omitting the constants. Thus:

$$P_{2k}(x) = (-1)^{k-1} \sum_{n=1}^{\infty} \frac{\cos 2n\pi x}{2^{2k-1}n^{2k}\pi^{2k}} \quad (5)$$

and

$$P_{2k+1}(x) = (-1)^{k-1} \sum_{n=1}^{\infty} \frac{\sin 2n\pi x}{2^{2k}n^{2k+1}\pi^{2k+1}}. \quad (6)$$

Since all the series except that for $P_1(x)$ are dominated by $\sum 1/n^2$, for all values of x, they converge uniformly and thus have as their sums continuous functions. Thus, for $k \geq 2$, all the functions $P_k(x)$ are continuous functions for all values of x. We may obtain the Fourier coefficients of the functions by termwise integration of the series, after multiplication by factors 1, $\sin 2n\pi x$ or $\cos 2n\pi x$. For, since these factors are numerically at most unity they do not disturb the uniform convergence. This shows that the coefficients of the expansions (5) and (6) are Fourier coefficients, and these series are the Fourier series of the Bernoulli periodic functions.

As all of these functions, including $P_1(x)$, are functions whose squares are integrable, by section 297 their Fourier series converge in the mean to the functions, and the series obtained by termwise integration over any finite interval converges to the integral of the function. Thus, from the method by which $P_{k+1}(x)$ was obtained from $P_k(x)$, we have

$$\int_a^x P_k(x) \, dx = P_{k+1}(x) - P_{k+1}(a). \quad (7)$$

This shows that, at all points of continuity of $P_k(x)$,

$$P_k(x) = \frac{d}{dx}[P_{k+1}(x)] = P'_{k+1}(x). \quad (8)$$

Thus this equation holds for all values of x if $k > 1$, and for all non-integral values of x if $k = 1$.

If we put $a = 0$, $x = 1$ in the relation (7), and recall that $P_{k+1}(x)$ is of period unity, we find:

$$\int_0^1 P_k(x)\, dx = 0. \tag{9}$$

The equations (8) and (9) enable us to determine expressions for the value of $P_k(x)$ in the interval 0,1. We first note that for $0 < x < 1$,

$$P'_2(x) = x - \tfrac{1}{2},\ P_2(x) = \frac{x^2}{2} - \frac{x}{2} + C, \tag{10}$$

and since

$$\int_0^1 P_2(x)\, dx = 0,\ C = \frac{1}{12}, \tag{11}$$

This shows that:

$$P_2(x) = \frac{x^2}{2} - \frac{x}{2} + \frac{1}{12},\ \ 0 < x < 1. \tag{12}$$

By the same procedure we find that

$$P_3(x) = \frac{x^3}{6} - \frac{x^2}{4} + \frac{x}{12},\ \ 0 < x < 1. \tag{13}$$

We could continue in this way to find a sequence of polynomials such that the kth one is of degree k, and equals $P_k(x)$ in the open interval 0,1. For $k > 1$, we could use the closed interval 0,1 since both $P_k(x)$ and the polynomial of the kth degree are continuous at the end points. These polynomials are called the *Bernoulli polynomials*.

319. Bernoulli Polynomials. We denote the Bernoulli polynomial of degree k by $B_k(x)$, so that:

$$B_1(x) = x - \tfrac{1}{2},\ B_2(x) = \frac{x^2}{2} - \frac{x}{2} + \frac{1}{12},\ \ \text{etc.} \tag{14}$$

Practical methods of finding the $B_k(x)$ for larger values of k will be given in section 321. We complete the sequence at the beginning by putting

$$B_0(x) = B'_1(x) = 1. \tag{15}$$

From this and equation (8)

$$B'_{k+1}(x) = B_k(x) \text{ for } k = 0, 1, 2, \cdots. \tag{16}$$

From equation (9),

$$\int_0^1 B_k(x)\, dx = 0 \quad \text{for} \quad k = 1, 2, \cdots . \tag{17}$$

This does not hold for $k = 0$.

The expansion (5) shows that the function $P_{2k}(1 - x) = P_{2k}(x)$. If we put $u = x - \frac{1}{2}$, $x = u + \frac{1}{2}$ and $1 - x = -u + \frac{1}{2}$. Thus $P_{2k}(u + \frac{1}{2})$ is an even function of u. Hence $B_{2k}(x)$ will be an even function of $u = x - \frac{1}{2}$ for $|u| < \frac{1}{2}$, and hence for all values. Thus, if $B_{2k}(x)$ is expressed in powers of $(x - \frac{1}{2})$, only even powers will appear. Similarly, if $B_{2k+1}(x)$ is expressed in powers of $(x - \frac{1}{2})$, only odd powers will appear.

For polynomials of index at least 2, $B_k(x) = P_k(x)$ on the closed interval 0,1. Hence, from equation (6)

$$B_{2k+1}(0) = B_{2k+1}(\tfrac{1}{2}) = B_{2k+1}(1) = 0, \; k = 1, 2, \cdots . \tag{18}$$

And, from equation (5):

$$B_{2k}(0) = B_{2k}(1) = \frac{(-1)^{k-1}}{2^{2k-1}\pi^{2k}} \sum_{n=1}^{\infty} \frac{1}{n^{2k}}, \quad k = 1, 2, \cdots . \tag{19}$$

Equation (18) shows that, in the closed interval 0,1 each polynomial of odd index at least 3 has the three zeros $0, \frac{1}{2}, 1$. Moreover, it can have no more, since if any odd polynomial $B_{2k+1}(x)$ had an additional root, by Rolle's theorem, its derivative $B_{2k}(x)$ would have a root between each pair of those of $B_{2k+1}(x)$. Thus $B_{2k}(x)$ would have at least three

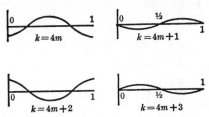

Typical shapes of $B_k(x)$, $k > 2$.

Fig. 27.

roots in the open interval 0,1 and by similar reasoning $B_{2k-1}(x)$ would have at least two roots in this open interval, and hence with 0 and 1 at least four roots. Continuing in this way, we would come to a contradiction since $B_3(x)$, being of the third degree, can have only three roots. The reasoning also shows that no even polynomial $B_{2k}(x)$ can have more than two roots in the interval 0,1. By considering $B_{2k+1}(x)$, and using Rolle's theorem, we see that it has two, one in each of the open intervals

$0,\frac{1}{2}$ and $\frac{1}{2},1$. In fact, since $B_{2k}(x)$ is an even function of $u = x - \frac{1}{2}$, it follows that they are symmetrically disposed about the point $\frac{1}{2}$. Hence, in the closed interval $0,1$ each odd function of index at least 3 has three roots given by equation (18), and each even function of index at least 2 has two roots, separated by these. Hence all these roots are simple, since no function has a common root with its derivative in the interval $0,1$.

320. Bernoulli Numbers. The Bernoulli numbers are defined in terms of the Bernoulli polynomials by putting:

$$B_n = n \,!\, B_n(0). \tag{20}$$

We take $0\,! = 1$, so that $B_0 = 1$. The method of computation already indicated shows that the coefficients of the polynomials, and hence $B_n(0)$ and B_n are all rational numbers. Also, for odd subscripts,

$$B_1 = -\tfrac{1}{2} \quad \text{and} \quad B_{2k+1} = 0, \quad k = 1, 2, 3, \cdots. \tag{21}$$

The first few B_n with even subscripts are:

$$B_2 = \frac{1}{6}, \; B_4 = -\frac{1}{30}, \; B_6 = \frac{1}{42}, \; B_8 = -\frac{1}{30}, \; \cdots. \tag{22}$$

The signs alternate, as we see from equation (19).

Since the series with term $1/n^{2k}$, for $k \geqq 1$, is dominated by the series $\Sigma 1/n^2$, it converges uniformly in k. Hence

$$\lim_{k \to \infty} \sum_{n=1}^{\infty} \frac{1}{n^k} = \sum_{n=1}^{\infty} \left(\lim_{k \to \infty} \frac{1}{n^k} \right) = 1. \tag{23}$$

Thus, from equation (19),

$$\lim_{k \to \infty} B_{2k}(0) = 0. \tag{24}$$

However, we have:

$$\lim_{k \to \infty} \left| B_{2k} \right| = \lim_{k \to \infty} \frac{(2k)\,!}{2^{2k-1} \pi^{2k}} = \infty, \tag{25}$$

since for $k = p + q$, with p fixed but $> 2\pi$, we have:

$$\frac{(2k)\,!}{2^{2k-1} \pi^{2k}} > \frac{(2p)\,!}{2^{2p-1} \pi^{2p}} 2^{2q}, \tag{26}$$

which becomes infinite when q becomes infinite.

321. Recursion Formulas. We proceed to prove that the Bernoulli polynomials may be symbolically expressed in terms of the Bernoulli numbers by the formula:

$$B_n(x) = \frac{1}{n\,!} \, (x + B)^n, \tag{27}$$

where in the expression on the right, each power of B, B^k is to be replaced by the kth Bernoulli number, B_k, after expansion. It follows from equation (27) that the polynomials $B_n(x)$ defined by it satisfy the relation:

$$B'_{n+1}(x) = \frac{1}{n!}(x + B)^n = B_n(x), \qquad (28)$$

the differentiation rule for the right member persisting just as if the B^k were powers of a constant, since no combination of separate powers is made.

But, the equation (27) gives the correct value for the first two Bernoulli polynomials:

$$B_0(x) = 1, \quad B_1(x) = x - \tfrac{1}{2}, \qquad (29)$$

so that when the remaining polynomials are determined in succession by integration, in accordance with equation (28), they must give the same value as before, except perhaps for the constant of integration. But this is right, since equation (27) makes

$$B_n(0) = \frac{B_n}{n!}, \qquad (30)$$

and the Bernoulli numbers were defined by this relation. This completes the proof that the polynomials $B_n(x)$ defined by the relation (27) are the Bernoulli polynomials.

For n at least 2, it follows from equations (18) and (19) that $B_n(1) - B_n(0) = 0$. From this and equation (27), we have:

$$(B + 1)^n - B^n = 0, \quad n = 2, 3, \cdots. \qquad (31)$$

If we put $n = 2k + 1$, expand and use equation (21) as well as $B_0 = 1$, we find:

$$(2k + 1)B_{2k} + {}^{2k+1}C_3 B_{2k-2} + {}^{2k+1}C_5 B_{2k-4} + \cdots$$
$$+ {}^{2k+1}C_{2k-1}B_2 + (2k + 1)(-\tfrac{1}{2}) + 1 = 0, \quad k = 1, 2, \cdots. \qquad (32)$$

This may be used as a recursion formula to compute the Bernoulli numbers with even subscripts. In succession, each B_{2k} is given as a linear combination of those already found. The values given in equation (22) may be checked by this process.

After the Bernoulli numbers have been found, the Bernoulli polynomials may be obtained from equation (27).

We may use the symbolic relations (27) and (31) to establish the generating functions for the Bernoulli numbers and polynomials. Let us start with

$$e^{(B+1)t} = e^{Bt}e^t. \qquad (33)$$

This relation holds if B is a number, and hence the coefficients of B^n on both sides will be the same functions of t. Thus, the relation continues to hold as a formal identity if B^n is replaced by B_n. But, for this interpretation of B^n, we have in consequence of equation (31):

$$e^{(B+1)t} - e^{Bt} = t, \tag{34}$$

where the term on the right results from the relation

$$(B + 1)^1 - B^1 = B_1 + 1 - B_1 = 1, \tag{35}$$

which replaces equation (31) for $n = 1$.

From the symbolic equations (33) and (34), we have:

$$e^{Bt}(e^t - 1) = t, \tag{36}$$

as a formal identity when B^n is replaced by B_n. Hence:

$$\frac{t}{e^t - 1} = e^{Bt} = \sum_{n=0}^{\infty} B_n \frac{t^n}{n!}. \tag{37}$$

Thus the function on the left is a generating function for the numbers $B_n/n!$, since these are the coefficients of its expansion.

Analogous to equation (33), we have

$$e^{(B+x)t} = e^{Bt}e^{xt}, \tag{38}$$

which may be used in conjunction with equation (37) to deduce:

$$\frac{te^{xt}}{e^t - 1} = e^{xt}e^{Bt} = e^{(B+x)t} = \sum_{n=1}^{\infty} (B + x)^n \frac{t^n}{n!}$$

$$= \sum_{n=1}^{\infty} B_n(x)t^n, \tag{39}$$

by equation (27). Thus the function on the left is a generating function for the Bernoulli polynomials.

The equation (37) enables us to find the coefficients of the power series expansions of several related functions in terms of the Bernoulli numbers. In particular $t \coth t$, $\tanh t$, $t \operatorname{csch} t$ as well as $t \cot t$, $\tan t$, $t \csc t$ are such functions. Similarly the coefficients of the expansion of $\operatorname{sech} t$ and $\sec t$ may be expressed in terms of the Bernoulli polynomials by means of equation (39). For the details see problems 8 through 11 of Exercises XVI.

322. Euler-Maclaurin Sum Formula. We shall now prove a formula connecting the integral of a function with a finite sum. We assume that the function, $f(x)$, for all the real values of x considered, has continuous derivatives either of all orders, or at least of all orders up to the last one written in any of our equations. Then, in consequence of equations (1) and (2), we have for any integral value of k,

$$\int_k^{k+1} f(x)\, dx = \int_k^{k+1} f(x) P_1'(x)\, dx$$

$$= f(x) P_1(x) \Big|_{k+}^{k+1-} - \int_k^{k+1} P_1(x) f'(x)\, dx, \quad (40)$$

by an integration by parts. By equation (3) and the fact that $P_1(x)$ is of period unity, this may be written:

$$\int_k^{k+1} f(x)\, dx = \tfrac{1}{2}[f(k+1) + f(k)] - \int_k^{k+1} P_1(x) f'(x)\, dx. \quad (41)$$

By equation (8), we may replace $P_1(x)$ by $P_2'(x)$. We again use an integration by parts to obtain:

$$\int_k^{k+1} P_2'(x) f'(x)\, dx = f'(x) P_2(x) \Big|_k^{k+1} - \int_k^{k+1} P_2(x) f''(x)\, dx$$

$$= \frac{B_2}{2\,!}[f'(k+1) - f'(k)] - \int_k^{k+1} P_2(x) f''(x)\, dx, \quad (42)$$

since

$$P_2(k+1) = P_2(k) = P_2(0) = B_2(0) = \frac{B_2}{2\,!}. \quad (43)$$

When we continue this process, the integrated terms from the polynomials with odd subscripts will vanish in view of equation (18). Thus we find:

$$\int_k^{k+1} f(x)\, dx = \tfrac{1}{2}[f(k+1) + f(k)]$$

$$- \sum_{r=1}^n \frac{B_{2r}}{(2r)!}\,[f^{(2r-1)}(k+1) - f^{(2r-1)}(k)]$$

$$+ \int_k^{k+1} P_{2n}(x) f^{(2n)}(x)\, dx. \quad (44)$$

If we sum both sides of this equation, after making $k = 0, 1, 2, \cdots,$ $m-1$, we find:

$$\int_0^m f(x)\, dx = \tfrac{1}{2}[f(0) + f(m)] + \sum_{k=1}^{m-1} f(k)$$

$$- \sum_{r=1}^n \frac{B_{2r}}{(2r)\,!}\,[f^{(2r-1)}(m) - f^{(2r-1)}(0)] + R_n. \quad (45)$$

The remainder after the terms written explicitly is

$$R_n = \int_0^m P_{2n}(x)f^{(2n)}(x)\, dx. \tag{46}$$

Let us incorporate the last term of the sum:

$$\frac{B_{2n}}{(2n)!}[f^{(2n-1)}(m) - f^{(2n-1)}(0)] = P_{2n}(0)\int_0^m f^{(2n)}(x)\, dx, \tag{47}$$

with the term R_n, to give:

$$R_{n-1} = \int_0^m [P_{2n}(x) - P_{2n}(0)]f^{(2n)}(x)\, dx. \tag{48}$$

From equation (5) we see that $P_{2k}(0)$ is a maximum of the function $P_{2k}(x)$ when k is odd, and a minimum when k is even. Hence, in all cases the factor $[P_{2n}(x) - P_{2n}(0)]$ never changes its sign, and by the theorem of section 125, the remainder is:

$$R_{n-1} = f^{(2n)}(\theta m)\int_0^m [P_{2n}(x) - P_{2n}(0)]\, dx, \tag{49}$$

where θ is a suitably chosen number between 0 and 1. In view of equation (7) this may be simplified to

$$R_{n-1} = -f^{(2n)}(\theta m)mP_{2n}(0). \tag{50}$$

Thus we finally have the *Euler-Maclaurin sum formula*,

$$\int_0^m f(x)\, dx = \tfrac{1}{2}[f(0) + f(m)] + \sum_{k=1}^{m-1} f(k)$$
$$- \sum_{r=1}^{n-1} \frac{B_{2r}}{(2r)!}[f^{(2r-1)}(m) - f^{(2r-1)}(0)] - f^{(2n)}(\theta m)m\frac{B_{2n}}{(2n)!}. \tag{51}$$

Collectively, the terms involving derivatives express the error made in computing the integral by the trapezoidal rule for unit intervals. The case of equal intervals not unity could be treated by a change of scale, $u = hx$.

As written the equation expresses an integral in terms of a sum and a remainder term. We may also think of it as expressing a sum in terms of an integral and certain additional terms, together with a remainder term, by writing:

$$\sum_{k=0}^{m-1} f(k) = \int_0^m f(x)\, dx + \tfrac{1}{2}[f(0) - f(m)]$$
$$+ \sum_{r=1}^{n-1} \frac{B_{2r}}{(2r)!}[f^{(2r-1)}(m) - f^{(2r-1)}(0)]$$
$$+ f^{(2n)}(\theta m)m\frac{B_{2n}}{(2n)!}. \tag{52}$$

We may use this formula to sum the powers of the integers, x^p, where p is a positive integer. In this case the equation may be written:

$$\sum_{k=1}^{m-1} k^p = \frac{m^{p+1}}{p+1} - \tfrac{1}{2}m^p$$
$$+ \sum_{r=1}^{r'} \frac{B_{2r}}{(2r)!} p(p-1)\cdots(p-2r+2)m^{p-2r+1}, \quad (53)$$

where,

$$r' = \frac{p-1}{2} \text{ for } p \text{ odd, and } \frac{p}{2} \text{ for } p \text{ even.} \quad (54)$$

The terms on the right, combined, equal:

$$\frac{1}{p+1}\left(m^{p+1} + {}^{p+1}C_1 m^p B_1 + \sum_{r=1}^{r'} {}^{p+1}C_{2r} m^{p+1-2r} B_{2r}\right), \quad (55)$$

where the C's are binomial coefficients. And, since the B_k with odd subscripts greater than 1 are zero, this is the expansion of

$$\frac{1}{p+1}[(m+B)^{p+1} - B^{p+1}], \quad (56)$$

with B^k replaced by B_k. Hence, by using equation (27), we find:

$$\sum_{k=1}^{m-1} k^p = p![B_{p+1}(m) - B_{p+1}(0)]. \quad (57)$$

In the sum formula (51), a useful conclusion may be drawn about the relation of the remainder to the size of the last term retained, provided that, for the orders used, the even derivatives of $f(x)$ are all positive on the interval considered, 0 to m. If we denote by t_n the term in equation (45) involving B_{2n}, we have

$$R_{n-1} = t_n + R_n. \quad (58)$$

Our assumption, together with equation (50), shows that R_n and R_{n-1} are each distinct from zero. And, since the signs of $P_{2n}(0)$ alternate, R_n and R_{n-1} have opposite signs. Thus:

$$|t_n| = |R_n| + |R_{n-1}|, \quad (59)$$

and R_n and R_{n-1} are each numerically less than t_n. Consequently, from equation (58), R_{n-1} has the same sign as t_n.

A similar conclusion holds if the even derivative of $f(x)$ are all negative. Also, if $f(x)$ and all the derivatives used approach zero for $x \to \infty$, and the even derivatives are all different from zero and of the same sign, the formula holds with $m = \infty$ if the sum and integral converge. In all these cases, the remainder term is numerically less than the first term of the series omitted, and has the same sign as this term.   For the limits m and ∞, the sum formula becomes:

$$\sum_{k=m}^{\infty} f(k) = \int_{m}^{\infty} f(x)\,dx + \tfrac{1}{2}f(m) - \sum_{r=1}^{n-1} \frac{B_{2r}}{(2r)\,!} f^{(2r-1)}(m) - R_{n-1}. \qquad (60)$$

This applies if the conditions hold for $x \geq m$.   For example, we may put $f(x) = x^{-p}$, $p > 1$ with $m \geq 1$ to avoid the discontinuity at 0.   We thus find:

$$\sum_{k=m}^{\infty} k^{-p} = \frac{m^{1-p}}{p-1} + \frac{1}{2m^{p}}$$

$$+ \sum_{r=1}^{n-1} \frac{B_{2r}}{(2r)\,!}\, m^{-p-2r+1} p(p+1) \cdots (p+2r-2) - R_{n-1}. \qquad (61)$$

The infinite series obtained by letting n become infinite diverges.   In fact the terms ultimately increase numerically, as may be shown by reasoning similar to that used to establish equation (25).   However, for any finite value of n, the sum gives an approximation to within the magnitude of the first term neglected.   The series may be used to compute $\sum_{k=1}^{\infty} k^{-p}$, by actually adding up the first $m-1$ terms, and using equation (61) to calculate the remaining part of the sum.   If m is fairly large, say >10, a relatively few terms will give a good approximation. Expansions, whether convergent or not, are called *asymptotic expansions* if for a fixed number of terms, the remainder approaches zero when some parameter becomes infinite.   In the case of equation (61), $R_{n-1} \to 0$ when $m \to \infty$, so that this is an asymptotic expansion.   The sum formula (60) frequently gives asymptotic expansions.

323. Euler's Constant.   The sum and integral in equation (60) diverge if $f(x) = 1/x$, $m \geq 1$.   However, the limit process which established equation (60) shows that:

$$\lim_{M \to \infty} \left(\sum_{k=m}^{M} \frac{1}{k} - \int_{m}^{M} \frac{dx}{x} \right) = \frac{1}{2m} + \sum_{r=1}^{n-1} \frac{B_{2r}}{2r}\, m^{-2r} - R_{n-1}. \qquad (62)$$

For $m = 1$, the limit in the left member is known as Euler's constant, and is denoted by γ, so that:

$$\gamma = \lim_{M \to \infty} \left(1 + \frac{1}{2} + \frac{1}{3} + \cdots + \frac{1}{M} - \log M \right). \qquad (63)$$

That the limit in equation (63), and hence that in equation (62), exists follows from the Cauchy convergence criterion, and the sum formula from which (62) was obtained, taken between limits m and M.   For an elementary proof, compare problem 9 of Exercises IX.   By combining

$$\sum_{k=1}^{m-1} \frac{1}{k} - \int_1^m \frac{dx}{x} = \sum_{k=1}^m \frac{1}{k} - \log m - \frac{1}{m} \tag{64}$$

with equation (62) we find that:

$$\gamma = \sum_{k=1}^m \frac{1}{k} - \log m - \frac{1}{2m} + \sum_{r=1}^{n-1} \frac{B_{2r}}{2r} m^{-2r} - R_{n-1}. \tag{65}$$

For any fixed m, and $n \to \infty$, the series diverges. But R_{n-1} is numerically less than the first term omitted, and since this approaches zero for any fixed n, when $m \to \infty$, the series is an asymptotic expansion for γ.   It may be used to compute

$$\gamma = 0.5772157 \cdots, \tag{66}$$

for example by taking $m = 10$ as in problem 14 of Exercises XVI.

324. Stirling's Formula for Factorial m. For positive integral values of m,

$$m! = 1 \cdot 2 \cdot 3 \cdots m, \quad \text{and} \quad \log (m!) = \sum_{k=1}^m \log k. \tag{67}$$

Thus we may use the methods under discussion to obtain an asymptotic expansion for $\log (m!)$. We put $f(x) = \log x$ in the sum formula (52), with lower limit 1, and find:

$$\sum_{k=1}^{m-1} \log k = m \log m - m - \tfrac{1}{2} \log m + 1$$
$$+ \sum_{r=1}^{n-1} \frac{B_{2r}(m^{-2r+1} - 1)}{(2r)(2r-1)} - R_{n-1}. \tag{68}$$

By equation (46), the remainder after one term is here:

$$-R_1 = - \int_1^m P_2(x) f''(x) \, dx = \int_1^m \frac{P_2(x)}{x^2} \, dx. \tag{69}$$

Since the Bernoulli periodic function $P_2(x)$ is bounded for all values of x this integral is dominated by that of a constant times x^{-2}, and so converges for $m \to \infty$.   This shows that

$$\lim_{M \to \infty} [\log (M!) - (M + \tfrac{1}{2}) \log M + M] = K \tag{70}$$

exists.   Moreover, if we apply the sum formula from m to M, and let M become infinite, we find, analogous to equation (65):

$$K = \log (m!) - (m + \tfrac{1}{2}) \log m + m$$
$$- \sum_{r=1}^{n-1} \frac{B_{2r} m^{-2r+1}}{(2r)(2r-1)} + R_{n-1}. \tag{71}$$

This equation could be used as an asymptotic expansion for K. However, we shall prove that, in fact, $K = \log \sqrt{2\pi}$, so that instead we use this expansion to calculate $\log (m !)$ for large values of m.

To evaluate K, we recall the product expansion for $\sin z$,

$$\sin z = z \prod_{n=1}^{\infty} \left(1 - \frac{z^2}{n^2\pi^2}\right), \tag{72}$$

of section 285. For $z = \pi/2$, this gives:

$$1 = \frac{\pi}{2} \prod_{n=1}^{\infty} \left[1 - \frac{1}{(2n)^2}\right]. \tag{73}$$

But, for the product to m terms:

$$p_m = \prod_{n=1}^{m} \frac{(2n - 1)(2n + 1)}{(2n)(2n)} = \frac{1 \cdot 3 \cdot 3 \cdot 5 \cdots (2m - 1)(2m + 1)}{2 \cdot 2 \cdot 4 \cdot 4 \cdots (2m)(2m)}$$

$$= \frac{(2m) ! \, (2m + 1) !}{(m !)^4 2^{4m}}. \tag{74}$$

By using equation (70) with $M = 2m$ and $M = m$, we find that as $m \to \infty$ the limit of

$$\log p_m = 2 \log (2m) ! + \log (2m + 1) - 4 \log m ! - 4m \log 2, \tag{75}$$

equals the limit of

$$2(2m + \tfrac{1}{2}) \log 2m - 2(2m) + 2K + \log (2m + 1)$$
$$- 4(m + \tfrac{1}{2}) \log m + 4m - 4K - 4m \log 2. \tag{76}$$

Consequently:

$$\lim (\log p_m) = \lim \left[\log \frac{2m + 1}{m} + \log 2 - 2K\right] = 2 \log 2 - 2K. \tag{77}$$

On combining this with equation (73), we have:

$$0 = \log \frac{\pi}{2} + \lim (\log p_m) = \log 2\pi - 2K, \tag{78}$$

so that

$$K = \tfrac{1}{2} \log 2\pi = \log \sqrt{2\pi}, \tag{79}$$

as we stated.

We may deduce from equations (70) and (79) that

$$\lim_{m \to \infty} \frac{m !}{\sqrt{2\pi} m^{m+\frac{1}{2}} e^{-m}} = 1. \tag{80}$$

The denominator of this expression is known as *Stirling's formula for factorial m*. In evaluating a limit involving $m !$ as a factor, we may replace m ! by $\sqrt{2\pi}\,m^{m+\frac{1}{2}}e^{-m}$. Equation (80) suggests that Stirling's formula gives an approximation to factorial m with a small percentage error for large values of m, and actually the percentage error is small even for moderate values of m.   Compare problem 15 of Exercises XVI.

325. The Gamma Function for Positive Real Values.   We have

$$\lim_{x \to \infty} x^{p+1}e^{-x} = 0 \tag{81}$$

for all values of p, by section 92.   It follows that for a sufficiently large value of M depending on p,

$$|x^{p-1}e^{-x}| < x^{-2}, \quad x > M. \tag{82}$$

Thus by section 166 the improper integral

$$\int_1^\infty x^{p-1}e^{-x}\,dx \tag{83}$$

converges for all values of p.

Again, since for positive values of x

$$x^{p-1}e^{-x} < x^{p-1}, \tag{84}$$

the integral

$$\int_0^1 x^{p-1}e^{-x}\,dx, \tag{85}$$

which is improper for $p < 1$, converges if p is positive.

It follows that if we set

$$\Gamma(p) = \int_0^\infty x^{p-1}e^{-x}\,dx = \int_0^\infty t^{p-1}e^{-t}\,dt, \quad p > 0, \tag{86}$$

the function $\Gamma(p)$ will be defined for all positive values of p.   It is called the *Gamma function*, as we anticipated in the notation $\Gamma(p)$.

For a and b positive, we may integrate the proper integral by parts to obtain:

$$\int_a^b x^p e^{-x}\,dx = -x^p e^{-x}\Big|_a^b + p\int_a^b x^{p-1}e^{-x}\,dx. \tag{87}$$

If $p > 1$, and we let $a \to 0$ and $b \to \infty$, this equation leads to:

$$\Gamma(p + 1) = p\Gamma(p), \quad p > 0. \tag{88}$$

By repeated use of this relation we find:

$$\Gamma(p + 1) = p(p - 1) \cdots (p - k)\Gamma(p - k), \quad p > k. \tag{89}$$

In particular, if p is an integer, n, we find:

$$\Gamma(n + 1) = n(n - 1) \cdots 2 \cdot 1\,\Gamma(1) = n\,!, \tag{90}$$

since direct integration shows that $\Gamma(1) = 1$.

In any range between two positive values, $0 < p_1 \leqq p \leqq p_2$, the improper integral which defines the Gamma function converges uni-

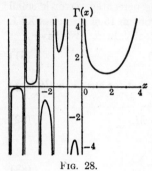

formly. Thus the function is analytic, since the integrand is an analytic function of p, and hence the proper integrals are analytic functions of p.

Equation (90) shows that the Gamma function of $n + 1$ is a generalization of the factorial function. The function $\Gamma(n + 1)$ is defined for all real values of n greater than -1. And for positive integral values of n, the only ones for which $n!$ was originally defined, $\Gamma(n + 1) = n!$.

Fig. 28.

326. The Gamma Function for Complex Values. An argument similar in character to that given in the last section shows that the function

$$\Gamma(z) = \int_0^\infty t^{z-1}e^{-t}\,dt, \quad \mathbf{R}(z) > 0, \tag{91}$$

defines a function of z for all complex values of z with positive real part. Here t is real, and we define the power by

$$t^z = e^{z \log t}, \quad \text{with } \log t \text{ real,} \tag{92}$$

so that if

$$z = p + is; \quad |t^{z-1}e^{-t}| = t^{p-1}e^{-t}. \tag{93}$$

Hence, if $p > 0$, the absolute convergence of the integral for $\Gamma(z)$ of equation (91) follows from the convergence of the integral for $\Gamma(p)$ of equation (86). Also, the convergence is uniform for $0 < p_1 \leqq p \leqq p_2$, so that $\Gamma(z)$ is analytic when $p > 0$.

We deduce as before that:

$$\Gamma(z + 1) = z\Gamma(z), \tag{94}$$

and hence that:

$$\Gamma(z + 1) = z(z - 1) \cdots (z - k)\Gamma(z - k), \tag{95}$$

or

$$\Gamma(z) = \frac{\Gamma(z + 1)}{z} = \frac{\Gamma(z + k)}{(z + k - 1)(z + k - 2) \cdots z}. \tag{96}$$

This last equation may be used to define $\Gamma(z)$ for values of z with negative real part, by taking k so that $(z + k)$ has a positive real part. The result will not depend on the value of k used, since equations (94) and (95) hold when the real part of z is positive.

This procedure defines a function $\Gamma(z)$, analytic for all finite values of z with the exception of zero and the negative integers. For these values the function becomes infinite and has a pole of the first order since one factor in the denominator of the expression (96) is zero.

The equation

$$z\,! = \Gamma(z+1), \tag{97}$$

which holds for positive integral values, is sometimes taken as the definition of $z\,!$ when z is not a positive integer. In particular, this makes $0\,! = 1$, the usual convention.

327. The Beta Function. For positive values of p and q the integral

$$\int_0^1 x^{p-1}(1-x)^{q-1}\,dx \tag{98}$$

converges. For, at each limit, one factor of the integrand is finite and the other is, at worst, a negative power less than unity of a factor with a simple zero. Thus the equation

$$B(p,q) = \int_0^1 x^{p-1}(1-x)^{q-1}\,dx, \quad p>0, \; q>0, \tag{99}$$

defines a function of the two positive real variables p and q. It is known as the *Beta function*.

We may express the Beta function in terms of Gamma functions by the following device. We have, on putting $t = y^2$,

$$\Gamma(p) = \int_0^\infty t^{p-1}e^{-t}\,dt = 2\int_0^\infty y^{2p-1}e^{-y^2}\,dy. \tag{100}$$

Now multiply $\Gamma(p)$ by $\Gamma(q)$, using this form with the dummy variable y replaced by x in the integral for $\Gamma(q)$. Thus:

$$\Gamma(p)\Gamma(q) = 2\int_0^\infty y^{2p-1}e^{-y^2}\,dy\,2\int_0^\infty x^{2q-1}e^{-x^2}\,dx. \tag{101}$$

We may consider this product as a repeated integral equal to a double integral which is improper but converges absolutely. Hence, by the reasoning similar to that of section 244 used in problem 32 of Exercises XII, we may show that it equals the corresponding repeated integral in polar coördinates, and

$$\Gamma(p)\Gamma(q) = 4\int_0^{\frac{\pi}{2}} d\theta \int_0^\infty \sin^{2p-1}\theta \, \cos^{2q-1}\theta \; r^{2p+2q-1}e^{-r^2}\,dr. \tag{102}$$

By equation (100), with y replaced by r, we have:

$$2 \int_0^\infty r^{2p+2q-1} e^{-r^2} \, dr = \Gamma(p+q). \qquad (103)$$

Again, if we put

$$\sin^2 \theta = u, \quad 2 \sin \theta \cos \theta = du, \quad \cos^2 \theta = 1 - u, \qquad (104)$$

we have

$$2 \int_0^{\frac{\pi}{2}} \sin^{2p-1} \theta \cos^{2q-1} d\theta = \int_0^1 u^{p-1} (1-u)^{q-1} \, du = B(p,q). \qquad (105)$$

It follows from equations (102), (103) and (105) that

$$\Gamma(p)\Gamma(q) = \Gamma(p+q)B(p,q), \qquad (106)$$

or:

$$B(p,q) = \frac{\Gamma(p)\Gamma(q)}{\Gamma(p+q)}. \qquad (107)$$

This shows that the function $B(p,q)$ is symmetrical in p and q.

If we put $p = q = \frac{1}{2}$ in equation (102), we find on evaluating the right member that:

$$[\Gamma(\tfrac{1}{2})]^2 = \pi, \quad \text{and} \quad \Gamma(\tfrac{1}{2}) = \sqrt{\pi}. \qquad (108)$$

From this and equation (100), with $p = \frac{1}{2}$, we find

$$\int_0^\infty e^{-v^2} \, dy = \frac{\sqrt{\pi}}{2}. \qquad (109)$$

For negative or complex values of the variables, we may use the equation (107) to define the Beta function. Thus

$$B(z,w) = \frac{\Gamma(z)\Gamma(w)}{\Gamma(z+w)}, \qquad (110)$$

for all values of the complex arguments z and w. For complex values with positive real parts, the discussion of this section applies with slight modification, and the function may be defined by an integral similar to that of equation (99).

328. Product Representations. There are two expressions for the Gamma function involving products. These may be derived from the following equation, in which n is a positive integer,

$$\Gamma(z) = \lim_{n \to \infty} \int_0^n \left(1 - \frac{t}{n}\right)^n t^{z-1} \, dt, \quad \mathbf{R}(z) > 0, \qquad (111)$$

which we proceed to establish.   This result is suggested by the relation

$$\lim_{n \to \infty} \left(1 - \frac{t}{n}\right)^n = \lim_{h \to 0} \left[(1 + h)^{\frac{1}{h}}\right]^{-t} = e^{-t}, \qquad (112)$$

but we require more precise relations to establish the desired result. Specifically, we have, for $0 \leqq t \leqq n$:

$$1 - \frac{t}{n} \leqq e^{-\frac{t}{n}}, \qquad (113)$$

$$1 + \frac{t}{n} \leqq e^{\frac{t}{n}}, \qquad (114)$$

$$1 - \frac{t^2}{n} \leqq \left(1 - \frac{t^2}{n^2}\right)^n. \qquad (115)$$

These relations are all equalities for $t = 0$, and for other values of $t \leqq n$ follow since in each case the derivative of the left member is less than that of the right member.   The form of the left members is suggested by the Taylor's expansions of the functions on the right.

For $\mathbf{R}(z) > 0$, we have from equation (91)

$$\Gamma(z) = \int_0^\infty e^{-t} t^{z-1}\, dt = \lim_{n \to \infty} \int_0^n e^{-t} t^{z-1}\, dt, \qquad (116)$$

since the integral converges.   Thus equation (111) will follow if we show that

$$\int_0^n e^{-t} t^{z-1}\, dt - \int_0^n \left(1 - \frac{t}{n}\right)^n t^{z-1}\, dt$$
$$= \int_0^n \left[1 - e^t \left(1 - \frac{t}{n}\right)^n\right] e^{-t} t^{z-1}\, dt \quad (117)$$

approaches zero as n becomes infinite.

It follows from the relation (113) that

$$\left(1 - \frac{t}{n}\right)^n \leqq e^{-t} \quad \text{or} \quad e^t \left(1 - \frac{t}{n}\right)^n \leqq 1. \qquad (118)$$

And, from the relations (114) and (115) we may deduce that

$$e^t \left(1 - \frac{t}{n}\right)^n \geqq \left(1 + \frac{t}{n}\right)^n \left(1 - \frac{t}{n}\right)^n \geqq 1 - \frac{t^2}{n}. \qquad (119)$$

The relations (118) and (119) may be combined to give

$$0 \leqq 1 - e^t \left(1 - \frac{t}{n}\right)^n \leqq \frac{t^2}{n}. \qquad (120)$$

As in equation (93), when

$$z = p + is; \quad |t^{z-1}e^{-t}| = t^{p-1}e^{-t}, \tag{121}$$

and we have for the integrand of equation (117)

$$\left| \left[1 - e^t \left(1 - \frac{t}{n} \right)^n \right] e^{-t} t^{z-1} \right| \leqq \frac{t^2}{n} e^{-t} t^{p-1} \quad \text{or} \quad \frac{1}{n} e^{-t} t^{p+1}. \tag{122}$$

Consequently the absolute value of the integral in the right member of equation (117) cannot exceed

$$\frac{1}{n} \int_0^n e^{-t} t^{p+1} \, dt < \frac{1}{n} \int_0^\infty e^{-t} t^{p+1} \, dt \quad \text{or} \quad \frac{1}{n} \Gamma(p+2). \tag{123}$$

As this approaches zero when n becomes infinite, the relation (111) is now established.

If we put $t = nu$ in the integral of equation (111), we find:

$$\int_0^n \left(1 - \frac{t}{n} \right)^n t^{z-1} \, dt = n^z \int_0^1 u^{z-1} (1 - u)^n \, du. \tag{124}$$

An integration by parts gives

$$\int_0^1 u^{z-1} (1 - u)^n \, du = \frac{u^z}{z} (1 - u)^n \Big|_0^1 + \frac{n}{z} \int_0^1 u^z (1 - u)^{n-1} \, du. \tag{125}$$

The integrated part is zero, since $\mathbf{R}(z) > 0$, if $n > 0$. If we repeat this process until we come to

$$\int_0^1 u^{z+n-1} \, du = \frac{1}{z + n}, \tag{126}$$

we find that

$$\int_0^1 u^{z-1} (1 - u)^n \, du = \frac{n(n-1) \cdots 2 \cdot 1}{z(z+1) \cdots (z+n-1)(z+n)}. \tag{127}$$

This is in agreement with the equations (110) and (95), since by the remark made at the end of section 327 the integral is

$$B(z, n+1) = \frac{\Gamma(z)\Gamma(n+1)}{\Gamma(z+n+1)}$$

$$= \frac{n!}{(z+n)(z+n-1) \cdots (z+1)z}. \tag{128}$$

From equations (111), (124) and (127) we find

$$\Gamma(z) = \lim_{n \to \infty} \frac{n! \, n^z}{z(z+1) \cdots (z+n)}. \tag{129}$$

This expression was known to Euler and was used by Gauss as the fundamental definition of the Gamma function.

The reciprocal of the fraction in equation (129) is

$$z\left(1 + \frac{z}{1}\right)\left(1 + \frac{z}{2}\right)\cdots\left(1 + \frac{z}{n}\right)e^{-z\log n}$$

$$= z\left(1 + \frac{z}{1}\right)e^{-z}\left(1 + \frac{z}{2}\right)e^{-\frac{z}{2}}\cdots\left(1 + \frac{z}{n}\right)e^{-\frac{z}{n}}e^{g_n z}, \qquad (130)$$

where

$$g_n = 1 + \frac{1}{2} + \frac{1}{3} + \cdots + \frac{1}{n} - \log n. \qquad (131)$$

By equation (63),

$$\lim_{n\to\infty} g_n = \gamma, \quad \text{and} \quad \lim_{n\to\infty} e^{g_n z} = e^{\gamma z}. \qquad (132)$$

As the terms multiplying the last may be regarded as the nth partial product of an infinite product, we have:

$$\frac{1}{\Gamma(z)} = e^{\gamma z} z \prod_{n=1}^{\infty}\left(1 + \frac{z}{n}\right)e^{-\frac{z}{n}}. \qquad (133)$$

This form is due to Weierstrass, and was used by him as the starting point of the theory of $\Gamma(z)$.

Let us consider the logarithm of the typical term of the product,

$$\log\left(1 + \frac{z}{n}\right) - \frac{z}{n} = \int_0^z\left(\frac{1}{z + n} - \frac{1}{n}\right)dz. \qquad (134)$$

Since

$$\left|\frac{1}{z + n} - \frac{1}{n}\right| = \left|\frac{-z}{n(z + n)}\right| \leq \left|\frac{2z}{n^2}\right| \quad \text{if} \quad n \geq |2z|, \qquad (135)$$

the series of integrands converges uniformly in any finite region not including any of the negative integers. Thus, on choosing branches of the logarithmic function as in section 285, we see that the integrated series converges uniformly in any such region. We may include any one of the negative integers without disturbing the uniform convergence, if we omit the corresponding factor from the product. Thus the function defined by the right member of equation (133) is analytic for all finite values of z. It is distinct from zero if z is not zero or a negative integer. Consequently its reciprocal, the Gamma function as defined by this relation, is analytic at all points except zero and the negative integers. The derivation only proves directly that the definition of $\Gamma(z)$ by equation (133), which is equivalent to equation (129), agrees with that previously given by equation (91) for $\mathbf{R}(z) > 0$. However, both the function defined by combining equation (96) with (91), and that defined by equation (133) are analytic for all finite values except zero and the negative integers. Hence the difference of the two functions is analytic except, perhaps, for zero and the negative integral values. And, since this difference is zero for all z with $\mathbf{R}(z) > 0$, it must be zero throughout its region of analyticity, and the two definitions agree for all values of z.

If we replace z by $-z$ in equation (133), we find:

$$\frac{1}{\Gamma(z)}\frac{1}{\Gamma(-z)} = -z^2 \prod_{n=-\infty}^{\infty}{}' \left(1 + \frac{z}{n}\right)e^{-\frac{z}{n}} = -z^2 \prod_{n=1}^{\infty}\left(1 - \frac{z^2}{n^2}\right). \tag{136}$$

But, by section 285,

$$\sin \pi z = \pi z \prod_{n=-\infty}^{\infty}{}' \left(1 - \frac{z}{n}\right)e^{\frac{z}{n}} = \pi z \prod_{n=1}^{\infty}\left(1 - \frac{z^2}{n^2}\right). \tag{137}$$

A comparison of these expressions shows that

$$\frac{\sin \pi z}{\pi} = \frac{1}{\Gamma(z)(-z)\Gamma(-z)} = \frac{1}{\Gamma(z)\Gamma(1-z)}, \tag{138}$$

by equation (94), which holds for all values of z, and hence when z is replaced by $-z$. Thus we have, finally,

$$\Gamma(z)\Gamma(1-z) = \frac{\pi}{\sin \pi z}. \tag{139}$$

329. Stirling's Formula for Complex Values. The Euler-Maclaurin sum formula, as given by equations (45) and (46) holds even if the function $f(x)$ is a complex function of a real variable as in section 119. From equation (129), $\log \Gamma(z)$ is the limit of

$$L(z,m) = z \log m + \sum_{k=1}^{m} \log k - \sum_{k=0}^{m} \log (z + k). \tag{140}$$

If we put $n = 2$ in equation (68), replace the remainder by its value from equation (69), and insert $1/6$ for B_2 in accordance with equation (22), we may write the result:

$$\sum_{k=1}^{m} \log k = m \log m - m + \tfrac{1}{2} \log m + 1 + \frac{1}{12}\left(\frac{1}{m} - 1\right)$$
$$+ \int_{1}^{m} \frac{P_2(x)}{x^2}\,dx. \tag{141}$$

For $f(x) = \log (z + x)$, an analogous relation is:

$$\sum_{k=0}^{m} \log (z + k) = (z + m) \log (z + m) - z \log z - m$$
$$+ \tfrac{1}{2} \log (z + m) + \tfrac{1}{2} \log z + \frac{1}{12}\left(\frac{1}{z + m} - \frac{1}{z}\right)$$
$$+ \int_{0}^{m} \frac{P_2(x)}{(z + x)^2} \, dx. \quad (142)$$

It follows from the last three equations that:

$$L(z,m) = - (z + m + \tfrac{1}{2}) \log \left(1 + \frac{z}{m}\right) + (z - \tfrac{1}{2}) \log z$$
$$+ K_m - \frac{1}{12}\left(\frac{1}{z + m} - \frac{1}{z}\right) - \int_{0}^{m} \frac{P_2(x)}{(z + x)^2} \, dx, \quad (143)$$

where K_m is given by

$$K_m = 1 + \frac{1}{12}\left(\frac{1}{m} - 1\right) + \int_{1}^{m} \frac{P_2(x)}{x^2} \, dx,$$

and

$$\lim_{m = \infty} K_m = K = \log \sqrt{2\pi}, \quad (144)$$

by equations (141), (70), and (79). For z fixed, not a negative real number or zero, we may let m become infinite. The integral in equation (143) will converge, since $P_2(x)$ is bounded, and the integrand is ultimately dominated by A/x^2, for a suitable value of A. Thus we find:

$$\log \Gamma(z) = -z + (z - \tfrac{1}{2}) \log z + K + \frac{1}{12z} - \int_{0}^{\infty} \frac{P_2(x)}{(z + x)^2} \, dx. \quad (145)$$

If the expansion of equation (142) were carried out to more terms, we should find:

$$\log \Gamma(z) = -z + (z - \tfrac{1}{2}) \log z + K + \sum_{r=1}^{n} \frac{B_{2r}}{2r(2r - 1)} \frac{1}{z^{2r-1}} + R_n,$$
$$(146)$$

where, by analogy with equation (46),

$$R_n = - \int_{0}^{\infty} \frac{P_{2n}(x)(2n - 1)\,!}{(z + x)^{2n}} \, dx. \quad (147)$$

Throughout this section, the branch of the logarithms to be used is that determined by taking the negative real axis as a cut, and the values real for positive real values. The expansion just obtained is valid for any fixed n, and any fixed z not on the cut. It is also an asymptotic expansion if z becomes infinite in certain restricted ways, for example if z remains outside a sector including the negative real axis. This will follow after we prove that, if

$$z = re^{i\theta} = r\cos\theta + ir\sin\theta, \quad -\pi + \delta < \theta < \pi - \delta, \quad (148)$$

the remainder term has a numerical value less than $\csc^{2n}(\delta/2)$ times that of the last term retained.

We begin by showing that

$$|z + x| \geqq \sin\frac{\delta}{2}(|z| + x). \tag{149}$$

Since

$$(r - x)^2 \geqq 0; \quad (r + x)^2 \geqq 4rx.$$

But $|\theta| < \pi - \delta$ implies $\left|\sin\dfrac{\theta}{2}\right| < \left|\cos\dfrac{\delta}{2}\right|$, so that

$$-4rx\sin^2\frac{\theta}{2} \geqq -(r + x)^2\cos^2\frac{\delta}{2}. \tag{150}$$

Consequently,

$$r^2 + x^2 + 2rx\cos\theta = (r + x)^2 - 4rx\sin^2\frac{\theta}{2} \geqq (r + x)^2\sin^2\frac{\delta}{2}. \tag{151}$$

That is,

$$|z + x|^2 \geqq (|z| + x)^2\sin^2\frac{\delta}{2}, \tag{152}$$

and the inequality (149) follows by taking the positive square root.

It follows by the argument used to show that the remainder term is numerically less than the last term retained when z is real and positive that

$$\int_0^\infty \frac{|P_{2n}(x)|(2n - 1)!}{(|z| + x)^{2n}}\,dx < \frac{|B_{2n}|}{2n(2n - 1)}\frac{1}{|z|^{2n-1}}. \tag{153}$$

But by equation (147) and the relation (149) we have:

$$|R_n| \leqq \int_0^\infty \frac{|P_{2n}(x)|(2n - 1)!}{|z + x|^{2n}}\,dx$$

$$\leqq \csc^{2n}\frac{\delta}{2}\int_0^\infty \frac{P_{2n}(x)(2n - 1)!}{(|z| + x)^{2n}}\,dx. \tag{154}$$

A comparison of the last two relations shows the relation of the remainder to the last term retained stated above, and the asymptotic character of the expansion (146) then follows.

330. Integral Representations of Euler's Constant. Certain important definite integrals are simply related to Euler's constant, which we have defined by:

$$\gamma = \lim_{n \to \infty} \left(1 + \frac{1}{2} + \frac{1}{3} + \cdots + \frac{1}{n} - \log n \right). \tag{155}$$

We begin with:

$$1 + t + t^2 + \cdots + t^{n-1} = \frac{1 - t^n}{1 - t}. \tag{156}$$

On integrating this from 0 to 1 we find:

$$1 + \frac{1}{2} + \frac{1}{3} + \cdots + \frac{1}{n} = \int_0^1 \frac{1 - t^n}{1 - t} \, dt. \tag{157}$$

Let us replace the dummy variable t by a new variable y, where

$$t = 1 - \frac{y}{n}. \tag{158}$$

Then

$$\int_0^1 \frac{1 - t^n}{1 - t} \, dt = \int_0^n \left[1 - \left(1 - \frac{y}{n} \right)^n \right] \frac{dy}{y}. \tag{159}$$

Since

$$-\log n = -\int_1^n \frac{dy}{y}, \tag{160}$$

it follows from equations (157) and (159) that γ is the limit of

$$1 + \frac{1}{2} + \frac{1}{3} + \cdots + \frac{1}{n} - \log n = \int_0^n \left[1 - \left(1 - \frac{y}{n} \right)^n \right] \frac{dy}{y} - \int_1^n \frac{dy}{y}$$

$$= \int_0^1 \left[1 - \left(1 - \frac{y}{n} \right)^n \right] \frac{dy}{y} - \int_1^n \left(1 - \frac{y}{n} \right)^n \frac{dy}{y}. \tag{161}$$

The relation (112) suggests that the limit of the last expression is the same as that of

$$\int_0^1 (1 - e^{-y}) \frac{dy}{y} - \int_1^n e^{-y} \frac{dy}{y}. \tag{162}$$

To verify this conjecture, we note that for $0 \le y \le n$

$$0 \le e^{-y} - \left(1 - \frac{y}{n} \right)^n \le e^{-y} \frac{y^2}{n}, \tag{163}$$

as a consequence of the relation (120). Consequently, the final member of equation (161) exceeds the expression (162) by a positive quantity which does not exceed

$$\int_0^n e^{-y} \frac{y^2}{n} \frac{dy}{y} \leqq \frac{1}{n} \int_0^\infty y e^{-y} \, dy \quad \text{or} \quad \frac{\Gamma(2)}{n} = \frac{1}{n}. \tag{164}$$

As this has a limit zero, when $n \to \infty$, the number γ is the limit of the expression (162), and

$$\gamma = \int_0^1 (1 - e^{-y}) \frac{dy}{y} - \int_1^\infty e^{-y} \frac{dy}{y}. \tag{165}$$

This expresses Euler's constant in terms of improper integrals.

The first integral may be computed from the rapidly convergent series which results by replacing e^{-y} by its power series expansion and integrating termwise. The second integral may then be found by combining this with the value of γ, equation (66), determined by the method of section 323. The results are:

$$\int_0^1 (1 - e^{-y}) \frac{dy}{y} = 0.79660 \cdots$$

and

$$\int_1^\infty e^{-y} \frac{dy}{y} = 0.21938 \cdots . \tag{166}$$

We may obtain another expression for γ in terms of an integral involving trigonometric functions, by the method of residues of section 278. The function $(1 - e^{-z})/z$ has a removable singularity at the origin, but otherwise is analytic for all finite values. Hence by integrating around a quadrant of a circle of radius unity in the first quadrant, we find:

$$\int_0^1 (1 - e^{-x}) \frac{dx}{x} + \int_{Q_1} (1 - e^{-z}) \frac{dz}{z} - \int_0^1 (1 - e^{-iy}) \frac{dy}{y} = 0, \tag{167}$$

where Q_1 is the circular arc. Similarly, by using a quadrant of a circle with arc Q_2, in the fourth quadrant, we find:

$$\int_0^1 (1 - e^{iy}) \frac{dy}{y} + \int_{Q_2} (1 - e^{-z}) \frac{dz}{z} - \int_0^1 (1 - e^{-x}) \frac{dx}{x} = 0, \tag{168}$$

where we have put $z = -iy$ on the y-axis.

Again, the function e^{-z}/z is analytic for all finite values except zero, so that its integral around a quarter of a ring bounded by the arc Q_1, a large quadrant Q_1' in the first quadrant, and portions of the x- and y-

axes will be zero.   The reasoning of section 281 shows that the integral around the large quadrant Q_1' approaches zero as its radius becomes infinite, and hence:

$$\int_1^\infty e^{-x} \frac{dx}{x} - \int_1^\infty e^{-iy} \frac{dy}{y} - \int_{Q_1} e^{-z} \frac{dz}{z} = 0. \qquad (169)$$

A similar quarter ring in the fourth quadrant may be used to give

$$\int_1^\infty e^{iy} \frac{dy}{y} - \int_1^\infty e^{-x} \frac{dx}{x} - \int_{Q_2} e^{-z} \frac{dz}{z} = 0, \qquad (170)$$

where we have again put $z = -iy$ on the y-axis.

If we add the members of equations (167) and (170), and subtract those of equations (168) and (169), we find:

$$2 \int_0^1 (1 - e^{-x}) \frac{dx}{x} - 2 \int_1^\infty e^{-x} \frac{dx}{x} + \int_0^1 (-2 + e^{iy} + e^{-iy}) \frac{dy}{y}$$

$$+ \int_1^\infty (e^{iy} + e^{-iy}) \frac{dy}{y} + \int_{Q_1} \frac{dz}{z} - \int_{Q_2} \frac{dz}{z} = 0. \quad (171)$$

But, by putting $z = e^{i\theta}$ in each case, we find

$$\int_{Q_1} \frac{dz}{z} = \int_{Q_2} \frac{dz}{z} = \frac{i\pi}{2}. \qquad (172)$$

This shows that the last two terms of equation (171) cancel, and the equation may be written:

$$\int_0^1 (1 - e^{-x}) \frac{dx}{x} - \int_1^\infty e^{-x} \frac{dx}{x} =$$

$$\int_0^1 (1 - \cos y) \frac{dy}{y} - \int_1^\infty \cos y \frac{dy}{y}. \quad (173)$$

From this and equation (165) we obtain

$$\gamma = \int_0^1 (1 - \cos y) \frac{dy}{y} - \int_1^\infty \cos y \frac{dy}{y}, \qquad (174)$$

the expression for γ in terms of integrals of trigonometric functions which we were seeking.

331. Some Non-elementary Integrals.   Consider the exponential integral

$$EI(x) = \int_x^\infty \frac{e^{-t}}{t} dt, \ x > 0. \qquad (175)$$

We find by successive integration by parts that

$$EI(x) = e^{-x}\left[\frac{1}{x} - \frac{1}{x^2} + \frac{2\,!}{x^3} - \cdots + (-1)^n\,\frac{n\,!}{x^{n+1}}\right] + R_{n+1}, \quad (176)$$

where

$$R_{n+1} = (-1)^{n+1}(n+1)\,!\int_x^\infty e^{-t}t^{-n-2}\,dt. \quad (177)$$

As x is positive, the integral is increased by replacing the power of t by the corresponding power of x, so that

$$|R_{n+1}| \le (n+1)\,!\,e^{-x}x^{-n-2}. \quad (178)$$

Thus the remainder term is numerically less than the term following the last term used in the expansion (176). For sufficiently large values of x, one of the early terms will be small, and the series may be used to compute the integral. It is only an asymptotic series, however, since although for fixed n and increasing x the remainder approaches zero, for fixed x and increasing n the series diverges. This follows from the fact that the ratio of consecutive terms is numerically n/x, which becomes infinite with n.

An expansion of $EI(x)$, convergent for all values of x, may be obtained by using a result based on equation (165). We have:

$$EI(x) = \int_x^\infty e^{-t}\frac{dt}{t} = \int_x^1 e^{-t}\frac{dt}{t} + \int_1^\infty e^{-t}\frac{dt}{t}$$

$$= \int_x^1 e^{-t}\frac{dt}{t} + \int_0^1 (1 - e^{-t})\frac{dt}{t} - \gamma \quad (179)$$

$$= \int_0^x (1 - e^{-t})\frac{dt}{t} - \log x - \gamma. \quad (180)$$

If the first integral is expanded in a power series, we find:

$$EI(x) = -\gamma - \log x + x - \frac{x^2}{2\cdot 2\,!} + \frac{x^3}{3\cdot 3\,!} - \cdots. \quad (181)$$

The logarithmic integral,

$$\text{li}\,x = \int_0^x \frac{dt}{\log t}, \quad 0 \le x < 1, \quad (182)$$

may be transformed into the exponential integral, by $t = e^{-u}$,

$$\text{li}\,x = -\int_{-\log x}^\infty e^{-u}\frac{du}{u} = -EI(-\log x). \quad (183)$$

We may treat the cosine integral,

$$CI(x) = \int_x^\infty \cos t \frac{dt}{t}, \tag{184}$$

in a manner similar to that used for the exponential integral. The asymptotic formula for large values of x is:

$$CI(x) = -\frac{\sin x}{x} + \frac{\cos x}{x^2} + 2! \frac{\sin x}{x^3} - 3! \frac{\cos x}{x^4} - \cdots \tag{185}$$

By using equation (174) we find that:

$$CI(x) = \int_0^x (1 - \cos t) \frac{dt}{t} - \log x - \gamma \tag{186}$$

$$= -\gamma - \log x + \frac{x^2}{2 \cdot 2!} - \frac{x^4}{4 \cdot 4!} + \cdots, \tag{187}$$

which may be used to calculate the integral for all values of x.

For the sine integral

$$SI(x) = \int_x^\infty \sin t \frac{dt}{t}, \tag{188}$$

we may use integration by parts to obtain the asymptotic expansion:

$$SI(x) = \frac{\cos x}{x} + \frac{\sin x}{x^2} - 2! \frac{\cos x}{x^3} - 3! \frac{\sin x}{x^4} + \cdots. \tag{189}$$

To obtain an expansion convergent for all values of x, we recall equation (221) of section 281, namely,

$$\int_0^\infty \sin t \frac{dt}{t} = \frac{\pi}{2}. \tag{190}$$

It follows from this that

$$SI(x) = \int_0^\infty \sin t \frac{dt}{t} - \int_0^x \sin t \frac{dt}{t}$$

$$= \frac{\pi}{2} - x + \frac{x^3}{3 \cdot 3!} - \frac{x^5}{5 \cdot 5!} + \cdots. \tag{191}$$

Similar methods apply to the probability integral,

$$\int_0^x e^{-x^2} dx = x - \frac{x^3}{3} + \frac{x^5}{5 \cdot 2!} - \frac{x^7}{7 \cdot 3!} + \cdots, \tag{192}$$

the Fresnel sine integral

$$\int_0^x \sin x^2 \, dx = \frac{x^3}{3} - \frac{x^7}{7 \cdot 3!} + \frac{x^{11}}{11 \cdot 5!} - \cdots \tag{193}$$

and the Fresnel cosine integral

$$\int_0^x \cos x^2 \, dx = x - \frac{x^5}{5 \cdot 2!} + \frac{x^9}{9 \cdot 4!} - \cdots. \tag{194}$$

These power series converge for all values of x.

The integrals from x to ∞ may be obtained from those from 0 to x by using the evaluation:

$$\int_0^\infty e^{-x^2} \, dx = \frac{\sqrt{\pi}}{2}, \tag{195}$$

found in equation (109), and the two derived from it in problem 47 of Exercises XIII:

$$\int_0^\infty \sin x^2 \, dx = \frac{\sqrt{2\pi}}{4} \quad \text{and} \quad \int_0^\infty \cos x^2 \, dx = \frac{\sqrt{2\pi}}{4}. \tag{196}$$

For the integrals from x to ∞, the asymptotic formulas:

$$\int_x^\infty e^{-x^2} \, dx = e^{-x^2}\left(\frac{1}{2x} - \frac{1}{2^2 x^3} + \frac{3}{2^3 x^5} - \frac{3 \cdot 5}{2^4 x^7} + \cdots \right), \tag{197}$$

$$\int_x^\infty \sin x^2 \, dx = \frac{\cos x^2}{2x} + \frac{\sin x^2}{2^2 x^3} - \frac{3 \cos x^2}{2^3 x^5} - \frac{3 \cdot 5 \sin x^2}{2^4 x^7} + \cdots, \tag{198}$$

$$\int_x^\infty \cos x^2 \, dx = -\frac{\sin x^2}{2x} + \frac{\cos x^2}{2^2 x^3} + \frac{3 \sin x^2}{2^3 x^5} - \frac{3 \cdot 5 \cos x^2}{2^4 x^7} - \cdots, \tag{199}$$

may be found by integrating by parts, in each case taking as the factor to be integrated xe^{-x^2}, $x \sin x^2$, or $x \cos x^2$. For sufficiently large values of x, these may be used to compute the integrals from x to ∞, and the values of the integrals from 0 to x may then be found for these large values by making use of equations (195) and (196).

EXERCISES XVI

1. Show that

$$\int_0^\infty x^m e^{-px^q} \, dx = \frac{\Gamma\left(\dfrac{m+1}{q}\right)}{qp^{\frac{m+1}{q}}}, \quad \text{if } m > -1, \ p > 0, \ q > 0.$$

Hint: Change the variable from x to $t = px^q$.

2. Show that

$$\int_0^1 x^n \, (\log x)^m \, dx = \frac{(-1)^m \Gamma(m+1)}{(n+1)^{m+1}}, \quad \text{if} \quad m > -1, \, n > -1.$$

Hint: Change the variable from x to $t = -(n+1) \log x$.

3. Let

$$H_p = \sum_{k=1}^{\infty} \frac{1}{k^p}, \; s_p = \sum_{k=0}^{\infty} \frac{1}{(2k+1)^p} \quad \text{and} \quad t_p = \sum_{k=1}^{\infty} \frac{(-1)^{k-1}}{k^p}$$

where $p > 1$ and need not be integral. Show that $s_p = (1 - 2^{-p})H_p$ and $t_p = (1 - 2^{-p+1})H_p$. When p is not an even integer, H_p may be computed by equation (61), but if p is an even integer the value is determined exactly by equation (5) as

$$H_{2n} = \frac{2^{2n-1} \pi^{2n} (-1)^{n-1} B_{2n}}{(2n)\,!}.$$

Hence, in particular,

$$H_2 = \frac{\pi^2}{6}, \quad s_2 = \frac{\pi^2}{8}, \quad t_2 = \frac{\pi^2}{12}.$$

4. Show that

$$\int_0^1 \frac{(-\log x)^p}{1-x} \, dx = \Gamma(p+1) \sum_{k=1}^{\infty} \frac{1}{k^{p+1}} \quad \text{if} \quad p > 0.$$

For the calculation of the sum, or exact evaluation when p is an odd integer, see problem 3. *Hint:* Expand $1/(1-x)$ in a power series and integrate termwise. The process is valid by section 247. Since for $0 < x < 1$, the partial sum $\sum_{i=0}^{n} x^i = \frac{1-x^{n+1}}{1-x} < \frac{2}{1-x}$, the partial sums are dominated by twice the original integrand.

5. Show that

$$\int_0^1 \frac{(-\log x)^m}{1+x} \, dx = \Gamma(m+1) \sum_{k=1}^{\infty} \frac{(-1)^{k-1}}{k^{m+1}}, \quad \text{if} \quad m > -1.$$

For the calculation of the sum, or exact evaluation when m is an odd integer, see problem 3. *Hint:* Proceed as in problem 4.

6. Show that

$$\int_0^1 \log \, (1-x) \, \frac{dx}{x} = \int_0^1 \frac{\log x}{1-x} \, dx = -\frac{\pi^2}{6}.$$

Hint: Integrate by parts or put $x = 1 - u$, and use problem 4.

7. Show that

$$\int_0^1 \log \, (1+x) \, \frac{dx}{x} = \int_0^1 \frac{-\log x}{1+x} \, dx = \frac{\pi^2}{12}.$$

Hint: Integrate by parts, and use problem 5.

8. Verify that

$$t \coth t - t = \frac{2t}{e^{2t} - 1} = \sum_{n=0}^{\infty} B_n \frac{(2t)^n}{n!},$$

and deduce that

$$\coth z = \frac{1}{z} + \sum_{k=1}^{\infty} B_{2k} \frac{2^{2k}}{(2k)!} z^{2k-1},$$

and hence

$$\cot z = \frac{1}{z} + \sum_{k=1}^{\infty} B_{2k} \frac{(-1)^k 2^{2k}}{(2k)!} z^{2k-1}.$$

By problem 3, the last result is in accord with that of problem 51, Exercises XIII.

9. Prove the identity $\tanh z = 2 \coth 2z - \coth z$, and deduce that

$$\tanh z = \sum_{k=1}^{\infty} \frac{(2^{2k} - 1) 2^{2k}}{(2k)!} B_{2k} z^{2k-1}.$$

Similarly deduce that

$$\tan z = \sum_{k=1}^{\infty} \frac{(2^{2k} - 1) 2^{2k} (-1)^{k-1}}{(2k)!} B_{2k} z^{2k-1},$$

either from the identity $\tan z = -2 \cot 2z + \cot z$, or from the result for $\tanh z$. *Hint:* Use problem 8.

10. Prove the identity $\operatorname{csch} z = -\coth z + \coth \frac{z}{2}$, and from this and problem 8 deduce that $\operatorname{csch} z = \frac{1}{z} + \sum_{k=1}^{\infty} \frac{(2 - 2^{2k})}{(2k)!} B_{2k} z^{2k-1}$. Also, either from this or the identity $\csc z = -\cot z + \cot \frac{z}{2}$, deduce that

$$\csc z = \frac{1}{z} + \sum_{k=1}^{\infty} \frac{(2 - 2^{2k})(-1)^k}{(2k)!} B_{2k} z^{2k-1}.$$

11. Verify the identity $2t \operatorname{sech} t = 4te^{3t}/(e^{4t} - 1) - 4te^t/(e^{4t} - 1)$. By equation (39), the right member is

$$\sum_{n=1}^{\infty} [B_n(\tfrac{3}{4}) - B_n(\tfrac{1}{4})](4t)^n, \quad \text{or} \quad \sum_{k=0}^{\infty} -2B_{2k+1}(\tfrac{1}{4})(4t)^{2k+1}$$

by section 319. Hence

$$\operatorname{sech} z = \sum_{k=0}^{\infty} -B_{2k+1}(\tfrac{1}{4}) 4^{2k+1} z^{2k},$$

and

$$\sec z = \sum_{k=0}^{\infty} (-1)^{k+1} B_{2k+1}(\tfrac{1}{4}) 4^{2k+1} z^{2k}.$$

12. *Operational notation.* Let D denote the operation of differentiation, and Δ denote the operation of increasing x by a and taking a difference, as in section

93. Then $1 + \Delta = e^{aD}$ is an abbreviation for Taylor's series, since when e^{aD} is expanded in a power series, and we operate on F with each side:

$$(1 + \Delta)F = F(x) + F(x + a) - F(x) = F(x + a),$$

and

$$\left(1 + aD + \frac{a^2D^2}{2!} + \cdots \right)F = F(x) + aF'(x) + \frac{a^2F''(x)}{2!} + \cdots.$$

The abbreviation for the Euler-Maclaurin sum formula may be found by formal transformations of $1 + \Delta = e^{aD}$ into $aD = \Delta aD/(e^{aD} - 1)$. If we expand the right member into $\sum_{n=0}^{\infty} \Delta B_n \dfrac{(aD)^n}{n!}$ by equation (37), and operate with each side on $F = \displaystyle\int_0^x f(t)\, dt$, we find:

$$af(x) = aDF = \sum_{n=0}^{\infty} \Delta B_n \frac{a^n}{n!} D^n F = \int_x^{x+a} f(t)\, dt - \frac{a}{2}[f(x + a) - f(x)]$$

$$+ \sum_{r=1}^{\infty} \frac{B_{2r}a^{2r}}{(2r)!} [f^{(2r-1)}(x + a) - f^{(2r-1)}(x)].$$

With $a = 1$ and $x = k$, and the infinite series replaced by a finite sum and a remainder term, this is essentially equation (44), from which we derived the Euler-Maclaurin sum formula.

13. While the operational procedure of problem 12 proves nothing, it frequently suggests expansions which may be shown to be convergent or asymptotic by other means. For example, an expansion in terms of differences useful for numerical integration is suggested by transforming $e^{aD} = 1 + \Delta$ into $\Delta/D = a\Delta/\log(1 + \Delta)$. This suggests $\displaystyle\int_x^{x+a} f(t)\, dt = a(1 + \Delta/2 - \Delta^2/12 + \Delta^3/24 - \cdots)f$. Show that, if all differences after the fourth are zero, the result obtained by using this for x to $x + a$ and $x + a$ to $x + 2a$ is the same as that found by Simpson's rule, section 145, for the single interval from x to $x + 2a$. *Hint:* For $x + a$ to $x + 2a$ we operate with $(1 + \Delta)$, and the first result is $a(2 + \Delta)(1 + \Delta/2 - \Delta^2/12 + \Delta^3/24)f$. The result from Simpson's rule is $a/3[1 + 4(1 + \Delta) + (1 + \Delta)^2]f$. These agree since $\Delta^4 f = 0$.

14. Show that the value of γ in equation (66) may be found from equation (65) with $m = 10$ and the terms in B_2 and B_4, since the term in B_6, and hence the remainder is less than $5 \cdot 10^{-9}$.

15. The percentage error made by replacing $m!$ by Stirling's approximation, $\sqrt{2\pi}m^{m+1/2}e^{-m}$ is less than 0.1 per cent if m exceeds 100, less than 1 per cent if m exceeds 10, and less than 10 per cent if m exceeds 1.

16. Show that $\displaystyle\int_a^b (x - a)^m(b - x)^n\, dx = (b - a)^{m+n+1}B(m + 1, n + 1)$, if $b > a$ and $m > -1, n > -1$. *Hint:* Replace x by t, where $x - a = (b - a)t$.

17. Show that

$$\int_0^p x^m (p^q - x^q)^n \, dx = \frac{p^{qn+m+1}}{q} B\left(n+1, \frac{m+1}{q}\right)$$

if $p > 0$, $q > 0$, $m > -1$ and $n > -1$. *Hint:* Replace x by t where $x^q = p^q t$.

18. Show that

$$\int_0^{\frac{\pi}{2}} \sin^m x \cos^n x \, dx = \frac{1}{2} B\left(\frac{m+1}{2}, \frac{n+1}{2}\right)$$

if $m > -1$, $n > -1$. *Hint:* Change the variable to $t = \sin^2 x$.

19. As a special case of problem 17 or 18, we have:

$$\int_0^1 \frac{x^m \, dx}{\sqrt{1 - x^2}} = \int_0^{\frac{\pi}{2}} \sin^m t \, dt = \int_0^{\frac{\pi}{2}} \cos^m t \, dt = \frac{1}{2} B\left(\frac{m+1}{2}, \frac{1}{2}\right), \quad m > -1.$$

The right member is $\frac{1}{2}[\Gamma(\{m+1\}/2)\Gamma(1/2)]/[\Gamma(m/2 + 1)]$, and for m an even integer, $2n$, is $\dfrac{1 \cdot 3 \cdot 5 \cdots (2n-1)}{2 \cdot 4 \cdot 6 \cdots (2n)} \dfrac{\pi}{2}$; while for m an odd integer, $2n + 1$, it is $\dfrac{2 \cdot 4 \cdot 6 \cdots (2n)}{3 \cdot 5 \cdot 7 \cdots (2n+1)}$.

20. *Wallis's product for π.* Show that the integral of problem 19 decreases as m increases through integral values, so that

$$\frac{2 \cdot 4 \cdot 6 \cdots (2n)}{3 \cdot 5 \cdot 7 \cdots (2n+1)} < \frac{1 \cdot 3 \cdot 5 \cdots (2n-1)}{2 \cdot 4 \cdot 6 \cdots (2n)} \frac{\pi}{2} < \frac{2 \cdot 4 \cdot 6 \cdots (2n-2)}{3 \cdot 5 \cdot 7 \cdots (2n-1)}.$$

Deduce from this that

$$\frac{\pi}{2} = \frac{2 \cdot 2 \cdot 4 \cdot 4 \cdot 6 \cdot 6}{1 \cdot 3 \cdot 3 \cdot 5 \cdot 5 \cdot 7} \cdots,$$

where the partial products are alternately in excess and defect. This is essentially equation (73). This derivation may be made " elementary " since the integrals of problem 19 may be evaluated without using the theory of the Gamma function, for example by integrating by parts.

21. Show that $\displaystyle\int_0^\infty \frac{x^m}{(1 + px^q)^k} \, dx = \frac{1}{qp^{(m+1)/q}} B\left(\frac{m+1}{q}, k - \frac{m+1}{q}\right)$ if $p > 0$, $q > 0$, $m > -1$ and $k > (m+1)/q$. *Hint:* Replace the variable x by t where $(1 + px^q)^{-1} = 1 - t$.

22. It was proved by contour integration in problem 40 of Exercises XIII that $\displaystyle\int_0^\infty \frac{x^{-p}}{1 + x} \, dx = \frac{\pi}{\sin p\pi}$, if $0 < p < 1$. Verify this result by using Gamma functions.

Hint: By problem 21 the integral equals $B(1 - p, p) = \Gamma(1 - p)\Gamma(p) = \dfrac{\pi}{\sin p\pi}$ by equation (139).

23. In n dimensions, let V_n be the volume for which $x_i \geqq 0$, $\sum\limits_{i=1}^{n} x_i \leqq a$.

Then $\displaystyle\int_{V_n} x_1^{m_1} x_2^{m_2} \cdots x_n^{m_n}\, dV_n = I(n,a)$, where $m_i > -1$, equals

$$a^{\Sigma m_i + n}\, \frac{\prod \Gamma(m_i + 1)}{\Gamma(\sum m_i + n + 1)},$$

with i from 1 to n in the sums and product. *Hint:* For $n = 1$,

$I(1,a) = \displaystyle\int_0^a x^{m_1}\, dx$ and $a^{m_1+1}\,[\Gamma(m_1 + 1)]/[\Gamma(m_1 + 2)] = a^{m_1+1}/(m_1 + 1)$.

Now use mathematical induction. $I(n,a) = \displaystyle\int_0^a x_n^{m_n}\, dx_n I(n-1,\, a - x_n) =$

$I(n-1,1)\displaystyle\int_0^a x_n^{m_n}(a - x_n)^J\, dx_n = a^{m_n+J+1}B(m_n + 1,\, J + 1)I(n-1,1) =$

$a^{m_n+J+1}\,[\Gamma(m_n + 1)\Gamma(J + 1)]/[\Gamma(m_n + J + 2)]I(n-1,1)$, where throughout

$J = \displaystyle\sum_{j=1}^{n-1} m_j + n - 1$. Thus $m_n + J + 1 = \sum m_i + n$, and the calculation

shows the result true for n if true for $n - 1$.

24. If V_n is defined by $x_i \geqq 0$, $\displaystyle\sum_{i=1}^{n} \left(\frac{x_i}{a_i}\right)^{p_i} \leqq 1$, and $m_i > -1$,

$$\int_{V_n} x_1^{m_1} x_2^{m_2} \cdots x_n^{m_n}\, dV_n = \frac{\displaystyle\prod_{i=1}^{n}\left[\frac{a_i^{m_i+1}}{p_i}\, \Gamma\left(\frac{m_i + 1}{p_i}\right)\right]}{\Gamma\left[\displaystyle\sum_{i=1}^{n}\left(\frac{m_i + 1}{p_i}\right) + 1\right]}.$$

The integrals of this problem are known as *Dirichlet's integrals.* In three dimensions they enable us to compute the volume, first and second moments, and hence centers of gravity and moments of inertia of octants of solids bounded by

surfaces $\left(\dfrac{x}{a}\right)^p + \left(\dfrac{y}{b}\right)^q + \left(\dfrac{z}{c}\right)^r = 1$, e.g., an ellipsoid. Similarly in two dimen-

sions for the areas and moments of quadrants of areas bounded by

$\left(\dfrac{x}{a}\right)^p + \left(\dfrac{y}{b}\right)^q = 1$, e.g., an ellipse. *Hint:* Reduce this integral to that of prob-

lem 23 by the change of variable $(x_i/a_i)^{p_i} = u_i$.

25. If $F(u)$ is continuous, V_n is the volume of problem 23, and $m_i > -1$,

then $\displaystyle\int_{V_n} F\left(\sum_{i=1}^{n} x_i\right) x_1^{m_1} x_2^{m_2} \cdots x_n^{m_n}\, dV_n = \frac{\prod \Gamma(m_i + 1)}{\Gamma(\sum m_i + n)} \int_0^a F(u) u^{\Sigma m_i + n - 1}\, du$.

Hint: Approximate the multiple integral by a single sum, using as element of volume that between $\sum x_i = u$ and $\sum x_i = u + \Delta u$. This element is Δu times an intermediate value of $dI(n,u)/du$, where $I(n,u)$ is the integral of problem 23 with u in place of a.

26. If $F(u)$ is continuous, V_n is the volume of problem 24, and $m_i > -1$, then

$$\int_{V_n} F\left[\sum_{i=1}^{n}\left(\frac{x_i}{a_i}\right)^{p_i}\right] x_1^{m_1} x_2^{m_2} \cdots x_n^{m_n}\, dV_n =$$

$$\frac{(\sum m_i + n)\, \Pi\left[\dfrac{a_i^{m_i+1}}{p_i}\, \Gamma\left(\dfrac{m_i+1}{p_i}\right)\right]}{\Gamma\left[\sum\left(\dfrac{m_i+1}{p_i}\right)+1\right]} \int_0^1 F(u) u^{\Sigma m_i + n - 1}\, du.$$

Hint: Use the result of problem 24, with a_i replaced by $a_i u$, and then proceed as in the preceding problem.

27. If U denotes the volume of a " sphere " in n dimensions, made up of points such that $\sum x_i^2 \leq R^2$, show that $\displaystyle\int_U \frac{1}{\sqrt{R^2 - \sum x_i^2}}\, dV_n = \frac{\pi^{(n+1)/2}}{\Gamma[(n+1)/2]}\, R^{n-1}$.

Hint: The integral is 2^n times the part with positive coördinates. By problem 26 this is reducible to that found in problem 17.

28. The " volume " of an n-dimensional " sphere " of radius R is equal to $\pi^{n/2} R^n / \Gamma[(n/2)+1]$ and the " surface " is $n\pi^{n/2} R^{n-1}/\Gamma[(n/2)+1]$. For $n = 2, 3, 4$ the " volumes " are πR^2, $\frac{4}{3}\pi R^3$ and $\frac{1}{2}\pi^2 R^4$, while the " surfaces " are $2\pi R$, $4\pi R^2$ and $2\pi^2 R^3$. *Hint:* Use problem 24, and the hint to problem 27, for the " volume." The " surface " is the derivative of the " volume " with respect to R.

29. Show that $\displaystyle\int_0^1 \frac{x^{-p} + x^{-q}}{(1+x)^{2-p-q}}\, dx = B(1-p,\ 1-q)$ if $0 < p < 1$, $0 < q < 1$. *Hint:* $\displaystyle\int_0^1 \frac{x^{-p}\, dx}{(1+x)^{2-p-q}} = \int_1^\infty \frac{u^{-q}\, du}{(1+u)^{2-p-q}}$ if $x = \dfrac{1}{u}$. Now use problem 21 to evaluate $\displaystyle\int_0^\infty \frac{u^{-q}\, du}{(1+u)^{2-p-q}}$.

30. The function $\displaystyle\int_0^\infty x^q e^{-xz}\, dx$, for $q > -1$ and z complex is an analytic function of z for all z with positive real part, by the argument of section 303. Deduce that $\displaystyle\int_0^\infty x^q e^{-xz}\, dx = \Gamma(q+1)/z^{q+1}$. If $z = a + bi = re^{i\theta}$, with $a > 0$, $-\pi/2 < \theta < \pi/2$, we have:

$$\int_0^\infty e^{-ax} \cos bx\, x^q\, dx = \frac{\Gamma(q+1)}{r^{q+1}} \cos (q+1)\theta \quad \text{and}$$

$$\int_0^\infty e^{-ax} \sin bx\, x^q\, dx = \frac{\Gamma(q+1)}{r^{q+1}} \sin (q+1)\theta.$$

31. If $\mathbf{R}(p) > \mathbf{R}(r)$, and $q > -1$, the function whose Laplace transform is $1/(p-r)^{q+1}$ is $x^q e^{rx}/\Gamma(q+1)$. For q an integer this agrees with problem 50 of Exercises XIV. *Hint:* Put $z = p - r$ in the integral of problem 30.

32. By inverting the order of integration in $\int_0^\infty dx \int_0^\infty dy \cos bx \, y^{p-1} e^{-xy} \, dy$,

show that if $b > 0$ and $0 < p < 1$, $\int_0^\infty \dfrac{\cos bx}{x^p} \, dx = \dfrac{b^{p-1}\pi}{\Gamma(p) \, 2 \cos (p\pi /2)}$. *Hint:*

For the original order, use $\int_0^\infty y^{p-1} e^{-xy} \, dy = \dfrac{\Gamma(p)}{x^p}$, obtained by putting

$xy = u$. For the other order, $\int_0^\infty \cos bx \, e^{-xy} \, dx = \dfrac{y}{b^2 + y^2}$ by section 135, and

$\int_0^\infty \dfrac{y^p \, dy}{b^2 + y^2} = \dfrac{b^{p-1}}{2} \int_0^\infty \dfrac{u^{(p-1)/2}}{1 + u} \, du$, if $b^2 u = y^2$. By problem 22 this is

$\dfrac{b^{p-1}}{2} \dfrac{\pi}{\sin\left(\dfrac{1 - p}{2}\right)\pi}$.

33. Prove that $\int_0^\infty \dfrac{\sin bx}{x^p} \, dx = \dfrac{b^{p-1}\pi}{\Gamma(p) \, 2 \sin (p\pi /2)}$, if $b > 0$ and $0 < p < 1$.

Hint: Proceed as in problem 32. Here $\int_0^\infty \sin bx \, e^{-xy} \, dx = \dfrac{b}{b^2 + y^2}$.

34. Show that $\int_0^\infty \dfrac{\cos bx}{x^p} \, dx = b^{p-1}\Gamma(1 - p) \sin \dfrac{p\pi}{2}$,

and

$$\int_0^\infty \dfrac{\sin bx}{x^p} \, dx = b^{p-1}\Gamma(1 - p) \cos \dfrac{p\pi}{2},$$

if $b > 0$ and $0 < p < 1$. *Hint:* Use equation (139), and the results of problems 32 and 33. Or replace q, a, r, θ by $-p$, 0, b, $\pi/2$ in problem 30. That this process is valid follows from the fact that the difference between the integral in a and that with $a = 0$ is dominated by the integral of problem 30 of Exercises XII.

35. Show that

$$\int_0^\infty \cos (bx^k) \, dx = \dfrac{\Gamma\left(\dfrac{1}{k}\right)}{kb^{\frac{1}{k}}} \cos \left(\dfrac{\pi}{2k}\right) \quad \text{and} \quad \int_0^\infty \sin (bx^k) \, dx = \dfrac{\Gamma\left(\dfrac{1}{k}\right)}{kb^{\frac{1}{k}}} \sin \left(\dfrac{\pi}{2k}\right),$$

if $b > 0$, $k > 1$. The special case $\int_0^\infty \cos x^2 \, dx = \int_0^\infty \sin x^2 \, dx = \dfrac{\sqrt{\pi}}{2\sqrt{2}}$

agrees with equation (196). *Hint:* Put $u = x^k$, and use problem 34.

36. Establish the duplication formula for $\Gamma(z)$:

$$\Gamma(2z) = \dfrac{1}{\sqrt{\pi}} 2^{2z-1}\Gamma(z)\Gamma\left(z + \dfrac{1}{2}\right).$$

(Legendre.) *Hint:*

$$\int_0^{\pi/2} \sin^n x \cos^n x \, dx = 2^{-1-n} \int_0^\pi \sin^n u \, du, \text{ if } u = 2x, \text{ or } 2^{-n} \int_0^{\pi/2} \sin^n u \, du.$$

Evaluate the first and last integral by problem 18, with $n = 2z - 1$, to get

$$\frac{\Gamma(z)\Gamma(z)}{\Gamma(2z)} = \frac{\Gamma(z)\,\Gamma\left(\dfrac{1}{2}\right)}{\Gamma\left(z + \dfrac{1}{2}\right)}\, 2^{1-2z}.$$

In the proof z is real, but the result extends to other z by analytic continuation.

37. Show that if z is not a negative integer,

$$\frac{\Gamma'(z)}{\Gamma(z)} = -\gamma - \frac{1}{z} + \sum_{n=1}^{\infty} \left(\frac{1}{n} - \frac{1}{z+n}\right).$$

Hence, in particular, if z is a positive integer, k,

$$\frac{\Gamma'(k)}{\Gamma(k)} = -\gamma + 1 + \frac{1}{2} + \frac{1}{3} + \cdots + \frac{1}{k-1}.$$

Hint: Use equation (133), take logarithms and differentiate.

38. If $\mathbf{R}(z) > 0$, the kth derivative of $\Gamma(z)$ is given by

$$\frac{d^k\Gamma(z)}{dz^k} = \int_0^{\infty} t^{z-1} e^{-t} (\log t)^k \, dt.$$

Hint: Use the uniform convergence, for $\mathbf{R}(z) > p > 0$, and reason from this as in section 273.

39. Prove that

$$|B_{2n}| = B_{2n}(-1)^{n-1} = 4n \int_0^{\infty} \frac{t^{2n-1}}{e^{2\pi t} - 1}\, dt$$

$$= \frac{2n(2n-1)}{\pi} \int_0^{\infty} t^{2n-2} \log\left(\frac{1}{1 - e^{-2\pi t}}\right) dt$$

$$= 4\pi \int_0^{\infty} \frac{t^{2n} e^{2\pi t}}{(e^{2\pi t} - 1)^2}\, dt.$$

Hint: Use problem 4, with $-\log x = 2\pi t$, $p = 2n - 1$ for the first integral, and integrate this by parts for the others.

40. Show that $\displaystyle\int_0^{\infty} \frac{x^{2n}}{\sinh^2 x}\, dx = \pi^{2n} B_{2n}(-1)^{n-1}$.   *Hint:* Use the last integral of problem 39, with $\pi t = x$.

41. Show that $\displaystyle\int_0^{\infty} \frac{x^{2n-1}}{\sinh x}\, dx = \frac{\pi^{2n} B_{2n}(-1)^{n-1}(2^{2n} - 1)}{2n}$.   *Hint:* Replace $1/\sinh x$ by $2/(e^x - 1) - 2/(e^{2x} - 1)$, and evaluate by putting $2\pi t = x$ and $\pi t = x$ in the first integral of problem 39.

42. Show that $\Gamma(1/m)\Gamma(2/m) \cdots \Gamma[(m-1)/m] = (2\pi)^{(m-1)/2}/\sqrt{m}$, m a positive integer.   *Hint:* $\displaystyle\sum_{k=0}^{m-1} z^k = \frac{z^m - 1}{z - 1} = \prod_{k=1}^{m-1}(z - e^{2k\pi i/m})$.   Put $z = 1$, and

$(1 - e^{2k\pi i/m}) = (-2ie^{k\pi i/m}) \sin k\pi/m$. Then $\prod_{k=1}^{m-1} e^{k\pi i/m} = e^{(m-1)\pi i/2} = i^{m-1}$.

Thus $m = \prod_{k=1}^{m-1} (1 - e^{2k\pi i/m}) = 2^{m-1} \prod_{k=1}^{m-1} \sin \dfrac{k\pi}{m}$.

Put $\Gamma(1/m)\Gamma(2/m) \cdots \Gamma[(m-1)/m] = P$. Then $P > 0$. Furthermore

$$P^2 = \prod_{k=1}^{m-1} \Gamma\left(\frac{k}{m}\right) \Gamma\left(\frac{m-k}{m}\right) = \prod_{k=1}^{m-1} \frac{\pi}{\sin \dfrac{k\pi}{m}}, \quad \text{by equation (139).} \quad \text{Thus}$$

$P^2 = (2\pi)^{m-1}/m$, by the result just proved, and $P = (2\pi)^{(m-1)/2}/\sqrt{m}$.

43. Demonstrate that $\Gamma(z)\Gamma(z + 1/m) \cdots \Gamma[z + (m-1)/m] = G(z) = (2\pi)^{(m-1)/2}m^{1/2-mz} \Gamma(mz)$. (Gauss.) *Hint:* By equation (129), $1/G(z)$ is the limit of

$$\frac{mz(mz + 1) \cdots (mz + mn + m - 1)}{n^{mz + \frac{m-1}{2}} (n\,!)^m m^{m(n+1)}} ;$$

while $\Gamma(mz)$ is the limit of $\dfrac{(mn)^{mz}(mn)\,!}{mz(mz + 1) \cdots (mz + mn)}$. Thus $m^{-mz} \dfrac{\Gamma(mz)}{G(z)}$ is

the limit of $\dfrac{(mn)\,! \, (mz + mn + 1)(mz + mn + 2) \cdots (mz + mn + m - 1)}{n^{(m-1)/2}(n\,!)^m m^{m(n+1)}}$ or

$$\frac{(mn - 1)\,! \, n^{\frac{m+1}{2}}}{(n\,!)^m m^{mn}} \left(1 + \frac{mz + 1}{mn}\right)\left(1 + \frac{mz + 2}{mn}\right) \cdots \left(1 + \frac{mz + m - 1}{mn}\right).$$

When $n \to \infty$, the factors involving z approach 1, and $G(z) = Qm^{-mz}\Gamma(mz)$,

with $Q = \lim_{n\to\infty} \dfrac{(n\,!)^m m^{mn}}{(mn - 1)\,! \, n^{(m+1)/2}}$. To evaluate Q, put $z = 1/m$ and use

problem 42. Thus $P = G\left(\dfrac{1}{m}\right) = Qm^{-1}$, and $Q = mP$.

For $m = 2$ the relation of this problem reduces to the duplication formula of problem 36.

44. Show that the expression of the Beta function in terms of Gamma functions, equation (107), may be proved by inverting the order of integration in

$\displaystyle\int_0^\infty e^{-y}y^{p+q-1}\, dy \int_0^\infty e^{-xy}x^{p-1}\, dx$. *Hint:* If $u = xy$, $y^p \displaystyle\int_0^\infty e^{-xy}x^{p-1}\, dx =$

$\displaystyle\int_0^\infty e^{-u}u^{p-1}\, du = \Gamma(p)$, so that in the order given the integral is $\Gamma(q)\Gamma(p)$.

Similarly, $(1 + x)^{p+q} \displaystyle\int_0^\infty e^{-(1+x)y}y^{p+q-1}\, dy = \Gamma(p + q)$. Also

$$\int_0^\infty x^{p-1}(1 + x)^{-p-q}\, dx = B(p,q)$$

by problem 21. Thus in the other order the integral is $\Gamma(p + q)B(p,q)$. The inversion is justified by section 244, since the integrals converge absolutely.

BIBLIOGRAPHY

(Arranged by subject matter)

ALGEBRA, INCLUDING DETERMINANTS AND A DETAILED DEVELOPMENT OF THE NUMBER SYSTEM OF ALGEBRA

1. FINE, H. B., *College Algebra*, Boston, 1905.

FUNDAMENTAL CONCEPTS OF ANALYSIS

2. HARDY, G. H., *Course of Pure Mathematics*, Cambridge, 1938.
3. KNOPP, K., *Theory and Application of Infinite Series*, translation by R. C. Young, London, 1928.
4. LANDAU, E. G. H., *Einführung in die Differential- und Integralrechnung*, Groningen, 1934.
5. OSGOOD, W. F., *Functions of a Complex Variable*, Peiping, 1936.
6. OSGOOD, W. F., *Functions of Real Variables*, Peiping, 1936.
7. VEBLEN, O., and LENNES, N. J., *Introduction to Infinitesimal Analysis, Functions of One Real Variable*, New York, 1907.

THE THEORY AND APPLICATION OF THE CALCULUS

8. COURANT, R., *Differential and Integral Calculus*, translation by E. J. McShane, London, vol. I, 1934, II, 1936.
9. FINE, H. B., *The Calculus*, New York, 1929.
10. GOURSAT, E., *A Course in Mathematical Analysis*, translation by E. R. Hedrick, vol. I, Boston, 1904.
11. LA VALLÉE POUSSIN, C.-J. DE, *Cours d'analyse infinitésimale*, Paris, vol. I, 1923 (the 1914 edition includes the theory of the Lebesgue integral), vol. II, 1928.
12. WILSON, E. B., *Advanced Calculus*, Boston, 1912.

TABLES

13. DAVIS, H. T., *Tables of the Higher Mathematical Functions*, Bloomington, Indiana, vol. I, 1933, II, 1935.
14. JAHNKE, E., and EMDE, F., *Tables of Functions with Formulae and Curves*, Leipzig, 1933.
15. PEIRCE, B. O., *A Short Table of Integrals*, Boston, 1929.

THE THEORY OF FUNCTIONS OF COMPLEX VARIABLES

16. COURANT, R., and HURWITZ, A., *Vorlesungen über allgemeine Funktionentheorie und elliptische Funktionen*, Berlin, 1925.
17. DEINES, P., *The Taylor Series*, Oxford, 1931.
18. GOURSAT, E., *A Course in Mathematical Analysis*, translation by E. R. Hedrick and O. Dunkel, vol. II, part 1, Boston, 1916.

585

19. Osgood, W. F., *Lehrbuch der Funktionentheorie*, Leipzig, vol. I, 1928, II, 1932.
20. Pierpont, J., *Functions of a Complex Variable*, New York, 1914.
21. Titchmarsh, E. C., *The Theory of Functions*, Oxford, 1932. (This includes real variables and Lebesgue integration).
22. Whittaker, E. T., and Watson, G. N., *Course of Modern Analysis*, Cambridge, 1927.

The Theory of Functions of Real Variables and the Theory of Integration

23. Carathéodory, C., *Vorlesungen über reelle Funktionen*, Leipzig, 1927.
24. Hobson, E. W., *The Theory of Functions of a Real Variable and the Theory of Fourier's Series*, Cambridge, vol. I, 1927, vol. II, 1926.
25. Saks, S., *Theory of the Integral*, translation by L. C. Young, with notes by S. Banach, New York, 1937.

Fourier Series, the Fourier Integral and the Laplace Integral

26. Bochner, S., *Vorlesungen über Fouriersche Integrale*, Leipzig, 1932.
27. McLachlan, N. W., *Complex Variable and Operational Calculus with Technical Applications*, Cambridge, 1939.
28. Titchmarsh, E. C., *Introduction to the Theory of Fourier Integrals*, Oxford, 1937,
29. Wiener, N., *The Fourier Integral and Certain of its Applications*, Cambridge, 1933.
30. Zygmund, A., *Trigonometrical Series*, Warsaw, 1935.

Differential Equations

31. Bieberbach, L., *Theorie der Differentialgleichungen*, Berlin, 1926.
32. Birkhoff, G. D., *Dynamical Systems*, Chapter I, New York, 1927.
33. Goursat, E., *A Course in Mathematical Analysis*, translation by E. R. Hedrick, vol. II, part 2, Boston, 1917.

INDEX

Catalogue of Dover
SCIENCE BOOKS

BOOKS THAT EXPLAIN SCIENCE

THE NATURE OF LIGHT AND COLOUR IN THE OPEN AIR, M. Minnaert. Why is falling snow sometimes black? What causes mirages, the fata morgana, multiple suns and moons in the sky; how are shadows formed? Prof. Minnaert of U. of Utrecht answers these and similar questions in optics, light, colour, for non-specialists. Particularly valuable to nature, science students, painters, photographers. "Can best be described in one word—fascinating!" Physics Today. Translated by H. M. Kremer-Priest, K. Jay. 202 illustrations, including 42 photos. xvi + 362pp. 5⅜ x 8.　　　　　　　　　　　　　T196 Paperbound **$1.95**

THE RESTLESS UNIVERSE, Max Born. New enlarged version of this remarkably readable account by a Nobel laureate. Moving from sub-atomic particles to universe, the author explains in very simple terms the latest theories of wave mechanics. Partial contents: air and its relatives, electrons and ions, waves and particles, electronic structure of the atom, nuclear physics. Nearly 1000 illustrations, including 7 animated sequences. 325pp. 6 x 9.　　　　　　　　　　　　　　　　　　　　　　　　T412 Paperbound **$2.00**

MATTER AND LIGHT, THE NEW PHYSICS, L. de Broglie. Non-technical papers by a Nobel laureate explain electromagnetic theory, relativity, matter, light, radiation, wave mechanics, quantum physics, philosophy of science. Einstein, Planck, Bohr, others explained so easily that no mathematical training is needed for all but 2 of the 21 chapters. "Easy simplicity and lucidity . . . should make this source-book of modern physcis available to a wide public," Saturday Review. Unabridged. 300pp. 5⅜ x 8.　　　　　T35 Paperbound **$1.60**

THE COMMON SENSE OF THE EXACT SCIENCES, W. K. Clifford. Introduction by James Newman, edited by Karl Pearson. For 70 years this has been a guide to classical scientific, mathematical thought. Explains with unusual clarity basic concepts such as extension of meaning of symbols, characteristics of surface boundaries, properties of plane figures, vectors, Cartesian method of determining position, etc. Long preface by Bertrand Russell. Bibliography of Clifford. Corrected. 130 diagrams redrawn. 249pp. 5⅜ x 8.
　　　　　　　　　　　　　　　　　　　　　　　　　　　T61 Paperbound **$1.60**

THE EVOLUTION OF SCIENTIFIC THOUGHT FROM NEWTON TO EINSTEIN, A. d'Abro. Einstein's special, general theories of relativity, with historical implications, analyzed in non-technical terms. Excellent accounts of contributions of Newton, Riemann, Weyl, Planck, Eddington, Maxwell, Lorentz, etc., are treated in terms of space, time, equations of electromagnetics, finiteness of universe, methodology of science. "Has become a standard work," Nature. 21 diagrams. 482pp. 5⅜ x 8.　　　　　　　　　　　　　　T2 Paperbound **$2.00**

BRIDGES AND THEIR BUILDERS, D. Steinman, S. R. Watson. Engineers, historians, everyone ever fascinated by great spans will find this an endless source of information and interest. Dr. Steinman, recent recipient of Louis Levy Medal, is one of the great bridge architects, engineers of all time. His analysis of great bridges of history is both authoritative and easily followed. Greek, Roman, medieval, oriental bridges; modern works such as Brooklyn Bridge, Golden Gate Bridge, etc. described in terms of history, constructional principles, artistry, function. Most comprehensive, accurate semi-popular history of bridges in print in English. New, greatly revised, enlarged edition. 23 photographs, 26 line drawings. xvii + 401pp. 5⅜ x 8.　　　　　　　　　　　　　　　　　T431 Paperbound **$1.95**

CONCERNING THE NATURE OF THINGS, Sir William Bragg. Christmas lectures at Royal Society by Nobel laureate, dealing with atoms, gases, liquids, and various types of crystals. No scientific background is needed to understand this remarkably clear introduction to basic processes and aspects of modern science. "More interesting than any bestseller," London Morning Post. 32pp. of photos. 57 figures. xii + 232pp. 5⅜ x 8. T31 Paperbound **$1.35**

THE RISE OF THE NEW PHYSICS, A. d'Abro. Half million word exposition, formerly titled "The Decline of Mechanism," for readers not versed in higher mathematics. Only thorough explanation in everyday language of core of modern mathematical physical theory, treating both classical, modern views. Scientifically impeccable coverage of thought from Newtonian system through theories of Dirac, Heisenberg, Fermi's statistics. Combines history, exposition; broad but unified, detailed view, with constant comparison of classical, modern views. "A must for anyone doing serious study in the physical sciences," J. of the Franklin Inst. "Extraordinary faculty . . . to explain ideas and theories . . . in language of everyday life," Isis. Part I of set: philosophy of science, from practice of Newton, Maxwell, Poincaré, Einstein, etc. Modes of thought, experiment, causality, etc. Part II: 100 pp. on grammar, vocabulary of mathematics, discussions of functions, groups, series, Fourier series, etc. Remainder treats concrete, detailed coverage of both classical, quantum physics: analytic mechanics, Hamilton's principle, electromagnetic waves, thermodynamics, Brownian movement, special relativity, Bohr's atom, de Broglie's wave mechanics, Heisenberg's uncertainty, scores of other important topics. Covers discoveries, theories of d'Alembert, Born, Cantor, Debye, Euler, Foucault, Galois, Gauss, Hadamard, Kelvin, Kepler Laplace, Maxwell, Pauli, Rayleigh Volterra, Weyl, more than 180 others. 97 illustrations. ix + 982pp. 5⅜ x 8.
T3 Vol. 1 Paperbound **$2.00**
T4 Vol. II Paperbound **$2.00**

SPINNING TOPS AND GYROSCOPIC MOTION, John Perry. Well-known classic of science still unsurpassed for lucid, accurate, delightful exposition. How quasi-rigidity is induced in flexible, fluid bodies by rapid motions; why gyrostat falls, top rises; nature, effect of internal fluidity on rotating bodies; etc. Appendixes describe practical use of gyroscopes in ships, compasses, monorail transportation. 62 figures. 128pp. 5⅜ x 8.
T416 Paperbound **$1.00**

FOUNDATIONS OF PHYSICS, R. B. Lindsay, H. Margenau. Excellent bridge between semi-popular and technical writings. Discussion of methods of physical description, construction of theory; valuable to physicist with elementary calculus. Gives meaning to data, tools of modern physics. Contents: symbolism, mathematical equations; space and time; foundations of mechanics; probability; physics, continua; electron theory; relativity; quantum mechanics; causality; etc. "Thorough and yet not overdetailed. Unreservedly recommended," Nature. Unabridged corrected edition. 35 illustrations. xi + 537pp. 5⅜ x 8. S377 Paperbound **$2.45**

FADS AND FALLACIES IN THE NAME OF SCIENCE, Martin Gardner. Formerly entitled "In the Name of Science," the standard account of various cults, quack systems, delusions which have masqueraded as science: hollow earth fanatics, orgone sex energy, dianetics, Atlantis, Forteanism, flying saucers, medical fallacies like zone therapy, etc. New chapter on Bridey Murphy, psionics, other recent manifestations. A fair reasoned appraisal of eccentric theory which provides excellent innoculation. "Should be read by everyone, scientist or non-scientist alike," R. T. Birge, Prof. Emeritus of Physics, Univ. of Calif; Former Pres., Amer. Physical Soc. x + 365pp. 5⅜ x 8. T394 Paperbound **$1.50**

ON MATHEMATICS AND MATHEMATICIANS, R. E. Moritz. A 10 year labor of love by discerning, discriminating Prof. Moritz, this collection conveys the full sense of mathematics and personalities of great mathematicians. Anecdotes, aphorisms, reminiscences, philosophies, definitions, speculations, biographical insights, etc. by great mathematicians, writers: Descartes, Mill, Locke, Kant, Coleridge, Whitehead, etc. Glimpses into lives of great mathematicians, from Archimedes to Euler, Gauss, Weierstrass. To mathematicians, a superb browsing-book. To laymen, exciting revelation of fullness of mathematics. Extensive cross index. 410pp. 5⅜ x 8. T489 Paperbound **$1.95**

GUIDE TO THE LITERATURE OF MATHEMATICS AND PHYSICS, N. G. Parke III. Over 5000 entries under approximately 120 major subject headings, of selected most important books, monographs, periodicals, articles in English, plus important works in German, French, Italian, Spanish, Russian. (many recently available works). Covers every branch of physics, math, related engineering. Includes author, title, edition, publisher, place, date, number of volumes, number of pages. 40 page introduction on basic problems of research, study provides useful information on organization, use of libraries, psychology of learning, etc. Will save you hours of time. 2nd revised edition. Indices of authors, subjects. 464pp. 5⅜ x 8. S447 Paperbound **$2.49**

THE STRANGE STORY OF THE QUANTUM, An Account for the General Reader of the Growth of Ideas Underlying Our Present Atomic Knowledge, B. Hoffmann. Presents lucidly, expertly, with barest amount of mathematics, problems and theories which led to modern quantum physics. Begins with late 1800's when discrepancies were noticed; with illuminating analogies, examples, goes through concepts of Planck, Einstein, Pauli, Schroedinger, Dirac, Sommerfield, Feynman, etc. New postscript through 1958. "Of the books attempting an account of the history and contents of modern atomic physics which have come to my attention, this is the best," H. Margenau, Yale U., in Amer. J. of Physics. 2nd edition. 32 tables, illustrations. 275pp. 5⅜ x 8. T518 Paperbound **$1.45**

HISTORY OF SCIENCE
AND PHILOSOPHY OF SCIENCE

THE VALUE OF SCIENCE, Henri Poincaré. Many of most mature ideas of "last scientific universalist" for both beginning, advanced workers. Nature of scientific truth, whether order is innate in universe or imposed by man, logical thought vs. intuition (relating to Weierstrass, Lie, Riemann, etc), time and space (relativity, psychological time, simultaneity), Herz's concept of force, values within disciplines of Maxwell, Carnot, Mayer, Newton, Lorentz, etc. iii + 147pp. 5⅜ x 8. S469 Paperbound **$1.35**

PHILOSOPHY AND THE PHYSICISTS, L. S. Stebbing. Philosophical aspects of modern science examined in terms of lively critical attack on ideas of Jeans, Eddington. Tasks of science, causality, determinism, probability, relation of world physics to that of everyday experience, philosophical significance of Planck-Bohr concept of discontinuous energy levels, inferences to be drawn from Uncertainty Principle, implications of "becoming" involved in 2nd law of thermodynamics, other problems posed by discarding of Laplacean determinism. 285pp. 5⅜ x 8. T480 Paperbound **$1.65**

THE PRINCIPLES OF SCIENCE, A TREATISE ON LOGIC AND THE SCIENTIFIC METHOD, W. S. Jevons. Milestone in development of symbolic logic remains stimulating contribution to investigation of inferential validity in sciences. Treats inductive, deductive logic, theory of number, probability, limits of scientific method; significantly advances Boole's logic, contains detailed introduction to nature and methods of probability in physics, astronomy, everyday affairs, etc. In introduction, Ernest Nagel of Columbia U. says, "[Jevons] continues to be of interest as an attempt to articulate the logic of scientific inquiry." liii + 786pp. 5⅜ x 8. S446 Paperbound **$2.98**

A HISTORY OF ASTRONOMY FROM THALES TO KEPLER, J. L. E. Dreyer. Only work in English to give complete history of cosmological views from prehistoric times to Kepler. Partial contents: Near Eastern astronomical systems, Early Greeks, Homocentric spheres of Euxodus, Epicycles, Ptolemaic system, Medieval cosmology, Copernicus, Kepler, much more. "Especially useful to teachers and students of the history of science . . . unsurpassed in its field," Isis. Formerly "A History of Planetary Systems from Thales to Kepler." Revised foreword by W. H. Stahl. xvii + 430pp. 5⅜ x 8. S79 Paperbound **$1.98**

A CONCISE HISTORY OF MATHEMATICS, D. Struik. Lucid study of development of ideas, techniques, from Ancient Near East, Greece, Islamic science, Middle Ages, Renaissance, modern times. Important mathematicians described in detail. Treatment not anecdotal, but analytical development of ideas. Non-technical—no math training needed. "Rich in content, thoughtful in interpretations," U.S. Quarterly Booklist. 60 illustrations including Greek, Egyptian manuscripts, portraits of 31 mathematicians. 2nd edition. xix + 299pp. 5⅜ x 8. S255 Paperbound **$1.75**

THE PHILOSOPHICAL WRITINGS OF PEIRCE, edited by Justus Buchler. A carefully balanced expositon of Peirce's complete system, written by Peirce himself. It covers such matters as scientific method, pure chance vs. law, symbolic logic, theory of signs, pragmatism, experiment, and other topics. "Excellent selection . . . gives more than adequate evidence of the range and greatness," Personalist. Formerly entitled "The Philosophy of Peirce." xvi + 368pp. T217 Paperbound **$1.95**

SCIENCE AND METHOD, Henri Poincaré. Procedure of scientific discovery, methodology, experiment, idea-germination—processes by which discoveries come into being. Most significant and interesting aspects of development, application of ideas. Chapters cover selection of facts, chance, mathematical reasoning, mathematics and logic; Whitehead, Russell, Cantor, the new mechanics, etc. 288pp. 5⅜ x 8. S222 Paperbound **$1.35**

SCIENCE AND HYPOTHESIS, Henri Poincaré. Creative psychology in science. How such concepts as number, magnitude, space, force, classical mechanics developed, how modern scientist uses them in his thought. Hypothesis in physics, theories of modern physics. Introduction by Sir James Larmor. "Few mathematicians have had the breadth of vision of Poincaré, and none is his superior in the gift of clear exposition," E. T. Bell. 272pp. 5⅜ x 8. S221 Paperbound **$1.35**

ESSAYS IN EXPERIMENTAL LOGIC, John Dewey. Stimulating series of essays by one of most influential minds in American philosophy presents some of his most mature thoughts on wide range of subjects. Partial contents: Relationship between inquiry and experience; dependence of knowledge upon thought; character logic; judgments of practice, data, and meanings; stimuli of thought, etc. viii + 444pp. 5⅜ x 8. T73 Paperbound **$1.95**

WHAT IS SCIENCE, Norman Campbell. Excellent introduction explains scientific method, role of mathematics, types of scientific laws. Contents: 2 aspects of science, science and nature, laws of chance, discovery of laws, explanation of laws, measurement and numerical laws, applications of science. 192pp. 5⅜ x 8. S43 Paperbound **$1.25**

FROM EUCLID TO EDDINGTON: A STUDY OF THE CONCEPTIONS OF THE EXTERNAL WORLD, Sir Edmund Whittaker. Foremost British scientist traces development of theories of natural philosophy from western rediscovery of Euclid to Eddington, Einstein, Dirac, etc. 5 major divisions: Space, Time and Movement; Concepts of Classical Physics; Concepts of Quantum Mechanics; Eddington Universe. Contrasts inadequacy of classical physics to understand physical world with present day attempts of relativity, non-Euclidean geometry, space curvature, etc. 212pp. 5⅜ x 8. **T491 Paperbound $1.35**

THE ANALYSIS OF MATTER, Bertrand Russell. How do our senses accord with the new physics? This volume covers such topics as logical analysis of physics, prerelativity physics, causality, scientific inference, physics and perception, special and general relativity, Weyl's theory, tensors, invariants and their physical interpretation, periodicity and qualitative series. "The most thorough treatment of the subject that has yet been published," The Nation. Introduction by L. E. Denonn. 422pp. 5⅜ x 8. **T231 Paperbound $1.95**

LANGUAGE, TRUTH, AND LOGIC, A. Ayer. A clear introduction to the Vienna and Cambridge schools of Logical Positivism. Specific tests to evaluate validity of ideas, etc. Contents: function of philosophy, elimination of metaphysics, nature of analysis, a priori, truth and probability, etc. 10th printing. "I should like to have written it myself," Bertrand Russell. 160pp. 5⅜ x 8. **T10 Paperbound $1.25**

THE PSYCHOLOGY OF INVENTION IN THE MATHEMATICAL FIELD, J. Hadamard. Where do ideas come from? What role does the unconscious play? Are ideas best developed by mathematical reasoning, word reasoning, visualization? What are the methods used by Einstein, Poincaré, Galton, Riemann? How can these techniques be applied by others? One of the world's leading mathematicians discusses these and other questions. xiii + 145pp. 5⅜ x 8. **T107 Paperbound $1.25**

GUIDE TO PHILOSOPHY, C. E. M. Joad. By one of the ablest expositors of all time, this is not simply a history or a typological survey, but an examination of central problems in terms of answers afforded by the greatest thinkers: Plato, Aristotle, Scholastics, Leibniz, Kant, Whitehead, Russell, and many others. Especially valuable to persons in the physical sciences; over 100 pages devoted to Jeans, Eddington, and others, the philosophy of modern physics, scientific materialism, pragmatism, etc. Classified bibliography. 592pp. 5⅜ x 8. **T50 Paperbound $2.00**

SUBSTANCE AND FUNCTION, and EINSTEIN'S THEORY OF RELATIVITY, Ernst Cassirer. Two books bound as one. Cassirer establishes a philosophy of the exact sciences that takes into consideration new developments in mathematics, shows historical connections. Partial contents: Aristotelian logic, Mill's analysis, Helmholtz and Kronecker, Russell and cardinal numbers, Euclidean vs. non-Euclidean geometry, Einstein's relativity. Bibliography. Index. xxi + 464pp. 5⅜ x 8. **T50 Paperbound $2.00**

FOUNDATIONS OF GEOMETRY, Bertrand Russell. Nobel laureate analyzes basic problems in the overlap area between mathematics and philosophy: the nature of geometrical knowledge, the nature of geometry, and the applications of geometry to space. Covers history of non-Euclidean geometry, philosophic interpretations of geometry, especially Kant, projective and metrical geometry. Most interesting as the solution offered in 1897 by a great mind to a problem still current. New introduction by Prof. Morris Kline, N.Y. University. "Admirably clear, precise, and elegantly reasoned analysis," International Math. News. xii + 201pp. 5⅜ x 8. **S233 Paperbound $1.60**

THE NATURE OF PHYSICAL THEORY, P. W. Bridgman. How modern physics looks to a highly unorthodox physicist—a Nobel laureate. Pointing out many absurdities of science, demonstrating inadequacies of various physical theories, weighs and analyzes contributions of Einstein, Bohr, Heisenberg, many others. A non-technical consideration of correlation of science and reality. xi + 138pp. 5⅜ x 8. **S33 Paperbound $1.25**

EXPERIMENT AND THEORY IN PHYSICS, Max Born. A Nobel laureate examines the nature and value of the counterclaims of experiment and theory in physics. Synthetic versus analytical scientific advances are analyzed in works of Einstein, Bohr, Heisenberg, Planck, Eddington, Milne, others, by a fellow scientist. 44pp. 5⅜ x 8. **S308 Paperbound 60¢**

A SHORT HISTORY OF ANATOMY AND PHYSIOLOGY FROM THE GREEKS TO HARVEY, Charles Singer. Corrected edition of "The Evolution of Anatomy." Classic traces anatomy, physiology from prescientific times through Greek, Roman periods, dark ages, Renaissance, to beginning of modern concepts. Centers on individuals, movements, that definitely advanced anatomical knowledge. Plato, Diocles, Erasistratus, Galen, da Vinci, etc. Special section on Vesalius. 20 plates. 270 extremely interesting illustrations of ancient, Medieval, Renaissance, Oriental origin. xii + 209pp. 5⅜ x 8. **T389 Paperbound $1.75**

SPACE - TIME - MATTER, Hermann Weyl. "The standard treatise on the general theory of relativity," (Nature), by world renowned scientist. Deep, clear discussion of logical coherence of general theory, introducing all needed tools: Maxwell, analytical geometry, non-Euclidean geometry, tensor calculus, etc. Basis is classical space-time, before absorption of relativity. Contents: Euclidean space, mathematical form, metrical continuum, general theory, etc. 15 diagrams. xviii + 330pp. 5⅜ x 8. **S267 Paperbound $1.75**

4

DOVER SCIENCE BOOKS

MATTER AND MOTION, James Clerk Maxwell. Excellent exposition begins with simple particles, proceeds gradually to physical systems beyond complete analysis; motion, force, properties of centre of mass of material system; work, energy, gravitation, etc. Written with all Maxwell's original insights and clarity. Notes by E. Larmor. 17 diagrams. 178pp. 5⅜ x 8.

S188 Paperbound **$1.25**

PRINCIPLES OF MECHANICS, Heinrich Hertz. Last work by the great 19th century physicist is not only a classic, but of great interest in the logic of science. Creating a new system of mechanics based upon space, time, and mass, it returns to axiomatic analysis, understanding of the formal or structural aspects of science, taking into account logic, observation, a priori elements. Of great historical importance to Poincaré, Carnap, Einstein, Milne. A 20 page introduction by R. S. Cohen, Wesleyan University, analyzes the implications of Hertz's thought and the logic of science. 13 page introduction by Helmholtz. xlii + 274pp. 5⅜ x 8.

S316 Clothbound **$3.50**

S317 Paperbound **$1.75**

FROM MAGIC TO SCIENCE, Charles Singer. A great historian examines aspects of science from Roman Empire through Renaissance. Includes perhaps best discussion of early herbals, penetrating physiological interpretation of "The Visions of Hildegarde of Bingen." Also examines Arabian, Galenic influences; Pythagoras' sphere, Paracelsus; reawakening of science under Leonardo da Vinci, Vesalius; Lorica of Gildas the Briton; etc. Frequent quotations with translations from contemporary manuscripts. Unabridged, corrected edition. 158 unusual illustrations from Classical, Medieval sources. xxvii + 365pp. 5⅜ x 8.

T390 Paperbound **$2.00**

A HISTORY OF THE CALCULUS, AND ITS CONCEPTUAL DEVELOPMENT, Carl B. Boyer. Provides laymen, mathematicians a detailed history of the development of the calculus, from beginnings in antiquity to final elaboration as mathematical abstraction. Gives a sense of mathematics not as technique, but as habit of mind, in progression of ideas of Zeno, Plato, Pythagoras, Eudoxus, Arabic and Scholastic mathematicians, Newton, Leibniz, Taylor, Descartes, Euler, Lagrange, Cantor, Weierstrass, and others. This first comprehensive, critical history of the calculus was originally entitled "The Concepts of the Calculus." Foreword by R. Courant. 22 figures. 25 page bibliography. v + 364pp. 5⅜ x 8.

S509 Paperbound **$2.00**

A DIDEROT PICTORIAL ENCYCLOPEDIA OF TRADES AND INDUSTRY, Manufacturing and the Technical Arts in Plates Selected from "L'Encyclopédie ou Dictionnaire Raisonné des Sciences, des Arts, et des Métiers" of Denis Diderot. Edited with text by C. Gillispie. First modern selection of plates from high-point of 18th century French engraving. Storehouse of technological information to historian of arts and science. Over 2,000 illustrations on 485 full page plates, most of them original size, show trades, industries of fascinating era in such great detail that modern reconstructions might be made of them. Plates teem with men, women, children performing thousands of operations; show sequence, general operations, closeups, details of machinery. Illustrates such important, interesting trades, industries as sowing, harvesting, beekeeping, tobacco processing, fishing, arts of war, mining, smelting, casting iron, extracting mercury, making gunpowder, cannons, bells, shoeing horses, tanning, papermaking, printing, dying, over 45 more categories. Professor Gillispie of Princeton supplies full commentary on all plates, identifies operations, tools, processes, etc. Material is presented in lively, lucid fashion. Of great interest to all studying history of science, technology. Heavy library cloth. 920pp. 9 x 12.

T421 2 volume set **$18.50**

DE MAGNETE, William Gilbert. Classic work on magnetism, founded new science. Gilbert was first to use word "electricity," to recognize mass as distinct from weight, to discover effect of heat on magnetic bodies; invented an electroscope, differentiated between static electricity and magnetism, conceived of earth as magnet. This lively work, by first great experimental scientist, is not only a valuable historical landmark, but a delightfully easy to follow record of a searching, ingenious mind. Translated by P. F. Mottelay. 25 page biographical memoir. 90 figures. lix + 368pp. 5⅜ x 8.

S470 Paperbound **$2.00**

HISTORY OF MATHEMATICS, D. E. Smith. Most comprehensive, non-technical history of math in English. Discusses lives and works of over a thousand major, minor figures, with footnotes giving technical information outside book's scheme, and indicating disputed matters. Vol. I: A chronological examination, from primitive concepts through Egypt, Babylonia, Greece, the Orient, Rome, the Middle Ages, The Renaissance, and to 1900. Vol. II: The development of ideas in specific fields and problems, up through elementary calculus. "Marks an epoch . . . will modify the entire teaching of the history of science," George Sarton. 2 volumes, total of 510 illustrations, 1355pp. 5⅜ x 8. Set boxed in attractive container.

T429, 430 Paperbound, the set **$5.00**

THE PHILOSOPHY OF SPACE AND TIME, H. Reichenbach. An important landmark in development of empiricist conception of geometry, covering foundations of geometry, time theory, consequences of Einstein's relativity, including: relations between theory and observations; coordinate definitions; relations between topological and metrical properties of space; psychological problem of visual intuition of non-Euclidean structures; many more topics important to modern science and philosophy. Majority of ideas require only knowledge of intermediate math. "Still the best book in the field," Rudolf Carnap. Introduction by R. Carnap. 49 figures. xviii + 296pp. 5⅜ x 8.

S443 Paperbound **$2.00**

5

FOUNDATIONS OF SCIENCE: THE PHILOSOPHY OF THEORY AND EXPERIMENT, N. Campbell. A critique of the most fundamental concepts of science, particularly physics. Examines why certain propositions are accepted without question, demarcates science from philosophy, etc. Part I analyzes presuppositions of scientific thought: existence of material world, nature of laws, probability, etc; part 2 covers nature of experiment and applications of mathematics: conditions for measurement, relations between numerical laws and theories, error, etc. An appendix covers problems arising from relativity, force, motion, space, time. A classic in its field. "A real grasp of what science is," Higher Educational Journal. xiii + 565pp. 5⅜ x 8⅜. S372 Paperbound **$2.95**

THE STUDY OF THE HISTORY OF MATHEMATICS and THE STUDY OF THE HISTORY OF SCIENCE, G. Sarton. Excellent introductions, orientation, for beginning or mature worker. Describes duty of mathematical historian, incessant efforts and genius of previous generations. Explains how today's discipline differs from previous methods. 200 item bibliography with critical evaluations, best available biographies of modern mathematicians, best treatises on historical methods is especially valuable. 10 illustrations. 2 volumes bound as one. 113pp. + 75pp. 5⅜ x 8. T240 Paperbound **$1.25**

MATHEMATICAL PUZZLES

MATHEMATICAL PUZZLES OF SAM LOYD, selected and edited by **Martin Gardner.** 117 choice puzzles by greatest American puzzle creator and innovator, from his famous "Cyclopedia of Puzzles." All unique style, historical flavor of originals. Based on arithmetic, algebra, probability, game theory, route tracing, topology, sliding block, operations research, geometrical dissection. Includes famous "14-15" puzzle which was national craze, "Horse of a Different Color" which sold millions of copies. 120 line drawings, diagrams. Solutions. xx + 167pp. 5⅜ x 8. T498 Paperbound **$1.00**

SYMBOLIC LOGIC and THE GAME OF LOGIC, Lewis Carroll. "Symbolic Logic" is not concerned with modern symbolic logic, but is instead a collection of over 380 problems posed with charm and imagination, using the syllogism, and a fascinating diagrammatic method of drawing conclusions. In "The Game of Logic" Carroll's whimsical imagination devises a logical game played with 2 diagrams and counters (included) to manipulate hundreds of tricky syllogisms. The final section, "Hit or Miss" is a lagniappe of 101 additional puzzles in the delightful Carroll manner. Until this reprint edition, both of these books were rarities costing up to $15 each. Symbolic Logic: Index. xxxi + 199pp. The Game of Logic: 96pp. 2 vols. bound as one. 5⅜ x 8. T492 Paperbound **$1.50**

PILLOW PROBLEMS and A TANGLED TALE, Lewis Carroll. One of the rarest of all Carroll's works, "Pillow Problems" contains 72 original math puzzles, all typically ingenious. Particularly fascinating are Carroll's answers which remain exactly as he thought them out, reflecting his actual mental process. The problems in "A Tangled Tale" are in story form, originally appearing as a monthly magazine serial. Carroll not only gives the solutions, but uses answers sent in by readers to discuss wrong approaches and misleading paths, and grades them for insight. Both of these books were rarities until this edition, "Pillow Problems" costing up to $25, and "A Tangled Tale" $15. Pillow Problems: Preface and Introduction by Lewis Carroll. xx + 109pp. A Tangled Tale: 6 illustrations. 152pp. Two vols. bound as one. 5⅜ x 8. T493 Paperbound **$1.50**

NEW WORD PUZZLES, G. L. Kaufman. 100 brand new challenging puzzles on words, combinations, never before published. Most are new types invented by author, for beginners and experts both. Squares of letters follow chess moves to build words; symmetrical designs made of synonyms; rhymed crostics; double word squares; syllable puzzles where you fill in missing syllables instead of missing letter; many other types, all new. Solutions. "Excellent," Recreation. 100 puzzles. 196 figures. vi + 122pp. 5⅜ x 8. T344 Paperbound **$1.00**

MATHEMATICAL EXCURSIONS, H. A. Merrill. Fun, recreation, insights into elementary problem solving. Math expert guides you on by-paths not generally travelled in elementary math courses—divide by inspection, Russian peasant multiplication; memory systems for pi; odd, even magic squares; dyadic systems; square roots by geometry; Tchebichev's machine; dozens more. Solutions to more difficult ones. "Brain stirring stuff . . . a classic," Genie. 50 illustrations. 145pp. 5⅜ x 8. T350 Paperbound **$1.00**

THE BOOK OF MODERN PUZZLES, G. L. Kaufman. Over 150 puzzles, absolutely all new material based on same appeal as crosswords, deduction puzzles, but with different principles, techniques. 2-minute teasers, word labyrinths, design, pattern, logic, observation puzzles, puzzles testing ability to apply general knowledge to peculiar situations, many others. Solutions. 116 illustrations. 192pp. 5⅜ x 8. T143 Paperbound **$1.00**

MATHEMAGIC, MAGIC PUZZLES, AND GAMES WITH NUMBERS, R. V. Heath. Over 60 puzzles, stunts, on properties of numbers. Easy techniques for multiplying large numbers mentally, identifying unknown numbers, finding date of any day in any year. Includes The Lost Digit, 3 Acrobats, Psychic Bridge, magic squares, triangles, cubes, others not easily found elsewhere. Edited by J. S. Meyer. 76 illustrations. 128pp. 5⅜ x 8. T110 Paperbound **$1.00**

DOVER SCIENCE BOOKS

PUZZLE QUIZ AND STUNT FUN, J. Meyer. 238 high-priority puzzles, stunts, tricks—math puzzles like The Clever Carpenter, Atom Bomb, Please Help Alice; mysteries, deductions like The Bridge of Sighs, Secret Code; observation puzzlers like The American Flag, Playing Cards, Telephone Dial; over 200 others with magic squares, tongue twisters, puns, anagrams. Solutions. Revised, enlarged edition of "Fun-To-Do." Over 100 illustrations. 238 puzzles, stunts, tricks. 256pp. 5⅜ x 8.   T337 Paperbound **$1.00**

101 PUZZLES IN THOUGHT AND LOGIC, C. R. Wylie, Jr. For readers who enjoy challenge, stimulation of logical puzzles without specialized math or scientific knowledge. Problems entirely new, range from relatively easy to brainteasers for hours of subtle entertainment. Detective puzzles, find the lying fisherman, how a blind man identifies color by logic, many more. Easy-to-understand introduction to logic of puzzle solving and general scientific method. 128pp. 5⅜ x 8.   T367 Paperbound **$1.00**

CRYPTANALYSIS, H. F. Gaines. Standard elementary, intermediate text for serious students. Not just old material, but much not generally known, except to experts. Concealment, Transposition, Substitution ciphers; Vigenere, Kasiski, Playfair, multafid, dozens of other techniques. Formerly "Elementary Cryptanalysis." Appendix with sequence charts, letter frequencies in English, 5 other languages, English word frequencies. Bibliography. 167 codes. New to this edition: solutions to codes. vi + 230pp. 5⅜ x 8⅜.
T97 Paperbound **$1.95**

CRYPTOGRAPY, L. D. Smith. Excellent elementary introduction to enciphering, deciphering secret writing. Explains transposition, substitution ciphers; codes; solutions; geometrical patterns, route transcription, columnar transposition, other methods. Mixed cipher systems; single, polyalphabetical substitutions; mechanical devices; Vigenere; etc. Enciphering Japanese; explanation of Baconian biliteral cipher; frequency tables. Over 150 problems. Bibliography. Index. 164pp. 5⅜ x 8.   T247 Paperbound **$1.00**

MATHEMATICS, MAGIC AND MYSTERY, M. Gardner. Card tricks, metal mathematics, stage mind-reading, other "magic" explained as applications of probability, sets, number theory, etc. Creative examination of laws, applications. Scores of new tricks, insights. 115 sections on cards, dice, coins; vanishing tricks, many others. No sleight of hand—math guarantees success. "Could hardly get more entertainment . . . easy to follow," Mathematics Teacher. 115 illustrations. xii + 174pp. 5⅜ x 8.   T335 Paperbound **$1.00**

AMUSEMENTS IN MATHEMATICS, H. E. Dudeney. Foremost British originator of math puzzles, always witty, intriguing, paradoxical in this classic. One of largest collections. More than 430 puzzles, problems, paradoxes. Mazes, games, problems on number manipulations, unicursal, other route problems, puzzles on measuring, weighing, packing, age, kinship, chessboards, joiners', crossing river, plane figure dissection, many others. Solutions. More than 450 illustrations. viii + 258pp. 5⅜ x 8.   T473 Paperbound **$1.25**

THE CANTERBURY PUZZLES H. E. Dudeney. Chaucer's pilgrims set one another problems in story form. Also Adventures of the Puzzle Club, the Strange Escape of the King's Jester, the Monks of Riddlewell, the Squire's Christmas Puzzle Party, others. All puzzles are original, based on dissecting plane figures, arithmetic, algebra, elementary calculus, other branches of mathematics, and purely logical ingenuity. "The limit of ingenuity and intricacy," The Observer. Over 110 puzzles, full solutions. 150 illustrations. viii + 225 pp. 5⅜ x 8.   T474 Paperbound **$1.25**

MATHEMATICAL PUZZLES FOR BEGINNERS AND ENTHUSIASTS, G. Mott-Smith. 188 puzzles to test mental agility. Inference, interpretation, algebra, dissection of plane figures, geometry, properties of numbers, decimation, permutations, probability, all are in these delightful problems. Includes the Odic Force, How to Draw an Ellipse, Spider's Cousin, more than 180 others. Detailed solutions. Appendix with square roots, triangular numbers, primes, etc. 135 illustrations. 2nd revised edition. 248pp. 5⅜ x 8.   T198 Paperbound **$1.00**

MATHEMATICAL RECREATIONS, M. Kraitchik. Some 250 puzzles, problems, demonstrations of recreation mathematics on relatively advanced level. Unusual historical problems from Greek, Medieval, Arabic, Hindu sources; modern problems on "mathematics without numbers," geometry, topology, arithmetic, etc. Pastimes derived from figurative, Mersenne, Fermat numbers: fairy chess; latruncles: reversi; etc. Full solutions. Excellent insights into special fields of math. "Strongly recommended to all who are interested in the lighter side of mathematics," Mathematical Gaz. 181 illustrations. 330pp. 5⅜ x 8.
T163 Paperbound **$1.75**

FICTION

FLATLAND, E. A. Abbott. A perennially popular science-fiction classic about life in a 2-dimensional world, and the impingement of higher dimensions. Political, satiric, humorous, moral overtones. This land where women are straight lines and the lowest and most dangerous classes are isosceles triangles with 3° vertices conveys brilliantly a feeling for many concepts of modern science. 7th edition. New introduction by Banesh Hoffmann. 128pp. 5⅜ x 8.   T1 Paperbound **$1.00**

SEVEN SCIENCE FICTION NOVELS OF H. G. WELLS. Complete texts, unabridged, of seven of Wells' greatest novels: The War of the Worlds, The Invisible Man, The Island of Dr. Moreau, The Food of the Gods, First Men in the Moon, In the Days of the Comet, The Time Machine. Still considered by many experts to be the best science-fiction ever written, they will offer amusements and instruction to the scientific minded reader. "The great master," Sky and Telescope. 1051pp. 5⅜ x 8.
T264 Clothbound $3.95

28 SCIENCE FICTION STORIES OF H. G. WELLS. Unabridged! This enormous omnibus contains 2 full length novels—Men Like Gods, Star Begotten—plus 26 short stories of space, time, invention, biology, etc. The Crystal Egg, The Country of the Blind, Empire of the Ants, The Man Who Could Work Miracles, Aepyornis Island, A Story of the Days to Come, and 20 others "A master . . . not surpassed by . . . writers of today," The English Journal. 915pp. 5⅜ x 8.
T265 Clothbound $3.95

FIVE ADVENTURE NOVELS OF H. RIDER HAGGARD. All the mystery and adventure of darkest Africa captured accurately by a man who lived among Zulus for years, who knew African ethnology, folkways as did few of his contemporaries. They have been regarded as examples of the very best high adventure by such critics as Orwell, Andrew Lang, Kipling. Contents: She, King Solomon's Mines, Allan Quatermain, Allan's Wife, Maiwa's Revenge. "Could spin a yarn so full of suspense and color that you couldn't put the story down," Sat. Review. 821pp. 5⅜ x 8.
T108 Clothbound $3.95

CHESS AND CHECKERS

LEARN CHESS FROM THE MASTERS, Fred Reinfeld. Easiest, most instructive way to improve your game—play 10 games against such masters as Marshall, Znosko-Borovsky, Bronstein, Najdorf, etc., with each move graded by easy system. Includes ratings for alternate moves possible. Games selected for interest, clarity, easily isolated principles. Covers Ruy Lopez, Dutch Defense, Vienna Game openings; subtle, intricate middle game variations; all-important end game. Full annotations. Formerly "Chess by Yourself." 91 diagrams. viii + 144pp. 5⅜ x 8.
T362 Paperbound $1.00

REINFELD ON THE END GAME IN CHESS, Fred Reinfeld. Analyzes 62 end games by Alekhine, Flohr, Tarrasch, Morphy, Capablanca, Rubinstein, Lasker, Reshevsky, other masters. Only 1st rate book with extensive coverage of error—tell exactly what is wrong with each move you might have made. Centers around transitions from middle play to end play. King and pawn, minor pieces, queen endings; blockage, weak, passed pawns, etc. "Excellent . . . a boon," Chess Life. Formerly "Practical End Play." 62 figures. vi + 177pp. 5⅜ x 8.
T417 Paperbound $1.25

HYPERMODERN CHESS as developed in the games of its greatest exponent, ARON NIMZO-VICH, edited by Fred Reinfeld. An intensely original player, analyst, Nimzovich's approaches startled, often angered the chess world. This volume, designed for the average player, shows how his iconoclastic methods won him victories over Alekhine, Lasker, Marshall, Rubinstein, Spielmann, others, and infused new life into the game. Use his methods to startle opponents, invigorate play. "Annotations and introductions to each game . . . are excellent," Times (London). 180 diagrams. viii + 220pp. 5⅜ x 8. **T448 Paperbound $1.35**

THE ADVENTURE OF CHESS, Edward Lasker. Lively reader, by one of America's finest chess masters, including: history of chess, from ancient Indian 4-handed game of Chaturanga to great players of today; such delights and oddities as Maelzel's chess-playing automaton that beat Napoleon 3 times; etc. One of most valuable features is author's personal recollections of men he has played against—Nimzovich, Emanuel Lasker, Capablanca, Alekhine, etc. Discussion of chess-playing machines (newly revised). 5 page chess primer. 11 illustrations. 53 diagrams. 296pp. 5⅜ x 8.
S510 Paperbound $1.45

THE ART OF CHESS, James Mason. Unabridged reprinting of latest revised edition of most famous general study ever written. Mason, early 20th century master, teaches beginning, intermediate player over 90 openings; middle game, end game, to see more moves ahead, to plan purposefully, attack, sacrifice, defend, exchange, govern general strategy. "Classic . . . one of the clearest and best developed studies," Publishers Weekly. Also included, a complete supplement by F. Reinfeld, "How Do You Play Chess?", invaluable to beginners for its lively question-and-answer method. 448 diagrams. 1947 Reinfeld-Bernstein text. Bibliography. xvi + 340pp. 5⅜ x 8.
T463 Paperbound $1.85

MORPHY'S GAMES OF CHESS, edited by P. W. Sergeant. Put boldness into your game by flowing brilliant, forceful moves of the greatest chess player of all time. 300 of Morphy's best games, carefully annotated to reveal principles. 54 classics against masters like Anderssen, Harrwitz, Bird, Paulsen, and others. 52 games at odds; 54 blindfold games; plus over 100 others. Follow his interpretation of Dutch Defense, Evans Gambit, Giuoco Piano, Ruy Lopez, many more. Unabridged reissue of latest revised edition. New introduction by F. Reinfeld. Annotations, introduction by Sergeant. 235 diagrams. x + 352pp. 5⅜ x 8.
T386 Paperbound $1.75

DOVER SCIENCE BOOKS

WIN AT CHECKERS, M. Hopper. (Formerly "Checkers.") Former World's Unrestricted Checker Champion discusses principles of game, expert's shots, traps, problems for beginner, standard openings, locating best move, end game, opening "blitzkrieg" moves to draw when behind, etc. Over 100 detailed questions, answers anticipate problems. Appendix. 75 problems with solutions, diagrams. 79 figures. xi + 107pp. 5⅜ x 8.   T363 Paperbound $1.00

HOW TO FORCE CHECKMATE, Fred Reinfeld. If you have trouble finishing off your opponent, here is a collection of lightning strokes and combinations from actual tournament play. Starts with 1-move checkmates, works up to 3-move mates. Develops ability to look ahead, gain new insights into combinations, complex or deceptive positions; ways to estimate weaknesses, strengths of you and your opponent. "A good deal of amusement and instruction," Times, (London). 300 diagrams. Solutions to all positions. Formerly "Challenge to Chess Players." 111pp. 5⅜ x 8.   T417 Paperbound $1.25

A TREASURY OF CHESS LORE, edited by Fred Reinfeld. Delightful collection of anecdotes, short stories, aphorisms by, about masters; poems, accounts of games, tournaments, photographs; hundreds of humorous, pithy, satirical, wise, historical episodes, comments, word portraits. Fascinating "must" for chess players; revealing and perhaps seductive to those who wonder what their friends see in game. 49 photographs (14 full page plates). 12 diagrams. xi + 306pp. 5⅜ x 8.   T458 Paperbound $1.75

WIN AT CHESS, Fred Reinfeld. 300 practical chess situations, to sharpen your eye, test skill against masters. Start with simple examples, progress at own pace to complexities. This selected series of crucial moments in chess will stimulate imagination, develop stronger, more versatile game. Simple grading system enables you to judge progress. "Extensive use of diagrams is a great attraction," Chess. 300 diagrams. Notes, solutions to every situation. Formerly "Chess Quiz." vi + 120pp. 5⅜ x 8.   T433 Paperbound $1.00

MATHEMATICS:
ELEMENTARY TO INTERMEDIATE

HOW TO CALCULATE QUICKLY, H. Sticker. Tried and true method to help mathematics of everyday life. Awakens "number sense"—ability to see relationships between numbers as whole quantities. A serious course of over 9000 problems and their solutions through techniques not taught in schools: left-to-right multiplications, new fast division, etc. 10 minutes a day will double or triple calculation speed. Excellent for scientist at home in higher math, but dissatisfied with speed and accuracy in lower math. 256pp. 5 x 7¼.
Paperbound **$1.00**

FAMOUS PROBLEMS OF ELEMENTARY GEOMETRY, Felix Klein. Expanded version of 1894 Easter lectures at Göttingen. 3 problems of classical geometry: squaring the circle, trisecting angle, doubling cube, considered with full modern implications: transcendental numbers, pi, etc. "A modern classic . . . no knowledge of higher mathematics is required," Scientia. Notes by R. Archibald. 16 figures. xi + 92pp. 5⅜ x 8.   T298 Paperbound $1.00

HIGHER MATHEMATICS FOR STUDENTS OF CHEMISTRY AND PHYSICS, J. W. Mellor. Practical, not abstract, building problems out of familiar laboratory material. Covers differential calculus, coordinate, analytical geometry, functions, integral calculus, infinite series, numerical equations, differential equations, Fourier's theorem probability, theory of errors, calculus of variations, determinants. "If the reader is not familiar with this book, it will repay him to examine it," Chem. and Engineering News. 800 problems. 189 figures. xxi + 641pp. 5⅜ x 8.   S193 Paperbound $2.25

TRIGONOMETRY REFRESHER FOR TECHNICAL MEN, A. A. Klaf. 913 detailed questions, answers cover most important aspects of plane, spherical trigonometry—particularly useful in clearing up difficulties in special areas. Part I: plane trig, angles, quadrants, functions, graphical representation, interpolation, equations, logs, solution of triangle, use of slide rule, etc. Next 188 pages discuss applications to navigation, surveying, elasticity, architecture, other special fields. Part 3: spherical trig, applications to terrestrial, astronomical problems. Methods of time-saving, simplification of principal angles, make book most useful. 913 questions answered. 1738 problems, answers to odd numbers. 494 figures. 24 pages of formulas, functions. x + 629pp. 5⅜ x 8.   T371 Paperbound $2.00

CALCULUS REFRESHER FOR TECHNICAL MEN, A. A. Klaf. 756 questions examine most important aspects of integral, differential calculus. Part I: simple differential calculus, constants, variables, functions, increments, logs, curves, etc. Part 2: fundamental ideas of integrations, inspection, substitution, areas, volumes, mean value, double, triple integration, etc. Practical aspects stressed. 50 pages illustrate applications to specific problems of civil, nautical engineering, electricity, stress, strain, elasticity, similar fields. 756 questions answered. 566 problems, mostly answered. 36pp. of useful constants, formulas. v + 431pp. 5⅜ x 8.   T370 Paperbound $2.00

MONOGRAPHS ON TOPICS OF MODERN MATHEMATICS, edited by J. W. A. Young. Advanced mathematics for persons who have forgotten, or not gone beyond, high school algebra. 9 monographs on foundation of geometry, modern pure geometry, non-Euclidean geometry, fundamental propositions of algebra, algebraic equations, functions, calculus, theory of numbers, etc. Each monograph gives proofs of important results, and descriptions of leading methods, to provide wide coverage. "Of high merit," Scientific American. New introduction by Prof. M. Kline, N.Y. Univ. 100 diagrams. xvi + 416pp. 6⅛ x 9¼.
S289 Paperbound **$2.00**

MATHEMATICS IN ACTION, O. G. Sutton. Excellent middle level application of mathematics to study of universe, demonstrates how math is applied to ballistics, theory of computing machines, waves, wave-like phenomena, theory of fluid flow, meteorological problems, statistics, flight, similar phenomena. No knowledge of advanced math required. Differential equations, Fourier series, group concepts, Eigenfunctions, Planck's constant, airfoil theory, and similar topics explained so clearly in everyday language that almost anyone can derive benefit from reading this even if much of high-school math is forgotten. 2nd edition. 88 figures. viii + 236pp. 5⅜ x 8. T450 Clothbound **$3.50**

ELEMENTARY MATHEMATICS FROM AN ADVANCED STANDPOINT, Felix Klein. Classic text, an outgrowth of Klein's famous integration and survey course at Göttingen. Using one field to interpret, adjust another, it covers basic topics in each area, with extensive analysis. Especially valuable in areas of modern mathematics. "A great mathematician, inspiring teacher, . . . deep insight," Bul., Amer. Math Soc.

Vol. I. ARITHMETIC, ALGEBRA, ANALYSIS. Introduces concept of function immediately, enlivens discussion with graphical, geometric methods. Partial contents: natural numbers, special properties, complex numbers. Real equations with real unknowns, complex quantities. Logarithmic, exponential functions, infinitesimal calculus. Transcendence of e and pi, theory of assemblages. Index. 125 figures. ix + 274pp. 5⅜ x 8. S151 Paperbound **$1.75**

Vol. II. GEOMETRY. Comprehensive view, accompanies space perception inherent in geometry with analytic formulas which facilitate precise formulation. Partial contents: Simplest geometric manifold; line segments, Grassman determinant principles, classication of configurations of space. Geometric transformations: affine, projective, higher point transformations, theory of the imaginary. Systematic discussion of geometry and its foundations. 141 illustrations. ix + 214pp. 5⅜ x 8. S151 Paperbound **$1.75**

A TREATISE ON PLANE AND ADVANCED TRIGONOMETRY, E. W. Hobson. Extraordinarily wide coverage, going beyond usual college level, one of few works covering advanced trig in full detail. By a great expositor with unerring anticipation of potentially difficult points. Includes circular functions; expansion of functions of multiple angle; trig tables; relations between sides, angles of triangles; complex numbers; etc. Many problems fully solved. "The best work on the subject," Nature. Formerly entitled "A Treatise on Plane Trigonometry." 689 examples. 66 figures. xvi + 383pp. 5⅜ x 8. S353 Paperbound **$1.95**

NON-EUCLIDEAN GEOMETRY, Roberto Bonola. The standard coverage of non-Euclidean geometry. Examines from both a historical and mathematical point of view geometries which have arisen from a study of Euclid's 5th postulate on parallel lines. Also included are complete texts, translated, of Bolyai's "Theory of Absolute Space," Lobachevsky's "Theory of Parallels." 180 diagrams. 431pp. 5⅜ x 8. S27 Paperbound **$1.95**

GEOMETRY OF FOUR DIMENSIONS, H. P. Manning. Unique in English as a clear, concise introduction. Treatment is synthetic, mostly Euclidean, though in hyperplanes and hyperspheres at infinity, non-Euclidean geometry is used. Historical introduction. Foundations of 4-dimensional geometry. Perpendicularity, simple angles. Angles of planes, higher order. Symmetry, order, motion; hyperpyramids, hypercones, hyperspheres; figures with parallel elements; volume, hypervolume in space; regular polyhedroids. Glossary. 78 figures. ix + 348pp. 5⅜ x 8. S182 Paperbound **$1.95**

MATHEMATICS: INTERMEDIATE TO ADVANCED

GEOMETRY (EUCLIDEAN AND NON-EUCLIDEAN)

THE GEOMETRY OF RENÉ DESCARTES. With this book, Descartes founded analytical geometry. Original French text, with Descartes's own diagrams, and excellent Smith-Latham translation. Contains: Problems the Construction of Which Requires only Straight Lines and Circles; On the Nature of Curved Lines; On the Construction of Solid or Supersolid Problems. Diagrams. 258pp. 5⅜ x 8. S68 Paperbound **$1.50**

DOVER SCIENCE BOOKS

THE WORKS OF ARCHIMEDES, edited by T. L. Heath. All the known works of the great Greek mathematician, including the recently discovered Method of Archimedes. Contains: On Sphere and Cylinder, Measurement of a Circle, Spirals, Conoids, Spheroids, etc. Definitive edition of greatest mathematical intellect of ancient world. 186 page study by Heath discusses Archimedes and history of Greek mathematics. 563pp. 5⅜ x 8.   S9 Paperbound **$2.00**

COLLECTED WORKS OF BERNARD RIEMANN. Important sourcebook, first to contain complete text of 1892 "Werke" and the 1902 supplement, unabridged. 31 monographs, 3 complete lecture courses, 15 miscellaneous papers which have been of enormous importance in relativity, topology, theory of complex variables, other areas of mathematics. Edited by R. Dedekind, H. Weber, M. Noether, W. Wirtinger. German text; English introduction by Hans Lewy. 690pp. 5⅜ x 8.   S226 Paperbound **$2.85**

THE THIRTEEN BOOKS OF EUCLID'S ELEMENTS, edited by Sir Thomas Heath. Definitive edition of one of very greatest classics of Western world. Complete translation of Heiberg text, plus spurious Book XIV. 150 page introduction on Greek, Medieval mathematics, Euclid, texts, commentators, etc. Elaborate critical apparatus parallels text, analyzing each definition, postulate, proposition, covering textual matters, refutations, supports, extrapolations, etc. This is the full Euclid. Unabridged reproduction of Cambridge U. 2nd edition. 3 volumes. 995 figures. 1426pp. 5⅜ x 8.   S88, 89, 90, 3 volume set, paperbound **$6.00**

AN INTRODUCTION TO GEOMETRY OF N DIMENSIONS, D. M. Y. Sommerville. Presupposes no previous knowledge of field. Only book in English devoted exclusively to higher dimensional geometry. Discusses fundamental ideas of incidence, parallelism, perpendicularity, angles between linear space, enumerative geometry, analytical geometry from projective and metric views, polytopes, elementary ideas in analysis situs, content of hyperspacial figures. 60 diagrams. 196pp. 5⅜ x 8.   S494 Paperbound **$1.50**

ELEMENTS OF NON-EUCLIDEAN GEOMETRY, D. M. Y. Sommerville. Unique in proceeding step-by-step. Requires only good knowledge of high-school geometry and algebra, to grasp elementary hyperbolic, elliptic, analytic non-Euclidean Geometries; space curvature and its implications; radical axes; homopethic centres and systems of circles; parataxy and parallelism; Gauss' proof of defect area theorem; much more, with exceptional clarity. 126 problems at chapter ends. 133 figures. xvi + 274pp. 5⅜ x 8.   S460 Paperbound **$1.50**

THE FOUNDATIONS OF EUCLIDEAN GEOMETRY, H. G. Forder. First connected, rigorous account in light of modern analysis, establishing propositions without recourse to empiricism, without multiplying hypotheses. Based on tools of 19th and 20th century mathematicians, who made it possible to remedy gaps and complexities, recognize problems not earlier discerned. Begins with important relationship of number systems in geometrical figures. Considers classes, relations, linear order, natural numbers, axioms for magnitudes, groups, quasi-fields, fields, non-Archimedian systems, the axiom system (at length), particular axioms (two chapters on the Parallel Axioms), constructions, congruence, similarity, etc. Lists: axioms employed, constructions, symbols in frequent use. 295pp. 5⅜ x 8.
S481 Paperbound **$2.00**

CALCULUS, FUNCTION THEORY (REAL AND COMPLEX), FOURIER THEORY

FIVE VOLUME "THEORY OF FUNCTIONS" SET BY KONRAD KNOPP. Provides complete, readily followed account of theory of functions. Proofs given concisely, yet without sacrifice of completeness or rigor. These volumes used as texts by such universities as M.I.T., Chicago, N.Y. City College, many others. "Excellent introduction . . . remarkably readable, concise, clear, rigorous," J. of the American Statistical Association.

ELEMENTS OF THE THEORY OF FUNCTIONS, Konrad Knopp. Provides background for further volumes in this set, or texts on similar level. Partial contents: Foundations, system of complex numbers and Gaussian plane of numbers, Riemann sphere of numbers, mapping by linear functions, normal forms, the logarithm, cyclometric functions, binomial series. "Not only for the young student, but also for the student who knows all about what is in it," Mathematical Journal. 140pp. 5⅜ x 8.   S154 Paperbound **$1.35**

THEORY OF FUNCTIONS, PART I, Konrad Knopp. With volume II, provides coverage of basic concepts and theorems. Partial contents: numbers and points, functions of a complex variable, integral of a continuous function, Cauchy's intergral theorem, Cauchy's integral formulae, series with variable terms, expansion and analytic function in a power series, analytic continuation and complete definition of analytic functions, Laurent expansion, types of singularities. vii + 146pp. 5⅜ x 8.   S156 Paperbound **$1.35**

THEORY OF FUNCTIONS, PART II, Konrad Knopp. Application and further development of general theory, special topics. Single valued functions, entire, Weierstrass. Meromorphic functions: Mittag-Leffler. Periodic functions. Multiple valued functions. Riemann surfaces. Algebraic functions. Analytical configurations, Riemann surface. x + 150pp. 5⅜ x 8.
S157 Paperbound **$1.35**

PROBLEM BOOK IN THE THEORY OF FUNCTIONS, VOLUME I, Konrad Knopp. Problems in elementary theory, for use with Knopp's "Theory of Functions," or any other text. Arranged according to increasing difficulty. Fundamental concepts, sequences of numbers and infinite series, complex variable, integral theorems, development in series, conformal mapping. Answers. viii + 126pp. 5⅜ x 8.
S 158 **Paperbound $1.35**

PROBLEM BOOK IN THE THEORY OF FUNCTIONS, VOLUME II, Konrad Knopp. Advanced theory of functions, to be used with Knopp's "Theory of Functions," or comparable text. Singularities, entire and meromorphic functions, periodic, analytic, continuation, multiple-valued functions, Riemann surfaces, conformal mapping. Includes section of elementary problems. "The difficult task of selecting . . . problems just within the reach of the beginner is here masterfully accomplished," AM. MATH. SOC. Answers. 138pp. 5⅜ x 8.
S159 **Paperbound $1.35**

ADVANCED CALCULUS, E. B. Wilson. Still recognized as one of most comprehensive, useful texts. Immense amount of well-represented, fundamental material, including chapters on vector functions, ordinary differential equations, special functions, calculus of variations, etc., which are excellent introductions to these areas. Requires only one year of calculus. Over 1300 exercises cover both pure math and applications to engineering and physical problems. Ideal reference, refresher. 54 page introductory review. ix + 566pp. 5⅜ x 8.
S504 **Paperbound $2.45**

LECTURES ON THE THEORY OF ELLIPTIC FUNCTIONS, H. Hancock. Reissue of only book in English with so extensive a coverage, especially of Abel, Jacobi, Legendre, Weierstrass, Hermite, Liouville, and Riemann. Unusual fullness of treatment, plus applications as well as theory in discussing universe of elliptic integrals, originating in works of Abel and Jacobi. Use is made of Riemann to provide most general theory. 40-page table of formulas. 76 figures. xxiii + 498pp. 5⅜ x 8.
S483 **Paperbound $2.55**

THEORY OF FUNCTIONALS AND OF INTEGRAL AND INTEGRO-DIFFERENTIAL EQUATIONS, Vito Volterra. Unabridged republication of only English translation. General theory of functions depending on continuous set of values of another function. Based on author's concept of transition from finite number of variables to a continually infinite number. Includes much material on calculus of variations. Begins with fundamentals, examines generalization of analytic functions, functional derivative equations, applications, other directions of theory, etc. New introduction by G. C. Evans. Biography, criticism of Volterra's work by E. Whittaker. xxxx + 226pp. 5⅜ x 8.
S502 **Paperbound $1.75**

AN INTRODUCTION TO FOURIER METHODS AND THE LAPLACE TRANSFORMATION, Philip Franklin. Concentrates on essentials, gives broad view, suitable for most applications. Requires only knowledge of calculus. Covers complex qualities with methods of computing elementary functions for complex values of argument and finding approximations by charts; Fourier series; harmonic anaylsis; much more. Methods are related to physical problems of heat flow, vibrations, electrical transmission, electromagnetic radiation, etc. 828 problems, answers. Formerly entitled "Fourier Methods." x + 289pp. 5⅜ x 8.
S452 **Paperbound $1.75**

THE ANALYTICAL THEORY OF HEAT, Joseph Fourier. This book, which revolutionized mathematical physics, has been used by generations of mathematicians and physicists interested in heat or application of Fourier integral. Covers cause and reflection of rays of heat, radiant heating, heating of closed spaces, use of trigonometric series in theory of heat, Fourier integral, etc. Translated by Alexander Freeman. 20 figures. xxii + 466pp. 5⅜ x 8.
S93 **Paperbound $2.00**

ELLIPTIC INTEGRALS, H. Hancock. Invaluable in work involving differential equations with cubics, quatrics under root sign, where elementary calculus methods are inadequate. Practical solutions to problems in mathematics, engineering, physics; differential equations requiring integration of Lamé's, Briot's, or Bouquet's equations; determination of arc of ellipse, hyperbola, lemiscate; solutions of problems in elastics; motion of a projectile under resistance varying as the cube of the velocity; pendulums; more. Exposition in accordance with Legendre-Jacobi theory. Rigorous discussion of Legendre transformations. 20 figures. 5 place table. 104pp. 5⅜ x 8.
S484 **Paperbound $1.25**

THE TAYLOR SERIES, AN INTRODUCTION TO THE THEORY OF FUNCTIONS OF A COMPLEX VARIABLE, P. Dienes. Uses Taylor series to approach theory of functions, using ordinary calculus only, except in last 2 chapters. Starts with introduction to real variable and complex algebra, derives properties of infinite series, complex differentiation, integration, etc. Covers biuniform mapping, overconvergence and gap theorems, Taylor series on its circle of convergence, etc. Unabridged corrected reissue of first edition. 186 examples, many fully worked out. 67 figures. xii + 555pp. 5⅜ x 8.
S391 **Paperbound $2.75**

LINEAR INTEGRAL EQUATIONS, W. V. Lovitt. Systematic survey of general theory, with some application to differential equations, calculus of variations, problems of math, physics. Includes: integral equation of 2nd kind by successive substitutions; Fredholm's equation as ratio of 2 integral series in lambda, applications of the Fredholm theory, Hilbert-Schmidt theory of symmetric kernels, application, etc. Neumann, Dirichlet, vibratory problems. ix + 253pp. 5⅜ x 8.
S175 Clothbound **$3.50**
S176 Paperbound **$1.60**

DOVER SCIENCE BOOKS

DICTIONARY OF CONFORMAL REPRESENTATIONS, H. Kober. Developed by British Admiralty to solve Laplace's equation in 2 dimensions. Scores of geometrical forms and transformations for electrical engineers, Joukowski aerofoil for aerodynamics, Schwartz-Christoffel transformations for hydro-dynamics, transcendental functions. Contents classified according to analytical functions describing transformations with corresponding regions. Glossary. Topological index. 447 diagrams. 6⅛ x 9¼.   .S160 Paperbound **$2.00**

ELEMENTS OF THE THEORY OF REAL FUNCTIONS, J. E. Littlewood. Based on lectures at Trinity College, Cambridge, this book has proved extremely successful in introducing graduate students to modern theory of functions. Offers full and concise coverage of classes and cardinal numbers, well ordered series, other types of series, and elements of the theory of sets of points. 3rd revised edition. vii + 71pp. 5⅜ x 8.   S171 Clothbound **$2.85**
                                                                                        S172 Paperbound **$1.25**

INFINITE SEQUENCES AND SERIES, Konrad Knopp. 1st publication in any language. Excellent introduction to 2 topics of modern mathematics, designed to give student background to penetrate further alone. Sequences and sets, real and complex numbers, etc. Functions of a real and complex variable. Sequences and series. Infinite series. Convergent power series. Expansion of elementary functions. Numerical evaluation of series. v + 186pp. 5⅜ x 8.
                                                                                        S152 Clothbound **$3.50**
                                                                                        S153 Paperbound **$1.75**

THE THEORY AND FUNCTIONS OF A REAL VARIABLE AND THE THEORY OF FOURIER'S SERIES, E. W .Hobson. One of the best introductions to set theory and various aspects of functions and Fourier's series. Requires only a good background in calculus. Exhaustive coverage of: metric and descriptive properties of sets of points; transfinite numbers and order types; functions of a real variable; the Riemann and Lebesgue integrals; sequences and series of numbers; power-series; functions representable by series sequences of continuous functions; trigonometrical series; representation of functions by Fourier's series; and much more. "The best possible guide," Nature. Vol. I: 88 detailed examples, 10 figures. Index. xv + 736pp. Vol. II: 117 detailed examples, 13 figures. x + 780pp. 6⅛ x 9¼.
                                                            Vol. I: S387 Paperbound **$3.00**
                                                            Vol. II: S388 Paperbound **$3.00**

ALMOST PERIODIC FUNCTIONS, A. S. Besicovitch. Unique and important summary by a well known mathematician covers in detail the two stages of development in Bohr's theory of almost periodic functions: (1) as a generalization of pure periodicity, with results and proofs; (2) the work done by Stepanof, Wiener, Weyl, and Bohr in generalizing the theory. xi + 180pp. 5⅜ x 8.   S18 Paperbound **$1.75**

INTRODUCTION TO THE THEORY OF FOURIER'S SERIES AND INTEGRALS, H. S. Carslaw. 3rd revised edition, an outgrowth of author's courses at Cambridge. Historical introduction, rational, irrational numbers, infinite sequences and series, functions of a single variable, definite integral, Fourier series, and similar topics. Appendices discuss practical harmonic analysis, periodogram analysis, Lebesgue's theory. 84 examples. xiii + 368pp. 5⅜ x 8.
                                                                                        S48 Paperbound **$2.00**

SYMBOLIC LOGIC

THE ELEMENTS OF MATHEMATICAL LOGIC, Paul Rosenbloom. First publication in any language. For mathematically mature readers with no training in symbolic. logic. Development of lectures given at Lund Univ., Sweden, 1948. Partial contents: Logic of classes, fundamental theorems, Boolean algebra, logic of propositions, of propositional functions, expressive languages, combinatory logics, development of math within an object language, paradoxes, theorems of Post, Goedel, Church, and similar topics. iv + 214pp. 5⅜ x 8.
                                                                                        S227 Paperbound **$1.45**

INTRODUCTION TO SYMBOLIC LOGIC AND ITS APPLICATION, R. Carnap. Clear, comprehensive, rigorous, by perhaps greatest living master. Symbolic languages analyzed, one constructed. Applications to math (axiom systems for set theory, real, natural numbers), topology (Dedekind, Cantor continuity explanations), physics (general analysis of determination, causality, space-time topology), biology (axiom system for basic concepts). "A masterpiece," Zentralblatt für Mathematik und Ihre Grenzgebiete. Over 300 exercises. 5 figures. xvi + 241pp. 5⅜ x 8.   S453 Paperbound **$1.85**

AN INTRODUCTION TO SYMBOLIC LOGIC, Susanne K. Langer. Probably clearest book for the philosopher, scientist, layman—no special knowledge of math required. Starts with simplest symbols, goes on to give remarkable grasp of Boole-Schroeder, Russell-Whitehead systems, clearly, quickly. Partial Contents: Forms, Generalization, Classes, Deductive System of Classes, Algebra of Logic, Assumptions of Principia Mathematica, Logistics, Proofs of Theorems, etc. "Clearest . . . simplest introduction . . . the intelligent non-mathematician should have no difficulty," MATHEMATICS GAZETTE. Revised, expanded 2nd edition. Truth-value tables. 368pp. 5⅜ 8.   S164 Paperbound **$1.75**

TRIGONOMETRICAL SERIES, Antoni Zygmund. On modern advanced level. Contains carefully organized analyses of trigonometric, orthogonal, Fourier systems of functions, with clear adequate descriptions of summability of Fourier series, proximation theory, conjugate series, convergence, divergence of Fourier series. Especially valuable for Russian, Eastern European coverage. 329pp. 5⅜ x 8.
S290 Paperbound **$1.50**

THE LAWS OF THOUGHT, George Boole. This book founded symbolic logic some 100 years ago. It is the 1st significant attempt to apply logic to all aspects of human endeavour. Partial contents: derivation of laws, signs and laws, interpretations, eliminations, conditions of a perfect method, analysis, Aristotelian logic, probability, and similar topics. xvii + 424pp. 5⅜ x 8.
S28 Paperbound **$2.00**

SYMBOLIC LOGIC, C. I. Lewis, C. H. Langford. 2nd revised edition of probably most cited book in symbolic logic. Wide coverage of entire field; one of fullest treatments of paradoxes; plus much material not available elsewhere. Basic to volume is distinction between logic of extensions and intensions. Considerable emphasis on converse substitution, while matrix system presents supposition of variety of non-Aristotelian logics. Especially valuable sections on strict limitations, existence theorems. Partial contents: Boole-Schroeder algebra; truth value systems, the matrix method; implication and deductibility; general theory of propositions; etc. "Most valuable," Times, London. 506pp. 5⅜ x 8.   S170 Paperbound **$2.00**

GROUP THEORY AND LINEAR ALGEBRA, SETS, ETC.

LECTURES ON THE ICOSAHEDRON AND THE SOLUTION OF EQUATIONS OF THE FIFTH DEGREE, Felix Klein. Solution of quintics in terms of rotations of regular icosahedron around its axes of symmetry. A classic, indispensable source for those interested in higher algebra, geometry, crystallography. Considerable explanatory material included. 230 footnotes, mostly bibliography. "Classical monograph . . . detailed, readable book," Math. Gazette. 2nd edition. xvi + 289pp. 5⅜ x 8.
S314 Paperbound **$1.85**

INTRODUCTION TO THE THEORY OF GROUPS OF FINITE ORDER, R. Carmichael. Examines fundamental theorems and their applications. Beginning with sets, systems, permutations, etc., progresses in easy stages through important types of groups: Abelian, prime power, permutation, etc. Except 1 chapter where matrices are desirable, no higher math is needed. 783 exercises, problems. xvi + 447pp. 5⅜ x 8.
S299 Clothbound **$3.95**
S300 Paperbound **$2.00**

THEORY OF GROUPS OF FINITE ORDER, W. Burnside. First published some 40 years ago, still one of clearest introductions. Partial contents: permutations, groups independent of representation, composition series of a group, isomorphism of a group with itself, Abelian groups, prime power groups, permutation groups, invariants of groups of linear substitution, graphical representation, etc. "Clear and detailed discussion . . . numerous problems which are instructive," Design News. xxiv + 512pp. 5⅜ x 8.   S38 Paperbound **$2.45**

COMPUTATIONAL METHODS OF LINEAR ALGEBRA, V. N. Faddeeva, translated by C. D. Benster. 1st English translation of unique, valuable work, only one in English presenting systematic exposition of most important methods of linear algebra—classical, contemporary. Details of deriving numerical solutions of problems in mathematical physics. Theory and practice. Includes survey of necessary background, most important methods of solution, for exact, iterative groups. One of most valuable features is 23 tables, triple checked for accuracy, unavailable elsewhere. Translator's note. x + 252pp. 5⅜ x 8.   S424 Paperbound **$1.95**

THE CONTINUUM AND OTHER TYPES OF SERIAL ORDER, E. V. Huntington. This famous book gives a systematic elementary account of the modern theory of the continuum as a type of serial order. Based on the Cantor-Dedekind ordinal theory, which requires no technical knowledge of higher mathematics, it offers an easily followed analysis of ordered classes, discrete and dense series, continuous series, Cantor's transfinite numbers. "Admirable introduction to the rigorous theory of the continuum . . . reading easy," Science Progress. 2nd edition. viii + 82pp. 5⅜ x 8.
S129 Clothbound **$2.75**
S130 Paperbound **$1.00**

THEORY OF SETS, E. Kamke. Clearest, amplest introduction in English, well suited for independent study. Subdivisions of main theory, such as theory of sets of points, are discussed, but emphasis is on general theory. Partial contents: rudiments of set theory, arbitrary sets, their cardinal numbers, ordered sets, their order types, well-ordered sets, their cardinal numbers. vii + 144pp. 5⅜ x 8.
S141 Paperbound **$1.35**

CONTRIBUTIONS TO THE FOUNDING OF THE THEORY OF TRANSFINITE NUMBERS, Georg Cantor. These papers founded a new branch of mathematics. The famous articles of 1895-7 are translated, with an 82-page introduction by P. E. B. Jourdain dealing with Cantor, the background of his discoveries, their results, future possibiilties. ix + 211pp. 5⅜ x 8.
S45 Paperbound **$1.25**

DOVER SCIENCE BOOKS

NUMERICAL AND GRAPHICAL METHODS, TABLES

JACOBIAN ELLIPTIC FUNCTION TABLES, L. M. Milne-Thomson. Easy-to-follow, practical, not only useful numerical tables, but complete elementary sketch of application of elliptic functions. Covers description of principle properties; complete elliptic integrals; Fourier series, expansions; periods, zeros, poles, residues, formulas for special values of argument; cubic, quartic polynomials; pendulum problem; etc. Tables, graphs form body of book: Graph, 5 figure table of elliptic function sn (u m); cn (u m); dn (u m). 8 figure table of complete elliptic integrals K, K', E, E', nome q. 7 figure table of Jacobian zeta-function Z(u). 3 figures. xi + 123pp. 5⅜ x 8.   S194 Paperbound **$1.35**

TABLES OF FUNCTIONS WITH FORMULAE AND CURVES, E. Jahnke, F. Emde. Most comprehensive 1-volume English text collection of tables, formulae, curves of transcendent functions. 4th corrected edition, new 76-page section giving tables, formulae for elementary functions not in other English editions. Partial contents: sine, cosine, logarithmic integral; error integral; elliptic integrals; theta functions; Legendre, Bessel, Riemann, Mathieu, hypergeometric functions; etc. "Out-of-the-way functions for which we know no other source." Scientific Computing Service, Ltd. 212 figures. 400pp. 5⅝ x 8⅜.   S133 Paperbound **$2.00**

MATHEMATICAL TABLES, H. B. Dwight. Covers in one volume almost every function of importance in applied mathematics, engineering, physical sciences. Three extremely fine tables of the three trig functions, inverses, to 1000th of radian; natural, common logs; squares, cubes; hyperbolic functions, inverses; $(a^2 + b^2)$ exp. ½a; complete elliptical integrals of 1st, 2nd kind; sine, cosine integrals; exponential integrals; Ei(x) and Ei(−x); binomial coefficients; factorials to 250; surface zonal harmonics, first derivatives; Bernoulli, Euler numbers, their logs to base of 10; Gamma function; normal probability integral; over 60pp. Bessel functions; Riemann zeta function. Each table with formulae generally used, sources of more extensive tables, interpolation data, etc. Over half have columns of differences, to facilitate interpolation. viii + 231pp. 5⅜ x 8.   S445 Paperbound **$1.75**

PRACTICAL ANALYSIS, GRAPHICAL AND NUMERICAL METHODS, F. A. Willers. Immensely practical hand-book for engineers. How to interpolate, use various methods of numerical differentiation and integration, determine roots of a single algebraic equation, system of linear equations, use empirical formulas, integrate differential equations, etc. Hundreds of short-cuts for arriving at numerical solutions. Special section on American calculating machines, by T. W. Simpson. Translation by R. T. Beyer. 132 illustrations. 422pp. 5⅜ x 8.
S273 Paperbound **$2.00**

NUMERICAL SOLUTIONS OF DIFFERENTIAL EQUATIONS, H. Levy, E. A. Baggott. Comprehensive collection of methods for solving ordinary differential equations of first and higher order. 2 requirements: practical, easy to grasp; more rapid than school methods. Partial contents: graphical integration of differential equations, graphical methods for detailed solution. Numerical solution. Simultaneous equations and equations of 2nd and higher orders. "Should be in the hands of all in research and applied mathematics, teaching," Nature. 21 figures. viii + 238pp. 5⅜ x 8.   S168 Paperbound **$1.75**

NUMERICAL INTEGRATION OF DIFFERENTIAL EQUATIONS, Bennet, Milne, Bateman. Unabridged republication of original prepared for National Research Council. New methods of integration by 3 leading mathematicians: "The Interpolational Polynomial," "Successive Approximation," A. A. Bennett, "Step-by-step Methods of Integration," W. W. Milne. "Methods for Partial Differential Equations," H. Bateman. Methods for partial differential equations, solution of differential equations to non-integral values of a parameter will interest mathematicians, physicists. 288 footnotes, mostly bibliographical. 235 item classified bibliography. 108pp. 5⅜ x 8.   S305 Paperbound **$1.35**